Discoveries in
LITERATURE

AMERICA READS **CLASSIC EDITION**

AMERICA READS   CLASSIC EDITION

BEGINNINGS in Literature
Alan L. Madsen
Sarah Durand Wood
Philip M. Connors

DISCOVERIES in Literature
L. Jane Christensen
Edmund J. Farrell

EXPLORATIONS in Literature
Nancy C. Millett
Raymond J. Rodrigues

PATTERNS in Literature
Edmund J. Farrell
Ouida H. Clapp
Karen J. Kuehner

TRADITIONS in Literature
Helen McDonnell
James E. Miller, Jr.
Russell J. Hogan

THE UNITED STATES in Literature
The Red Badge of Courage edition
Three Long Stories edition
James E. Miller, Jr.
Kerry M. Wood
Carlota Cárdenas de Dwyer

ENGLAND in Literature
Macbeth edition
Hamlet edition
John Pfordresher
Gladys V. Veidemanis
Helen McDonnell

CLASSICS in World Literature
Kerry M. Wood
Helen McDonnell
John Pfordresher
Mary Alice Fite
Paul Lankford

The authors and editors wish to thank the following consultants for reading and teaching editorial material and proposed selections for America Reads.

■ Barbara E. Anderson, Junior Level Coordinator and Teacher, James B. Conant High School, Hoffman Estates, Illinois

■ Anita Arnold, Chairman, English Department, Thomas Jefferson High School, San Antonio, Texas

■ Pat Dudley, Principal, Jane Long Elementary School, Abilene ISD, Abilene, Texas

■ Dr. V. Pauline Hodges-McLain, Coordinator, Language Arts, Jefferson County Public Schools, Golden, Colorado

■ Rance Howe, English/Language Arts Consultant K-12, Anoka-Hennepin ISD 11, Coon Rapids, Minnesota

■ Lisbeth Johnson, English Teacher, Capital High School, Olympia, Washington

■ Daniel Lane, Supervisor of Humanities, Holmdel Twp. Public Schools, Holmdel, New Jersey

■ May Lee, English Teacher, Baldwin Senior High School, Baldwin, New York

■ Richard T. Martin, English Department Chairman, Burrillville Junior-Senior High School, Harrisville, Rhode Island

■ Barbara McCormick, Systemwide Chairman of English, Greenville Public Schools, Greenville, Mississippi

■ James McCullough, English Teacher, Carmel High School, Mundelein, Illinois

■ Cathy Nufer, Teacher, Grade 6, Elm School, Hinsdale, Illinois

■ Marlyn Payne, Teacher, Grade 7, Nichols Middle School, Evanston, Illinois

■ Sally P. Pfeifer, English Department Chair, Lewis and Clark High School, Spokane, Washington

■ James B. Phillips, Instructor in English and Reading, Norwood Senior High School, Norwood, Massachusetts

■ John Pratt, Language Arts Chairperson, Edison High School, Stockton, California

■ Cora Wolfe, English Department Chairperson, Antelope Union High School, Wellton, Arizona

Discoveries in LITERATURE

AMERICA READS   **CLASSIC EDITION**

L. Jane Christensen
Edmund J. Farrell

S C O T T,   F O R E S M A N

Scott, Foresman and Company   Editorial Offices: Glenview, Illinois
Regional Offices:
Sunnyvale, California   Tucker, Georgia   Glenview, Illinois   Oakland, New Jersey   Dallas, Texas

L. Jane Christensen

Associate Executive Director, National Council of Teachers of English. Editor of *Your Reading,* an annotated middle school/junior high booklist. Consultant for workshops on the teaching of composition and humanities. Formerly: teacher of English at junior high, high school, and college levels.

Edmund J. Farrell

Professor, English Education, University of Texas, Austin. Formerly: Associate Executive Director, National Council of Teachers of English; Chairman, English Department, James Lick High School, San Jose, California; Chairman, NCTE Commission on Literature. Past president of the California Association of Teachers of English and the Texas Joint Council of Teachers of English. Recipient, NCTE Distinguished Service Award, 1982.

Cover: Winslow Homer, *Breezing Up (A Fair Wind)* (detail), 1876, National Gallery of Art, Washington, D.C. Gift of the W. L. and May T. Mellon Foundation

Pronunciation key and dictionary entries are from *Scott, Foresman Advanced Dictionary* by E. L. Thorndike and Clarence L. Barnhart. Copyright © 1988 Scott, Foresman and Company.

ISBN: 0-673-29377-7

Copyright © 1991, 1989
Scott, Foresman and Company, Glenview, Illinois
All Rights Reserved. Printed in the United States of America.

2345678910-VHJ-969594939291

CONTENTS

UNIT 2   PLAYS

UNIT 3   NONFICTION

UNIT 4   POETRY

UNIT 5   SHORT STORY 2

THINKING CRITICALLY ABOUT LITERATURE

UNIT 6   FOLK LITERATURE

THINKING CRITICALLY ABOUT LITERATURE

UNIT 7   NOVEL

THINKING CRITICALLY ABOUT LITERATURE

UNIT 8   EPIC

THINKING CRITICALLY ABOUT LITERATURE

READING LITERATURE

COMMENT ARTICLES

THE WRITER'S CRAFT

HANDBOOK OF LITERARY TERMS

WRITER'S HANDBOOK

GLOSSARY OF LITERARY TERMS *687*

PREVIEW

★ *Discoveries in Literature* has six units containing short stories, poetry, plays, nonfiction, and folk literature. A seventh unit is made up of a novel, *Kävik, the Wolf Dog,* and the eighth unit is the story of Ulysses, a famous Greek hero, and his adventures with gods and goddesses.

UNIT ORGANIZATION

Units begin with an illustration and a unit preview to help you see what each unit contains. Many selections are preceded by a wide yellow bar at the top of a page. This bar directs you to the Handbook of Literary Terms at the back of the text, where you will learn about an essential literary term before you read the selection.

Think and Discuss questions follow each selection or group of selections. You may want to read the questions before you read the selection as a way of guiding your reading.

Applying/Reviewing questions about the literary term you have studied also appear after literary works. These are to help you make certain you understand how an author has developed plot, used figurative language, or made use of other techniques.

Reading Literature Skillfully lessons appear from time to time. Here you will see short exercises on topics such as cause and effect relationships, predicting outcomes, and summarizing. You will be able to do most of these lessons rather quickly and without your teacher's help.

Vocabulary exercises throughout the book will help you understand words or meanings new to you. They will also show you how to determine the meanings of words from context or from the parts of a word. You may be tested on the words in these exercises.

Thinking Skills lessons will help you learn to think about literature in some new ways by practicing *classifying, generalizing, synthesizing* (putting together parts and elements to form new ideas) and *evaluating*.

Composition assignments and ideas follow many selections. You will find it useful to refer to the Writer's Handbook at the back of this text for more help with some of these assignments.

Enrichment selections are also included and provide ideas for class projects and speaking and listening activities.

OTHER FEATURES

Three types of articles can be found throughout this anthology. Comment articles provide interesting sidelights on a work, an author, or a related subject. (See, for example, "The Detective Who Wouldn't Die," page 127.)

Articles titled "Writer's Craft" focus on how writers achieve their effects and help you to achieve similar effects in your writing. Finally, there are articles such as "Reading a Play," page 115, that will give you some helpful hints on reading various types of literature.

UNIT REVIEWS

Each unit ends with a three-part review titled "Thinking Critically About Literature." Here you will be asked to read a new, short work and answer questions to help you apply what you have learned. You will also review the selection or selections in the unit and complete a writing assignment related to the unit material.

END-OF-BOOK MATERIAL

At the back of this text on page 633 is a Handbook of Literary Terms followed by a Writer's Handbook. You will be referred to the Handbook of Literary Terms and the Writer's Handbook throughout earlier parts of the book. There is also a Glossary of Literary Terms and a Glossary that looks like a dictionary. Here are all words featured in Vocabulary exercises, plus other words you will encounter in your reading.

The stories, poems, and plays in this book were written by a wide variety of authors. Although some lived long ago, their work has survived because it is both meaningful and interesting. The work of those writers who are living today is included not only because it is well written but because it provides insights into life today—and even into the future.

Kathy Jakobsen, *Circus Parade*, 1979, Private Collection

PREVIEW

UNIT 1   SHORT STORY 1

Cutie Pie / Nicholas Fisk
The Widow and the Parrot / Virginia Woolf
Raymond's Run / Toni Cade Bambara
One Night Stand / Louis L'Amour
Gentleman of Río en Medio / Juan A. A. Sedillo
The Old Demon / Pearl S. Buck
Stolen Day / Sherwood Anderson
Rikki-tikki-tavi / Rudyard Kipling
The Circuit / Francisco Jiménez
The Fallen Angel / Evan Hunter
The Smallest Dragonboy / Anne McCaffrey
I'll Give You Law / Molly Picon

Features
Reading a Short Story
The Writer's Craft: Be Specific
Comment: The Story Behind the Story

Application of Literary Terms
plot   setting
characterization   theme

Reading Literature Skillfully
cause/effect relationships

Vocabulary
dictionary
context
pronunciation key
combining forms
word origins
synonyms and antonyms

Thinking Skills
classifying
generalizing
evaluating

Composition Assignments Include
Writing a Report
Writing a News Story
Writing About a Pet
Describing a Character
Writing About a Story
Being a Story Character
Writing a Journal Entry
Comparing Story Characters
Describing How Friends Help
Writing About an Experience

Enrichment
Working with a Group
Reading Dialogue Aloud
Reporting to the Class

Thinking Critically About Literature
Concept Review
Content Review
Composition Review

Cutie Pie

Nicholas Fisk

He was helpless and alone—stranded on an alien planet—but he fought his despair with all the courage of his race.

Some of the highest minds on Earth combined to build *Questar,* the spaceship that accidentally captured a creature living on the planet Quta-pi.[1]

Some of the lowest minds on Earth gave the creature its popular name: Cutie Pie. You see how these minds worked. "From Quta-pi we bring you—Cutie Pie!" Great. Fantastic. Listen, men, we've got a *property* here. Get out there and sell.

Heaven knows, the creature was "cute." So cute that all over Earth, millions of human eyes, glued to millions of color TV sets, goggled rapturously at the iridescent "feathers" (pearly down on the belly, radiant and shimmering patterns elsewhere) that covered Cutie Pie's curved, cozy, rounded body. Human hearts doted on his dark, liquid eyes; on the gentle mouth that seemed to smile; on the busy little "hands," complete with thumbs, that Cutie Pie used with such astonishing speed and skill.

"Aaah Aaah . . . !" crooned the world, "Aaah! Just look at him now! He's making his bed!"

"Oh! The colors! I could just cuddle him to death!"

"Oo, mummy do look! He's cleaning his whiskers again!"

Almost at once there were Cutie Pie dolls, coloring books, tee shirts, fan clubs, cereal cartons, cartoon serials—anything, everything. Fortunes were made instantly. How could the promoters fail? The creature was adorable. "Oh, he's just too sweet to *live!*" the world said.

How right the world was. Every day, Cutie Pie nearly died.

"If only I could actually *see* him—*touch* him—*hold* him!" people mewed. They could not. Cutie Pie—no, this is too much, let us give him his own, proper name, Ch-tsal[2]—Ch-tsal was hermetically sealed. He lived in a glass prison, a scientific tomb. Temperature—exactly 180°F; humidity—precisely 98 percent; atmosphere—hydrogen, oxygen, and

---

1. *Quta-pi* (kyü′tä pī′).
2. *Ch-tsal* (chə tsäl′).

careful proportions of a dozen exotic gases. This atmosphere imitated that of Quta-pi, the place where Ch-tsal had been captured. So, the Earth scientists agreed, it must be right.

Ch-tsal knew better. For him, every day was an agonizing fight for life. The 180°F temperature roasted him. The 98 percent humidity stifled him. The so carefully proportioned atmosphere choked him.

For although Ch-tsal was captured on Quta-pi, that planet was not his home. He merely chanced to be there. For Ch-tsal was, in our terms, an adolescent. The elders had sent him out to undertake what we would call an initiation: he went out as a "boy," to return with the dignity of a "man," having faced difficulties and dangers in strange places. Quta-pi was the strangest, most hostile place he had to visit. However, his stay there was to be brief.

Or so it was planned. But on Quta-pi the sky had split and thundered (that was our spaceship *Questar*). A *thing* had descended and scarred the planet's surface (that was *Questar's* scoop, a sort of rake gathering samples of soil, rock, shale). Ch-tsal, stunned, was scooped up too.

He shudderingly remembered silver creatures with bubble faces (those were the crew of *Questar*). He glimpsed them briefly, then lost consciousness. Now he was a prisoner of white-clad men with tube-and-goggle faces. They came into his glass prison fast and went out faster. They wore gas masks to protect themselves against the atmosphere they had created for Ch-tsal.

He knew these jailers did not mean to torture him. They were not wicked; he could feel that they meant well. But he could not talk to them, could not explain. Ch-tsal had no vocal chords; his race does not speak as we do. He could only look past the goggleglasses into the eyes, begging them to understand. But they could not, did not.

If Ch-tsal's eyes seemed liquid to the watching world, it was probably because of the endless tears he shed.

"Aaaah!" the world said. "Look! He's doing it again! He's *grooming* himself!" "Combing his lovely silky whiskers with his darling little hands!" "Cleaning his *booful* feathers!"

He was indeed. Ch-tsal unceasingly groomed his feathers because they were filters, temperature-controllers, respirators and much else. As for his whiskers—they were his receivers, antennae, language-carriers, voice, lifeline. They linked him to his people. So even at home, these precious whiskers were groomed frequently. They had to be kept working perfectly.

In the glass prison they did not work.

So Ch-tsal, to add to his physical miseries, was deaf, dumb and cut off. Alone. Alone, alone, alone. . . .

He fought his despair with all the courage and complex experience of his race (far older than ours). His five stomachs and numerous organic filters just about allowed him to stomach the food and atmosphere supplied him. His mind and hands could sometimes be forced for whole hours to entertain him ("Aaah, look! He's making something! A sort of game! Can you understand it? I can't. . . .").

Vincent DiFate

Best of all there was sleep—and dreams; he was home again, free again, loved and loving again. Such dreams!

On the nineteenth day, Earth time, of his captivity, Ch-tsal woke from a beautiful dream to an appalling reality.

Lying on the floor of his glass prison were—feathers. Jeweled feathers from his back, the longer, more boldly patterned feathers from his sides, and down from his belly. They had fallen out in the night.

To Ch-tsal, this calamity was what sudden growths of hair would be to a human. Imagine. You wake one morning to find your face, the backs of your hands, your arms, your body, covered with tufts of coarse hair! Unthinkable!

And even worse for Ch-tsal. He had dreamed of his mother: her beauty—the shapes and patterns and colors of her feathers—was largely of her own creation. Like all those of her race, she had created her own style of beauty; willed her own individual, self-expressive loveliness. So, in his different way, had Ch-tsal. His feathers said, "This is me, Ch-tsal. As you can see simply by looking at me, I am such-and-such an individual, with certain definite tastes and hopes and beliefs." To him, his feathers were what clothes may be to humans—but more.

To lose his feathers was to lose himself.

To become naked was to become a monster.

He wept, prayed and attended to himself incessantly but without hope. His feathers continued to fall, and his whiskers. The scientists attending him peered through the glass walls and creased their brows. The world at large at first said, "Oh, the poor thing!" "Surely something can be done?" "Poor Cutie Pie!"

Soon the pity soured. "Really, it's not nice!" "I think it's disgusting." "What's on the other channels?"

And then a baby panda was born—and the Olympic games came round, and a new girl singer arrived who wore a one-piece glitter swimsuit back to front. The Cutie Pie tee shirts and badges and books were thrown away. Ch-tsal was forgotten.

By now he was hideous and near to death. Naked, he crouched in a corner of his glass prison, his dull eyes staring back at the bright eyes of the TV cameras. His little hands plucked at the naked flesh or picked at his muzzle, where his whiskers had been. There was nothing left for him. He had long realized that the glass walls prevented him from sending or receiving messages. Now he realized that even if he escaped, he would be powerless. Without his whiskers, he could no longer contact home. And if the impossible happened—if he could find a way of reaching home—how could he reappear there naked, without his feathers?

His scientist-jailers were sympathetic, but they too were powerless. They were also a little annoyed with him. His sickness accused them of incompetence; his survival was an embarrassment. "Cutie Pie" were words they flinched from.

They did their best. One day, two scientists came into the prison to examine the slack, naked, ugly body of Ch-tsal. "We could try a change of diet," one said. "What, again? We've tried everything," the other replied. They put down the food bowl and examined Ch-tsal through the glass of their gas-mask goggles. They looked at him hard and long—too long: "We'd better get out!" they said and hastened from the glass cell, feeling the strange gases beginning to seep through the masks and into their noses. "Quick! The decontamination center!"

One of them pressed the button that closed the glass wall. The food bowl jammed it. It could not close, not completely. The food bowl squashed into a figure of eight and a small gap was left.

Ch-tsal thought, "I can get through that gap. Escape. But I am too tired and I no longer care." But then he thought of the heavens and the stars and planets—and among them, the little planet that was his home.

So he left his prison and escaped into the world of Earth.

Earth astonished him.

The air—he could breath it! The temperature—it was pleasant! There was even a sun (only one—his planet had three) to warm his decaying body, tingle his naked skin! Then shadow again, and coolness, and delight!

It rained; and Ch-tsal knew ecstasy. For the first time, his body was less than agony to him. For whole moments, as the raindrops beat on his tortured flesh, he felt even the gates of his mind open. He would have sent a message of thanks to his God, but of course he could not: his whiskers, his "voice," were gone. He gave thanks all the same, beaming his mind as hard as he could. Then alone, still alone, he enjoyed the rain.

He knew he had to hide and how to hide. He was efficient in everything, though deadly tired. His clever hands explored the facts and things of Earth and found them easy. You turn this knob or push this handle . . . you slide this up or pull this down. Everything was big and crude and simple. Child's play.

He found food in the extension to Mrs. Chatsworth's house on Cedar Avenue. She grew cacti. They tasted unpleasant but they were food, definitely food, not the poisonous stuff of the prison cell. He ate plants, made himself a carrying bag, cut himself a store of food and carried it off.

Now all he wanted was a friend: a creature, however simple or alien, to give him comfort. He had been alone so long.

He found a creature asleep. It was a handsome thing with fur that reminded Ch-tsal of his own feathers. The fur was colored and patterned, very elaborately; surely not by accident?

The creature awoke and opened golden eyes. It arched its back—saw Ch-tsal—and attacked, fast and viciously. It had white hooks set in its head and brown-black hooks at the end of its limbs.

It took all Ch-tsal's mental power to quiet the creature. When it was quiet, it turned out to be useless. It had only the simplest and crudest thoughts—comfort, hunting, mating, food, territory. It could not link its thoughts. He left the thing purring and went on his way.

After the cat, a dog. Ch-tsal, ashamed of his nakedness, was frightened to approach the well-covered, furry animal which radiated the sort of uncertain silly niceness that some of the creatures on Ch-tsal's own planet displayed. The dog growled and wagged its tail. Ch-tsal sensed that it might attack him, or adore him, or both. The dog licked him. Disgusted, Ch-tsal left it. The dog stared after him wagging its tail. It did not follow.

It rained again and Ch-tsal lay on his back, limbs spread, blessing every cold, clear, clean drop. He rubbed the wetness into his skin—and felt stubby prickles!

He felt his muzzle. Tiny, wiry projections tickled his fingers! His heart leapt with hope. He gave thanks. But still he had nobody to turn to. He was still alone.

He met the one he needed. The name of this person was Christopher Harry Winters. His age, at the first meeting, was six weeks and three days.

C. H. Winters was a good happy baby. Ch-tsal first saw him lying on a rug in a garden warmed by early summer sun. He was just the same size as Ch-tsal. Better still, he was completely naked. Ch-tsal did not have to feel ashamed in his company.

The baby kicked its legs and waved its clenched fists and made sounds. From his hiding place, a rhododendron bush, Ch-tsal could see that it leaked water from its mouth. Later, he learned that it was quite a leaky little creature altogether (which confirmed Ch-tsal's suspicion that this was an ungrown specimen of the senior species of Earth; babies were much the same on his home planet).

A big creature, not naked, came out to attend the baby. This, as Ch-tsal quickly deduced, was the mother. Ch-tsal could pick up the strong, thick waves of loving emotions that flowed between mother and baby. He remembered them from his own childhood.

He stayed in or near the rhododendron bush for three days, constantly gathering strength, often eating (by now he had the choice of a dozen foods), and always observing Christopher. Obviously he could not approach the baby in the daytime, his ugly, naked shape would be seen by the mother. In any case, the daytime Christopher was not what Ch-tsal wanted. Awake, the baby was just an active, healthy blob of animal matter, without reason or logic in its excellent mind.

It was the night-time Christopher he needed.

One night, Ch-tsal made his way into Christopher's nursery and lay down on the cot by the sleeping baby, who was almost exactly his size.

"Talk to me!" Ch-tsal said, probing with his mind. The baby stirred. "Please talk!" Ch-tsal said and laid his whiskery muzzle against the plump hand.

The baby smiled in its sleep. Its mind began talking.

It did not talk of what it knew now (which was next to nothing) but of what it had always known; its race memories. Ch-tsal learned what it was like for a human to plunge through a great wave, green and icy; to hunt down animals in dark forests; to let fly an arrow and somehow know for certain, as it left the bow, that it would hit its mark. He learned of the glories of battle, the terrors of defeat, the chill wickedness of snakes, the smell of wood smoke.

In his turn, Ch-tsal told the baby of the building of crystal cities, of creatures in caves, of the pioneer ships that opened up the galaxy, of the Venus invaders and how they were repulsed, of the five ways of knowing God, and of the taste of a certain food that grew only when his planet's three moons were full.

At last, both fell into the true sleep, when the mind closes itself to all but dreams. When morning came, Ch-tsal was gone. The mother fussed over her baby. By now he often laughed. He was made happier than ever by his talks with Ch-tsal. As he gurgled and bubbled, part of his unformed mind romped among the jewels of last night. He chuckled, and his mother nuzzled his neck. He laughed out loud and pulled her hair. His own hair grew longer and curlier each day.

So, too, did Ch-tsal's feathers and whiskers. He forced them to grow, mostly by will, but also by careful attention to them and to his person. He energetically searched for food, ate with careful greed, exercised furiously, groomed his plumage continuously. His feathers were still ugly, but this did not worry him. The important thing was that his whiskers grew. He took to crouching rigidly, for hours on end, head up, staring into the night sky, whiskers vibrating, reaching out to home; and trying not to despair when no answer came.

When Christopher was four months old, and the summer was fading, Ch-tsal's feathers were so splendid that he had to be still more careful about hiding himself. He glittered in the darkness; and knew that not all humans slept all night. Some were hunters, as Christopher had told him. They had killing weapons.

But one particular night when Ch-tsal was reaching out to the sky, he heard his mother's voice, very faintly and brokenly. He replied: she heard. There came all sorts of marvelous, tearful, joyous words. . . .

Ch-tsal forgot caution and went mad. In the dewy moonlight of the woods, he became a firework, a bombshell, a Catherine wheel,[3] spinning and zooming and bouncing off tree trunks. He whizzed and somersaulted and flashed and looped the loop on the wet leaves.

Two young men, hopefully poaching with airguns, saw him. But Ch-tsal saw them first and beamed a single pulse of ecstasy so powerful that the young men fell over backwards. They shook their heads and gaped.

They never mentioned the incident to each other or anyone else, fearing to be thought fools.

Nor did they ever mention the spaceship.

SPACESHIP LANDS IN HERTS[4] VILLAGE! The newspaper yelled it. TV followed it up. It seemed a big story: bigger than a baby panda, bigger than the girl singer, a real sensation.

It soon fizzled out. You can get only so much mileage from talking heads on TV screens—from long shots of scientists staring at burnt grass in a roped-off area—from a patch of burnt field with a furrow leading to a dimple like a "!"

WHATEVER BECAME OF CUTIE PIE? seemed a better story. Was there a link between the alien creature and the spaceship? But this faded too. The questions were fine—but where were the answers?

---

3. **Catherine wheel,** a type of firework that, when ignited, revolves on a pin, making a wheel of fire or sparks.
4. **Herts** (härts), Hertfordshire (härt'fərd shər), a county of southeastern England.

Only one person on Earth knows them and he is still too young to tell them to anyone but his mother. . . .

"He come. He did come."

"Did he, darling? I'm glad. Hold your mug properly."

"He did come last night, oh yes. It was nice."

"Drink up, darling. More. More."

"Telling stories he was, oh yes. And come again soon."

"You're sure *you're* not telling stories, darling? Drink it all up, there's a big boy."

Christopher sticks out his lower lip and stares at his mother. Why should she think him a liar? Why won't she accept a simple truth—that quite often, in the night, someone else is there beside him in bed (not actually there, only in his mind, but there all the same)—and that they tell each other stories—and that this friendship will last all his life?

His mother kisses C. H. Winters.

C. H. Winters forgives his mother and finishes his milk.

THINK AND DISCUSS
Understanding
1. How do the people on Earth react to Ch-tsal when they first see him on TV?
2. What is the greatest mistake that Earth scientists make about Ch-tsal?
3. What are the facts about Ch-tsal?
4. After escaping, what does Ch-tsal discover about Earth?

Analyzing
5. What do the reactions of Earth humans to Ch-tsal reveal about the lowest Earth minds?
6. What is the most extraordinary of Ch-tsal's qualities?
7. What kinds of thoughts do C. H. Winters and Ch-tsal share?

Extending
8. If an Earth person were accidentally taken to Ch-tsal's planet, what kinds of misunderstandings might occur there?

VOCABULARY
Context

He received the *wound*
when he *wound* the toy.

Which of the italicized words above means "injury"? What does the other italicized word mean? When a word has more than one meaning or pronunciation, the context often indicates which meaning or pronunciation is intended. The context of an unfamiliar word also can provide clues to its meaning.

On your paper write the letter of the correct meaning for each italicized word in the sentences that follow. Choice **d** ("no helpful clue") will be used once.

1. Two young men, hopefully *poaching* with airguns, saw Ch-tsal. (**a**) simmering food in a liquid; (**b**) trespassing on someone's land to hunt or fish; (**c**) knitting; (**d**) no helpful clue

2. When Ch-tsal's health grew worse, the doctors who took care of him feared that they would be accused of *incompetence*. (**a**) excellence; (**b**) cheating; (**c**) lack of ability; (**d**) no helpful clue

3. Later Ch-tsal saw that he had shed his *iridescent* feathers. (**a**) shabby; (**b**) gaudy; (**c**) dull; (**d**) no helpful clue

4. Ch-tsal worked *incessantly* to free himself, not even stopping to eat or sleep. (**a**) continually; (**b**) dispiritedly; (**c**) on and off; (**d**) no helpful clue

5. Though terrified by the *calamity* of having lost all his feathers, Ch-tsal pulled himself together and set about the task of growing new ones. (**a**) joy; (**b**) misfortune; (**c**) silliness; (**d**) no helpful clue

COMPOSITION
Writing a Report

Imagine you are Ch-tsal. Write a brief report to send back to your planet, through your whiskers, of course. What would you want to tell about life on Earth? Before you begin, reread parts of the story and list specific examples, such as color TV sets, tee shirts, and cats. How would you describe each of these for a person who had never seen one?

Writing a News Story

Write a short news story about Ch-tsal's capture. First review that part of the story. Take notes about *who* was involved, *what* happened, *where* and *when* the event occurred, and *why* it happened. Use these five Ws to write your news story. See Lesson 1, "Writing About Literature," in the Writer's Handbook.

ENRICHMENT
Working with a Group

Work with a small group of your classmates. Decide what happens to Ch-tsal after the spaceship lands in Herts Village. Does he return to his planet? Does he later come back to Earth to contact C. H.? Be creative. Suggest as many possibilities as you can, such as what he finds on his planet. Then, as a group, prepare an oral report for the others in the class.

BIOGRAPHY

Nicholas Fisk
1923–

Although he has done various kinds of writing, Nicholas Fisk prefers to write science fiction for young people. According to him, science-fiction writers are freer than other writers because they can make up characters and events that do not exist in the world today. Science fiction is often referred to as SF. Fisk thinks it should be "IF" because science-fiction stories are about possibilities, which are more interesting than facts. Fisk has been an actor, a publisher, a musician, an illustrator, and a photographer. Yet he says that, above all, he is a writer.

All human beings need food, sleep, shelter, and work—and many believe that people need stories as well. You probably tell stories every day as you talk with your friends about what is happening in your life. Through experience, you learn how to tell stories that will keep others interested. In a similar way, the author of a written story learns how to keep readers interested. A story may be adventurous, humorous, mysterious, suspenseful, or sad. Readers keep reading because they want to find out how it all turns out in the end.

A **short story** is much briefer than a novel, and it has fewer characters and situations. The reader may not get to know everything about the main character in a short story, but usually that character goes through some kind of experience or change. Readers learn about **characters** through the author's description of their physical appearances, actions, words, and inner thoughts. Authors also reveal their characters by showing how other characters feel about them.

The interactions between characters develop into the **plot.** A plot is a pattern of events in a **cause-and-effect relationship.** For example, in "Cutie Pie" Ch-tsal is able to escape his prison because the food bowl jams the glass wall as it is closing.

As characters interact, they come into conflict with each other, with nature, or with society, or they discover a conflict within themselves. If the conflict is with other forces, it is external; a conflict with

your friends is an external conflict. If the conflict is within a person, it is internal; if you feel guilt over some action, or have difficulty in making a decision, you have internal conflict. The conflict builds to a certain point, called the turning point, or the climax. This climax turns the story in a different direction, toward the conclusion, which is the wrapping up, or ending, of the story.

The **setting** in a ring is the part that holds the jewel in place. The word *setting* is used for the time and place of a story in that the setting—when and where the story takes place—holds the action. Time and place can be very important in some stories, maybe even the center of attention, and not so important in others. Sometimes the reader must guess where and when the story takes place, using clues given by the author.

A story sometimes has an underlying meaning, or **theme.** It may be stated but usually it isn't. As you read, think about the meaning behind the events and the characters' actions. For example, the theme of "Cutie Pie" could be stated as follows: When there is understanding and identification, communication is possible even though no words are spoken.

The individual techniques used by authors to develop plot, characters, setting, and theme work together smoothly so that you are not conscious that they are working to bring enjoyable reading. That is the end result—enjoyment.

See PLOT in the Handbook of Literary Terms, page 649.

The Widow and the Parrot

Virginia Woolf

"Bless us and save us!" the old woman cried out. "There's a house on fire—thanks be to the Lord!"

Some fifty years ago Mrs. Gage, an elderly widow, was sitting in her cottage in a village called Spilsby in Yorkshire.[1] Although lame and rather short sighted she was doing her best to mend a pair of clogs, for she had only a few shillings a week to live on. As she hammered at the clog, the postman opened the door and threw a letter into her lap.

It bore the address "Messrs. Stagg and Beetle, 67 High Street, Lewes,[2] Sussex."

Mrs. Gage opened it and read:

"Dear Madam: We have the honor to inform you of the death of your brother Mr. Joseph Brand."

"Lawk a mussy," said Mrs. Gage. "Old brother Joseph gone at last!"

"He has left you his entire property," the letter went on, "which consists of a dwelling house, stable, cucumber frames, mangles, wheelbarrows, etc., etc., in the village of Rodmell, near Lewes. He also bequeaths to you his entire fortune; Viz: £3,000 (three thousand pounds)[3] sterling."

Mrs. Gage almost fell into the fire with joy. She had not seen her brother for many years, and, as he did not even acknowledge the Christmas card which she sent him every year, she thought that his miserly habits, well known to her from childhood, made him grudge even a penny stamp for a reply. But now it had all turned out to her advantage. With three thousand pounds, to say nothing of house, etc., etc., she and her family could live in great luxury forever.

She determined that she must visit Rod-

---

1. **Yorkshire** (yôrk'shər), a county of northeastern England. In this story, the character Mrs. Gage travels from her home in Yorkshire to Sussex, a southern county.
2. **Lewes** (lü'is).
3. **three thousand pounds**, an amount of British money worth almost fifteen thousand dollars at the time.

mell at once. The village clergyman, the Rev. Samuel Tallboys, lent her two pound ten, to pay her fare, and by next day all preparations for her journey were complete. The most important of these was the care of her dog Shag during her absence, for in spite of her poverty she was devoted to animals, and often went short herself rather than stint her dog of his bone.

She reached Lewes late on Tuesday night. In those days, I must tell you, there was no bridge over the river at Southease, nor had the road to Newhaven yet been made. To reach Rodmell it was necessary to cross the river Ouse[4] by a ford, traces of which still exist, but this could only be attempted at low tide, when the stones on the river bed appeared above the water. Mr. Stacey, the farmer, was going to Rodmell in his cart, and he kindly offered to take Mrs. Gage with him. They reached Rodmell about nine o'clock on a November night and Mr. Stacey obligingly pointed out to Mrs. Gage the house at the end of the village which had been left her by her brother. Mrs. Gage knocked at the door. There was no answer. She knocked again. A very strange high voice shrieked out "Not at home." She was so much taken aback that if she had not heard footsteps coming she would have run away. However the door was opened by an old village woman, by name Mrs. Ford.

"Who was that shrieking out 'Not at home'?" said Mrs. Gage.

"Drat the bird!" said Mrs. Ford very peevishly, pointing to a large grey parrot. "He almost screams my head off. There he sits all day humped up on his perch like a monument screeching 'Not at home' if ever you go near his perch." He was a very handsome bird, as Mrs. Gage could see; but his feathers were sadly neglected. "Perhaps he is unhappy, or he may be hungry," she said. But Mrs. Ford said it was temper merely; he was a seaman's parrot and had learnt his language in the east. However, she added, Mr. Joseph was very fond of him, had called him James; and, it was said, talked to him as if he were a rational being. Mrs. Ford soon left. Mrs. Gage at once went to her box and fetched some sugar which she had with her and offered it to the parrot, saying in a very kind tone that she meant him no harm, but was his old master's sister, come to take possession of the house, and she would see to it that he was as happy as a bird could be. Taking a lantern she next went round the house to see what sort of property her brother had left her. It was a bitter disappointment. There were holes in all the carpets. The bottoms of the chairs had fallen out. Rats ran along the mantelpiece. There were large toadstools growing through the kitchen floor. There was not a stick of furniture worth seven pence halfpenny; and Mrs. Gage only cheered herself by thinking of the three thousand pounds that lay safe and snug in Lewes Bank.

She determined to set off to Lewes next day in order to claim her money from Messrs. Stagg and Beetle the solicitors,[5] and then to return home as quick as she could. Mr. Stacey, who was going in to market with some fine Berkshire pigs, again offered to

---

4. *Ouse* (üz).
5. *solicitor*, a lawyer in Britain who can advise clients and prepare cases but can plead cases only in a lower court.

take her with him, and told her some terrible stories of young people who had been drowned through trying to cross the river at high tide, as they drove. A great disappointment was in store for the poor old woman directly she got in to Mr. Stagg's office.

"Pray take a seat, Madam," he said, looking very solemn and grunting slightly. "The fact is," he went on, "that you must prepare to face some very disagreeable news. Since I wrote to you I have gone carefully through Mr. Brand's papers. I regret to say that I can find no trace whatever of the three thousand pounds. Mr. Beetle, my partner, went himself to Rodmell and searched the premises with the utmost care. He found absolutely nothing—no gold, silver, or valuables of any kind—except a fine grey parrot which I advise you to sell for whatever he will fetch. His language, Benjamin Beetle said, is very extreme. But that is neither here nor there. I much fear you have had your journey for nothing. The premises are dilapidated; and of course our expenses are considerable." Here he stopped, and Mrs. Gage well knew that he wished her to go. She was almost crazy with disappointment. Not only had she borrowed two pound ten from the Rev. Samuel Tallboys, but she would return home absolutely empty handed, for the parrot James would have to be sold to pay her fare. It was raining hard, but Mr. Stagg did not press her to stay, and she was too beside herself with sorrow to care what she did. In spite of the rain she started to walk back to Rodmell across the meadows.

Mrs. Gage, as I have already said, was lame in her right leg. At the best of times she walked slowly, and now, what with her disappointment and the mud on the bank, her progress was very slow indeed. As she plodded along, the day grew darker and darker, until it was as much as she could do to keep on the raised path by the river side. You might have heard her grumbling as she walked, and complaining of her crafty brother Joseph, who had put her to all this trouble "Express," she said, "to plague me. He was always a cruel little boy when we were children," she went on. "He liked worrying the poor insects, and I've known him trim a hairy caterpillar with a pair of scissors before my very eyes. He was such a miserly varmint too. He used to hide his pocket money in a tree, and if anyone gave him a piece of iced cake for tea, he cut the sugar off and kept it for his supper. I make no doubt he's all aflame at this very moment in Hell fire, but what's the comfort of that to me?" she asked, and indeed it was very little comfort, for she ran slap into a great cow which was coming along the bank, and rolled over and over in the mud.

She picked herself up as best she could and trudged on again. It seemed to her that she had been walking for hours. It was now pitch dark and she could scarcely see her own hand before her nose. Suddenly she bethought her of Farmer Stacey's words about the ford. "Lawk a mussy," she said, "however shall I find my way across? If the tide's in, I shall step into deep water and be swept out to sea in a jiffy! Many's the couple that been drowned here; to say nothing of horses, carts, herds of cattle, and stacks of hay."

Indeed what with the dark and the mud she had got herself into a pretty pickle. She

Will Barnet, *The Golden Thread*, 1980
Courtesy Kennedy Galleries, Inc., New York

could hardly see the river itself, let alone tell whether she had reached the ford or not. No lights were visible anywhere, for, as you may be aware, there is no cottage or house on that side of the river nearer than Asheham House, lately the seat of Mr. Leonard Woolf.[6] It seemed that there was nothing for it but to sit down and wait for the morning. But at her age, with the rheumatics in her system, she might well die of cold. On the other hand, if she tried to cross the river it was almost certain that she would be drowned. So miserable was her state that she would gladly have changed places with one of the cows in the field. No more wretched old woman could have been found in the whole county of Sussex; standing on the river bank, not knowing whether to sit or to swim, or merely to roll over in the grass, wet though it was, and sleep or freeze to death, as her fate decided.

At that moment a wonderful thing happened. An enormous light shot up into the sky, like a gigantic torch, lighting up every blade of grass, and showing her the ford not twenty yards away. It was low tide, and the crossing would be an easy matter if only the light did not go out before she had got over.

"It must be a Comet or some such wonderful monstrosity," she said as she hobbled across. She could see the village of Rodmell brilliantly lit up in front of her.

"Bless us and save us!" she cried out. "There's a house on fire—thanks be to the Lord"—for she reckoned that it would take some minutes at least to burn a house down, and in that time she would be well on her way to the village.

"It's an ill wind that blows nobody any good," she said as she hobbled along the Roman road. Sure enough, she could see every inch of the way, and was almost in the village street when for the first time it struck her: "Perhaps it's my own house that's blazing to cinders before my very eyes!"

She was perfectly right.

A small boy in his nightgown came capering up to her and cried out, "Come and see old Joseph Brand's house ablaze!"

All the villagers were standing in a ring round the house handing buckets of water which were filled from the well in Monk's house kitchen, and throwing them on the flames. But the fire had got a strong hold, and just as Mrs. Gage arrived, the roof fell in.

"Has anybody saved the parrot?" she cried.

"Be thankful you're not inside yourself, Madam," said the Rev. James Hawkesford, the clergyman. "Do not worry for the dumb creatures. I make no doubt the parrot was mercifully suffocated on his perch."

But Mrs. Gage was determined to see for herself. She had to be held back by the village people, who remarked that she must be crazy to hazard her life for a bird.

"Poor old woman," said Mrs. Ford, "she has lost all her property, save one old wooden box, with her night things in it. No doubt we should be crazed in her place too."

So saying, Mrs. Ford took Mrs. Gage by the hand and led her off to her own cottage, where she was to sleep the night. The fire was now extinguished, and everybody went home to bed. But poor Mrs. Gage could not sleep. She tossed and tumbled thinking of her mis-

6. **Mr. Leonard Woolf,** the husband of the author. (The setting of this story is the town where the author actually lived.) Here, *seat* means "home."

erable state, and wondering how she could get back to Yorkshire and pay the Rev. Samuel Tallboys the money she owed him. At the same time she was even more grieved to think of the fate of the poor parrot James. She had taken a liking to the bird, and thought that he must have an affectionate heart to mourn so deeply for the death of old Joseph Brand, who had never done a kindness to any human creature. It was a terrible death for an innocent bird, she thought; and if only she had been in time, she would have risked her own life to save his.

She was lying in bed thinking these thoughts when a slight tap at the window made her start. The tap was repeated three times over. Mrs. Gage got out of bed as quickly as she could and went to the window. There, to her utmost surprise, sitting on the window ledge, was an enormous parrot. The rain had stopped and it was a fine moonlight night. She was greatly alarmed at first, but soon recognized the grey parrot, James, and was overcome with joy at his escape. She opened the window, stroked his head several times, and told him to come in. The parrot replied by gently shaking his head from side to side, then flew to the ground, walked away a few steps, looked back as if to see whether Mrs. Gage were coming, and then returned to the window sill, where she stood in amazement.

"The creature has more meaning in its acts than we humans know," she said to herself. "Very well, James," she said aloud, talking to him as though he were a human being, "I'll take your word for it. Only wait a moment while I make myself decent."

So saying she pinned on a large apron, crept as lightly as possible downstairs, and let herself out without rousing Mrs. Ford.

The parrot James was evidently satisfied. He now hopped briskly a few yards ahead of her in the direction of the burnt house. Mrs. Gage followed as fast as she could. The parrot hopped, as if he knew his way perfectly, round to the back of the house, where the kitchen had originally been. Nothing now remained of it except the brick floor, which was still dripping with the water which had been thrown to put out the fire. Mrs. Gage stood still in amazement while James hopped about, pecking here and there, as if he were testing the bricks with his beak. It was a very uncanny sight, and had not Mrs. Gage been in the habit of living with animals, she would have lost her head, very likely, and hobbled back home. But stranger things yet were to happen. All this time the parrot had not said a word. He suddenly got into a state of the greatest excitement, fluttering his wings, tapping the floor repeatedly with his beak, and crying so shrilly, "Not at home! Not at home!" that Mrs. Gage feared that the whole village would be roused.

"Don't take on so, James; you'll hurt yourself," she said soothingly. But he repeated his attack on the bricks more violently than ever.

"Whatever can be the meaning of it?" said Mrs. Gage, looking carefully at the kitchen floor. The moonlight was bright enough to show her a slight unevenness in the laying of the bricks, as if they had been taken up and then relaid not quite flat with the others. She had fastened her apron with a large safety pin, and she now prized this pin between the bricks and found that they were only loosely laid together. Very soon she had taken one up in her hands. No sooner had she done this than the parrot hopped onto the brick next to it, and, tapping it smartly with his beak, cried, "Not at home!" which Mrs. Gage understood to mean that she was to move it. So they went on taking up the bricks in the moonlight until they had laid bare a space some six feet by four and a half. This the parrot seemed to think was enough. But what was to be done next?

Mrs. Gage now rested, and determined to be guided entirely by the behavior of the parrot James. She was not allowed to rest for long. After scratching about in the sandy foundations for a few minutes, as you may have seen a hen scratch in the sand with her claws, he unearthed what at first looked like a round lump of yellowish stone. His excitement became so intense that Mrs. Gage now went to his help. To her amazement she found that the whole space which they had uncovered was packed with long rolls of these round yellow stones, so neatly laid together that it was quite a job to move them. But what could they be? And for what purpose had they been hidden here? It was not until they had removed the entire layer on the top, and next a piece of oil cloth which lay beneath them, that a most miraculous sight was displayed before their eyes—there, in row after row, beautifully polished, and shining brightly in the moonlight, were thousands of brand new sovereigns!!!![7]

This, then, was the miser's hiding place; and he had made sure that no one would detect it by taking two extraordinary precautions. In the first place, as was proved later, he had built a kitchen range over the spot where his treasure lay hid, so that unless the fire had destroyed it, no one could have guessed its existence: and secondly he had coated the top layer of sovereigns with some sticky substance, then rolled them in the earth, so that if by any chance one had been laid bare no one would have suspected that it was anything but a pebble such as you may see for yourself any day in the garden. Thus, it was only by the extraordinary coincidence of the fire and the parrot's sagacity that old Joseph's craft was defeated.

Mrs. Gage and the parrot now worked hard and removed the whole hoard—which numbered three thousand pieces, neither more nor less—placing them in her apron which was spread upon the ground. As the three thousandth coin was placed on the top of the pile, the parrot flew up into the air in triumph and alighted very gently on the top of Mrs. Gage's head. It was in this fashion that they returned to Mrs. Ford's cottage, at a very slow pace, for Mrs. Gage was lame, as I have said, and now she was almost weighted to the ground by the contents of her apron. But she reached her room without any one knowing of her visit to the ruined house.

Next day she returned to Yorkshire. Mr. Stacey once more drove her into Lewes and was rather surprised to find how heavy Mrs. Gage's wooden box had become. But he was a quiet sort of man, and merely concluded that the kind people at Rodmell had given her a few odds and ends to console her for the dreadful loss of all her property in the fire.

---

7. *sovereigns* (sov′rənz), British gold coins worth one pound sterling.

Out of sheer goodness of heart Mr. Stacey offered to buy the parrot off her for half a crown; but Mrs. Gage refused his offer with such indignation, saying that she would not sell the bird for all the wealth of the Indies, that he concluded that the old woman had been crazed by her troubles.

It now only remains to be said that Mrs. Gage got back to Spilsby in safety; took her black box to the Bank; and lived with James the parrot and her dog Shag in great comfort and happiness to a very great age.

It was not till she lay on her death bed that she told the clergyman (the son of the Rev. Samuel Tallboys) the whole story, adding that she was quite sure that the house had been burnt on purpose by the parrot James, who, being aware of her danger on the river bank, flew into the scullery, and upset the oil stove which was keeping some scraps warm for her dinner. By this act, he not only saved her from drowning, but brought to light the three thousand pounds, which could have been found in no other manner. Such, she said, is the reward of kindness to animals.

The clergyman thought that she was wandering in her mind. But it is certain that the very moment the breath was out of her body, James the parrot shrieked out, "Not at home! Not at home!" and fell off his perch stone dead. The dog Shag had died some years previously.

Visitors to Rodmell may still see the ruins of the house, which was burnt down fifty years ago, and it is commonly said that if you visit it in the moonlight you may hear a parrot tapping with his beak upon the brick floor, while others have seen an old woman sitting there in a white apron.

THINK AND DISCUSS
Understanding
1. What is Mrs. Gage's financial condition at the beginning of the story?
2. What are Mrs. Gage's reactions to the letter she receives?
3. Draw a map and then explain how Mrs. Gage travels between each of the following two places: (a) from her home in Spilsby to her brother's home in Rodmell; (b) from Rodmell to Lewes; (c) from Lewes back to Rodmell.

Analyzing
4. What does Mrs. Gage's treatment of the dog, Shag, and her treatment of the parrot, James, show about the kind of person she is?
5. According to Mrs. Gage's memory of Joseph Brand, what kind of person was he?

Extending
6. Why do you think James said only the one phrase, "Not at home"?
7. When Mrs. Gage sees the house burning but realizes it allows her to cross the river by its light, she says, "It's an ill wind that blows nobody any good." When in your life or in the life of a character about whom you have read did an ill wind blow some good?

APPLYING: Plot H⟋
See Handbook of Literary Terms, p. 649.
In developing a **plot**, an author chooses a pattern of related events to present and resolve some conflict. The conflict may be external or internal. In the pattern of

events, each incident grows out of the one that happened before it.

1. What is the main conflict in "The Widow and the Parrot"?
2. Is the main conflict an external or an internal conflict? Explain.
3. Put the following events in the order in which they happen in the story.
   (a) The widow leaves home.
   (b) The widow meets James, the parrot.
   (c) A telegram is delivered to the widow.
   (d) James falls over dead.
   (e) The widow gets bad news from the bankers.
   (f) James leads the widow to the coins.
   (g) The widow crosses the river with the light from the burning house.
   (h) The widow and the parrot live in comfort and happiness.

READING LITERATURE SKILLFULLY
Cause/Effect Relationships

In a story, an incident often is caused by and logically follows the one that happened before it. For example, a shepherd boy in a well-known fable "cried wolf" all the time, even though there was no wolf in sight. The result was that the village people did not believe his cry for help when a wolf actually did come.

For each of the following effects, give the cause.

1. Mrs. Gage makes a trip to Rodmell.
2. Mrs. Gage is disappointed when she goes to the office of her solicitor, Mr. Stagg.
3. Mrs. Gage is able to cross the river on foot although it is dark.
4. She finds the coins.

VOCABULARY
Dictionary

A dictionary entry contains many kinds of information in addition to the definition of the word. Use the Glossary in the back of this book to answer the following questions.

1. The pronunciation key at the top of each right-hand page in the Glossary tells you how to pronounce the sound symbols in parentheses after the entry word. What words in the pronunciation key stand for the vowel sounds in *sagacity?*
2. Primary (') and secondary (') accent marks tell you which syllables to stress. Does the accented syllable in *sagacity* rhyme with *mass* or *may?*
3. Two pronunciations are given for *hoard.* According to the first one, does *hoard* rhyme with *curd, card,* or *cord?*
4. Separate numbered entries are given for two or more words that have the same spelling but different origins and meanings. Which entry for *mangle* fits the meaning of the word as it is used in the sixth paragraph of the first column on page 13?
5. A synonym is a word having the same or nearly the same meaning as another word. What are two synonyms for *uncanny?*
6. *Obligingly* is included as a run-on entry at the end of another entry. Under what entry word do you find *obligingly?*
7. What part of speech is *obligingly?*
8. The origin, or history, of a word is provided in brackets at the end of an entry. From what two languages does *hazard* come?
9. What was the original meaning of *hazard?*

THINKING SKILLS
Evaluating

To evaluate is to make a judgment based on some sort of standard. For example, a critic sees a movie and often gives a review that includes an evaluation of how true to life it is compared to other movies the critic has seen.

Compare the incidents that occur in this story with things you know are likely to happen in real life. Do you judge this story to be realistic, or do you think it is unlikely to have ever happened?

COMPOSITION
Writing About a Pet

Many pets have saved human lives. Write a paragraph or two about a situation in which a pet helps a person. You may choose to write about a pet you have owned or known or one you have read about. Begin by describing the person and the animal. Be sure to give specific details about how the animal acted.

Describing a Character

After reading this story, what idea do you have about the kind of person Mrs. Gage is? In your own words, write a short description of her for a friend who has not read the story. Include details about her physical appearance, her favorite sayings, her strong beliefs, and how she affects the people who meet and know her. Before you begin, go back to the story and find specific details. You may wish to write a second paragraph in which you contrast her with her brother, Joseph. See Lesson 2, "Supporting Your Ideas," in the Writer's Handbook.

BIOGRAPHY

Virginia Woolf
1882–1941

Virginia Woolf was educated at home by her father, Sir Leslie Stephen, a distinguished writer and critic. After his death she moved to London with her brother and sister. Their home in Bloomsbury, a district of London, was the meeting place of a number of famous intellectuals, who became known as the Bloomsbury Group. In 1912 she married Leonard Woolf and with him founded the Hogarth Press. The press published the early works of many noted writers. Virginia Woolf wrote several successful novels, as well as short stories and essays. Her long essay, *A Room of One's Own*, forcefully presented the difficulties facing the woman writer in 1929.

Review PLOT in the Handbook of Literary Terms, page 649.

Raymond's Run

Toni Cade Bambara

Just before I take off in a race, I always feel like I'm in a dream. . . .

I don't have much work to do around the house like some girls. My mother does that. And I don't have to earn my pocket money by running errands and selling Christmas cards. My brother George does that. And anything else that's got to get done, my father does.

All I have to do is mind my brother Raymond, which is enough. He's much bigger and he's older, too, but a lot of people call him my little brother because he's not quite right and needs looking after. And if any of these smart mouths try to pick on Raymond, they have to deal with me, and I don't believe in just standing around talking. I'd much rather knock them down and take my chances, even if I am a girl with skinny arms and a squeaky voice, which is how I got my nickname Squeaky. And if things get too rough, I run.

As anybody can tell you, I'm the fastest thing on two feet. There is no track meet where I don't win the first-place medal. I used to win the twenty-yard dash when I was a little kid. Nowadays it's the hundred-yard dash.

I'm the swiftest thing in the neighborhood. Everyone knows that except the two people who know better—my father and me. My father can beat me in a race to Amsterdam Avenue with me getting a head start and him running with his hands in his pockets and whistling. But can you imagine a thirty-five-year-old man stuffing himself into a pair of shorts just to beat his kid in a race?

So, as far as everyone's concerned, I'm the fastest. Except for Gretchen, who has put out the story that she is going to win the first-place medal this year. Ridiculous. No one can beat me, and that's all there is to that.

After school I usually take a walk down Broadway so I can practice my breathing exercises. I always keep Raymond walking on the inside, close to the buildings, because he's subject to fits of fantasy and sometimes starts thinking he's a circus performer and that the curb is a tightrope strung high in the air.

Or sometimes, if I don't watch him, he'll run across traffic to one of the parks and give the pigeons a fit. Then I have to go around apologizing to all the people sitting on the benches who are all shook up with the pigeons fluttering around them, scattering newspapers, and upsetting their sack lunches.

So I keep Raymond on the inside, and today he starts playing like he's driving a stagecoach. This is okay with me so long as he doesn't run over me or interrupt my breathing exercises, which I have to do on account of I'm serious about my running and don't care who knows it.

Now some people like to act like things come easy to them and won't let on that they practice. But not me. You can see me any time of the day practicing. I never walk if I can run, and Raymond always keeps up because, if he hangs back, someone is likely to walk up behind him and get smart and take his allowance.

So I'm going down Broadway breathing out and breathing in, in counts of seven. And suddenly here comes Gretchen with her sidekicks—Mary Louise, who used to be a friend of mine when she first moved to Harlem[1] from Cincinnati, and Rosie, who is as fat as I am skinny and has a big mouth where Raymond is concerned and is too stupid to know that there is not a big deal of difference between herself and Raymond.

So they are coming up Broadway, and I see right away that it's going to mean trouble because the street ain't that big. First I think I'll step into the candy store and look over the new comics and let them pass. But that's chicken, and I've got a reputation to consider. So then I think I'll just walk straight on through them, or over them if necessary. But as they get to me, they slow down.

"You signing up for the Field Day races?" smiles Mary Louise.

A dumb question like that doesn't deserve an answer.

"I don't think you're going to win this time," says Rosie, trying to signify[2] with her hands on her hips all salty.

"I always win 'cause I'm the best," I say straight at Gretchen.

Gretchen smiles. But it's not really a smile, and I'm thinking that girls never ever really smile at each other because they don't know how and don't want to know how.

Then Rosie looks at Raymond, who has just brought his make-believe stagecoach to a stop. And she's about to see what trouble she can stir up through him. "What grade you in now, Raymond?" she asks.

"You got anything to say to my brother, you say it to me," I tell her.

"What are you, his mother?" sasses Rosie.

"That's right, fatso."

So they just stand there, and Gretchen puts her hands on her hips and is about to say something but doesn't. Then she walks around me and looks me up and down, but she keeps moving up Broadway and her sidekicks follow her. So me and Raymond

---

1. *Harlem,* a region of New York City.
2. *signify,* make clever and insulting comments about the person you are speaking to. (Slang)

Hughie Lee-Smith, *Boy with Tire*, 1952, Detroit Institute of Arts

smile at each other and he says "Giddyap" to his team of horses and I continue with my breathing exercises.

On Field Day I take my time getting to the park because the track meet is the last thing on the program. I put Raymond in the swings. Then I look around for Mr. Pearson, who pins the numbers on. I'm really looking for Gretchen, if you want to know the truth, but she's not around.

The park is packed with parents in hats and little kids in white dresses and light blue suits. Some older guys with their caps on backwards are leaning against the fence swirling basketballs on the tips of their fingers, waiting for all these crazy people to clear out so they can play.

Then here comes Mr. Pearson with his clipboard and his cards and pencils and whistles and fifty million other things he's always dropping. He sticks out in a crowd because he looks like he's on stilts. We used to call him Jack the Beanstalk to get him mad. But I'm the only one who can outrun him and get away, and now I'm too grown for silly name calling.

"Well, Squeaky," he says, checking my name off the list, and handing me number seven and two pins.

I'm thinking he's got no right to call me Squeaky if I don't call him Beanstalk. "Hazel Elizabeth Deborah Parker," I correct him, and tell him to write it down that way on his board.

"Well, Hazel Elizabeth Deborah Parker, are you going to give someone else a break this year?"

I squint at him real hard to see if he is seriously thinking I should lose the race on purpose just to give someone else a break.

"Only eight girls running this time," he continues, shaking his head sadly like it's my fault all of New York didn't turn out in sneakers. "That new girl should give you a run for your money." He looks around the park for Gretchen like a periscope in a submarine movie. "Wouldn't it be a nice gesture if you were to . . . to ah . . ."

I give him such a look that he can't finish putting that idea into words. Then I pin number seven on myself and stomp away, I'm so burned. I go straight to the track and stretch out on the grass.

The man on the loudspeaker begins calling everyone over to the track for the first event, which is the twenty-yard dash. The race takes two minutes because most of the little kids don't know better than to run off the track or run the wrong way or run smack into the fence and fall down and cry.

Then comes the fifty-yard dash, and I don't even bother to turn my head to watch because Raphael Perez[3] always wins by psyching out the other runners, telling them they're going to fall on their faces or lose their shorts or something.

Then I hear my brother Raymond hollering from the swings. He knows I'm about to do my thing because the man on the loudspeaker has just announced the hundred-yard dash.

I get up and slip off my sweat pants and then I see Gretchen standing at the starting line, kicking her legs like a pro. Then as I get into place, I see Raymond on the other side of the fence, bending down with his fingers on the ground just like he knew what he was doing. I start to yell at him but I don't. It burns up your energy to holler.

Just before I take off in a race, I always feel like I'm in a dream, the kind of dream you have when you're sick with fever and feel all hot and weightless. I dream I'm flying over a sandy beach in the early morning sun, touching the leaves of the trees as I fly by. And all the time I feel myself getting lighter and lighter.

Then I spread my fingers in the dirt and crouch over for the Get-On-Your-Mark yell. I stop dreaming and I am solid again and telling myself, "Squeaky, you must win. You must win. You are the fastest thing in the world. You can even beat your father if you try."

And then I feel my weight coming back just behind my knees, then down to my feet, and the pistol shot explodes in my blood, and I am off and weightless again, flying past the other runners. My arms pump up and down, and the whole world is quiet except for the crunch-crunch as I zoom over the gravel on the track.

I glance to my left, and there is no one. But to my right is Gretchen, who's got her chin jutting out as if it would win the race all by itself. And on the other side of the fence is my brother Raymond with his arms down at his side and the palms tucked up behind him, running in his very own style. It's the first time I've ever seen him do that, and I almost stop to watch.

But the white ribbon is bouncing toward me, and I tear past it, running hard till my feet—with a mind of their own—start digging up footfuls of dirt and stop me. Then all the kids standing on the sidelines pile on me,

---

3. *Raphael Perez* (räf'ä əl pä'räs).

slapping me on the back with their Field Day programs because they think I've won again and everybody on 151st Street can walk tall for another year.

"In first place——" The man on the loudspeaker pauses, and the loudspeaker starts to whine. Then some static. I lean down to catch my breath, and I see Gretchen doing the same thing—huffing and puffing with her hands on her hips, taking it slow, breathing in steady time like a real pro—and I sort of like her a little for the first time.

"In first place——" Then three or four voices get all mixed up on the loudspeaker, and I dig my sneaker in the grass and stare at Gretchen who's staring back, both wondering just who did win. I can hear old Beanstalk arguing with the man on the loudspeaker about what the stopwatches say.

Then I hear Raymond yanking at the fence and calling me, and I wave to shush him. But he keeps rattling the fence like a gorilla in a cage, and he starts climbing up nice and easy. And it occurs to me, watching how smoothly he climbs and remembering how he looked running with the wind pulling his mouth back and his teeth showing and all, it occurs to me that Raymond would make a very fine runner. Doesn't he always keep up with me on my practices? And he surely knows how to breathe in counts of seven 'cause he's always doing it at the dinner table.

And I'm smiling to beat the band because if I've lost this race, or if me and Gretchen have tied, or even if I've won, I can always retire as a runner and begin a whole new career as a coach with Raymond as my champion.

I stand there laughing out loud as Ray-mond jumps down from the fence and runs over to me with his arms down at his side in his own running style. And by the time he comes over, I'm jumping up and down I'm so glad to see him.

But of course everyone thinks I'm jumping up and down because the men have finally gotten themselves together and the loudspeaker is announcing, "In first place—Miss Hazel Elizabeth Deborah Parker. In second place—Miss Gretchen B. Lewis."

And I look over at Gretchen wondering what the B stands for. And I smile. Maybe she'd like to help me coach Raymond because she's obviously serious about running. And she nods to congratulate me. Then she smiles, too, and it's about as real a smile as girls can do for each other.

THINK AND DISCUSS
Understanding
1. What is Squeaky's responsibility in her family?
2. In what ways does Squeaky work at being the fastest runner in her neighborhood?
3. Why does Squeaky become upset with what Mr. Pearson says on the day of the big race?

Analyzing
4. What kind of person is Squeaky? Give examples from the story to describe her appearance and her qualities.
5. After the race, what change seems to

occur in the relationship between Squeaky and Gretchen?

6. Is "Raymond's Run" a good title for this story? Explain.

Extending

7. Do you think Gretchen's smile at the end of the story is sincere? Why or why not?

REVIEWING: Plot H⯐

See Handbook of Literary Terms, p. 649.

In developing a **plot**, the author includes a climax, or turning point. It may be something a character does to cause a change, or it may be an event that takes place and brings about a change. The conclusion, or ending, is the solution of the conflict.

1. What do you think is the turning point of this story?

2. What happens in the conclusion?

THINKING SKILLS
Generalizing

To generalize is to draw a general conclusion from particular information.

Squeaky's statement that ". . . girls never ever really smile at each other because they don't know how and don't want to know how" is a generalization. Do you agree with it? If so, give examples to support your opinion. If not, explain why you think it is not sound.

COMPOSITION ⟸
Writing About a Story

Choose something from this story to which you relate because you find it exciting or because it is something you enjoy doing. For example, you might choose the Field Day races or Squeaky's ability to run fast. Write a paragraph or two explaining what part of the story you enjoyed most and why. Before you begin, review the story to find examples to support your choice.

Being a Story Character

Imagine you are Gretchen B. Lewis. Write a diary entry for the day you lost the race to Squeaky. Before beginning, reread the ending of the story. What do the girls' actions show about their feelings at this time?

BIOGRAPHY

Toni Cade Bambara

1939–

Many of Toni Cade Bambara's stories are about young people such as Squeaky in "Raymond's Run." These characters are often sensitive, yet tough and energetic individuals. Much of what Bambara writes is a reflection of her own active and varied life. Her published books include *Gorilla, My Love* and *Tales and Stories for Black Folks*.

Review PLOT in the Handbook of Literary Terms, page 649.

One Night Stand

Louis L'Amour

"Look, son," the man said, "you've undoubtedly got nerve, and probably you're a fine actor, but this man is a killer. . . . You wouldn't have a chance!"

tephen Malone was tall, handsome, immaculate, and broke. He lay on his back, hands clasped behind his head, trying not to think about breakfast. Three weeks ago he had been playing lead roles in *Hearts of Oak*, *Hamlet*, and *Davy Crockett* on successive nights. Then the bookings ran out, the play closed, and the manager skipped town with the company funds, leaving them stranded.

For some time he had been aware of voices in the next room. A girl was speaking. "He can't! He wouldn't dare!"

The man's tone was touched with despair. "They say he's killed fourteen men. For the kind of money Mason would pay, the Kid wouldn't hesitate to make it fifteen."

There was a pause. "Even before my hand was crippled I couldn't match him. Now I wouldn't stand a chance."

"But Pa, if Hickok comes——?"

"If he can get here in time! He's not the kind to forget what I did for him, but unless he shows up I'm finished. Else,[1] I'd give a thousand dollars to see Bill Hickok[2] walk through that door right now!"

Stephen Malone knew a cue when he heard one. He stepped into the hall and rapped on the door of their room.

"Who's there?" It was the man's voice.

"Bill Hickok."

The door opened and he was facing a thin old man with gray hair, and a pretty, dark-

---

1. *Else* (el'zə).

2. *Bill Hickok.* Else's father is referring to James Butler Hickok (1837–1876), an American frontier scout and U.S. marshal, better known as Wild Bill Hickok.

haired girl. "You aren't Bill Hickok!" The man was disgusted.

"No," Malone said, "but for a thousand dollars I will be."

"You're a gunfighter?" Else demanded.

"I'm an actor. It is my business to make people believe I am somebody else."

"This is different. This isn't playacting."

"He could kill you," Else said. "You wouldn't have a chance."

"Not if I'm a good enough actor. Not many men would try to draw a gun on Wild Bill Hickok."

"It's a fool idea," the man said.

"So there's an element of risk. I've played Hamlet, Macbeth, and Shylock.[3] Why not Wild Bill?"

"Look, son, you've undoubtedly got nerve, and probably you're a fine actor, but this man is a killer. Oh, I know he's a tinhorn,[4] but you wouldn't have a chance!"

"Not if I'm a good enough actor."

"He's talking nonsense, and you both know it!" Else protested.

"To play Hickok, son, you've got to be able to shoot like Hickok."

"Only if I play it badly. You say the Kid is a tinhorn, I'll trust to your judgment and my skill."

Brady walked to the window. "It might work, you know. It just might."

"It would be suicide!" Else objected.

Brady turned from the window. "I am Emmett Brady. This is my daughter, Else. Frank Mason wants my range, and the Pioche[5] Kid is a friend of his. He was brought here to kill me."

"The pleasure will be mine, sir," Malone bowed.

"Did anyone see you come into the hotel?" Brady asked.

"Only the man at the desk. It was two o'clock in the morning."

"Then it's all right. Jim Cooley is a friend of mine."

"Get him to spread the story that Hickok is in town, and once the story is around, I'll make my play."

"It's ridiculous!" Else declared. "Why should you risk your life for us?"

"Miss Brady, as much as I'd enjoy posing as Sir Galahad, I cannot. I'm no knight in armor, just a stranded actor. But for a thousand dollars? I haven't made that much in a whole season!"

"You've got sand, Malone. Else, fetch Jim Cooley."

"You've still time to back out," Else warned.

"I am grateful for your concern but this will be the first time I have been offered one thousand dollars for a single performance."

Returning to his room, Malone opened his trunk and chose a blond wig with hair to his shoulders. He selected a drooping mustache. ". . . And the buckskin jacket I wore as Davy Crockett.[6] Then I'll remove the plume from this hat I wore in *Shenandoah*——"

The Pioche Kid stared complacently into his glass. Brady was an old man with a bad right hand. He was nothing to worry about.

Jim Cooley came through the swinging

---

3. *Hamlet, Macbeth, and Shylock*, three characters in plays by William Shakespeare; all are demanding roles requiring talented actors.

4. *tinhorn*, a noisy show-off.

5. *Pioche* (pē ōch').

6. *Davy Crockett*, American hunter, scout, and congressman killed in 1836 at the Alamo.

H. H. Cross, *Wild Bill Hickok*
The Thomas Gilcrease Institute of American History and Art, Tulsa, Oklahoma

doors. "Give me a shot, Sam." He glanced around the room. "Wait until you boys hear who is in town! Wild Bill himself! Rode in last night, all the way from Kansas because he heard his old friend Emmett Brady needed help!"

The Pioche Kid went sick with shock. Somebody was asking what Brady had on Hickok. "Nursed him back to health after a gunshot wound. Hickok nearly killed a couple of horses getting here. He's sleeping it off over at the hotel now."

Wild Bill Hickok! The Kid hadn't bargained for this. He took up his whiskey and tossed it off, but the shudder that followed was not caused by the whiskey.

"Sam . . . ?" He pushed the empty glass toward him.

He could feel the excitement in the room. They were thinking they'd see the Pioche Kid shoot it out with Wild Bill Hickok, the most famous of them all.

Somebody mentioned the fourteen men the Kid was supposed to have killed, but the Kid himself knew there had been but four, and two of those had been drunken cowhands, and one of them a drunken farmer who had never held a pistol before.

Suddenly, desperately, he wanted out. How had he got into this, anyway? Hickok could *shoot!* He recalled the stories of Hickok's famous target matches with the renowned Major Talbot, at Cheyenne.[7]

"He's the best," Cooley was saying. "Eyes in the back of his head, seems like. Remember the time he killed Phil Coe, then turned and killed a man running up behind him?"

Cooley smiled at the Kid. "Should be something, you and him. You've killed more than he has if you discount those he killed while a sharp-shooter in the Army. But I did see him take four at once. Killed two, a third died later, and the fourth was never any good for anything after."

Cooley finished his drink. "I'm gettin' out of here. I've seen too many bystanders get gut-shot. Sorry I can't wish you luck, Kid, but Bill's a friend of mine."

Men moved to the tables, away from the bar. One hastily paid for his drink and left the bar. The Kid was alone, isolated, cut off.

What the blazes was happening? This was *Hickok!* If he won they'd all slap him on the back and buy him drinks, but if he lost they'd just stare at the body as they walked by. He mopped his face. He was soaked with sweat, and he knew why. He was scared.

Mason was at the door. "He's comin', Kid. Be something to be known as the man who killed Wild Bill."

Malone paused in the door to wave at someone down the street, then he walked to the bar. All eyes were on him. "Rye, if you please."

Sam put a bottle and a glass before him. The Kid licked dry lips with a fumbling tongue. Desperately he wanted to wipe his palm dry on his pants, but he was afraid Hickok would think he was going for a gun. Now was the time. He should open the ball. Sweat dripped from his face to the bar. He opened his mouth to speak, but Malone spoke first.

"Bartender, I'd like to find two men for a little job. I'll pay a dollar each. It's a digging job."

---

7. *Cheyenne* (shī an'), capital of Wyoming.

"You said . . . a *digging* job?"

"That's right. I want two men to dig a hole about—" he turned deliberately and looked right at the Kid, "—six feet long, six feet deep, and three wide."

"Whereabouts do you want it dug?"

"On Boot Hill."

"A grave?"

"Exactly."

Sam motioned to two men at a nearby table. "Tom? Joe? Mr. Hickok wants a couple of men." He hesitated ever so slightly. "To dig a grave."

"And to make a slab for a marker," Malone said.

Sam was loving every moment of it. "You want a name on it?"

"Don't bother with the name. Within the week they will have forgotten who he was, anyway. Just carve on it HE SHOULD HAVE LEFT BEFORE THE SUN WENT DOWN."

He finished his drink. "Good afternoon, gentlemen."

He strolled to the door, paused briefly with his hand on the door, then stepped out on the boardwalk and turned toward the hotel.

Within the saloon a chair creaked as someone shifted weight. The Kid lifted a fumbling hand to brush away the sweat from his face and the hand trembled. He tossed off his drink, spilling a little on his chin. Never had death seemed so close.

What kind of a fool was he, anyway? What did he have to do with Brady? Let Mason do his own killing. Suddenly all he wanted was to be away, away from those watching eyes, staring at him, so willing to see him die.

What did he owe Mason? All he had to do was cross the street, mount his horse and ride. Behind his back they would sneer, but what did that matter? He owed these people nothing, and there were a thousand towns like this. Moreover, he'd be alive . . . *alive!*

He wanted to feel the sunshine on his face, the wind in his hair, to drink a long, cold drink of water. He wanted to live!

Abruptly, he walked to the door. He had seen men die, seen them lie tormented in the bloody dust. He did not want to feel the tearing agony of a bullet in his guts.

There was Hickok, his broad back to him, only a few paces away. A quick shot . . . he could always say Hickok had turned.

Sweat dripped into his eyes, dimly he remembered *eyes in the back of his head.* On that other occasion Hickok had turned suddenly and fired . . . dead center.

The Kid let go of his gun as if it were red hot.

Yet he could still make it. He was a pretty good shot . . . well, a fair shot. He could——

Two men emerged from the livery stable, each carrying a shovel. Tom and Joe, to dig a grave . . . *his* grave?

He crossed the street, almost running, and jerked loose the tie-rope. He missed the stirrup with his first try, made it on the second, and was almost crying when he hit the saddle. He wheeled the horse from the hitch-rail and left town at a dead run.

His saddle was hot from the sun, but he could *feel* it. The wind was in his face . . . he was free! He was riding, he was living, and there were a lot of other towns, a lot of country.

Brady turned from the window. "He's gone, Else. Malone did it."

"Mason's leaving, too," she added.

The door opened behind them and Stephen Malone stepped in, removing his hat, then the wig and the mustache. "That's one part I never want to play again!"

"Here's your money, son. You earned it."

"Thanks."

"What would you have done, Malone," Cooley asked, "if the Kid had called your hand?"

"Done? Why this——!"

His draw was surprisingly fast, and he fired at Cooley, point-blank. Cooley sprang back, shocked. His hands clutched his abdomen.

His hands came away and he stared at them. No blood. No——!

Malone was smiling.

"Blanks!" Cooley exclaimed. "You faced the Kid with nothing in your gun but blanks!"

"Well, why not? It was all part of the act."

THINK AND DISCUSS
Understanding
1. What are the immediate problems of Stephen Malone and Emmett Brady as the story opens?
2. Why do the Bradys doubt that Malone can help them?
3. When is Malone's life most in danger?
4. What is the surprising last part of Malone's act?

Analyzing
5. What does the Kid think when he hears Malone's description of the grave and words to be carved on the marker?
6. Contrast the character traits shown by Stephen Malone and the Pioche Kid.
7. A story has suspense when its outcome is uncertain. What is the moment of greatest suspense in this story?

Extending
8. Suppose you are Malone and the Kid says to you, "Draw right now. Count to three." What would you do?

REVIEWING: Plot HΖ
See Handbook of Literary Terms, p. 649.

To develop a **plot**, an author chooses a pattern of events to present and resolve a conflict. The conflict may be external or internal. The incidents are arranged in a cause and effect relationship, with many of the incidents necessary links leading to the climax and conclusion of the work.

1. What characters are in conflict in this story?
2. Which character has the most inner conflict?
3. What important event has been omitted from this list?
   - (a) Frank Mason brings the Pioche Kid to town.
   - (b) Emmett Brady hires Malone.
   - (c) Jim Cooley announces that Hickok is in town.
   - (d) The Pioche Kid jumps on his horse and leaves town.

4. What is the climax, or turning point, in this story?
5. What is the conclusion of the story?

COMPOSITION
Writing a Journal Entry
If Malone had kept a journal about his performance as an actor, what might he have said about his meeting with the Pioche Kid? Pretend you are Malone and write a one-paragraph account, beginning with the words "Today I had the greatest challenge of my performing career." Include a description of the costume as well as the performance.

Writing a Scene
Imagine that the real Wild Bill Hickok arrives in town at the end of the story, right after Malone has fired the blank. Write a scene in which Hickok demands an explanation and listens to the story as told by Malone and Brady. You may write in paragraph form or in the form of a play.

Consider that Hickok would probably hear the firing of the blank and see Malone with a gun drawn. How do you think Hickok would respond?

ENRICHMENT
Reading Dialogue Aloud
Although the dialogue in short stories is often lean and short, its use helps to create lively stories. Note the conversation beginning on page 29 with "He can't! He wouldn't dare!" and ending on page 30 with "I am grateful for your concern . . . ."

Choose readers for the parts of Emmett Brady, his daughter, and Stephen Malone. Practice reading the parts, saying only the words that are in quotation marks. Remember to express the way the character feels. Those in the class who listen to the first reading may later take a turn, or they may read other sections of dialogue, such as the scene in which Cooley announces that Wild Bill has arrived in town.

BIOGRAPHY

Louis L'Amour
1908–1988

Louis L'Amour claimed that his writing began as a "spur-of-the-moment thing," encouraged by friends who enjoyed hearing his stories of the West. L'Amour's love for the western United States is evident in his more than two hundred novels and short stories. This love for the West came from his extensive travels and his adventurous life.

After leaving Jamestown, North Dakota, at fifteen, the self-educated L'Amour worked as a longshoreman, lumberjack, boxer, elephant handler, and freight hopper.

L'Amour, who wrote three novels a year, researched his stories carefully and read a great deal. Over thirty motion pictures have been based on his stories.

Writer's Craft

Be Specific

Good writers are specific. When they tell about a character or place, they want the reader to be able to see clearly what they are describing. To do this, they must use specifics, which are exact details and particular pieces of information. For example, "a shady, old oak" instead of "a tree" gives us a more complete picture. A "faint shower of piano notes" is more vivid than "soft music."

In "Cutie Pie," notice the details Nicholas Fisk uses to help the reader visualize a creature from another planet:

> . . . millions of human eyes, glued to millions of color TV sets, goggled rapturously at the iridescent "feathers" . . . that covered Cutie Pie's curved, cozy, rounded body. Human hearts doted on his dark, liquid eyes . . . .
>
> (page 3, column 1)

Good writers also use specifics to show us things about their characters that can't be seen, such as inner qualities and feelings. Virginia Woolf shows what a miser Joseph was in "The Widow and the Parrot" by including the following details from his past:

> He used to hide his pocket money in a tree, and if anyone gave him a piece of iced cake for tea, he cut the sugar off and kept it for his supper.
>
> (page 16, column 2)

In "One Night Stand," you know the Kid is scared because Louis L'Amour shows you this fear in a detailed and specific way:

> The Kid licked dry lips with a fumbling tongue. Desperately he wanted to wipe his palm dry . . . .
>
> (page 32, column 2)

As you can see, by using specifics, an author can make you feel that you are experiencing the story right along with the characters. The same goes for your own writing. A sure way to make it more lively and exciting is to be specific.

An article on writer's craft appears in every unit of this book. Each article covers a different technique used by good writers. As you study *Discoveries in Literature*, you might keep a **reading/writing log.** In it, record examples from your reading of the writing technique discussed in "The Writer's Craft." Reviewing your log before you write will help you use these techniques to improve your own composition. Suggestions about what to record are found after some selections in each unit.

Noticing specific details makes you a better reader.

Using specific details makes you a better writer.

See CHARACTERIZATION in the Handbook of Literary Terms, page 635.

Gentleman of Río en Medio

Juan A. A. Sedillo

The old man had agreed to sell his land, but there was one thing he couldn't sell . . .

It took months of negotiation to come to an understanding with the old man. He was in no hurry. What he had the most of was time. He lived up in Río en Medio,[1] where his people had been for hundreds of years. He tilled the same land they had tilled. His house was small and wretched, but quaint. The little creek ran through his land. His orchard was gnarled and beautiful.

The day of the sale he came into the office. His coat was old, green and faded. I thought of Senator Catron, who had been such a power with these people up there in the mountains. Perhaps it was one of his old Prince Alberts.[2] He also wore gloves. They were old and torn and his fingertips showed through them. He carried a cane, but it was only the skeleton of a worn-out umbrella. Behind him walked one of his innumerable kin —a dark young man with eyes like a gazelle.

The old man bowed to all of us in the room. Then he removed his hat and gloves, slowly and carefully. Chaplin[3] once did that in a picture, in a bank—he was the janitor. Then he handed his things to the boy, who stood obediently behind the old man's chair.

There was a great deal of conversation, about rain and about his family. He was very proud of his large family. Finally we got down to business. Yes, he would sell, as he had agreed, for twelve hundred dollars, in cash. We would buy, and the money was

---

Juan (hwän) Sedillo (se dē'yô)

1. *Río en Medio* (rē'ô en me'dyô), the name of a town, meaning "River in the Middle."
2. *Prince Alberts*, long, double-breasted coats, named after Prince Albert (1819–1861), husband of Queen Victoria of England.
3. *Chaplin*, Charles Chaplin (1889–1977), English-born motion-picture actor, especially noted for his comedy pantomime in early silent movies.

"Gentleman of Río en Medio" by Juan A. A. Sedillo from *The New Mexico Quarterly*, August 1939. Reprinted by permission of the author.

ready. "Don Anselmo,"[4] I said to him in Spanish, "we have made a discovery. You remember that we sent that surveyor, that engineer, up there to survey your land so as to make the deed. Well, he finds that you own more than eight acres. He tells us that your land extends across the river and that you own almost twice as much as you thought." He didn't know that. "And now, Don Anselmo," I added, "these Americans are *buena gente*,[5] they are good people, and they are willing to pay you for the additional land as well, at the same rate per acre, so that instead of twelve hundred dollars you will get almost twice as much, and the money is here for you."

The old man hung his head for a moment in thought. Then he stood up and stared at me. "Friend," he said, "I do not like to have you speak to me in that manner." I kept still and let him have his say. "I know these Americans are good people, and that is why I have agreed to sell to them. But I do not care to be insulted. I have agreed to sell my house and land for twelve hundred dollars and that is the price."

I argued with him but it was useless. Finally he signed the deed and took the money but refused to take more than the amount agreed upon. Then he shook hands all around, put on his ragged gloves, took his stick and walked out with the boy behind him.

A month later my friends had moved into Río en Medio. They had replastered the old adobe house, pruned the trees, patched the fence, and moved in for the summer. One day they came back to the office to complain. The children of the village were overrunning their property. They came every day and played under the trees, built little play fences around them, and took blossoms. When they were spoken to they only laughed and talked back good-naturedly in Spanish.

I sent a messenger up to the mountains for Don Anselmo. It took a week to arrange another meeting. When he arrived he repeated his previous preliminary performance. He wore the same faded cutaway, carried the same stick and was accompanied by the boy again. He shook hands all around, sat down with the boy behind his chair, and talked about the weather. Finally I broached the subject. "Don Anselmo, about the ranch you sold to these people. They are good people and want to be your friends and neighbors always. When you sold to them you signed a document, a deed, and in that deed you agreed to several things. One thing was that they were to have the complete possession of the property. Now, Don Anselmo, it seems that every day the children of the village overrun the orchard and spend most of their time there. We would like to know if you, as the most respected man in the village, could not stop them from doing so in order that these people may enjoy their new home more in peace."

Don Anselmo stood up. "We have all learned to love these Americans," he said, "because they are good people and good neighbors. I sold them my property because I knew they were good people, but I did not sell them the trees in the orchard."

This was bad. "Don Anselmo," I pleaded,

---

4. **Don Anselmo** (dôn än sel′mô). *Don* is a Spanish title meaning "Mr." or "Sir."
5. **buena gente** (bwä′nä hen′te), good people.

Paul Klee, *Kleine Rhythmische Landschaft*,
Piperdruck Nr. 181

"when one signs a deed and sells real property one sells also everything that grows on the land, and those trees, every one of them, are on the land and inside the boundaries of what you sold."

"Yes, I admit that," he said. "You know," he added, "I am the oldest man in the village. Almost everyone there is my relative and all the children of Río en Medio are my *sobrinos* and *nietos*,[6] my descendants. Every time a child has been born in Río en Medio since I took possession of that house from my mother I have planted a tree for that child. The trees in that orchard are not mine, *Señor*, they belong to the children of the village.

Every person in Río en Medio born since the railroad came to Santa Fe owns a tree in that orchard. I did not sell the trees because I could not. They are not mine."

There was nothing we could do. Legally we owned the trees but the old man had been so generous, refusing what amounted to a fortune for him. It took most of the following winter to buy the trees, individually, from the descendants of Don Anselmo in the valley of Río en Medio.

---

6. *sobrinos* (sô brē′nôs) *and nietos* (nē e′tôs), nephews and nieces, and grandchildren.

THINK AND DISCUSS
Understanding
1. How are the people of Río en Medio related to Don Anselmo?
2. How do the children bother the new American residents?
3. How does Don Anselmo explain why he never sold the trees in the first place?

Analyzing
4. The **narrator** is the person telling the story. What is the narrator's feeling about Don Anselmo?
5. How is Don Anselmo a gentleman?

Extending
6. Do you think that the narrator takes advantage of Don Anselmo, or that Don Anselmo takes advantage of the narrator? Explain.

APPLYING: Characterization H𝒯
See Handbook of Literary Terms, p. 635.
Characterization is the method an author uses to create a fictional person. One way an author may develop a character is through describing the character's physical appearance.
1. What details do you remember about the physical appearance of Don Anselmo?
2. Which of the following details might the author have chosen to include in describing Don Anselmo? Be sure any new detail supports his total image.
   (a) a new silk scarf at his neck
   (b) worn leather boots
   (c) a top hat turned gray with time
   (d) a diamond stickpin in his tie

3. Don Anselmo reminds the narrator of Senator Catron and of Charles Chaplin. Explain how he is like each man.

VOCABULARY
Pronunciation Key

Use the Glossary or a dictionary to answer the questions about the words in italics in the following sentences.

1. What do the pronunciations of the words *gnarled* and *pneumonia* have in common?
2. Is the first syllable of *preliminary* pronounced the same as the first syllable of *predestine?*
3. What two letters represent the sound spelled *qu* in the word *quaint?*
4. Does the *a* in *gazelle* represent the sound of *a* in *hat, about,* or *far?*
5. Is the vowel sound in the first syllable of *innumerable* like the vowel sound in *let, it,* or *ice?*

COMPOSITION
Reading/Writing Log

In this story, the narrator uses many specific words to describe Don Anselmo's appearance. Two examples are given. Copy the examples in your **reading/writing log.** Then find at least four other examples in the story and add them to your log.

old man
coat is old (page 37, column 1)

Being a Story Character

Imagine that you are the young man who accompanies Don Anselmo to the lawyer's office. Write a brief account of what happens during the second trip for future generations to read. Before you begin to write, list details of what happens during that visit. If you are keeping a **reading/writing log,** note the describing words that you recorded earlier and try to be as specific when you make your own list.

Describing a Character

Choose an older person you have known and write a one-paragraph description of this person. Be sure to describe the person's appearance and tell about any actions that have impressed you. Before you begin to write, list details for the paragraph. If you are keeping a **reading/writing log,** refer to it for ideas.

BIOGRAPHY
Juan A. A. Sedillo
1902–1982

Juan A. A. Sedillo was born in New Mexico. He was descended from the earliest Spanish settlers of the southwestern United States and Mexico. He lived in both countries and worked as a lawyer and judge in the city of Santa Fe. He also shared his experiences by writing newspaper columns and stories such as this tale based on memories of an incident from his legal career.

Review CHARACTERIZATION in the Handbook of Literary Terms, page 635.

The Old Demon

Pearl S. Buck

Two very different enemies in two very different conflicts—how could old Mrs. Wang win against either?

ld Mrs. Wang knew of course that there was a war. Everybody had known for a long time that there was war going on and that Japanese were killing Chinese. But still it was not real and no more than hearsay since none of the Wangs had been killed. The Village of Three Mile Wangs on the flat banks of the Yellow River, which was old Mrs. Wang's clan village, had never even seen a Japanese. This was how they came to be talking about Japanese at all.

It was evening and early summer, and after her supper Mrs. Wang had climbed the dike steps, as she did every day, to see how high the river had risen. She was much more afraid of the river than of the Japanese. She knew what the river would do. And one by one the villagers had followed her up the dike, and now they stood staring down at the malicious yellow water, curling along like a lot of snakes, and biting at the high dike banks.

"I never saw it as high as this so early," Mrs. Wang said. She sat down on a bamboo stool that her grandson, Little Pig, had brought for her, and spat into the water.

"It's worse than the Japanese, this old devil of a river," Little Pig said recklessly.

"Fool!" Mrs. Wang said quickly. "The river god will hear you. Talk about something else."

So they had gone on talking about the Japanese. . . . How, for instance, asked Wang, the baker, who was old Mrs. Wang's nephew twice removed, would they know the Japanese when they saw them?

Mrs. Wang at this point said positively, "You'll know them. I once saw a foreigner.

He was taller than the eaves of my house and he had mud-colored hair and eyes the color of a fish's eyes. Anyone who does not look like us—that is a Japanese."

Everybody listened to her since she was the oldest woman in the village and whatever she said settled something.

Then Little Pig spoke up in his disconcerting way. "You can't see them, Grandmother. They hide up in the sky in airplanes."

Mrs. Wang did not answer immediately. Once she would have said positively, "I shall not believe in an airplane until I see it." But so many things had been true which she had not believed—the Empress, for instance, whom she had not believed dead, was dead. The Republic,[1] again, she had not believed in because she did not know what it was. She still did not know, but they had said for a long time there had been one. So now she merely stared quietly about the dike where they all sat around her. It was very pleasant and cool, and she felt nothing mattered if the river did not rise to flood.

"I don't believe in the Japanese," she said flatly.

They laughed at her a little, but no one spoke. Someone lit her pipe—it was Little Pig's wife, who was her favorite, and she smoked it.

"Sing, Little Pig!" someone called.

So Little Pig began to sing an old song in a high, quavering voice, and old Mrs. Wang listened and forgot the Japanese. The evening was beautiful, the sky so clear and still that the willows overhanging the dike were reflected even in the muddy water. Everything was at peace. The thirty-odd houses which made up the village straggled along beneath them. Nothing could break this peace. After all, the Japanese were only human beings.

"I doubt those airplanes," she said mildly to Little Pig when he stopped singing. But without answering her, he went on to another song.

Year in and year out she had spent the summer evenings like this on the dike. The first time she was seventeen and a bride, and her husband had shouted to her to come out of the house and up the dike, and she had come, blushing and twisting her hands together, to hide among the women while the men roared at her and made jokes about her. All the same, they had liked her. "A pretty piece of meat in your bowl," they had said to her husband. "Feet a trifle big," he had answered deprecatingly. But she could see he was pleased, and so gradually her shyness went away.

He, poor man, had been drowned in a flood when he was still young. And it had taken her years to get him prayed out of Buddhist purgatory.[2] Finally she had grown tired of it, what with the child and the land all on her back, and so when the priest said coaxingly, "Another ten pieces of silver and he'll be out entirely," she asked, "What's he got in there yet?"

"Only his right hand," the priest said, encouraging her.

---

1. **The Republic.** For thousands of years China was an empire ruled by a succession of emperors and empresses. In 1912 the Republic of China was established. It lasted until 1949.
2. **Buddhist purgatory.** Buddhism as a religion held a position in the Orient similar to that of Christianity in the western world. Some forms of Buddhism teach of a heaven, hell, and purgatory where souls are purified.

Well, then, her patience broke. Ten dollars! It would feed them for the winter. Besides, she had had to hire labor for her share of repairing the dike, too, so there would be no more floods.

"If it's only one hand, he can pull himself out," she said firmly.

She often wondered if he had, poor silly fellow. As like as not, she had often thought gloomily in the night, he was still lying there, waiting for her to do something about it. That was the sort of man he was. Well, some day, perhaps, when Little Pig's wife had had the first baby safely and she had a little extra, she might go back to finish him out of purgatory. There was no real hurry, though. . . .

"Grandmother, you must go in," Little Pig's wife's soft voice said. "There is a mist rising from the river now that the sun is gone."

"Yes, I suppose I must," old Mrs. Wang agreed. She gazed at the river a moment. That river—it was full of good and evil together. It would water the fields when it was curbed and checked, but then if an inch were allowed it, it crashed through like a roaring dragon. That was how her husband had been swept away—careless, he was, about his bit of the dike. He was always going to mend it, always going to pile more earth on top of it, and then in a night the river rose and broke through. He had run out of the house, and she had climbed on the roof with the child and had saved herself and it while he was drowned. Well, they had pushed the river back again behind its dikes, and it had stayed there this time. Every day she herself walked up and down the length of the dike for which the village was responsible and examined it.

The men laughed and said, "If anything is wrong with the dikes, Granny will tell us."

It had never occurred to any of them to move the village away from the river. The Wangs had lived there for generations, and some had always escaped the floods and had fought the river more fiercely than ever afterward.

Little Pig suddenly stopped singing.

"The moon is coming up!" he cried. "That's not good. Airplanes come out on moonlight nights."

"Where do you learn all this about airplanes?" old Mrs. Wang exclaimed. "It is tiresome to me," she added, so severely that no one spoke. In this silence, leaning upon the arm of Little Pig's wife, she descended slowly the earthen steps which led down into the village, using her long pipe in the other hand as a walking stick. Behind her the villagers came down, one by one, to bed. No one moved before she did, but none stayed long after her.

And in her own bed at last, behind the blue cotton mosquito curtains which Little Pig's wife fastened securely, she fell peacefully asleep.

She had lain awake a little while thinking about the Japanese and wondering why they wanted to fight. Only very coarse persons wanted wars. In her mind she saw large coarse persons. If they came one must wheedle them, she thought, invite them to drink tea, and explain to them, reasonably— only why should they come to a peaceful farming village . . . ?

So she was not in the least prepared for Little Pig's wife screaming at her that the

Keith Ferris, *Damaged Mitsubishi "Zero" Aircraft*, 1977

Japanese had come. She sat up in bed muttering, "The tea bowls—the tea——"

"Grandmother, there's no time!" Little Pig's wife screamed. "They're here—they're here!"

"Where?" old Mrs. Wang cried, not awake.

"In the sky!" Little Pig's wife wailed.

They had all run out at that, into the clear early dawn, and gazed up. There, like the wild geese flying in autumn, were great bird-like shapes.

"But what are they?" old Mrs. Wang cried.

And then, like a silver egg dropping, something drifted straight down and fell at the far end of the village in a field. A fountain of earth flew up, and they all ran to see it. There was a hole thirty feet across, as big as a pond. They were so astonished they could not speak, and then, before anyone could say anything, another and another egg began to fall and everybody was running, running. . . .

Everybody, that is, but Mrs. Wang. When Little Pig's wife seized her hand to drag her along, old Mrs. Wang pulled away and sat down against the bank of the dike.

"I can't run," she remarked. "I haven't run in seventy years, since before my feet were bound.[3] You go on. Where's Little Pig?" She looked around. Little Pig was already gone. "Like his grandfather," she remarked, "always the first to run."

But Little Pig's wife would not leave her, not, that is, until old Mrs. Wang reminded her that it was her duty.

"If Little Pig is dead," she said, "then it is necessary that his son be born alive." And when the girl still hesitated, she struck at her gently with her pipe. "Go on—go on," she exclaimed.

So unwillingly, because now they could scarcely hear each other speak for the roar of the dipping planes, Little Pig's wife went on with the others.

By now, although only a few minutes had passed, the village was in ruins and the straw roofs and wooden beams were blazing. Everybody was gone. As they passed they had shrieked at old Mrs. Wang to come on, and she had called back pleasantly:

"I'm coming—I'm coming!"

But she did not go. She sat quite alone watching now what was an extraordinary spectacle. For soon other planes came, from where she did not know, but they attacked the first ones. The sun came up over the fields of ripening wheat, and in the clear summery air the planes wheeled and darted and spat at each other. When this was over, she thought, she would go back into the village and see if anything was left. Here and there a wall stood, supporting a roof. She could not see her own house from here. But she was not unused to war. Once bandits had looted their village, and houses had been burned then, too. Well, now it had happened again. Burning houses one could see often, but not this darting silvery shining battle in the air. She understood none of it—not what those things were, nor how they stayed up in the sky. She simply sat, growing hungry, and watching.

---

3. before my feet were bound. Among certain classes, it once was a custom to wrap the feet of young girls in tight bindings. The resulting deformity was considered attractive and further signified that these girls need not work.

"I'd like to see one close," she said aloud. And at that moment, as though in answer, one of them pointed suddenly downward, and, wheeling and twisting as though it were wounded, it fell head down in a field which Little Pig had ploughed only yesterday for soybeans. And in an instant the sky was empty again, and there was only this wounded thing on the ground and herself.

She hoisted herself carefully from the earth. At her age she need be afraid of nothing. She could, she decided, go and see what it was. So, leaning on her bamboo pipe, she made her way slowly across the fields. Behind her in the sudden stillness two or three village dogs appeared and followed, creeping close to her in their terror. When they drew near to the fallen plane, they barked furiously. Then she hit them with her pipe.

"Be quiet," she scolded, "there's already been noise enough to split my ears!"

She tapped the airplane.

"Metal," she told the dogs. "Silver, doubtless," she added. Melted up, it would make them all rich.

She walked around it, examining it closely. What made it fly? It seemed dead. Nothing moved or made a sound within it. Then, coming to the side to which it tipped, she saw a young man in it, slumped into a heap in a little seat. The dogs growled, but she struck at them again and they fell back.

"Are you dead?" she inquired politely.

The young man moved a little at her voice, but did not speak. She drew nearer and peered into the hole in which he sat. His side was bleeding.

"Wounded!" she exclaimed. She took his wrist. It was warm, but inert, and when she let it go, it dropped against the side of the hole. She stared at him. He had black hair and a dark skin like a Chinese and still he did not look like a Chinese.

"He must be a Southerner," she thought. Well, the chief thing was, he was alive.

"You had better come out," she remarked. "I'll put some herb plaster on your side."

The young man muttered something dully.

"What did you say?" she asked. But he did not say it again.

"I am still quite strong," she decided after a moment. So she reached in and seized him about the waist and pulled him out slowly, panting a good deal. Fortunately he was rather a little fellow and very light. When she had him on the ground, he seemed to find his feet; and he stood shakily and clung to her, and she held him up.

"Now if you can walk to my house," she said, "I'll see if it is there."

Then he said something, quite clearly. She listened and could not understand a word of it. She pulled away from him and stared.

"What's that?" she asked.

He pointed at the dogs. They were standing growling, their ruffs up. Then he spoke again, and as he spoke he crumpled to the ground. The dogs fell on him, so that she had to beat them off with her hands.

"Get away!" she shouted. "Who told *you* to kill him?"

And then, when they had slunk back, she heaved him somehow onto her back; and, trembling, half carrying, half pulling him, she dragged him to the ruined village and laid him in the street while she went to find her house, taking the dogs with her.

Her house was quite gone. She found the

place easily enough. This was where it should be, opposite the water gate into the dike. She had always watched that gate herself. Miraculously it was not injured now, nor was the dike broken. It would be easy enough to rebuild the house. Only, for the present, it was gone.

So she went back to the young man. He was lying as she had left him, propped against the dike, panting and very pale. He had opened his coat and he had a little bag from which he was taking out strips of cloth and a bottle of something. And again he spoke, and again she understood nothing. Then he made signs and she saw it was water he wanted, so she took up a broken pot from one of many blown about the street, and, going up the dike, she filled it with river water and brought it down again and washed his wound, and she tore off the strips he made from the rolls of bandaging. He knew how to put the cloth over the gaping wound and he made signs to her, and she followed these signs. All the time he was trying to tell her something, but she could understand nothing.

"You must be from the South, sir," she said. It was easy to see he had education. He looked very clever. "I have heard your language is different from ours." She laughed a little to put him at his ease, but he only stared at her somberly with dull eyes. So she said brightly, "Now if I could find something for us to eat, it would be nice."

He did not answer. Indeed he lay back, panting still more heavily, and stared into space as though she had not spoken.

"You would be better with food," she went on. "And so would I," she added. She was beginning to feel unbearably hungry.

It occurred to her that in Wang, the baker's shop, there might be some bread. Even if it were dusty with fallen mortar, it would still be bread. She would go and see. But before she went she moved the soldier a little so that he lay in the edge of the shadow cast by a willow tree that grew in the bank of the dike. Then she went to the baker's shop. The dogs were gone.

The baker's shop was, like everything else, in ruins. No one was there. At first she saw nothing but the mass of crumpled earthen walls. But then she remembered that the oven was just inside the door, and the door frame still stood erect, supporting one end of the roof. She stood in this frame, and, running her hand in underneath the fallen roof inside, she felt the wooden cover of the iron caldron. Under this there might be steamed bread. She worked her arm delicately and carefully in. It took quite a long time, but, even so, clouds of lime and dust almost choked her. Nevertheless she was right. She squeezed her hand under the cover and felt the firm smooth skin of the big steamed bread rolls, and one by one she drew out four.

"It's hard to kill an old thing like me," she remarked cheerfully to no one, and she began to eat one of the rolls as she walked back. If she had a bit of garlic and a bowl of tea—but one couldn't have everything in these times.

It was at this moment that she heard voices. When she came in sight of the soldier, she saw surrounding him a crowd of other soldiers, who had apparently come from nowhere. They were staring down at the wounded soldier, whose eyes were now closed.

"Where did you get this Japanese, Old Mother?" they shouted at her.

"What Japanese?" she asked, coming to them.

"This one!" they shouted.

"Is he a Japanese?" she cried in the greatest astonishment. "But he looks like us—his eyes are black, his skin——"

"Japanese!" one of them shouted at her.

"Well," she said quietly, "he dropped out of the sky."

"Give me that bread!" another shouted.

"Take it," she said, "all except this one for him."

"A Japanese monkey eat good bread?" the soldier shouted.

"I suppose he is hungry also," old Mrs. Wang replied. She began to dislike these men. But then, she had always disliked soldiers.

"I wish you would go away," she said. "What are you doing here? Our village has always been peaceful."

"It certainly looks very peaceful now," one of the men said, grinning, "as peaceful as a grave. Do you know who did that, Old Mother? The Japanese!"

"I suppose so," she agreed. Then she asked, "Why? That's what I don't understand."

"Why? Because they want our land, that's why!"

"Our land!" she repeated. "Why, they can't have our land!"

"Never!" they shouted.

But all this time while they were talking and chewing the bread they had divided among themselves, they were watching the eastern horizon.

"Why do you keep looking east?" old Mrs. Wang now asked.

"The Japanese are coming from there," the man replied who had taken the bread.

"Are you running away from them?" she asked, surprised.

"There are only a handful of us," he said apologetically.

"We were left to guard a village—Pao An, in the county of——"

"I know that village," old Mrs. Wang interrupted. "You needn't tell me. I was a girl there. How is the old Pao who keeps the teashop in the main street. He's my brother."

"Everybody is dead there," the man replied. "The Japanese have taken it—a great army of men came with their foreign guns and tanks, so what could we do?"

"Of course, only run," she agreed. Nevertheless she felt dazed and sick. So he was dead, that one brother she had left! She was now the last of her father's family.

But the soldiers were straggling away again leaving her alone.

"They'll be coming, those little black dwarfs," they were saying. "We'd best go on."

Nevertheless, one lingered a moment, the one who had taken the bread, to stare down at the young wounded man, who lay with his eyes shut, not having moved at all.

"Is he dead?" he inquired. Then, before Mrs. Wang could answer, he pulled a short knife out of his belt. "Dead or not, I'll give him a punch or two with this——"

But old Mrs. Wang pushed his arm away.

"No, you won't," she said with authority. "If he is dead, then there is no use in sending him into purgatory all in pieces. I am a good Buddhist myself."

The man laughed. "Oh well, he is dead," he answered; and then, seeing his comrades already at a distance, he ran after them.

A Japanese, was he? Old Mrs. Wang, left alone with this inert figure, looked at him tentatively. He was very young, she could see, now that his eyes were closed. His hand, limp in unconsciousness, looked like a boy's hand, unformed and still growing. She felt his wrist but could discern no pulse. She leaned over him and held to his lips the half of her roll which she had not eaten.

"Eat," she said very loudly and distinctly. "Bread!"

But there was no answer. Evidently he was dead. He must have died while she was getting the bread out of the oven.

There was nothing to do then but to finish the bread herself. And when that was done, she wondered if she ought not to follow after Little Pig and his wife and all the villagers. The sun was mounting and it was growing hot. If she were going, she had better go. But first she would climb the dike and see what the direction was. They had gone straight west, and as far as eye could look westward was a great plain. She might even see a good-sized crowd miles away. Anyway, she could see the next village, and they might all be there.

So she climbed the dike slowly, getting very hot. There was a slight breeze on top of the dike and it felt good. She was shocked to see the river very near the top of the dike. Why, it has risen in the last hour!

"You old demon!" she said severely. Let the river god hear it if he liked. He was evil, that he was—so to threaten flood when there had been all this other trouble.

She stooped and bathed her cheeks and her wrists. The water was quite cold, as though with fresh rains somewhere. Then she stood up and gazed around her. To the west there was nothing except in the far distance the soldiers still half-running, and beyond them the blur of the next village, which stood on a long rise of ground. She had better set out for that village. Doubtless Little Pig and his wife were there waiting for her.

Just as she was about to climb down and start out, she saw something on the eastern horizon. It was at first only an immense cloud of dust. But, as she stared at it, very quickly it became a lot of black dots and shining spots. Then she saw what it was. It was a lot of men—an army. Instantly she knew what army.

"That's the Japanese," she thought. Yes, above them were the buzzing silver planes. They circled about, seeming to search for someone.

"I don't know who you're looking for," she muttered, "unless it's me and Little Pig and his wife. We're the only ones left. You've already killed my brother Pao."

She had almost forgotten that Pao was dead. Now she remembered it acutely. He had such a nice shop—always clean, and the tea good and the best meat dumplings to be had and the price always the same. Pao was a good man. Besides, what about his wife and his seven children? Doubtless they were all killed, too. Now these Japanese were looking for her. It occurred to her that on the dike she could easily be seen. So she clambered hastily down.

It was when she was about halfway down that she thought of the water gate. This old river—it had been a curse to them since time began. Why should it not make up a little now for all the wickedness it had done? It was plotting wickedness again, trying to steal over its banks. Well, why not? She wavered a moment. It was a pity, of course, that the young dead Japanese would be swept into the flood. He was a nice-looking boy, and she had saved him from being stabbed. It was not quite the same as saving his life, of course, but still it was a little the same. If he had been alive, he would have been saved. She went over to him and tugged at him until he lay well near the top of the bank. Then she went down again.

She knew perfectly how to open the water gate. Any child knew how to open the sluice for crops. But she knew also how to swing open the whole gate. The question was, could she open it quickly enough to get out of the way?

"I'm only one old woman," she muttered. She hesitated a second more. Well, it would be a pity not to see what sort of a baby Little Pig's wife would have, but one could not see everything. She had seen a great deal in this life. There was an end to what one could see, anyway.

She glanced again to the east. There were the Japanese coming across the plain. They were a long clear line of black, dotted with thousands of glittering points. If she opened this gate, the impetuous water would roar toward them, rushing into the plains, rolling into a wide lake, drowning them, maybe. Certainly they could not keep marching nearer and nearer to her and to Little Pig and his wife who were waiting for her. Well, Little Pig and his wife—they would wonder about her—but they would never dream of this. It would make a good story—she would have enjoyed telling it.

She turned resolutely to the gate. Well, some people fought with airplanes and some with guns, but you could fight with a river, too, if it were a wicked one like this one. She wrenched out a huge wooden pin. It was slippery with silvery green moss. The rill of water burst into a strong jet. When she wrenched one more pin, the rest would give way themselves. She began pulling at it, and felt it slip a little from its hole.

"I might be able to get myself out of purgatory with this," she thought, "and maybe they'll let me have that old man of mine, too. What's a hand of his to all this? Then we'll——

The pin slipped away suddenly, and the gate burst flat against her and knocked her breath away. She had only time to gasp, to the river:

"Come on, you old demon!"

Then she felt it seize her and lift her up to the sky. It was beneath her and around her. It rolled her joyfully hither and thither, and then, holding her close and enfolded, it went rushing against the enemy.

THINK AND DISCUSS

Understanding

1. Why does Mrs. Wang say she doubts the existence of the Japanese and of airplanes?
2. Why doesn't Mrs. Wang flee with the other villagers when the bombing begins?
3. When does Mrs. Wang find out that the wounded soldier is Japanese?
4. What news that affects her personally does she learn from the Chinese soldiers?

Analyzing

5. What has been the role of the river in the lives of the villagers?
6. Why does Mrs. Wang show kindness to the wounded Japanese soldier yet open the water gate when the Japanese army approaches?
7. Does Mrs. Wang triumph or suffer defeat at the end? Explain.

Extending

8. Do you think that the villagers will ever know that Mrs. Wang has opened the flood gate? Give examples to support your opinion.

REVIEWING: Characterization HⱫ
See Handbook of Literary Terms, p. 635.

Characterization is the method an author uses to create a fictional person. An author may develop a character through speech, actions, and inner thoughts or by revealing the attitudes and reactions of other characters.

1. Give an example of Mrs. Wang's actions or words to illustrate each of the following characteristics or traits.
   (**a**) practical
   (**b**) considerate
   (**c**) peace-loving
   (**d**) resourceful
   (**e**) physically strong
   (**f**) courageous
2. How do the villagers regard Mrs. Wang, and what does this show about her character?
3. What do Mrs. Wang's inner thoughts just before the conclusion of the story reveal about her character?

VOCABULARY

Combining Forms

The Yellow River in "The Old Demon" is described as *malicious*. *Malicious* is a form of the word *malice*, which comes from the Latin word *malus*, meaning "poor" or "evil."

The combining form *mal-* is found in many English words. Read the sentences below and explain how the italicized word in each is related to "evil" or "poor" in meaning.

1. An unhappy patient accused Dr. Bache of *malpractice*.
2. The humane society was on hand to make certain that the animals were not *maltreated*.
3. My father told me to stop behaving like a *malcontent* and return to school.
4. We own a normal cat and an unsettled, *maladjusted* poodle.
5. Throughout the world, millions of people suffer from *malnutrition*.

COMPOSITION
Writing a Tribute

Imagine that later in his life Little Pig wants to compose a tribute to his grandmother. Consider what you think Little Pig would say and write two or three paragraphs under the title "An Extraordinary Woman." Choose at least three traits and give examples of Mrs. Wang's actions that show those traits.

Comparing Story Characters

Write two or three paragraphs in which you compare and contrast Mrs. Wang and Don Anselmo, the Gentleman from Río en Medio. Tell ways that they are alike and ways that they are different. Consider where they live, their families and how they feel about them, character traits they share, how the villagers regard them, and how they act to benefit their villages. See Lesson 4, "Writing to Compare and Contrast," in the Writer's Handbook.

ENRICHMENT
Reporting to the Class

Pearl Buck wrote many other stories and novels about China, where she lived with her parents. Her short story "The Big Wave" tells about a family's struggle with a tidal wave. Her book *The Good Earth* won a Nobel Prize in Literature. Find out more about her life or read something she has written. Then choose your own way of reporting to the class.

 ## BIOGRAPHY

Pearl S. Buck
1892–1973

At one time, Pearl Buck was as much at home in China as she was in America. Born in West Virginia, she journeyed to China with her missionary parents when she was only five months old. After growing up in China, she spent her college years back in the United States. Then she returned to China to teach for five years.

Buck's first book appeared in 1930. A year later she published *The Good Earth*, a novel about China. A best seller for nearly two years, *The Good Earth* was produced both as a play and as a movie, and it has been translated into more than thirty languages. Many of her novels, stories, and other writings have revealed in great depth the people of China to readers in the western world—an accomplishment seldom equaled by any westerner.

Review **CHARACTERIZATION** in the Handbook of Literary Terms, page 635.

Stolen Day

Sherwood Anderson

I limped painfully away. I kept on limping until I got out of the schoolhouse street.

---

t must be that all children are actors. The whole thing started with a boy on our street named Walter, who had inflammatory rheumatism.[1] That's what they called it. He didn't have to go to school.

Still he could walk about. He could go fishing in the creek or the waterworks pond. There was a place up at the pond where in the spring the water came tumbling over the dam and formed a deep pool. It was a good place. Sometimes you could get some big ones there.

I went down that way on my way to school one spring morning. It was out of my way but I wanted to see if Walter was there.

He was, inflammatory rheumatism and all. There he was, sitting with a fish pole in his hand. He had been able to walk down there all right.

It was then that my own legs began to hurt. My back too. I went on to school but, at the recess time, I began to cry. I did it when the teacher, Sarah Suggett, had come out into the schoolhouse yard.

She came right over to me.

"I ache all over," I said. I did, too.

I kept on crying and it worked all right.

"You'd better go on home," she said.

So I went. I limped painfully away. I kept on limping until I got out of the schoolhouse street.

Then I felt better. I still had inflammatory rheumatism pretty bad but I could get along better.

I must have done some thinking on the way home.

"I'd better not say I have inflammatory

---

1. *inflammatory rheumatism,* a disease of the joints, usually marked by heat, redness, swelling, and pain.

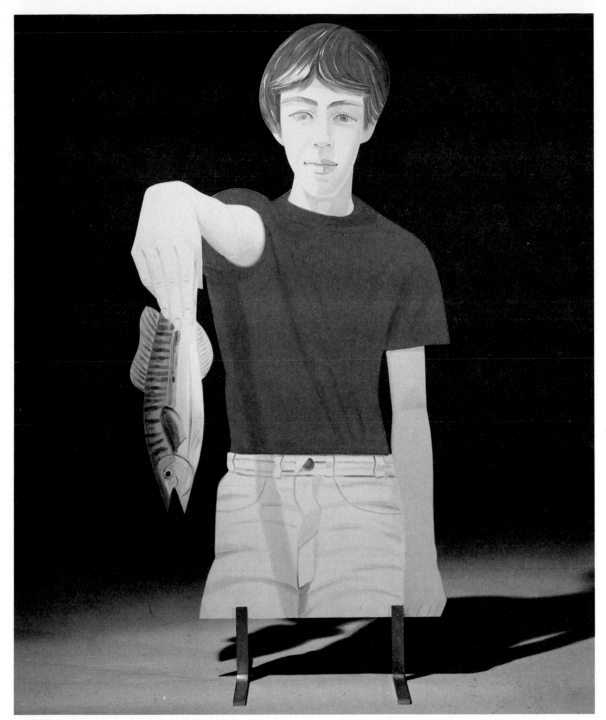

Alex Katz, *Trophy III*, 1973, oil on aluminum
Marlborough Gallery, Inc.

rheumatism," I decided. "Maybe if you've got that you swell up."

I thought I'd better go around to where Walter was and ask him about that, so I did—but he wasn't there.

"They must not be biting today," I thought.

I had a feeling that, if I said I had inflammatory rheumatism, Mother or my brothers and my sister Stella might laugh. They did laugh at me pretty often and I didn't like it at all.

"Just the same," I said to myself, "I have got it." I began to hurt and ache again.

I went home and sat on the front steps of our house. I sat there a long time. There wasn't anyone at home but Mother and the two little ones. Ray would have been four or five then and Earl might have been three.

It was Earl who saw me there. I had got tired sitting and was lying on the porch. Earl was always a quiet, solemn little fellow.

He must have said something to Mother for presently she came.

"What's the matter with you? Why aren't you in school?" she asked.

I came pretty near telling her right out that I had inflammatory rheumatism but I thought I'd better not. Mother and Father had been speaking of Walter's case at the table just the day before. "It affects the heart," Father had said. That frightened me when I thought of it. "I might die," I thought. "I might just suddenly die right here; my heart might stop beating."

On the day before I had been running a race with my brother Irve. We were up at the fairgrounds after school and there was a half-mile track.

"I'll bet you can't run a half mile," he said. "I bet you I could beat you running clear around the track."

And so we did it and I beat him, but afterward my heart did seem to beat pretty hard. I remembered that lying there on the porch. "It's a wonder, with my inflammatory rheumatism and all, I didn't just drop down dead," I thought. The thought frightened me a lot. I ached worse than ever.

"I ache, Ma," I said. "I just ache."

She made me go in the house and upstairs and get into bed.

It wasn't so good. It was spring. I was up there for perhaps an hour, maybe two, and then I felt better.

I got up and went downstairs. "I feel better, Ma," I said.

Mother said she was glad. She was pretty busy that day and hadn't paid much attention to me. She had made me get into bed upstairs and then hadn't even come up to see how I was.

I didn't think much of that when I was up there but when I got downstairs where she was, and when, after I had said I felt better and she only said she was glad and went right on with her work, I began to ache again.

I thought, "I'll bet I die of it. I bet I do."

I went out to the front porch and sat down. I was pretty sore at Mother.

"If she really knew the truth, that I have inflammatory rheumatism and I may just drop down dead any time, I'll bet she wouldn't care about that either," I thought.

I was getting more and more angry the more thinking I did.

"I know what I'm going to do," I thought; "I'm going to go fishing."

I thought that, feeling the way I did, I might be sitting on the high bank just above the deep pool where the water went over the dam, and suddenly my heart would stop beating.

And then, of course, I'd pitch forward, over the bank into the pool and, if I wasn't dead when I hit the water, I'd drown sure.

They would all come home to supper and they'd miss me.

"But where is he?"

Then Mother would remember that I'd come home from school aching.

She'd go upstairs and I wouldn't be there. One day during the year before, there was a child got drowned in a spring. It was one of the Wyatt children.

Right down at the end of the street there was a spring under a birch tree and there had been a barrel sunk in the ground.

Everyone had always been saying the spring ought to be kept covered, but it wasn't.

So the Wyatt child went down there, played around alone, and fell in and got drowned.

Mother was the one who had found the drowned child. She had gone to get a pail of water and there the child was, drowned and dead.

This had been in the evening when we were all at home, and Mother had come running up the street with the dead, dripping child in her arms. She was making for the Wyatt house as hard as she could run, and she was pale.

She had a terrible look on her face, I remembered then.

"So," I thought, "they'll miss me and there'll be a search made. Very likely there'll be someone who has seen me sitting by the pond fishing, and there'll be a big alarm and all the town will turn out and they'll drag the pond."

I was having a grand time, having died. Maybe, after they found me and had got me out of the deep pool, Mother would grab me up in her arms and run home with me as she had run with the Wyatt child.

I got up from the porch and went around the house. I got my fishing pole and lit out for the pool below the dam. Mother was busy—she always was—and didn't see me go. When I got there I thought I'd better not sit too near the edge of the high bank.

By this time I didn't ache hardly at all, but I thought:

"With inflammatory rheumatism you can't tell," I thought.

"It probably comes and goes," I thought.

"Walter has it and he goes fishing," I thought.

I had got my line into the pool and suddenly I got a bite. It was a regular whopper: I knew that. I'd never had a bite like that.

I knew what it was. It was one of Mr. Fenn's big carp.

Mr. Fenn was a man who had a big pond of his own. He sold ice in the summer and the pond was to make the ice. He had bought some big carp and put them into his pond and then, earlier in the spring when there was a freshet, his dam had gone out.

So the carp had got into our creek and one or two big ones had been caught—but none of them by a boy like me.

The carp was pulling and I was pulling and I was afraid he'd break my line, so I just tumbled down the high bank, holding onto the line and got right into the pool. We had it out, there in the pool. We struggled. We wrestled. Then I got a hand under his gills and got him out.

He was a big one all right. He was nearly half as big as I was myself. I had him on the bank and I kept one hand under his gills and I ran.

I never ran so hard in my life. He was slippery, and now and then he wriggled out of my arms; once I stumbled and fell on him, but I got him home.

So there it was. I was a big hero that day. Mother got a washtub and filled it with water. She put the fish in it and all the neighbors came to look. I got into dry clothes and went down to supper—and then I made a break that spoiled my day.

There we were, all of us, at the table, and suddenly Father asked what had been the matter with me at school. He had met the teacher, Sarah Suggett, on the street and she had told him how I had become ill.

"What was the matter with you?" Father asked, and before I thought what I was saying I let it out.

"I had the inflammatory rheumatism," I said—and a shout went up. It made me sick to hear them, the way they all laughed.

It brought back all the aching pain again, and like a fool I began to cry.

"Well, I *have* got it—I *have*, I *have*," I cried, and I got up from the table and ran upstairs.

I stayed there until Mother came up. I knew it would be a long time before I heard the last of the inflammatory rheumatism. I was sick all right, but the aching I now had wasn't in my legs or in my back.

THINK AND DISCUSS
Understanding
1. When does the narrator first think he has inflammatory rheumatism?
2. What is the attitude of the narrator's mother when he comes home from school?
3. How does the narrator try to convince his teacher and his mother that he has inflammatory rheumatism?

Analyzing
4. What clues in the story convince you as a reader that the narrator does not have inflammatory rheumatism?

5. Do you think the narrator convinces himself that he is ill? Explain.
6. Is the main conflict in this story a conflict between characters or is it within one character?
7. What is the climax, or turning point, of the story?
8. What is the conclusion of the story?

Extending
9. Suppose that the narrator did not catch the carp while fishing. How long do you think he would have gone on having inflammatory rheumatism?

REVIEWING: Characterization
See Handbook of Literary Terms, p. 635.

Characterization is the method an author uses to create a fictional person. An author may develop a character through describing the character's physical appearance, speech, actions, and inner thoughts or by revealing attitudes and reactions of other characters.

1. When the narrator comes home from school, does he tell his mother what he really thinks is the matter?
2. What do the narrator's inner thoughts reveal about his feelings toward Walter?
3. From his inner thoughts, how does the narrator feel about his mother on the day he comes home from school?
4. Which of the following methods used by an author to develop a character seems to be least important in this story?
   (**a**) physical appearance
   (**b**) inner thoughts
   (**c**) attitudes and reactions of others

COMPOSITION
Writing About an Experience

Write one or two paragraphs about an incident when you imagined or pretended illness to stay home or to get out of going somewhere. If this has never happened in your life, you may make up a character and situation. Before you begin to write, make a list of symptoms for the illness. When you write, let the reader know how you or your made-up character feels by revealing your inner thoughts, as the narrator of "Stolen Day" does.

Writing a News Story

For a local newspaper, write a brief story about the narrator catching the big carp. Newspaper reports usually include the five Ws: *who* was involved, *what* happened, *when* and *where* it took place, and *why* it happened. Before you begin, list the five Ws on a sheet of paper. Then reread the part of the story in which the narrator catches the carp and make notes of the answers next to the five Ws. Use your list as you write.

BIOGRAPHY

Sherwood Anderson
1876–1941

Sherwood Anderson grew up in Clyde, Ohio, where he learned much about storytelling from his father, a wandering house painter and harness maker. At the age of fourteen, Anderson quit school and for the next twenty years worked at various jobs, although at one point during these years he did return to school. In 1919 he published his first book of short stories, titled *Winesburg, Ohio*. His stories are often about events in the lonely, sometimes frustrated lives of people in small towns. His work influenced other American writers of short stories. Later in life he settled in Virginia, where he bought two newspapers and became the managing editor for both of them.

See SETTING in the Handbook of Literary Terms, page 656.

Rikki-tikki-tavi

Rudyard Kipling

**Enemies lurk in the garden, and Death terrorizes the neighborhood—
until Rikki-tikki-tavi arrives.**

---

his is the story of the great war that Rikki-tikki-tavi[1] fought single-handed, through the bathrooms of the big bungalow in Segowlee cantonment.[2] Darzee[3] the Tailorbird helped him, and Chuchundra[4] the Muskrat, who never comes out into the middle of the floor, but always creeps round by the wall, gave him advice, but Rikki-tikki did the real fighting.

He was a mongoose, rather like a little cat in his fur and his tail, but quite like a weasel in his head and his habits. His eyes and the end of his restless nose were pink. He could scratch himself anywhere he pleased with any leg, front or back, that he chose to use. He could fluff up his tail till it looked like a bottle brush, and his war cry as he scuttled through the long grass was: *Rikk-tikk-tikki-tikki-tchk!*

One day, a high summer flood washed him out of the burrow where he lived with his father and mother, and carried him, kicking and clucking, down a roadside ditch. He found a little wisp of grass floating there, and clung to it till he lost his senses. When he revived, he was lying in the hot sun on the middle of a garden path, very draggled indeed, and a small boy was saying, "Here's a dead mongoose. Let's have a funeral."

"No," said his mother, "let's take him in and dry him. Perhaps he isn't really dead."

They took him into the house, and a big man picked him up between his finger and thumb and said he was not dead but half choked. So they wrapped him in cotton wool, and warmed him over a little fire, and he opened his eyes and sneezed.

---

1. *Rikki-tikki-tavi* (rik′ē ti′kē tav′ē).
2. *Segowlee* (sə gou′lē) *cantonment* (kan ton′mənt), the British military station at Segowlee, India.
3. *Darzee* (där zē′).
4. *Chuchundra* (chü chun′drə).

"Rikki-tikki-tavi" from *The Jungle Book* by Rudyard Kipling. Reprinted by permission of The National Trust and Macmillan, London, Limited.

"Now," said the big man (he was an Englishman who had just moved into the bungalow), "don't frighten him, and we'll see what he'll do."

It is the hardest thing in the world to frighten a mongoose, because he is eaten up from nose to tail with curiosity. The motto of all the mongoose family is "Run and find out," and Rikki-tikki was a true mongoose. He looked at the cotton wool, decided that it was not good to eat, ran all around the table, sat up and put his fur in order, scratched himself, and jumped on the small boy's shoulder.

"Don't be frightened, Teddy," said his father. "That's his way of making friends."

"Ouch! He's tickling under my chin," said Teddy.

Rikki-tikki looked down between the boy's collar and neck, snuffed at his ear, and climbed down to the floor, where he sat rubbing his nose.

"Good gracious," said Teddy's mother, "and that's a wild creature! I suppose he's so tame because we've been kind to him."

"All mongooses are like that," said her husband. "If Teddy doesn't pick him up by the tail, or try to put him in a cage, he'll run in and out of the house all day long. Let's give him something to eat."

They gave him a little piece of raw meat. Rikki-tikki liked it immensely, and when it was finished he went out into the veranda and sat in the sunshine and fluffed up his fur to make it dry to the roots. Then he felt better.

"There are more things to find out about in this house," he said to himself, "than all my family could find out in all their lives. I shall certainly stay and find out."

He spent all that day roaming over the house. He nearly drowned himself in the bathtubs, put his nose into the ink on a writing table, and burned it on the end of the big man's cigar, for he climbed up in the big man's lap to see how writing was done. At nightfall he ran into Teddy's nursery to watch how kerosene lamps were lighted, and when Teddy went to bed Rikki-tikki climbed up too. But he was a restless companion, because he had to get up and attend to every noise all through the night, and find out what made it. Teddy's mother and father came in, the last thing, to look at their boy, and Rikki-tikki was awake on the pillow.

"I don't like that," said Teddy's mother. "He may bite the child."

"He'll do no such thing," said the father. "Teddy is safer with that little beast than if he had a bloodhound to watch him. If a snake came into the nursery now——"

But Teddy's mother wouldn't think of anything so awful.

Early in the morning Rikki-tikki came to early breakfast in the veranda riding on Teddy's shoulder, and they gave him banana and some boiled egg. He sat on all their laps one after the other, because every well-brought-up mongoose always hopes to be a house mongoose some day and have rooms to run about in; and Rikki-tikki's mother (she used to live in the general's house at Segowlee) had carefully told Rikki what to do if ever he came across white men.

Then Rikki-tikki went out into the garden to see what was to be seen. It was a large garden, only half cultivated, with bushes, as big as summer houses, of Marshal Niel roses, lime and orange trees, clumps of bamboos, and thickets of high grass. Rikki-tikki licked his lips. "This is a splendid hunting ground," he said, and his tail grew bottle-brushy at the thought of it, and he scuttled up and down the garden, snuffing here and there till he heard very sorrowful voices in a thornbush. It was Darzee the Tailorbird and his wife. They had made a beautiful nest by pulling two big leaves together and stitching them up the edges with fibers, and had filled the hollow with cotton and downy fluff. The nest swayed to and fro, as they sat on the rim and cried.

"What is the matter?" asked Rikki-tikki.

"We are very miserable," said Darzee. "One of our babies fell out of the nest yesterday and Nag[5] ate him."

"H'm," said Rikki-tikki, "that is very sad—but I am a stranger here. Who is Nag?"

Darzee and his wife only cowered down in the nest without answering, for from the thick grass at the foot of the bush there came a low hiss—a horrid cold sound that made Rikki-tikki jump back two clear feet. Then inch by inch out of the grass rose up the head and spread hood of Nag, the big black cobra, and he was five feet long from tongue to tail. When he had lifted one-third of himself clear of the ground, he stayed balancing to and fro exactly as a dandelion tuft balances in the wind, and he looked at Rikki-tikki with the wicked snake's eyes that never change their expression, whatever the snake may be thinking of.

"Who is Nag?" said he. "*I* am Nag. The great God Brahm[6] put his mark upon all our people, when the first cobra spread his hood to keep the sun off Brahm as he slept. Look, and be afraid!"

He spread out his hood more than ever, and Rikki-tikki saw the spectacle mark on the back of it that looks exactly like the eye part of a hook-and-eye fastening. He was afraid for the minute, but it is impossible for a mongoose to stay frightened for any length of time, and though Rikki-tikki had never met a live cobra before, his mother had fed him on dead ones, and he knew that all a grown mongoose's business in life was to fight and eat snakes. Nag knew that too and, at the bottom of his cold heart, he was afraid.

"Well," said Rikki-tikki, and his tail began to fluff up again, "marks or no marks, do you think it is right for you to eat fledglings out of a nest?"

Nag was thinking to himself, and watching the least little movement in the grass behind Rikki-tikki. He knew that mongooses in the garden meant death sooner or later for him and his family, but he wanted to get Rikki-tikki off his guard. So he dropped his head a little, and put it on one side.

"Let us talk," he said. "You eat eggs. Why should not I eat birds?"

"Behind you! Look behind you!" sang Darzee.

Rikki-tikki knew better than to waste time in staring. He jumped up in the air as high as he could go, and just under him whizzed by the head of Nagaina,[7] Nag's wicked wife. She had crept up behind him as he was talking, to make an end of him. He heard her savage hiss as the stroke missed. He came down almost across her back, and if he had been an old

---

5. *Nag* (näg).
6. *The great God Brahm* (bräm), the supreme god of the Hindu religion, usually known as Brahma (brä′mə).
7. *Nagaina* (nä gān′ə).

mongoose he would have known that then was the time to break her back with one bite; but he was afraid of the terrible lashing return stroke of the cobra. He bit, indeed, but did not bite long enough, and he jumped clear of the whisking tail, leaving Nagaina torn and angry.

"Wicked, wicked Darzee!" said Nag, lashing up as high as he could reach toward the nest in the thornbush. But Darzee had built it out of reach of snakes, and it only swayed to and fro.

Rikki-tikki felt his eyes growing red and hot (when a mongoose's eyes grow red, he is angry), and he sat back on his tail and hind legs like a little kangaroo, and looked all round him, and chattered with rage. But Nag and Nagaina had disappeared into the grass. When a snake misses its stroke, it never says anything or gives any sign of what it means to do next. Rikki-tikki did not care to follow them, for he did not feel sure that he could manage two snakes at once. So he trotted off to the gravel path near the house, and sat down to think. It was a serious matter for him.

If you read the old books of natural history, you will find they say that when the mongoose fights the snake and happens to get bitten, he runs off and eats some herb that cures him. That is not true. The victory is only a matter of quickness of eye and quickness of foot—snake's blow against mongoose's jump—and as no eye can follow the motion of a snake's head when it strikes, this makes things much more wonderful than any magic herb. Rikki-tikki knew he was a young mongoose, and it made him all the more pleased to think that he had managed to escape a blow from behind.

It gave him confidence in himself, and when Teddy came running down the path, Rikki-tikki was ready to be petted. But just as Teddy was stooping, something wriggled a little in the dust, and a tiny voice said: "Be careful. I am Death!" It was Karait,[8] the dusty brown snakeling that lies for choice on the dusty earth; and his bite is as dangerous as the cobra's. But he is so small that nobody thinks of him, and so he does the more harm to people.

Rikki-tikki's eyes grew red again, and he danced up to Karait with the peculiar rocking, swaying motion that he had inherited from his family. It looks very funny, but it is so perfectly balanced a gait that you can fly off from it at any angle you please, and in dealing with snakes this is an advantage.

If Rikki-tikki had only known, he was doing a much more dangerous thing than fighting Nag, for Karait is so small, and can turn so quickly, that unless Rikki bit him close to the back of the head, he would get the return stroke in his eye or his lip. But Rikki did not know. His eyes were all red, and he rocked back and forth, looking for a good place to hold. Karait struck out. Rikki jumped sideways and tried to run in, but the wicked little dusty gray head lashed within a fraction of his shoulder, and he had to jump over the body, and the head followed his heels close.

Teddy shouted to the house: "Oh, look here! Our mongoose is killing a snake." And Rikki-tikki heard a scream from Teddy's mother. His father ran out with a stick, but by the time he came up, Karait had lunged out once too far, and Rikki-tikki had sprung, jumped on the snake's back, dropped his head far between his forelegs, bitten as high up the back as he could get hold, and rolled away.

That bite paralyzed Karait, and Rikki-tikki was just going to eat him up from the tail, after the custom of his family at dinner, when he remembered that a full meal makes a slow mongoose, and if he wanted all his strength and quickness ready, he must keep himself thin. He went away for a dust bath under the castor-oil bushes, while Teddy's father beat the dead Karait.

"What is the use of that?" thought Rikki-tikki. "I have settled it all."

And then Teddy's mother picked him up from the dust and hugged him, crying that he had saved Teddy from death, and Teddy's father said that he was a providence, and Teddy looked on with big scared eyes. Rikki-tikki was rather amused at all the fuss, which, of course, he did not understand. Teddy's mother might just as well have petted Teddy for playing in the dust. Rikki was thoroughly enjoying himself.

That night at dinner, walking to and fro

---

8. *Karait* (kä rīt′).

among the wineglasses on the table, he might have stuffed himself three times over with nice things. But he remembered Nag and Nagaina, and though it was very pleasant to be patted and petted by Teddy's mother, and to sit on Teddy's shoulder, his eyes would get red from time to time, and he would go off into his long war cry of *"Rikk-tikk-tikki-tikki-tchk!"*

Teddy carried him off to bed and insisted on Rikki-tikki sleeping under his chin. Rikki-tikki was too well bred to bite or scratch, but as soon as Teddy was asleep he went off for his nightly walk round the house, and in the dark he ran up against Chuchundra the Muskrat creeping around by the wall. Chuchundra is a brokenhearted little beast. He whimpers and cheeps all the night, trying to make up his mind to run into the middle of the room. But he never gets there.

"Don't kill me," said Chuchundra, almost weeping. "Rikki-tikki, don't kill me!"

"Do you think a snake-killer kills muskrats?" said Rikki-tikki scornfully.

"Those who kill snakes get killed by snakes," said Chuchundra, more sorrowfully than ever. "And how am I to be sure that Nag won't mistake me for you some dark night?"

"There's not the least danger," said Rikki-tikki. "But Nag is in the garden, and I know you don't go there."

"My cousin Chua[9] the Rat told me——" said Chuchundra, and then he stopped.

"Told you what?"

"H'sh! Nag is everywhere, Rikki-tikki. You should have talked to Chua in the garden."

"I didn't—so you must tell me. Quick, Chuchundra, or I'll bite you!"

Chuchundra sat down and cried till the tears rolled off his whiskers. "I am a very poor man," he sobbed. "I never had spirit enough to run out into the middle of the room. H'sh! I mustn't tell you anything. Can't you *hear*, Rikki-tikki?"

Rikki-tikki listened. The house was as still as still, but he thought he could just catch the faintest *scratch-scratch* in the world—a noise as faint as that of a wasp walking on the windowpane—the dry scratch of a snake's scales on brick work.

"That's Nag or Nagaina," he said to himself, "and he is crawling into the bathroom sluice. You're right, Chuchundra; I should have talked to Chua."

He stole off to Teddy's bathroom, but there was nothing there, and then to Teddy's mother's bathroom. At the bottom of the smooth plaster wall there was a brick pulled out to make a sluice for the bath water, and as Rikki-tikki stole in by the masonry curb where the bath is put, he heard Nag and Nagaina whispering together outside in the moonlight.

"When the house is emptied of people," said Nagaina to her husband, *"he* will have to go away, and then the garden will be our own again. Go in quietly, and remember that the big man who killed Karait is the first one to bite. Then come out and tell me, and we will hunt for Rikki-tikki together."

"But are you sure that there is anything to be gained by killing the people?" said Nag.

"Everything. When there were no people

---

9. *Chua* (chü′ə).

in the bungalow, did we have any mongoose in the garden? So long as the bungalow is empty, we are king and queen of the garden; and remember that as soon as our eggs in the melon bed hatch (as they may tomorrow), our children will need room and quiet."

"I had not thought of that," said Nag. "I will go, but there is no need that we should hunt for Rikki-tikki afterwards. I will kill the big man and his wife, and the child if I can, and come away quietly. Then the bungalow will be empty, and Rikki-tikki will go."

Rikki-tikki tingled all over with rage and hatred at this, and then Nag's head came through the sluice, and his five feet of cold body followed it. Angry as he was, Rikki-tikki was very frightened as he saw the size of the big cobra. Nag coiled himself up, raised his head, and looked into the bathroom in the dark, and Rikki could see his eyes glitter.

"Now, if I kill him here, Nagaina will know; and if I fight him on the open floor, the odds are in his favor. What am I to do?" said Rikki-tikki-tavi.

Nag waved to and fro, and then Rikki-tikki heard him drinking from the biggest water jar that was used to fill the bath. "That is good," said the snake. "Now, when Karait was killed, the big man had a stick. He may have that stick still, but when he comes in to bathe in the morning he will not have a stick. I shall wait here till he comes. Nagaina—do you hear me?—I shall wait here in the cool till daytime."

There was no answer from outside, so Rikki-tikki knew Nagaina had gone away. Nag coiled himself down, coil by coil, round the bulge at the bottom of the water jar, and Rikki-tikki stayed still as death. After an hour he began to move, muscle by muscle, toward the jar. Nag was asleep, and Rikki-tikki looked at his big back, wondering which would be the best place for a good hold. "If I don't break his back at the first jump," said Rikki, "he can still fight. And if he fights—O Rikki!" He looked at the thickness of the neck below the hood, but that was too much for him; and a bite near the tail would only make Nag savage.

"It must be the head," he said at last; "the head above the hood. And, when I am once there, I must not let go."

Then he jumped. The head was lying a little clear of the water jar, under the curve of it; and, as his teeth met, Rikki braced his back against the bulge of the red earthenware to hold down the head. This gave him just one second's purchase, and he made the most of it. Then he was battered to and fro as a rat is shaken by a dog—to and fro on the floor, up and down, and around in great circles, but his eyes were red and he held on as the body cartwhipped over the floor, upsetting the tin dipper and the soap dish and the flesh brush, and banged against the tin side of the bath.

As he held he closed his jaws tighter and tighter, for he made sure he would be banged to death, and, for the honor of his family, he preferred to be found with his teeth locked. He was dizzy, aching, and felt shaken to pieces when something went off like a thunderclap just behind him. A hot wind knocked him senseless and red fire singed his fur. The big man had been wakened by the noise, and had fired both barrels of a shotgun into Nag just behind the hood.

Rikki-tikki held on with his eyes shut, for now he was quite sure he was dead. But the head did not move, and the big man picked him up and said, "It's the mongoose again, Alice. The little chap has saved *our* lives now."

Then Teddy's mother came in with a very white face, and saw what was left of Nag, and Rikki-tikki dragged himself to Teddy's bedroom and spent half the rest of the night shaking himself tenderly to find out whether he really was broken into forty pieces, as he fancied.

When morning came he was very stiff, but well pleased with his doings. "Now I have Nagaina to settle with, and she will be worse than five Nags, and there's no knowing when the eggs she spoke of will hatch. Goodness! I must go and see Darzee," he said.

Without waiting for breakfast, Rikki-tikki ran to the thornbush where Darzee was singing a song of triumph at the top of his voice. The news of Nag's death was all over the garden, for the sweeper had thrown the body on the rubbish heap.

"Oh, you stupid tuft of feathers!" said Rikki-tikki angrily. "Is this the time to sing?"

"Nag is dead—is dead—is dead!" sang Darzee. "The valiant Rikki-tikki caught him by the head and held fast. The big man brought the bang stick, and Nag fell in two pieces! He will never eat my babies again."

"All that's true enough. But where's Nagaina?" said Rikki-tikki, looking carefully round him.

"Nagaina came to the bathroom sluice and called for Nag," Darzee went on, "and Nag came out on the end of a stick—the sweeper picked him up on the end of a stick and threw him upon the rubbish heap. Let us sing about the great, the red-eyed Rikki-tikki!" And Darzee filled his throat and sang.

"If I could get up to your nest, I'd roll your babies out!" said Rikki-tikki. "You don't know when to do the right thing at the right time. You're safe enough in your nest there, but it's war for me, down here. Stop singing a minute, Darzee."

"For the great, the beautiful Rikki-tikki's sake I will stop," said Darzee. "What is it, O Killer of the terrible Nag?"

"Where is Nagaina, for the third time?"

"On the rubbish heap by the stables, mourning for Nag. Great is Rikki-tikki with the white teeth."

"Bother my white teeth! Have you ever heard where she keeps her eggs?"

"In the melon bed, on the end nearest the wall, where the sun strikes nearly all day. She hid them there weeks ago."

"And you never thought it worthwhile to tell me? The end nearest the wall, you said?"

"Rikki-tikki, you are not going to eat her eggs?"

"Not eat exactly, no. Darzee, if you have a grain of sense you will fly off to the stables and pretend that your wing is broken, and let Nagaina chase you away to this bush. I must get to the melon bed, and if I went there now she'd see me."

Darzee was a feather-brained little fellow who could never hold more than one idea at a time in his head. And just because he knew that Nagaina's children were born in eggs like his own, he didn't think at first that it was fair to kill them. But his wife was a sensible bird, and she knew that cobra's eggs meant young cobras later on. So she flew off from the nest, and left Darzee to keep the babies warm, and continue his song about the death of Nag. Darzee was very like a man in some ways.

She fluttered in front of Nagaina by the rubbish heap and cried out, "Oh, my wing is broken! The boy in the house threw a stone at me and broke it." Then she fluttered more desperately than ever.

Nagaina lifted up her head and hissed. "You warned Rikki-tikki when I would have killed him. Indeed and truly, you've chosen a bad place to be lame in." And she moved toward Darzee's wife, slipping along over the dust.

"The boy broke it with a stone!" shrieked Darzee's wife.

"Well! It may be some consolation to you when you're dead to know that I shall settle accounts with the boy. My husband lies on the rubbish heap this morning, but before night the boy in the house will lie very still. What is the use of running away? I am sure to catch you. Little fool, look at me!"

Darzee's wife knew better than to do *that*, for a bird who looks at a snake's eyes gets so frightened that she cannot move. Darzee's wife fluttered on, piping sorrowfully, and never leaving the ground, and Nagaina quickened her pace.

Rikki-tikki heard them going up the path from the stables, and he raced for the end of the melon patch near the wall. There, in the warm litter above the melons, very cunningly hidden, he found twenty-five eggs, about the size of a bantam's eggs, but with whitish skins instead of shells.

"I was not a day too soon," he said, for he could see the baby cobras curled up inside the skin, and he knew that the minute they were hatched they could each kill a man or a mongoose. He bit off the tops of the eggs as fast as he could, taking care to crush the young cobras, and turned over the litter from time to time to see whether he had missed any. At last there were only three eggs left, and Rikki-tikki began to chuckle to himself, when he heard Darzee's wife screaming:

"Rikki-tikki, I led Nagaina toward the house, and she has gone into the veranda, and—oh, come quickly—she means killing!"

Rikki-tikki smashed two eggs, and tumbled backward down the melon bed with the third egg in his mouth, and scuttled to the veranda as hard as he could put foot to the ground. Teddy and his mother and father were there at early breakfast, but Rikki-tikki saw that they were not eating anything. They sat stone-still, and their faces were white. Nagaina was coiled up on the matting by Teddy's chair, within easy striking distance of Teddy's bare leg, and she was swaying to and fro, singing a song of triumph.

"Son of the big man that killed Nag," she hissed, "stay still. I am not ready yet. Wait a little. Keep very still, all you three! If you move I strike, and if you do not move I strike. Oh, foolish people who killed my Nag!"

Teddy's eyes were fixed on his father, and all his father could do was to whisper, "Sit still, Teddy. You mustn't move. Teddy, keep still."

Then Rikki-tikki came up and cried, "Turn round, Nagaina. Turn and fight!"

"All in good time," said she, without moving her eyes. "I will settle my account with *you* presently. Look at your friends, Rikki-tikki. They are still and white. They are afraid. They dare not move, and if you come a step nearer I strike."

"Look at your eggs," said Rikki-tikki, "in the melon bed near the wall. Go and look, Nagaina!"

The big snake turned half around, and saw the egg on the veranda. "Ah-h! Give it to me," she said.

Rikki-tikki put his paws one on each side of the egg, and his eyes were blood-red. "What price for a snake's egg? For a young cobra? For a young king cobra? For the last—the very last of the brood? The ants are eating all the others down by the melon bed."

Nagaina spun clear round, forgetting everything for the sake of the one egg. Rikki-tikki saw Teddy's father shoot out a big hand, catch Teddy by the shoulder, and drag him across the little table with the teacups, safe and out of reach of Nagaina.

"Tricked! Tricked! Tricked! *Rikk-tck-tck!*" chuckled Rikki-tikki. "The boy is safe, and it was I—I—I that caught Nag by the hood last night in the bathroom." Then he began to jump up and down, all four feet together, his head close to the floor. "He threw me to and fro, but he could not shake me off. He was dead before the big man blew him in two. I did it! *Rikki-tikki-tck-tck!* Come then, Nagaina. Come and fight with me. You shall not be a widow long."

Nagaina saw that she had lost her chance of killing Teddy, and the egg lay between Rikki-tikki's paws. "Give me the egg, Rikki-tikki. Give me the last of my eggs, and I will go away and never come back," she said, lowering her hood.

"Yes, you will go away, and you will never come back. For you will go to the rubbish heap with Nag. Fight, widow! The big man has gone for his gun. Fight!"

Rikki-tikki was bounding all round Nagaina, keeping just out of reach of her stroke, his little eyes like hot coals. Nagaina gathered herself together and flung out at him. Rikki-tikki jumped up and backward. Again and again and again she struck, and each time her head came with a whack on the matting of the veranda and she gathered herself together like a watch spring. Then Rikki-tikki danced in a circle to get behind her, and Nagaina spun round to keep her head to his head, so that the rustle of her tail on the matting sounded like dry leaves blown along by the wind.

He had forgotten the egg. It still lay on the veranda, and Nagaina came nearer and nearer to it, till at last, while Rikki-tikki was drawing breath, she caught it in her mouth, turned to the veranda steps, and flew like an arrow down the path, with Rikki-tikki behind her. When the cobra runs for her life, she goes like a whiplash flicked across a horse's neck. Rikki-tikki knew that he must catch her, or all the trouble would begin again.

She headed straight for the long grass by the thornbush, and as he was running Rikki-tikki heard Darzee still singing his foolish little song of triumph. But Darzee's wife was wiser. She flew off her nest as Nagaina came along, and flapped her wings about Nagaina's head. If Darzee had helped her they might have turned her, but Nagaina only lowered her hood and went on. Still, the instant's delay brought Rikki-tikki up to her, and as she plunged into the rathole where she and Nag used to live, his little white teeth were clenched on her tail, and he went down with her—and very few mongooses, however wise and old they may be, care to follow a cobra into its hole.

It was dark in the hole; and Rikki-tikki never knew when it might open out and give Nagaina room to turn and strike at him. He held on savagely, and stuck out his feet to act as brakes on the dark slope of the hot, moist earth.

Then the grass by the mouth of the hole stopped waving, and Darzee said, "It is all over with Rikki-tikki! We must sing his death song. Valiant Rikki-tikki is dead! For Nagaina will surely kill him underground."

So he sang a very mournful song that he made up on the spur of the minute, and just as he got to the most touching part, the grass quivered again, and Rikki-tikki, covered with dirt, dragged himself out of the hole leg by leg, licking his whiskers. Darzee stopped with a little shout. Rikki-tikki shook some of the dust out of his fur and sneezed. "It is all over," he said. "The widow will never come out again." And the red ants that live between the grass stems heard him, and began to troop down one after another to see if he had spoken the truth.

Rikki-tikki curled himself up in the grass and slept where he was—slept and slept till it was late in the afternoon, for he had done a hard day's work.

"Now," he said, when he awoke, "I will go back to the house. Tell the Coppersmith, Darzee, and he will tell the garden that Nagaina is dead."

The Coppersmith is a bird who makes a noise exactly like the beating of a little hammer on a copper pot. The reason he is always making it is because he is the town crier to every Indian garden, and tells all the news to everybody who cares to listen. As Rikki-tikki went up the path, he heard his "attention" notes like a tiny dinner gong, and then the steady "*Ding-dong-tock! Nag is dead—dong! Nagaina is dead! Ding-dong-tock!*" That set all the birds in the garden singing, and the frogs croaking, for Nag and Nagaina used to eat frogs as well as little birds.

When Rikki got to the house, Teddy and Teddy's mother (she looked very white still, for she had been fainting) and Teddy's father came out and almost cried over him; and that night he ate all that was given him till he could eat no more, and went to bed on Teddy's shoulder, where Teddy's mother saw him when she came to look late at night.

"He saved our lives and Teddy's life," she said to her husband. "Just think, he saved all our lives."

Rikki-tikki woke up with a jump, for the mongooses are light sleepers.

"Oh, it's you," said he. "What are you bothering for? All the cobras are dead. And if they weren't, I'm here."

Rikki-tikki had a right to be proud of himself. But he did not grow too proud, and he kept that garden as a mongoose should keep it, with tooth and jump and spring and bite, till never a cobra dared show its head inside the walls.

THINK AND DISCUSS
Understanding
1. Find examples of how Rikki-tikki-tavi shows courage.
2. In what ways is Rikki foolish?
3. How does Rikki prove the motto "Run and find out" fits him?
4. Why do the snakes want to kill the people in the house?

Analyzing
5. What is the moment of greatest suspense in the story?
6. Why do you think Rikki feels such loyalty to the family?
7. **Character** is revealed through physical appearance, speech, actions, and inner thoughts and by the reactions of others to the character. Find examples of each method of characterization in this story.

Extending
8. If this story took place in a garden in the United States today, which kinds of animals could you substitute for the mongoose, the king cobra, the Indian tailorbird, the muskrat, and the coppersmith?

APPLYING: Setting HZ
See Handbook of Literary Terms, p. 656.

Setting is the time, place, and general environment in which the events of a story take place. The setting may be stated directly or only suggested by the author.
1. Where does this story take place and at what time in history?
2. How does the setting influence the story?

VOCABULARY
Word Origins
Because India was for many years a British colony, a number of Indian words have become common in English. For example, our word *bandanna* comes from a Hindi word for a dyeing process that involves tying the cloth in knots—what is now called "tie-dyeing." *Bandanna* has come to mean, in English, a large scarf or handkerchief.

The words listed in the left-hand column below have come to us from India. Match them with their original Indian meanings given at the right. Use the Glossary if necessary.

1. veranda   (**a**) bracelet
2. bungalow   (**b**) house
3. cot   (**c**) bed frame
4. shampoo   (**d**) to press; knead
5. bangle   (**e**) porch

THINKING SKILLS
Classifying
To classify things is to arrange them into classes or groups according to some system. For example, snakes and birds are both classified as animals, but each can be further classified into certain distinct kinds. Note that the karait and cobra are snakes, and that the tailorbird and the coppersmith are birds.

Both animal and human traits are attributed to animals in the story. Classify each description as a human trait or an animal trait.
1. . . . he is eaten up from nose to tail with curiosity.

2. The Coppersmith is a bird who makes a noise exactly like the beating of a little hammer on a copper pot.
3. Darzee was a feather-brained little fellow who could never hold more than one idea at a time in his head.
4. It gave him confidence in himself. . . .
5. He spread out his hood more than ever. . . .

COMPOSITION

Reading/Writing Log

In this story Rudyard Kipling uses many specific words in describing the animals, the sounds they make, and the way they move. Some examples are given below. Copy them in your **reading/writing log.** Then find at least ten additional examples in the story and add them to the log.

> like a weasel in his head and habits
> war cry of *Rikk-tikk-tikki-tikki-tchk*
> scuttled through the long grass
> > (page 60, column 1)
> sorrowful voices in a thornbush
> > (page 62, column 1)

Writing About Differences

There are differences between the way the mongoose and the snakes fight. Write a paragraph or two contrasting the fighting styles of Rikki and the two snakes. Before you begin to write, it may help you to go back over the story to find descriptions of the animals' eyes, body movements, sounds, and ways of striking. If you are keeping a **reading/writing log,** note the specific words from "Rikki-tikki-tavi" that you recorded earlier.

Describing an Animal

Choose a pet you have had or one that belongs to someone you know. Write a paragraph explaining how the animal got its name and whether it is trusted or not. Describe any of the pet's human traits, as the author of "Rikki-tikki-tavi" does. Before you begin, you may want to reread some of the descriptions of animals in this story. For help, see Lesson 3, "Writing a Clear Description," in the Writer's Handbook.

BIOGRAPHY

Rudyard Kipling
1865–1936

Rudyard Kipling is known throughout the world for his poems and tales of India, the land where he was born. Of special interest are his *Just So Stories, The Jungle Book,* and *The Second Jungle Book,* all of which deal with animals, as well as *Kim,* an adventure story about an English orphan in India, and *Captains Courageous,* the story of a spoiled American boy on a fishing schooner.

Review SETTING in the Handbook of Literary Terms, page 656.

The Circuit

Francisco Jiménez

It was that time of year. Everything was neatly packed—again.

 t was that time of year again. Ito, the strawberry sharecropper, did not smile. It was natural. The peak of the strawberry season was over and the last few days the workers, most of them *braceros*,[1] were not picking as many boxes as they had during the months of June and July.

As the last days of August disappeared, so did the number of *braceros*. Sunday, only one—the best picker—came to work. I liked him. Sometimes we talked during our half-hour lunch break. That is how I found out he was from Jalisco,[2] the same state in Mexico my family was from. That Sunday was the last time I saw him.

When the sun had tired and sunk behind the mountains, Ito signaled us that it was time to go home. "*Ya esora*,"[3] he yelled in his broken Spanish. Those were the words I waited for twelve hours a day, everyday, seven days a week, week after week. And the thought of not hearing them again saddened me.

As we drove home Papa did not say a word. With both hands on the wheel, he stared at the dirt road. My older brother, Roberto, was also silent. He leaned his head back and closed his eyes. Once in a while he cleared from his throat the dust that blew in from outside.

Yes, it was that time of year. When I opened the front door to the shack, I stopped. Everything we owned was neatly packed in cardboard boxes. Suddenly I felt even more the weight of hours, days, weeks, and months of work. I sat down on a box. The thought of having to move to Fresno and knowing what was in store for me there brought tears to my eyes.

That night I could not sleep. I lay in bed

Francisco Jiménez (frän sēs′kō hē mä′nes).

1. *braceros* (brä sä′rōs), Mexicans allowed to enter the United States to do farm work.
2. *Jalisco* (hä lēs′kō).
3. *Ya esora* (yä äs ō′rä), a contraction of *ya es la hora*, which means "Now it's time."

thinking about how much I hated this move.

A little before five o'clock in the morning, Papa woke everyone up. A few minutes later, the yelling and screaming of my little brothers and sisters, for whom the move was a great adventure, broke the silence of dawn. Shortly, the barking of the dogs accompanied them.

While we packed the breakfast dishes, Papa went outside to start the "Carcanchita." That was the name Papa gave his old '38 black Plymouth. He bought it in a used-car lot in Santa Rosa in the winter of 1949. Papa was very proud of his car. "*Mi Carcanchita*,"[4] my little jalopy, he called it. He had a right to be proud of it. He spent a lot of time looking at other cars before buying this one. When he finally chose the "Carcanchita," he checked it thoroughly before driving it out of the car lot. He examined every inch of the car. He listened to the motor, tilting his head from side to side like a parrot, trying to detect any noises that spelled car trouble. After being satisfied with the looks and sounds of the car, Papa then insisted on knowing who the original owner was. He never did find out from the car salesman. But he bought the car anyway. Papa figured the original owner must have been an important man because behind the rear seat of the car he found a blue necktie.

Papa parked the car out in front and left the motor running. "*Listo*"[5] (ready), he yelled. Without saying a word, Roberto and I began to carry the boxes out to the car. Roberto carried the two big boxes and I carried the two smaller ones. Papa then threw the mattress on top of the car roof and tied it with ropes to the front and rear bumpers.

Everything was packed except Mama's pot. It was an old large galvanized pot she had picked up at an army surplus store in Santa Maria the year I was born. The pot was full of dents and nicks, and the more dents and nicks it had, the more Mama liked it. "*Mi olla*"[6] (my pot), she used to say proudly.

I held the front door open as Mama carefully carried out her pot by both handles, making sure not to spill the cooked beans. When she got to the car, Papa reached out to help her with it. Roberto opened the rear car door and Papa gently placed it on the floor behind the front seat. All of us then climbed in. Papa sighed, wiped the sweat off his forehead with his sleeve, and said wearily: "*Es todo*"[7] (that's it).

As we drove away, I felt a lump in my throat. I turned around and looked at our little shack for the last time.

At sunset we drove into a labor camp near Fresno. Since Papa did not speak English, Mama asked the camp foreman if he needed any more workers. "We don't need no more," said the foreman, scratching his head. "Check with Sullivan down the road. Can't miss him. He lives in a big white house with a fence around it."

When we got there, Mama walked up to the house. She went through a white gate, past a row of rose bushes, up the stairs to the front door. She rang the doorbell. The porch light went on and a tall husky man came out. They exchanged a few words. After the man went in, Mama clasped her hands and hur-

---

4. **Mi Carcanchita** (mē kär′kän chē′tä).
5. **Listo** (lēs′tō).
6. **Mi olla** (mē ô′yä).
7. **Es todo** (ās tō′dō).

E. John Robinson, *Autumn Vineyards*
Private Collection

ried back to the car. "We have work! Mr. Sullivan said we can stay there the whole season," she said gasping and pointing to an old garage near the stables.

The garage was worn out by the years. It had no windows. The walls, eaten by termites, strained to support the roof full of holes. The loose dirt floor, populated by earthworms, looked like a gray road map.

That night, by the light of a kerosene lamp, we unpacked and cleaned our new home. Roberto swept away the loose dirt, leaving the hard ground. Papa plugged the holes in the walls with old newspapers and tin can tops. Mama fed my little brothers and sisters. Papa and Roberto then brought in the mattress and placed it on the far corner of the garage. "Mama, you and the little ones sleep on the mattress. Roberto, Panchito, and I will sleep outside under the trees," Papa said.

Early next morning Mr. Sullivan showed us where his crop was, and after breakfast, Papa, Roberto, and I headed for the vineyard to pick.

Around nine o'clock the temperature had risen to almost one hundred degrees. I was completely soaked in sweat and my mouth felt as if I had been chewing on a handkerchief. I walked over to the end of the row, picked up the jug of water we had brought, and began drinking. "Don't drink too much; you'll get sick," Roberto shouted. No sooner had he said that than I felt sick to my stomach. I dropped to my knees and let the jug roll off my hands. I remained motionless with my eyes glued on the hot sandy ground. All I could hear was the drone of insects. Slowly I began to recover. I poured water over my face and neck and watched the black mud run down my arms and hit the ground.

I still felt a little dizzy when we took a break to eat lunch. It was past two o'clock and we sat underneath a large walnut tree that was on the side of the road. While we ate, Papa jotted down the number of boxes we had picked. Roberto drew designs on the ground with a stick. Suddenly I noticed Papa's face turn pale as he looked down the road. "Here comes the school bus," he whispered loudly in alarm. Instinctively, Roberto and I ran and hid in the vineyards. We did not want to get in trouble for not going to school. The yellow bus stopped in front of Mr. Sullivan's house. Two neatly dressed boys about my age got off. They carried books under their arms. After they crossed the street, the bus drove away. Roberto and I came out from hiding and joined Papa. *"Tienen que tener cuidado"*[8] (you have to be careful), he warned us.

After lunch we went back to work. The sun kept beating down. The buzzing insects, the wet sweat, and the hot dry dust made the afternoon seem to last forever. Finally the mountains around the valley reached out and swallowed the sun. Within an hour it was too dark to continue picking. The vines blanketed the grapes, making it difficult to see the bunches. *"Vámonos,"*[9] said Papa, signaling to us that it was time to quit work. Papa then took out a pencil and began to figure out how much we had earned our first day. He wrote down numbers, crossed some out, wrote down some more. *"Quince"*[10] (fifteen dollars), he murmured.

---

8. *Tienen que tener cuidado* (tyä′nen kā tā när′ kwē dä′dō).
9. *Vámonos* (bvä′mō nōs), "Let's go."
10. *Quince* (kēn′se).

When we arrived home, we took a cold shower underneath a waterhose. We then sat down to eat dinner around some wooden crates that served as a table. Mama had cooked a special meal for us. We had rice and tortillas with *carne con chile*, my favorite dish.

The next morning I could hardly move. My body ached all over. I felt little control over my arms and legs. This feeling went on every morning for days until my muscles finally got used to the work.

It was Monday, the first week of November. The grape season was over and I could now go to school. I woke up early that morning and lay in bed, looking at the stars and savoring the thought of not going to work and of starting sixth grade for the first time that year. Since I could not sleep, I decided to get up and join Papa and Roberto at breakfast. I sat at the table across from Roberto, but I kept my head down. I did not want to look up and face him. I knew he was sad. He was not going to school today. He was not going tomorrow, or next week, or next month. He would not go until the cotton season was over, and that was sometime in February. I rubbed my hands together and watched the dry, acid-stained skin fall to the floor in little rolls.

When Papa and Roberto left for work, I felt relief. I walked to the top of a small grade next to the shack and watched the "Carcanchita" disappear in the distance in a cloud of dust.

Two hours later, around eight o'clock, I stood by the side of the road waiting for school bus number twenty. When it arrived I climbed in. No one noticed me. Everyone was busy either talking or yelling. I sat in an empty seat in the back.

When the bus stopped in front of the school, I felt very nervous. I looked out the bus window and saw boys and girls carrying books under their arms. I felt empty. I put my hands in my pants pockets and walked to the principal's office. When I entered I heard a woman's voice say: "May I help you?" I was startled. I had not heard English for months. For a few seconds I remained speechless. I looked at the lady who waited for an answer. My first instinct was to answer her in Spanish, but I held back. Finally, after struggling for English words I managed to tell her that I wanted to enroll in the sixth grade. After answering many questions, I was led to the classroom.

Mr. Lema, the sixth-grade teacher, greeted me and assigned me a desk. He then introduced me to the class. I was so nervous and scared at that moment when everyone's eyes were on me that I wished I were with Papa and Roberto picking cotton. After taking roll, Mr. Lema gave the class the assignment for the first hour. "The first thing we have to do this morning is finish reading the story we began yesterday," he said enthusiastically. He walked up to me, handed me an English book, and asked me to read. "We are on page 125," he said politely. When I heard this, I felt my blood rush to my head; I felt dizzy. "Would you like to read?" he asked hesitantly. I opened the book to page 125. My mouth was dry. My eyes began to water. I could not begin. "You can read later," Mr. Lema said understandingly.

For the rest of the reading period I kept getting angrier and angrier with myself. I should have read, I thought to myself.

During recess I went into the restroom and opened my English book to page 125. I began to read in a low voice, pretending I was in class. There were many words I did not know. I closed the book and headed back to the classroom.

Mr. Lema was sitting at his desk correcting papers. When I entered he looked up at me and smiled. I felt better. I walked up to him and asked if he could help me with the new words. "Gladly," he said.

The rest of the month I spent my lunch hours working on English with Mr. Lema, my best friend at school.

One Friday during lunch hour Mr. Lema asked me to take a walk with him to the music room. "Do you like music?" he asked me as we entered the building.

"Yes, I like Mexican *corridos*,"[11] I answered. He then picked up a trumpet, blew on it and handed it to me. The sound gave me goose bumps. I knew that sound. I had heard it in many Mexican *corridos*. "How would you like to learn how to play it?" he asked. He must have read my face because before I could answer, he added: "I'll teach you how to play it during our lunch hours."

That day I could hardly wait to get home to tell Papa and Mama the great news. As I got off the bus, my little brothers and sisters ran up to meet me. They were yelling and screaming. I thought they were happy to see me, but when I opened the door to our shack, I saw that everything we owned was neatly packed in cardboard boxes.

---

11. *corridos* (kôr rē′dōs), Mexican folk ballads, usually telling of the adventures of a hero.

THINK AND DISCUSS
Understanding
1. Describe the family's most prized possession, the "Carcanchita."
2. Why doesn't the narrator go to school until November?
3. What makes the teacher so special to the narrator?

Analyzing
4. How would you describe the concern and respect shown each other by the family members?
5. What are the narrator's attitudes toward his work?
6. What specific occurrences make the narrator feel uncomfortable and self-conscious at school?
7. In what way is the ending of the story like the beginning?

Extending
8. Can you think of a time when you entered a new class or school and felt lonely and self-conscious? What advice would you give to others in a similar situation?

REVIEWING: Setting HⱫ
See Handbook of Literary Terms, p. 656.
Setting is the time, place, and general environment in which the events of a narrative occur. The details of setting may be directly stated or only suggested.
1. Describe the setting in "The Circuit."
2. What details of setting are directly stated, and what details are suggested?
3. How does the setting influence the way the family lives?

THINKING SKILLS
Classifying

To classify things is to arrange them into classes or groups according to some system. Consider the problems faced by the narrator of this account. Which are problems he faces because of his culture, and which are problems shared by most students?

1. Feeling lonely on the school bus
2. Hiding from the school bus
3. Starting school in November
4. Nervous and scared when introduced to the class
5. Mouth goes dry when asked to read aloud

COMPOSITION
Being a Story Character

Imagine you are Roberto. Write a paragraph to add some of your own memories to the account. Before you begin, choose an incident and list descriptions for how Roberto may have felt at the time.

Writing About a Teacher

You may remember a teacher who was special, just as Mr. Lema was special. Write a paragraph or two about that teacher, giving specific details about the teacher's character traits and actions that help your reader understand your appreciation for the person.

The Story Behind the Story

"The Circuit" is an autobiographical short story based on my experiences as a child growing up in a migrant family. "Roberto" is my older brother's real name; "Panchito" is my Spanish nickname.

The idea for the story goes back many years to the time when I was in Miss Bell's English class at Santa Maria High School. Miss Bell encouraged the class to write detailed narrative accounts of personal experiences. Even though I had difficulty expressing myself in English, I enjoyed the assignments, and with much effort I wrote about what I knew best. The remarks she made about what I wrote were so reassuring that long after I left her class I continued to reflect upon my life experiences and often thought of expressing them in writing. Whenever I could, I would jot down recollections on a piece of paper, hoping to write about them in the future.

In 1972, I shared two autobiographical narrative accounts with Professor Andrés Iduarte, my mentor in graduate school. He liked them very much and urged me to publish my work.

Encouraged by his positive remarks, I decided to write a short story describing in detail the joys and disappointments I encountered as I grew up in a migrant setting. I chose to treat my experiences during the time I was in the sixth grade because that school year had a great influence on me, especially the relationship I had with Mr. Lema, the sixth-grade teacher.

Francisco Jiménez

See THEME in the Handbook of Literary Terms, page 662.

The Fallen Angel

Evan Hunter

He claimed people wanted to watch him break his neck. Was he right?

---

e first came in one morning while I was making out the payroll for my small circus. We were pulling up stakes, ready to roll on to the next town, and I was bent over the books, writing down what I was paying everybody, and maybe that is why I did not hear the door open. When I looked up, this long, lanky fellow was standing there, and the door was shut tight behind him.

I looked at the door, and then I looked at him. He had a thin face with a narrow mustache, and black hair on his head that was sort of wild and sticking up in spots. He had brown eyes and a funny, twisted sort of mouth, with very white teeth which he was showing me at the moment.

"Mr. Mullins?" he asked.

"Yes," I said, because that is my name. Not Moon Mullins, which a lot of the fellows jokingly call me, but Anthony Mullins. And that is my real name, with no attempt to sound showmanlike; a good name, you will admit. "I am busy."

"I won't take much time," he said very softly. He walked over to the desk with a smooth, sideward step, as if he were on greased ball bearings.

"No matter how much time you will take," I said, "I am still busy."

"My name is Sam Angeli,"[1] he said.

"Pleased to meet you, Mr. Angeli," I told him. "My name is Anthony Mullins, and I am sorry you must be running along so quickly, but . . ."

"I'm a trapeze artist," he said.

"We already have three trapeze artists," I informed him, "and they are all excellent performers, and the budget does not call for . . ."

---

1. *Angeli* (än′jə lē).

"They are not Sam Angeli," he said, smiling and touching his chest with his thumb.

"That is true," I answered. "They are, in alphabetical order: Sue Ellen Bradley, Edward the Great and Arthur Farnings."

"But not Sam Angeli," he repeated softly.

"No," I said. "It would be difficult to call them all Sam Angeli since they are not even related, and even if they were related, it is unlikely they would all have the same name—even if they were triplets, which they are not."

"*I* am Sam Angeli," he said.

"So I have gathered. But I already have three . . ."

"I'm better," he said flatly.

"I have never met a trapeze artist who was not better than any other trapeze artist in the world," I said.

"In my case it happens to be true," he said.

I nodded and said nothing. I chewed my cigar awhile and went back to my books, and when I looked up he was still standing there, smiling.

"Look, my friend," I said, "I am earnestly sorry there is no opening for you, but . . ."

"Why not watch me a little?"

"I am too busy."

"It'll take five minutes. Your big top is still standing. Just watch me up there for a few minutes, that's all."

"My friend, what would be the point? I already have . . ."

"You can take your books with you, Mr. Mullins; you won't be sorry."

I looked at him again, and he stared at me levelly, and he had a deep, almost blazing, way of staring that made me believe I would really not be sorry if I watched him perform. Besides, I could take the books with me.

"All right," I said, "but we're only wasting each other's time."

"I've got all the time in the world," he answered.

We went outside, and sure enough the big top was still standing, so I bawled out Warren for being so slow to get a show on the road, and then this Angeli and I went inside, and he looked up at the trapeze, and I very sarcastically said, "Is that high enough for you?"

He shrugged and looked up and said, "I've been higher, my friend. Much higher." He dropped his eyes to the ground then, and I saw that the net had already been taken up.

"This exhibition will have to be postponed," I informed him. "There is no net."

"I don't need a net," he answered.

"No?"

"No."

"Do you plan on breaking your neck under one of my tops? I am warning you that my insurance doesn't cover . . ."

"I won't break my neck," Angeli said. "Sit down."

I shrugged and sat down, thinking it was his neck and not mine. I opened the books on my lap and got to work, and he walked across the tent and started climbing up to the trapeze. I got involved with the figures, and finally he yelled, "Okay, you ready?"

"I'm ready," I said.

I looked up to where he was sitting on one trapeze, holding the bar of the other trapeze in his big hands.

"Here's the idea," he yelled down. He had to yell because he was a good hundred feet in the air. "I'll set the second trapeze swinging, and then I'll put the one I'm on in motion. Then I'll jump from one trapeze to the other one. Understand?"

"I understand," I yelled back. I'm a quiet man by nature, and I have never liked yelling. Besides, he was about to do a very elementary trapeze routine, so there was nothing to get excited and yelling about.

He pushed out the second trapeze, and it swung away out in a nice clean arc, and then it came back and he shoved it out again and it went out farther and higher this time. He set his own trapeze in motion then, and both trapezes went swinging up there, back and forth, back and forth, higher and higher. He stood up on the bar and watched the second trapeze, timing himself, and then he shouted down, "I'll do a somersault to make it interesting."

"Go ahead," I said.

"Here I go," he said.

His trapeze came back and started forward, and the second trapeze reached the end of its arc and started back, and I saw him bend a little from the knees, calculating his timing, and then he leaped off, and his head ducked under, and he went into the somersault.

He did a nice clean roll, and then he stretched out his hands for the bar of the second trapeze, but the bar was nowhere near him. His fingers closed on air, and my eyes popped wide open as he sailed past the trapeze and then started a nose dive for the ground.

I jumped to my feet with my mouth open, remembering there was no net under him, and thinking of the mess he was going to make all over my tent. I watched him falling like a stone, and then I closed my eyes as he came closer to the ground. I clenched my fists and waited for the crash, and then the crash came, and there was a deathly silence in the tent afterward. I sighed and opened my eyes.

Sam Angeli got up and casually brushed the sawdust from his clothes. "How'd you like it?" he asked.

I stood stiff as a board and stared at him.

"How'd you like it?" he repeated.

"Dr. Lipsky!" I shouted. "Doc, come quick!"

"No need for a doctor," Angeli said, smiling and walking over to me. "How'd you like the fall?"

"The . . . the fall?"

"The fall," Angeli said, smiling. "Looked like the real McCoy, didn't it?"

"What do you mean?"

"Well, you don't think I missed that bar accidentally, do you? I mean, after all, that's a kid stunt."

"You fell on purpose?" I kept staring at him, but all his bones seemed to be in the right places, and there was no blood on him anywhere.

"Sure," he said. "My specialty. I figured it all out, Mr. Mullins. Do you know why people like to watch trapeze acts? Not because there's any skill or art attached. Oh, no." He smiled, and his eyes glowed, and I watched him, still amazed. "They like to watch because they are inherently evil, Mr. Mullins. They watch because they think that fool up there is going to fall and break his neck, and they want to be around when he does it." Angeli nodded. "So I figured it all out."

"You did?"

Grand Entry, 1890, Library of Congress
This circus poster is an early lithograph.

"I did. I figured if the customers wanted to see me fall, then I would fall. So I practiced falling."

"You did?"

"I did. First I fell out of bed, and then I fell from a first-story window, and then I fell off the roof. And then I took my biggest fall, the fall that . . . But I'm boring you. The point is, I can fall from any place now. In fact, that trapeze of yours is rather low."

"Rather low," I repeated softly.

"Yes."

"What's up?" Dr. Lipsky shouted, rushing into the tent, his shirttails trailing. "What happened, Moon?"

"Nothing," I said, wagging my head. "Nothing, Doc."

"Then why'd you . . . ?"

"I wanted to tell you," I said slowly, "that I've just hired a new trapeze artist."

We rolled on to the next town, and I introduced Angeli to my other trapeze artists: Sue Ellen, Farnings, and Edward the Great. I told them I wanted Angeli to have exclusive use of the tent that afternoon, and all afternoon I sat and watched him while he jumped for trapezes and missed and went flying down on his nose or head or his back or whatever he landed on. I kept watching him when he landed, but the sawdust always came up around him like a big cloud, and I never could see what he did inside that cloud. All I know is that he got up every time, and he brushed himself off, and each time I went over to him and expected to find a hundred broken bones and maybe a fractured skull, but each time he just stood up with that handsome smile on his face as if

he hadn't just fallen from away up there.

"This is amazing," I told him. "This is almost supernatural!"

"I know," he said.

"We'll start you tonight," I said, getting excited about it now. "Can you start tonight?"

"I can start anytime," he said.

"Sam Angeli," I announced, spreading my hand across the air as if I were spelling it out in lights. "Sam An——" I paused and let my hand drop. "That's terrible," I said.

"I know," Angeli answered. "But I figured that out, too."

"What?"

"A name for me. I figured this all out."

"And what's the name?" I asked.

"The Fallen Angel," he said.

There wasn't much of a crowd that night. Sue Ellen, Farnings, and Edward the Great went up there and did their routines, but they were playing to cold fish, and you could have put all the applause they got into a sardine can. Except mine. Whenever I saw Sue Ellen, I clapped my heart out, and I never cared what the crowd was doing. I went out after Edward the Great wound up his act, and I said, "Ladeeeees and Gentulmennnn, it gives me great pleasure to introduce at this time, in his American première, for the first time in this country, the Fallen Angel!"

I don't know what I expected, but no one so much as batted an eyelid.

"You will note," I said, "that the nets are now being removed from beneath the trapezes, and that the trapezes are being raised to the uppermost portion of the tent. The Fallen Angel will perform at a height of one hundred and fifty feet above the ground, without benefit of a net, performing his death-defying feats of skill for your satisfaction."

The crowd murmured a little, but you could see they still weren't very excited about it all.

"And now," I shouted, "the Fallen Angel!"

Angeli came into the ring, long and thin, muscular in his red tights, the sequins shining so that they could almost blind you. He began climbing up to the bars, and everyone watched him, a little bored by now with all these trapeze acts. Angeli hopped aboard and then worked out a little, swinging to and fro, leaping from one trapeze to another, doing a few difficult stunts. He looked down to the band then, and Charlie started a roll on the drums, and I shouted into my megaphone, "And now, a blood-chilling, spine-tingling double somersault from one moving trapeze to another at one hundred and fifty feet above the ground—*without a net!*"

The crowd leaned forward a little, the way they always will when a snare drum starts rolling, and Angeli set the bars in motion, and then he tensed, with all the spotlights on him. The drum kept going, and then Angeli leaped into space, and he rolled over once, twice, and then his arms came out straight for the bar, and his hands clutched nothing, and he started to fall.

A woman screamed, and then they all were on their feet, a shocked roar leaping from four hundred throats all together. Angeli dropped and dropped and dropped, and women covered their eyes and screamed and brave men turned away, and then he hit the

sawdust, and the cloud rolled up around him, and an *Ohhhhhhh* went up from the crowd. They kept standing, shocked, silent, like a bunch of pallbearers.

Then suddenly, casually, the Fallen Angel got to his feet and brushed off his red-sequined costume. He turned to the crowd and smiled a big, happy smile, and then he turned to face the other half of the tent, smiling again, extending his arms and hands to his public, almost as if he were silently saying, "My children! My nice children!"

The crowd cheered and whistled and shouted and stamped. Sue Ellen, standing next to me, sighed and said, "Tony, he's wonderful," and I heard her, and I heard the yells of "Encore!" out there, but I didn't bring Angeli out again that night. I tucked him away and then waited for the landslide.

The landslide came the next night. We were playing in a small town, but I think everyone who could walk turned out for the show. They fidgeted through all the acts, crowding the tent, standing in the back, shoving and pushing. They were bored when my aerial artists went on, but the boredom was good because they were all waiting for the Fallen Angel, all waiting to see if the reports about him were true.

When I introduced him, there was no applause. There was only an awful hush. Angeli came out and climbed up to the bars and then began doing his tricks again, and everyone waited, having heard that he took his fall during the double somersault.

But Angeli was a supreme showman, and he realized that the value of his trick lay in its surprise element. So he didn't wait for the double somersault this time. He simply swung out one trapeze and then made a leap for it, right in the middle of his other routine stunts, only this time he missed, and down he dropped with the crowd screaming to its feet.

A lot of people missed the fall, and that was the idea, because those same people came back the next night, and Angeli never did it the same way twice. He'd fall in the middle of his act, or at the end, or once he fell the first time he jumped for the trapeze. Another time he didn't fall at all during the act, and then, as he was coming down the ladder, he missed a rung and down he came, and the crowd screamed.

And Angeli would come to me after each performance and his eyes would glow, and he'd say, "Did you hear them, Tony? They want me to fall, they want me to break my neck!"

And maybe they did. Or maybe they were just very happy to see him get up after he fell, safe and sound. Whatever it was, it was wonderful. Business was booming, and I began thinking of getting some new tops, and maybe a wild-animal act. I boosted everybody's salary, and I began taking a larger cut myself, and I was finally ready to ask Sue Ellen something I'd wanted to ask her for a long, long time. And Sam Angeli had made it all possible. I spoke to her alone one night, over by the stakes where the elephants were tied.

"Sue Ellen," I said, "there's something that's been on my mind for a long time now."

"What is it, Tony?" she said.

"Well, I'm just a small-time circus man, and I never had much money, you know, and so I never had the right. But things have picked up considerably, and . . . "

"Don't, Tony," she said.

I opened my eyes wide. "I beg your pardon, Sue Ellen?"

"Don't ask me. Maybe it could have been, and maybe it couldn't. But no more now, Tony. Not since I met Sam. He's everything I want, Tony; can you understand that?"

"I suppose," I said.

"I think I love him, Tony."

I nodded and said nothing.

"I'm awfully sorry," Sue Ellen said.

"If it makes you happy, honey . . . " I couldn't think of any way to finish it.

I started work in earnest. Maybe I should have fired Angeli on the spot, but you can't fire love, and that's what I was battling. So instead I worked harder, and I tried not to see Sue Ellen around all the time. I began to figure crowd reactions, and I realized the people would not hold still for my other aerial artists once they got wind of the Fallen Angel. So we worked Farnings and Edward (whose "Great" title we dropped) into one act, and we worked Sue Ellen into Angeli's act. Sue Ellen dressed up the act a lot, and it gave Angeli someone to kid around with up there, making his stunts before the fall more interesting.

Sue Ellen never did any of the fancy stuff. She just caught Angeli, or was caught by him—all stuff leading up to Angeli's spectacular fall. The beautiful part was that Sue Ellen never had to worry about timing. I mean, if she missed Angeli—so he fell. I thought about his fall a lot, and I tried to figure it out, but I never could, and after a while I stopped figuring. I never stopped thinking about Sue Ellen, though, and it hurt me awful to watch her looking at him with those eyes full of worship, but if she was happy, that was all that counted.

And then I began to get bigger ideas. Why fool around with a small-time circus? I wondered. Why not expand? Why not incorporate?

I got off a few letters to the biggest circuses I knew of. I told them what I had, and I told them the boy was under exclusive contract to me, and I told them he would triple attendance, and I told them I was interested in joining circuses, becoming partners sort of, with the understanding that the Fallen Angel would come along with me. I guess the word got around by then because all the big-shot letters were very cordial and very nice, and they all asked me when they could get a look at Angeli because they would certainly be interested in incorporating my fine little outfit on a partnership basis if my boy were all I claimed him to be, sincerely yours.

I got off a few more letters, asking all the big shots to attend our regular Friday night performance so that they could judge the crowd reaction and see the Fallen Angel under actual working conditions. All my letters were answered with telegrams, and we set the ball rolling.

That Friday afternoon was pure bedlam.

There's always a million things happening around a circus, anyway, but this Friday everything seemed to pile up at once. Like Fifi, our bareback rider, storming into the tent in her white ruffles.

"My horse!" she yelled, her brown eyes flashing. "My horse!"

"Is something wrong with him?" I asked.

"No, nothing's wrong with him," she screamed. "But something's wrong with José Esperanza,[2] and I'm going to wring his neck unless . . ."

"Now easy, honey," I said, "let us take it easy."

"I told him a bucket of *rye*. I did *not* say a bucket of oats. JuJu does not eat oats; he eats rye. And my safety and health and life depend on JuJu, and I will not have him eating some foul-smelling oats when I distinctly told José . . ."

"José!" I bellowed. "José Esperanza, come here."

José was a small Puerto Rican we'd picked up only recently. A nice young kid with big brown eyes and a small timid smile. He poked his head into the wagon and smiled, and then he saw Fifi and the smile dropped from his face.

"Is it true you gave JuJu oats, José, when you were told to give him rye?" I asked.

"Yes, *Señor*,[3] José said, "that is true."

"But why, José? Why on earth . . ."

José lowered his head. "The horse, *Señor*, I like him. He is a nice horse. He is always good to me."

"What's that got to do with the bucket of rye?"

"*Señor*," José said pleadingly, "I did not want to get the horse drunk."

"Drunk? Drunk?"

"Yes, *Señor*, a bucket of rye. Even for a horse, that is a lot of whiskey. I did not think . . ."

"Oh," Fifi wailed, "of all the— I'll feed

---

2. *José Esperanza* (hô sä′ es pe rän′sä).
3. *Señor* (se nyôr′), in Spanish, Mister or Sir.

the horse myself. I'll feed him myself. Never mind!"

She stormed out of the wagon, and José smiled sheepishly and said, "I did wrong, *Señor?*"

I shook my head, and José left, and when I turned around Sam Angeli was standing there. I hadn't heard him come in, and I wondered how long he'd been there, so I said, "A good kid, José."

"If you like good kids," Angeli answered.

"He'll go to heaven, that one," I said. "Mark my words."

Angeli smiled. "We'll see," he said. "I wanted to talk to you, Tony."

"Oh? What about?"

"About all these people coming tonight. The big shots, the ones coming to see me."

"What about them?"

"Nothing, Tony. But suppose—just suppose, mind you—suppose I don't fall?"

"What do you mean?" I said.

"Just that. Suppose I don't fall tonight?"

"That's silly," I said. "You have to fall."

"Do I? Where does it say I have to fall?"

"Your contract. You signed a . . ."

"The contract doesn't say anything about my having to fall, Tony. Not a word."

"Well . . . say, what is this? A holdup?"

"No. Nothing of the sort. I just got to thinking. If this works out tonight, Tony, you're going to be a big man. But what do I get out of it?"

"Do you want a salary boost? Is that it? O.K. You've got a salary boost. How's that?"

"I don't want a salary boost."

"What, then?"

"Something of very little importance. Something of no value whatever."

"What?" I said. "What is it?"

"Suppose we make a deal, Tony?" Angeli said. "Suppose we shake on it? If I fall tonight, I get this little something that I want."

"What's this little something that you want?"

"Is it a deal?"

"I have to know first."

"Well, let's forget it then," Angeli said.

"Now wait a minute, wait a minute. Is this 'thing'—Sue Ellen?"

Angeli smiled. "I don't have to make a deal to get her, Tony."

"Well, is it money?"

"No. This thing has no material value."

"Then why do you want it?"

"I collect them."

"And I've got one?"

"Yes."

"Well, what . . . ?"

"Is it a deal, or isn't it?"

"I don't know. I mean, this is a peculiar way to . . ."

"Believe me, this thing is of no material value to you. You won't even know it's gone. But if I go through with my fall tonight, all I ask is that you give it to me. A handshake will be binding as far as I'm concerned."

I shrugged. "All right, all right, a deal. Provided you haven't misrepresented this thing, whatever it is. Provided it's not of material value to me."

"I haven't misrepresented it. Shall we shake, Tony?"

He extended his hand, and I took it, and his eyes glowed, but his skin was very cold to the touch. I pulled my hand away.

"Now," I said, "what's this thing you want from me?"

Angeli smiled. "Your soul."

I was suddenly alone in the wagon. I looked around, but Angeli was gone, and then the door opened and Sue Ellen stepped in, and she looked very grave and very upset.

"I heard," she said. "Forgive me. I heard. I was listening outside. Tony, what are you going to do? What are *we* going to do?"

"Can it be?" I said. "Can it be, Sue Ellen? He looks just like you and me. How'd I get into this?"

"We've got to do something," Sue Ellen said. "Tony, we've got to stop him!"

We packed them in that night. They sat, and they stood, and they climbed all over the rafters; they were everywhere. And right down front, I sat with the big shots, and they all watched my small, unimportant show until it was time for the Fallen Angel to go on.

I got up and smiled weakly and said, "If you gentlemen will excuse me, I have to introduce the next act."

They all smiled back knowingly, and nodded their heads, and their gold stickpins and pinky rings winked at me, and they blew out expensive cigar smoke, and I was thinking, *Mullins, you can blow out expensive cigar smoke, too, but you won't have any soul left.*

I introduced the act, and I was surprised to see all my aerial artists run out onto the sawdust: Sue Ellen, Farnings, Edward and the Fallen Angel. I watched Angeli as he crossed one of the spotlights, and if I'd had any doubts they all vanished right then. Angeli cast no shadow on the sawdust.

I watched in amazement as the entire troupe went up the ladder to the trapezes. There was a smile on Angeli's face, but Sue Ellen and the rest had tight, set mouths.

They did a few stunts, and I watched the big shots, and it was plain they were not impressed at all by these routine aerial acrobatics. I signaled the band, according to schedule, and I shouted, "And now, ladies and gentlemen, the Fallen Angel in a death-defying, spine-tingling, bloodcurdling triple somersault at one hundred and fifty feet above the ground, *without a net!*"

Sue Ellen swung her trapeze out, and Angeli swung his, and then Sue Ellen dropped head downward and extended her hands, and Angeli swung back and forth, and the crowd held its breath, waiting for him to take his fall, and the big shots held their breaths, waiting for the same thing. Only I knew what would happen if he did take that fall. Only I knew about our agreement. Only I—and Sue Ellen, waiting up there for Angeli to jump.

Charlie started the roll on his snare, and then the roll stopped abruptly, and Angeli released his grip on the bar and he swung out into space, and over he went, once, twice, three times—and *slap*. Sue Ellen's hands clamped around his wrists, and she held on for dear life. I couldn't see Angeli's face from so far below, but he seemed to be struggling to get away. Sue Ellen held him for just an instant, just long enough for Edward to swing his trapeze into position.

She flipped Angeli out then, and over he went—and *wham*. Edward grabbed his ankles. Angeli flapped his arms and kicked his legs, trying to get free, but Edward—Edward the Great!—wouldn't drop him. Instead, he swung his trapeze back, and then gave Angeli a flip and Farnings grabbed Angeli's wrists.

Farnings flipped Angeli up, and Sue Ellen caught him, and then Sue Ellen swung her trapeze all the way back and tossed Angeli to Edward, and I began to get the idea of what was going on up there.

Edward tossed Angeli, and Farnings caught him, and then Farnings tossed him to Sue Ellen, and Sue Ellen tossed him right back again. Then Farnings climbed onto Sue Ellen's trapeze, and they both swung back to the platform.

Edward took a long swing, and then he tossed Angeli head over heels, right back to the platform, where Sue Ellen and Farnings grabbed him with four eager arms.

I was grinning all over by this time, and the crowd was booing at the top of its lungs. Who cared? The big shots were stirring rest-lessly, but they'd probably heard that Angeli sometimes fell coming down the ladder, and so they didn't leave their seats.

Only tonight, Angeli wasn't doing any falling coming down any ladder. Because Sue Ellen had one of his wrists and Farnings had one of his ankles, and one was behind him, and the other was ahead of him; and even if he pitched himself off into space, he wouldn't have gone far, not with the grips they had on both him and the ladder. I saw the big shots get up and throw away their cigars, and then everybody began booing as if they wanted to tear down the top with their voices. Angeli came over to me, and his face didn't hold a pleasant smile this time. His face was in rage, and it turned red, as if he would explode.

"You tricked me!" he screamed. "You tricked me!"

And all at once he wasn't there any more.

THINK AND DISCUSS
Understanding
1. Who is the narrator of this story, and what are his interests?
2. What is Sam Angeli's specialty?
3. What are the reactions to Sam Angeli from the audiences and from the other performers?
4. Why does Angeli think people like his act?

Analyzing
5. Describe the **character** Sam Angeli. Consider his physical appearance, actions, and beliefs.

6. How does Sam Angeli misjudge Anthony Mullins?
7. Why does Angeli become so angry when he feels he has been tricked?
8. What hints are given early in the story that Angeli is not what he pretends to be?

Extending
9. If this story were to be continued, what do you think would happen to Mullins, Sue Ellen, and Angeli?

APPLYING: Theme H✐

See Handbook of Literary Terms, p. 662.

The **theme** of a literary work is its underlying meaning. A theme may be directly stated, but more often it is implied.

1. Who or what do you think Angeli is?
2. What causes Angeli to fail in the end?
3. In what ways is the title "The Fallen Angel" appropriate to the story?
4. What do you think is the theme of the story?

COMPOSITION ✐

Reading/Writing Log

The author of "The Fallen Angel" provides specific details and information to help you picture Anthony Mullins and Sam Angeli. Copy the headings and examples below in your **reading/writing log.** Then find additional examples for each character.

Mullins	Angeli
quiet man by nature	long, lanky fellow
never liked yelling	thin face
	narrow mustache

Writing About Characters

Write two paragraphs showing the differences between Mullins and Angeli. Consider their physical appearances, their beliefs about other people, and their interests in life. Before you begin, list details about each character. If you are keeping a **reading/writing log,** note the specific details about Mullins and Angeli that you listed earlier. Refer to your log as you write. See Lesson 7, "Writing About Characters," in the Writer's Handbook.

Describing How Friends Help

Anthony Mullins's friends come to his aid when he is in danger of losing his soul. Write a paragraph about a time when one or more of your friends helped you get through a difficult situation. Be sure to give specific details so that the reader understands how your friends supported you and how the situation turned out.

BIOGRAPHY

Evan Hunter

1926–

Evan Hunter has had a varied work background, from selling lobsters to teaching high-school classes, but his career as a writer has included an even greater range: novels, short stories, stage plays, and screenplays, appealing to readers of crime and mystery fiction, science fiction and fantasy, romances, and children's literature. His novel *The Blackboard Jungle* was made into a motion picture. He also wrote the screenplay for another well-known film, Alfred Hitchcock's *The Birds*, adapting a story by another author.

Review **THEME** in the Handbook of Literary Terms, page 662.

The Smallest Dragonboy

Anne McCaffrey

If Keevan should be chosen by a dragon, he would achieve the only goal of his life—to become a dragonrider!

Pern—the setting of "The Smallest Dragonboy" and other stories by Anne McCaffrey—is an imaginary planet on which people often must struggle to survive. The Pernese people live in volcanic rock holdings called weyrs. *Each of these communities has a* Weyrleader *and other officers called* wingseconds.

The Pernese dwell in caves to protect themselves from the evil Thread. *This silver spore-life comes from a stray planet, the Red Star, which after regular intervals passes in its orbit close to Pern. During these times of* Threadfall, *the spores try to cross the space gap to live on the more temperate planet of Pern. Once grounded, the spores devour organic matter.*

To combat the life-threatening Thread, the Pernese have bred a new form of life—telepathic dragons who exhale flaming gas and travel from place to place and from time to time instantaneously (called going between). *Because the dragons can fly, they meet and char the Thread in midair. They fly with* dragonriders *whom they have chosen (or* Impressed) *at hatching time. A dragonrider and his dragon become lifelong companions.*

This story takes place in Benden Weyr—a large Pernese settlement in the Benden Mountains—during dragon hatching.

Characters, Places, and Terms to Know

Keevan	main character; a dragonrider candidate	Pern	imaginary planet
Beterli	oldest and largest dragonrider candidate	weyr	community or settlement
		Thread	evil spore-life from stray planet
Mende	Keevan's foster mother	going between	to travel from place to place and from time to time
K'last	Keevan's father, a dragonrider		
F'lar	Weyrleader of the settlement		
Lessa	Weyrwoman, a wise ruler	Benden Weyr	a large settlement on Pern
L'vel	dragonrider	turn	a year

lthough Keevan lengthened his walking stride as far as his legs would stretch, he couldn't quite keep up with the other candidates. He knew he would be teased again.

Just as he knew many other things that his foster mother told him he ought not to know, Keevan knew that Beterli, the most senior of the boys, set that spanking pace just to embarrass him, the smallest dragonboy. Keevan would arrive, tail fork-end of the group, breathless, chest heaving, and maybe get a stern look from the instructing wingsecond.

Dragonriders, even if they were still only hopeful candidates for the glowing eggs which were hardening on the hot sands of the Hatching Ground cavern, were expected to be punctual and prepared. Sloth was not tolerated by the Weyrleader of Benden Weyr. A good record was especially important now. It was very near hatching time, when the baby dragons would crack their mottled shells, and stagger forth to choose their lifetime companions. The very thought of that glorious moment made Keevan's breath catch in his throat. To be chosen—to be a dragonrider! To sit astride the neck of a winged beast with jeweled eyes: to be his friend, in telepathic communion with him for life; to be his companion in good times and fighting extremes; to fly effortlessly over the lands of Pern! Or, thrillingly, *between* to any point anywhere on the world! Flying *between* was done on dragonback or not at all, and it was dangerous.

Keevan glanced upward, past the black mouths of the weyr caves in which grown dragons and their chosen riders lived, toward the Star Stones that crowned the ridge of the old volcano that was Benden Weyr. On the height, the blue watch dragon, his rider mounted on his neck, stretched the great transparent pinions that carried him on the winds of Pern to fight the evil Thread that fell at certain times from the skies. The many-faceted rainbow jewels of his eyes glistened fleetingly in the greeny sun. He folded his great wings to his back, and the watch pair resumed their statuelike pose of alertness.

Then the enticing view was obscured as Keevan passed into the Hatching Ground cavern. The sands underfoot were hot, even through heavy wher-hide boots. How the bootmaker had protested having to sew so small! Keevan was forced to wonder why being small was reprehensible. People were always calling him "babe" and shooing him away as being "too small" or "too young" for this or that. Keevan was constantly working, twice as hard as any other boy his age, to prove himself capable. What if his muscles weren't as big as Beterli's? They were just as hard. And if he couldn't overpower anyone in a wrestling match, he could outdistance everyone in a footrace.

"Maybe if you run fast enough," Beterli had jeered on the occasion when Keevan had been goaded to boast of his swiftness, "you could catch a dragon. That's the only way you'll make a dragonrider!"

"You just wait and see, Beterli, you just wait," Keevan had replied. He would have liked to wipe the contemptuous smile from Beterli's face, but the guy didn't fight fair even when a wingsecond was watching. "No one knows what Impresses a dragon!"

"They've got to be able to *find* you first, babe!"

Yes, being the smallest candidate was not an enviable position. It was therefore imperative that Keevan Impress a dragon in his first hatching. That would wipe the smile off every face in the cavern and accord him the respect due any dragonrider, even the smallest one.

Besides, no one knew exactly what Impressed the baby dragons as they struggled from their shells in search of their lifetime partners.

"I like to believe that dragons see into a man's heart," Keevan's foster mother, Mende, told him. "If they find goodness, honesty, a flexible mind, patience, courage—and you've got that in quantity, dear Keevan—that's what dragons look for. I've seen many a well-grown lad left standing on the sands, Hatching Day, in favor of someone not so strong or tall or handsome. And if my memory serves me"—which it usually did: Mende knew every word of every Harper's tale worth telling, although Keevan did not interrupt her to say so—"I don't believe that F'lar, our Weyrleader, was all that tall when bronze Mnementh chose him. And Mnementh was the only bronze dragon of that hatching."

Dreams of Impressing a bronze were beyond Keevan's boldest reflections, although that goal dominated the thoughts of every other hopeful candidate. Green dragons were small and fast and more numerous. There was more prestige to Impressing a blue or brown than a green. Being practical, Keevan seldom dreamed as high as a big fighting brown, like Canth, F'nor's fine fellow, the biggest brown on all Pern. But to fly a bronze? Bronzes were almost as big as the queen, and only they took the air when a queen flew at mating time. A bronze rider could aspire to become Weyrleader! Well, Keevan would console himself, brown riders could aspire to become wingseconds, and that wasn't bad. He'd even settle for a green dragon: they were small, but so was he. No matter! He simply had to Impress a dragon his first time in the Hatching Ground. Then no one in the Weyr would taunt him anymore for being so small.

Shells, Keevan thought now, but the sands are hot!

"Impression time is imminent, candidates," the wingsecond was saying as everyone crowded respectfully close to him. "See the extent of the striations on this promising egg." The stretch marks *were* larger than yesterday.

Everyone leaned forward and nodded thoughtfully. That particular egg was the one Beterli had marked as his own, and no other candidate dared, on pain of being beaten by Beterli at his first opportunity, to approach it. The egg was marked by a large yellowish splotch in the shape of a dragon backwinging to land, talons outstretched to grasp rock. Everyone knew that bronze eggs bore distinctive markings. And naturally, Beterli, who'd been presented at eight Impressions already and was the biggest of the candidates, had chosen it.

"I'd say that the great opening day is almost upon us," the wingsecond went on, and then his face assumed a grave expression. "As we well know, there are only forty eggs and seventy-two candidates. Some of you may be disappointed on the great day. That doesn't necessarily mean you aren't dragonrider material, just that *the* dragon for you hasn't been shelled. You'll have other hatchings, and it's no disgrace to be left behind an Impression or two. Or more."

Keevan was positive that the wingsecond's eyes rested on Beterli, who'd been stood off at so many Impressions already. Keeven tried to squinch down so the wingsecond wouldn't notice him. Keeven had been reminded too often that he was eligible to be a candidate by one day only. He, of all the hopefuls, was most likely to be left standing on the great day. One more reason why he simply had to Impress at his first hatching.

"Now move about among the eggs," the wingsecond said. "Touch them. We don't know that it does any good, but it certainly doesn't do any harm."

Some of the boys laughed nervously, but everyone immediately began to circulate among the eggs. Beterli stepped up officiously to "his" egg, daring anyone to come near it. Keevan smiled, because he had already touched it—every inspection day, when the others were leaving the Hatching Ground and no one could see him crouch to stroke it.

Keevan had an egg he concentrated on, too, one drawn slightly to the far side of the others. The shell had a soft greenish-blue tinge with a faint creamy swirl design. The consensus was that this egg contained a mere green, so Keevan was rarely bothered by rivals. He was somewhat perturbed then to see Beterli wandering over to him.

"I don't know why you're allowed in this Impression, Keevan. There are enough of us without a babe," Beterli said, shaking his head.

"I'm of age." Keevan kept his voice level, telling himself not to be bothered by mere words.

"Yah!" Beterli made a show of standing in his toe-tips. "You can't even see over an egg; Hatching Day, you better get in front or the dragons won't see you at all. 'Course, you could get run down that way in the mad scramble. Oh, I forget, you can run fast, can't you?"

"You'd better make sure a dragon sees *you*, this time, Beterli," Keevan replied. "You're almost overage, aren't you?"

Beterli flushed and took a step forward,

hand half-raised. Keevan stood his ground, but if Beterli advanced one more step, he would call the wingsecond. No one fought on the Hatching Ground. Surely Beterli knew that much.

Fortunately, at that moment, the wingsecond called the boys together and led them from the Hatching Ground to start on evening chores. There were "glows" to be replenished in the main kitchen caverns and sleeping cubicles, the major hallways, and the queen's apartment. Firestone sacks had to be filled against Thread attack, and black rock brought to the kitchen hearths. The boys fell to their chores, tantalized by the odors of roasting meat. The population of the Weyr began to assemble for the evening meal, and the dragonriders came in from the Feeding Ground on their sweep checks.

It was the time of day Keevan liked best: once the chores were done but before dinner was served, a fellow could often get close enough to the dragonriders to hear their talk. Tonight, Keevan's father, K'last, was at the main dragonrider table. It puzzled Keevan how his father, a brown rider and a tall man, could *be* his father—because he, Keevan, was so small. It obviously puzzled K'last, too, when he deigned to notice his small son: "In a few more Turns, you'll be as tall as I am—or taller!"

K'last was pouring Benden wine all around the table. The dragonriders were relaxing. There'd be no Thread attack for three more days, and they'd be in the mood to tell tall tales, better than Harper yarns, about impossible maneuvers they'd done a-dragonback. When Thread attack was closer, their talk would change to a discussion of tactics of eva-

sion, of going *between*, how long to suspend there until the burning but fragile Thread would freeze and crack and fall harmlessly off dragon and man. They would dispute the exact moment to feed firestone to the dragon so he'd have the best flame ready to sear Thread midair and render it harmless to ground—and man—below. There was such a lot to know and understand about being a dragonrider that sometimes Keevan was overwhelmed. How would he ever be able to remember everything he ought to know at the right moment? He couldn't dare ask such a question; this would only have given additional weight to the notion that he was too young yet to be a dragonrider.

"Having older candidates makes good sense," L'vel was saying, as Keevan settled down near the table. "Why waste four to five years of a dragon's fighting prime until his rider grows up enough to stand the rigors?" L'vel had Impressed a blue of Ramoth's first clutch. Most of the candidates thought L'vel was marvelous because he spoke up in front of the older riders, who awed them. "That was well enough in the Interval when you didn't need to mount the full Weyr complement to fight Thread. But not now. Not with more eligible candidates than ever. Let the babes wait."

"Any boy who is over twelve Turns has the right to stand in the Hatching Ground," K'last replied, a slight smile on his face. He never argued or got angry. Keevan wished he were more like his father. And oh, how he wished he were a brown rider! "Only a dragon—each particular dragon—knows what he wants in a rider. We certainly can't tell. Time and again the theorists," K'last's smile deepened as his eyes swept those at the table, "are surprised by dragon choice. *They* never seem to make mistakes, however."

"Now, K'last, just look at the roster this Impression. Seventy-two boys and only forty eggs. Drop off the twelve youngest, and there's still a good field for the hatchlings to choose from. Shells! There are a couple of weyrlings unable to see over a wher egg much less a dragon! And years before they can ride Thread."

"True enough, but the Weyr is scarcely under fighting strength, and if the youngest Impress, they'll be old enough to fight when the oldest of our current dragons go *between* from senility."

"Half the Weyr-bred lads have already been through several Impressions," one of the bronze riders said then. "I'd say drop some of *them* off this time. Give the untried a chance."

"There's nothing wrong in presenting a clutch with as wide a choice as possible," said the Weyrleader, who had joined the table with Lessa, the Weyrwoman. "Has there ever been a case," she said, smiling in her odd way at the riders, "where a hatchling didn't choose?"

Her suggestion was almost heretical and drew astonished gasps from everyone, including the boys.

F'lar laughed. "You say the most outrageous things, Lessa."

"Well, *has* there ever been a case where a dragon didn't choose?"

"Can't say as I recall one," K'last replied.

"Then we continue in this tradition," Lessa said firmly, as if that ended the matter.

But it didn't. The argument ranged from one table to the other all through dinner, with some favoring a weeding out of the candidates to the most likely, lopping off those who were very young or who had had multiple opportunities to Impress. All the candidates were in a swivet, though such a departure from tradition would be to the advantage of many. As the evening progressed, more riders were favoring eliminating the youngest and those who'd passed four or more Impressions unchosen. Keevan felt he could bear such a dictum only if Beterli were also eliminated. But this seemed less likely than that Keevan would be turfed out, since the Weyr's need was for fighting dragons and riders.

By the time the evening meal was over, no decision had been reached, although the Weyrleader had promised to give the matter due consideration.

He might have slept on the problem, but few of the candidates did. Tempers were uncertain in the sleeping caverns next morning as the boys were routed out of their beds to carry water and black rock and cover the "glows." Twice Mende had to call Keevan to order for clumsiness.

"Whatever is the matter with you, boy?" she demanded in exasperation when he tipped black rock short of the bin and sooted up the hearth.

"They're going to keep me from this Impression."

"What?" Mende stared at him. "Who?"

"You heard them talking at dinner last night. They're going to turf the babes from the hatching."

Mende regarded him a moment longer before touching his arm gently. "There's lots of talk around a supper table, Keevan. And it cools as soon as the supper. I've heard the same nonsense before every hatching, but nothing is ever changed."

"There's always a first time," Keevan answered, copying one of her own phrases.

"That'll be enough of that, Keevan. Finish your job. If the clutch does hatch today, we'll need full rock bins for the feast, and you won't be around to do the filling. All my fosterlings make dragonriders."

"The first time?" Keevan was bold enough to ask as he scooted off with the rockbarrow.

Perhaps, Keevan thought later, if he hadn't been on that chore just when Beterli was also fetching black rock, things might have turned out differently. But he had dutifully trundled the barrow to the outdoor bunker for another load just as Beterli arrived on a similar errand.

"Heard the news, babe?" Beterli asked. He was grinning from ear to ear, and he put an unnecessary emphasis on the final insulting word.

"The eggs are cracking?" Keevan all but dropped the loaded shovel. Several anxieties flicked through his mind then: he was black with rock dust—would he have time to wash before donning the white tunic of candidacy? And if the eggs were hatching, why hadn't the candidates been recalled by the wingsecond?

"Naw! Guess again!" Beterli was much too pleased with himself.

With a sinking heart, Keeven knew what the news must be, and he could only stare with intense desolation at the older boy.

"C'mon! Guess, babe!"

"I've no time for guessing games," Keevan managed to say with indifference. He began to shovel black rock into the barrow as fast as he could.

"I said, guess." Beterli grabbed the shovel.

"And I said I have no time for guessing games."

Beterli wrenched the shovel from Keevan's hands. "Guess!"

"I'll have that shovel back, Beterli." Keevan straightened up, but he didn't come to Beterli's bulky shoulder. From somewhere, other boys appeared, some with barrows, some mysteriously alerted to the prospect of a confrontation among their numbers.

"Babes don't give orders to candidates around here, babe!"

Someone sniggered and Keevan, incredulous, knew that he must've been dropped from the candidacy.

He yanked the shovel from Beterli's loosened grasp. Snarling, the older boy tried to regain possession, but Keevan clung with all his strength to the handle, dragged back and forth as the stronger boy jerked the shovel about.

With a sudden, unexpected movement, Beterli rammed the handle into Keevan's chest, knocking him over the barrow handles. Keevan felt a sharp, painful jab behind his left ear, an unbearable pain in his left shin, and then a painless nothingness.

Mende's angry voice roused him, and startled, he tried to throw back the covers, thinking he'd overslept. But he couldn't move, so firmly was he tucked into his bed. And then the constriction of a bandage on his head and the dull sickishness in his leg brought back recent occurrences.

"Hatching?" he cried.

"No, lovey," Mende said in a kind voice. Her hand was cool and gentle on his forehead. "Though there's some as won't be at any hatching again." Her voice took on a stern edge.

Keeven looked beyond her to see the Weyrwoman, who was frowning with irritation.

"Keevan, will you tell me what occurred at the black-rock bunker?" asked Lessa in an even voice.

He remembered Beterli now and the quarrel over the shovel and . . . what had Mende said about some not being at any hatching? Much as he hated Beterli, he couldn't bring himself to tattle on Beterli and force him out of candidacy.

"Come, lad," and a note of impatience crept into the Weyrwoman's voice. "I merely want to know what happened from you, too. Mende said she sent you for black rock. Beterli—and every Weyrling in the cavern—seems to have been on the same errand. What happened?"

"Beterli took my shovel. I hadn't finished with it."

"There's more than one shovel. What did he *say* to you?"

"He'd heard the news."

"What news?" The Weyrwoman was suddenly amused.

"That . . . that . . . there'd been changes."

"Is that what he said?"

"Not exactly."

"What did he say? C'mon, lad, I've heard from everyone else, you know."

"He said for me to guess the news."

"And you fell for that old gag?" The Weyrwoman's irritation returned.

"Consider all the talk last night at supper, Lessa," Mende said. "Of course the boy would think he'd been eliminated."

"In effect, he is, with a broken skull and leg." Lessa touched his arm in a rare gesture of sympathy. "Be that as it may, Keevan, you'll have other Impressions. Beterli will not. There are certain rules that must be observed by all candidates, and his conduct proves him unacceptable to the Weyr."

She smiled at Mende and then left.

"I'm still a candidate?" Keevan asked urgently.

"Well, you are and you aren't, lovey," his foster mother said. "Is the numbweed working?" she asked, and when he nodded, she said, "You just rest. I'll bring you some nice broth."

At any other time in his life, Keevan would have relished such cosseting, but now he just lay there worrying. Beterli had been dismissed. Would the others think it was his fault? But everyone was there! Beterli provoked that fight. His worry increased, because although he heard excited comings and goings in the passageway, no one tweaked back the curtain across the sleeping alcove he shared with five other boys. Surely one of them would have to come in sometime. No, they were all avoiding him. And something else was wrong. Only he didn't know what.

Mende returned with broth and beachberry bread.

"Why doesn't anyone come see me, Mende? I haven't done anything wrong, have I? I didn't ask to have Beterli turfed out."

Mende soothed him, saying everyone was busy with noontime chores and no one was angry with him. They were giving him a chance to rest in quiet. The numbweed made him drowsy, and her words were fair enough. He permitted his fears to dissipate. Until he heard a hum. Actually, he felt it first, in the broken shin bone and his sore head. The hum began to grow. Two things registered suddenly in Keevan's groggy mind: the only white candidate's robe still on the pegs in the chamber was his; and the dragons hummed when a clutch was being laid or being hatched. Impression! And he was flat abed.

Bitter, bitter disappointment turned the warm broth sour in his belly. Even the small voice telling him that he'd have other opportunities failed to alleviate his crushing depression. *This* was the Impression that mattered! This was his chance to show *everyone*, from Mende to K'last to L'vel and even the Weyrleader that he, Keevan, was worthy of being a dragonrider.

He twisted in bed, fighting against the tears that threatened to choke him. Dragonmen don't cry! Dragonmen learn to live with pain.

Pain? The leg didn't actually pain him as he rolled about on his bedding. His head felt sort of stiff from the tightness of the bandage. He sat up, an effort in itself since the numbweed made exertion difficult. He touched the splinted leg; the knee was unhampered. He had no feeling in his bone, really. He swung himself carefully to the side of his bed and stood slowly. The room wanted to swim about him. He closed his eyes, which made the dizziness worse, and he had to clutch the wall.

Gingerly, he took a step. The broken leg dragged. It hurt in spite of the numbweed, but what was pain to a dragonman?

No one had said he couldn't go to the Impression. "You are and you aren't," were Mende's exact words.

Clinging to the wall, he jerked off his bedshirt. Stretching his arm to the utmost, he jerked his white candidate's tunic from the peg. Jamming first one arm and then the other into the holes, he pulled it over his head. Too bad about the belt. He couldn't wait. He hobbled to the door, hung on to the curtain to steady himself. The weight on his leg was unwieldy. He wouldn't get very far without something to lean on. Down by the bathing pool was one of the long crooknecked poles used to retrieve clothes from the hot washing troughs. But it was down there, and he was on the level above. And there was no one nearby to come to his aid: everyone would be in the Hatching Ground right now, eagerly waiting for the first egg to crack.

The humming increased in volume and tempo, an urgency to which Keevan responded, knowing that his time was all too limited if he was to join the ranks of the hopeful boys standing around the cracking eggs. But if he hurried down the ramp, he'd fall flat on his face.

He could, of course, go flat on his rear end, the way crawling children did. He sat down, sending a jarring stab of pain through his leg and up to the wound on the back of his head. Gritting his teeth and blinking away tears, Keevan scrabbled down the ramp. He had to wait a moment at the bottom to catch his breath. He got to one knee, the injured leg straight out in front of him. Somehow, he managed to push himself erect, though the room seemed about to tip over his ears. It

Wayne Anderson

wasn't far to the crooked stick, but it seemed an age before he had it in his hand.

Then the humming stopped!

Keevan cried out and began to hobble frantically across the cavern, out to the bowl of the Weyr. Never had the distance between living caverns and the Hatching Ground seemed so great. Never had the Weyr been so breathlessly silent. It was as if the multitude of people and dragons watching the hatching held every breath in suspense. Not even the wind muttered down the steep sides of the bowl. The only sounds to break the stillness were Keevan's ragged gasps and the thump-thud of his stick on the hard-packed ground. Sometimes he had to hop twice on his good leg to maintain his balance. Twice he fell into the sand and had to pull himself up on the stick, his white tunic no longer spotless.

Once he jarred himself so badly he couldn't get up immediately.

Then he heard the first exhalation of the crowd, the oohs, the muted cheer, the susurrus of excited whispers. An egg had cracked, and the dragon had chosen his rider. Desperation increased Keevan's hobble. Would he never reach the arching mouth of the Hatching Ground?

Another cheer and an excited spate of applause spurred Keevan to greater effort. If he didn't get there in moments, there'd be no unpaired hatchling left. Then he was actually staggering to the Hatching Ground, the sands hot on his bare feet.

No one noticed his entrance or his halting progress. And Keevan could see nothing but the backs of the white-robed candidates, seventy of them ringing the area around the eggs. Then one side would surge forward or back and there'd be a cheer. Another dragon had been Impressed. Suddenly a large gap appeared in the white human wall, and Keevan had his first sight of the eggs. There didn't seem to be *any* left uncracked, and he could see the lucky boys standing beside wobble-legged dragons. He could hear the unmistakable plaintive crooning of hatchlings and their squawks of protest as they'd fall awkwardly in the sand.

Suddenly he wished that he hadn't left his bed, that he'd stayed away from the Hatching Ground. Now everyone would see his ignominious failure. So he scrambled as desperately to reach the shadowy walls of the Hatching Ground as he had struggled to cross the bowl. He mustn't be seen.

He didn't notice, therefore, that the shifting group of boys remaining had begun to drift in his direction. The hard pace he set himself and his cruel disappointment took their double toll of Keevan. He tripped and collapsed sobbing to the warm sands. He didn't see the consternation in the watching Weyrfolk above the Hatching Ground, nor did he hear the excited whispers of speculation. He didn't know that the Weyrleader and Weyrwoman had dropped to the arena and were making their way toward the knot of boys slowly moving in the direction of the entrance.

"Never seen anything like it," the Weyrleader was saying. "Only thirty-nine riders chosen. And the bronze trying to leave the Hatching Ground without making Impression."

"A case in point of what I said last night," the Weyrwoman replied, "where a hatchling makes no choice because the right boy isn't there."

"There's only Beterli and K'last's young one missing. And there's a full wing of likely boys to choose from . . ."

"None acceptable, apparently. Where is the creature going? He's not heading for the entrance after all. Oh, what have we there, in the shadows?"

Keevan heard with dismay the sound of voices nearing him. He tried to burrow into the sand. The mere thought of how he would be teased and taunted now was unbearable.

Don't worry! Please don't worry! The thought was urgent, but not his own.

Someone kicked sand over Keevan and butted roughly against him.

"Go away. Leave me alone!" he cried.

Why? was the injured-sounding question inserted into his mind. There was no voice, no tone, but the question was there, perfectly clear, in his head.

Incredulous, Keevan lifted his head and stared into the glowing jeweled eyes of a small bronze dragon. His wings were wet, the tips drooping in the sand. And he sagged in the middle on his unsteady legs, although he was making a great effort to keep erect.

Keevan dragged himself to his knees, oblivious of the pain in his leg. He wasn't even aware that he was ringed by the boys passed over, while thirty-one pairs of resentful eyes watched him Impress the dragon. The Weyrmen looked on, amused, and surprised at the draconic choice, which could not be forced. Could not be questioned. Could not be changed.

Why? asked the dragon again. *Don't you like me?* His eyes whirled with anxiety, and his tone was so piteous that Keevan staggered forward and threw his arms around the dragon's neck, stroking his eye ridges, patting the damp, soft hide, opening the fragile-looking wings to dry them, and wordlessly assuring the hatchling over and over again that he was the most perfect, most beautiful, most beloved dragon in the Weyr, in all the Weyrs of Pern.

"What's his name, K'van?" asked Lessa, smiling warmly at the new dragonrider. K'van stared up at her for a long moment. Lessa would know as soon as he did. Lessa was the only person who could "receive" from all dragons, not only her own Ramoth. Then he gave her a radiant smile, recognizing the traditional shortening of his name that raised him forever to the rank of dragonrider.

My name is Heth, the dragon thought mildly, then hiccuped in sudden urgency. *I'm hungry.*

"Dragons are born hungry," said Lessa, laughing. "F'lar, give the boy a hand. He can barely manage his own legs, much less a dragon's."

K'van remembered his stick and drew himself up. "We'll be just fine, thank you."

"You may be the smallest dragonrider ever, young K'van," F'lar said, "but you're one of the bravest!"

And Heth agreed! Pride and joy so leaped in both chests that K'van wondered if his heart would burst right out of his body. He looped an arm around Heth's neck and the pair, the smallest dragonboy and the hatchling who wouldn't choose anybody else, walked out of the Hatching Ground together forever.

THINK AND DISCUSS
Understanding
1. What are some of Keevan's worries as he thinks about becoming a dragonrider?
2. How is Keevan injured?
3. What clues alert Keevan that the hatching may have begun?
4. What are the colors and special qualities of the dragons on Pern?

Analyzing
5. How is Keevan **characterized?** Consider his physical appearance, actions, and inner thoughts.

6. Compare Keevan to his rival, Beterli. Include examples of Beterli's physical appearance and actions.
7. Which people support Keevan in his hope of becoming a dragonrider, and how does each give him support?

Extending
8. What do you think would have happened if Keevan had not made it to the Hatching Ground in time to be chosen?
9. Is the civilization on Pern more or less advanced than our own? Explain.

REVIEWING: Theme H₳

See Handbook of Literary Terms, p. 662.

The **theme** of a literary work is its underlying meaning. A theme may be directly stated, but more often it is implied.

1. What qualities does Mende believe the dragons look for in choosing riders?
2. Find examples of Keevan's qualities and actions that seem to justify Heth's choice of him.
3. What is the theme, or underlying meaning, of this story?

VOCABULARY

Synonyms and Antonyms

Synonyms are words that mean the same or almost the same thing. Antonyms are words with opposite meanings.

On a sheet of paper, write the headings for three columns: Words in Sentences, Synonyms, and Antonyms. Write the words in italics in the sentences under the first heading. Then in the second and third columns, write the correct synonym and antonym for each word. Use the lists of synonyms and antonyms. You will not use all of the choices.

1. The climate on the planet Pern is *temperate* compared to the climate on Red Star.
2. Laziness is not *tolerated* in Benden Weyr.
3. Keevan's view of the dragon and his rider are *obscured* as he goes into the cavern.
4. Beterli gives Keevan a mocking, *contemptuous* look.
5. Lessa's *outrageous* suggestion brings gasps from everyone.
6. Keevan's excitement and joy make him *oblivious* of the pain in his leg.

Synonyms: forgetful, hidden, scornful, shocking, allowed, moderate, necessary

Antonyms: mild, prohibited, aware, unpleasant, clear, approving, extreme

BIOGRAPHY

Anne McCaffrey
1926–

When Anne McCaffrey was a girl, her family had an old typewriter, and she remembers using it to write her first "novel" at the age of nine. The work was four pages long. She is now known as the author of a number of fantasy novels set in the fictional world of Pern, including the best sellers *The White Dragon* and *Moreta: Dragonlady of Pern*. She has won the Hugo and Nebula awards for science fiction.

McCaffrey was born in Massachusetts and once directed opera in Delaware, but she now lives and writes in Ireland.

THINKING CRITICALLY
ABOUT LITERATURE

UNIT 1   SHORT STORY 1

■ CONCEPT REVIEW

At the end of each unit in *Discoveries in Literature* is a selection for you to use in reviewing the important ideas and literary terms found in the selections in that unit. It contains notes and questions designed to help you think critically about your reading. Page numbers in the notes refer to an application. A more extensive discussion of these terms is in the Handbook of Literary Terms.

I'll Give You Law

Molly Picon

When I read the newspaper, there is always a must section in it that I never pass by. This is the lost and found advertisements usually buried in the back pages. This is a habit I picked up from my grandmother. She always took a keen interest in who had lost what, and who was honestly reporting on items found. She could people a whole colony from just a couple of advertisements.

"Lost—one black puppy with a white patch around its eye. Answers to the name 'Spot.' Please call Beaver 6-5000. Reward."

■ As you read, look for details that characterize Mrs. Ostrow, the grandmother.

Molly Picon (pē′con).

From this my grandmother would draw for me a picture of a child sobbing itself to sleep at night, of parents out searching the streets anxiously, calling in hopeless voices, "Spot. Come on, Spot. Here, boy."

The picture was so real to both of us we used to sit there with tears in our eyes, willing Spot to answer, wanting the child to cry with joy and not in sorrow.

We thought about all the lost items with equal interest. We wondered about the found items as well, visualizing the happy claimants, and the honest finders handsomely rewarded. At such moments, God was in Heaven, and all was right with the world.

And then one day, we moved swiftly from the land of fantasy to a world of realities. My grandmother found something!

"What is it? What is it?" I asked, hopping with excitement.

"A lavaliere!" My grandmother was absolutely overwhelmed. She had never found anything in her life, and now, here in her hand, was this magnificent lavaliere.

■ lavaliere (lav′ə lir′ or lä′və lir′): jewelry hanging from a chain, worn around the neck
■ Cause/effect: The cause of their excitement is the finding of a lavaliere.
■ Note that the grandmother believes the lavaliere is worth a great deal of money.

"It must be very expensive," I said, running my fingers over it.

"A fortune," my grandmother said positively. She held it up against her. "A regular fortune," she breathed.

"Are you going to keep it?" I asked.

She gave me a sharp look. If the thought entered her mind, she wasn't going to admit it to me.

"Am I going to keep it?" she asked. "Such a question." She threw her shawl over her head.

■ Characterization (page 40): The grandmother never questions whether or not to return the lavaliere.

"Where are you going?" I asked. "Can I go, too?"

"I'm going to the police station. Let them worry about it. You can't come," she added firmly. "A police station is not respectable."

At the police station, the property clerk informed her politely that if the lavaliere was not claimed within ninety days, the police department would turn the jewelry over to her, and she would be its rightful and legal owner. He took her name and address and wrote it down. They would let her know, he said indifferently.

"Oh, I hope nobody claims it," I said fervently. "Oh, Grandma, I hope whoever lost it doesn't even know they lost it."

Such a dilemma for my grandmother. If ever she yearned for anything, it was for this lavaliere. On the other hand, her active imagination conjured up for her such tearful scenes that she couldn't wait for the loser to come and claim her property.

■ Plot (page 20): Note the grandmother's inner conflict.

Meanwhile, my grandmother took to haunting the police station and the property clerk. "How are you," she would ask, "and how is the family?" In the beginning he would dismiss this with a curt "fine we haven't heard don't call on us we'll let you know" attitude. But my grandmother began to take a personal interest in the policemen at the precinct. She knew their names and the names of their wives and children. She knew how hard it was to make ends meet on a police-man's salary, what policeman was going to night school to study law and improve his station in life, what policeman was smarting at being passed over when promotions were handed out. Only the property clerk held out. When he would look up and see my grandmother, he would mutter and groan.

■ **Characterization:** The grandmother is persistent.

"Mrs. Ostrow," he would say, "don't you have anything to do at home?"

■ **Plot:** Note the external conflict Mrs. Ostrow has.

"Why don't I have something to do at home?" My grandmother would regard him scornfully. "You think I like to come here day after day?"

"So why do you come?" he would ask logically.

"To see what I have to see," she would tell him. And then she would demand to see the lavaliere with "my own eyes." And then she would subject him to a searching questioning. Who had come today, and what had they claimed, and wasn't it possible the lavaliere had belonged to one of the people who had come, and had he told anybody about it, and if he was keeping it such a big secret, how could anybody know he had it in the first place?

As hard as I prayed that no one would show up, he prayed that someone—anyone—would.

"Ninety days," he would cry, clutching his hair. "I'll never survive it."

I never knew that ninety days could last so long. But eventually the ninetieth day arrived, bringing with it much excitement. My grand-mother and I dressed as though we were going to a party. She was going to allow me to go with her for the presentation. On the way we discussed her immense good fortune.

"When I die," she said to me, "I want you to have it."

"Please, Grandma," I said, uncomfortably. It seemed like a grim note to inject in an otherwise cloudless day.

"No," she insisted seriously. "I want you to have it. It will be like a—what is the word I want, Molly?"

"An heirloom?"

"That's the word." She pounced on it with satisfaction. "And when you die, your children will have it."

In two sentences, my grandmother had disposed of us both.

At the police station, my grandmother was greeted with happy smiles, even from the property clerk. I should say, especially from the property clerk. It was the happiest day of his life.

When my grandmother finally held the lavaliere in her hand, her eyes misted over. She couldn't speak, but she nodded her head at the policemen.

■ Characterization: The property clerk is happy because he no longer will be bothered by Mrs. Ostrow's questions.

"Don't be a stranger," they urged her. "Don't wait till you find something before you drop in."

"Such nice boys," my grandmother said, as we left the station. She touched her eyes with her handkerchief. "Such good boys, even him," she said, referring to the property clerk. "He had his eye on it, but out of respect, he didn't touch it." I believed my grandmother. I didn't see how that property clerk could have looked at that lavaliere for ninety days and so nobly fought off temptation.

■ Characterization: Mrs. Ostrow believes the best of everyone.

When we got home, my grandmother promptly put the lavaliere on.

"I'll wear it night and day," she vowed. "I'll never take it off." For a week she was as good as her word.

Then one day there came a knock at the door, and tragedy swept in, escorted by an embarrassed property clerk from the police station.

"Where is it?" cried the woman he had brought to the door. She looked at my grandmother. "My lavaliere she's wearing," she cried in horror, pointing to my grandmother.

■ Plot: Note the climax, or turning point.

My grandmother looked at both of them, shocked. Her hand went up automatically to clutch the lavaliere.

"It's mine," she said. "You told me, after ninety days . . ."

"That's right," the property clerk said promptly. "Legally it is yours. That's what I've been trying to tell this lady. She didn't claim it in ninety days, and the law says . . ."

"I'll give you law," the lady shouted vigorously, pounding him on the arm. "Does the law say after ninety days thieves and murderers can do whatever they want? Law! I'll give you law!"

"Please, lady," the property clerk pleaded. "Let's try to be calm."

"Calm!" she took up the cry. "I'll give you calm!"

My grandmother entered the fray briskly.

"So much commotion," she said. "You want the neighbors to think

■ Characterization: Mrs. Ostrow cares what the neighbors think.

we're killing you on the doorstep. Come inside." She urged them in and closed the door. "So if you'll stop talking and tell me where you were," she said, guiding the distracted woman to a seat, "we'll listen and we'll be the same good friends."

"Where was I?" the woman said, shaking her head. "My daughter was having her baby, so she says to me, 'Ma,' she says, 'if you don't come, I won't have it, that's all.'

"So I had to go to Scranton yet. One month in advance, just in case. And then, with God's help, the baby comes. Now she's afraid to hold it, it might break. And she's afraid to wash it. It might come apart in the water. One month. Two months. Finally I say to her, 'Rebeccah,' I say, 'enough is enough already. Whatever you'll do, you'll do.'"

■ **Setting** (page 71): Scranton is in Pennsylvania. The story may take place near there.

My grandmother was already making tea for everybody, bustling about the kitchen, putting crackers and jam on the table.

"The young people today," she commented.

"So when I come back, I first realized my lavaliere is gone. I'm not hung with jewelry, and between you and me and the lamppost," she added confidentially to my grandmother, "I need a lavaliere like I need a hole in the head. But when I need a little extra money in an emergency, that lavaliere saves my life."

"How does it save your life?" I asked.

"I bring it to the pawnshop and whatever few pennies he gives me . . ."

"The pawnshop!" I was indignant. "She doesn't even wear it, Grandma," I said passionately. "Don't give it back. You don't have to. The law says you don't have to."

"That's right," the property clerk said instantly. He was on his second cup of tea and using my grandmother's jam as if the jar had an endless bottom.

The woman opened her mouth to protest, but my grandmother stopped her by holding up her hand for silence.

"Molly," she said gently, "there is a law here, too." She laid her hand tenderly on my heart: "Look in your heart and tell me. Suppose it was your lavaliere. Suppose you lost it and somebody else found it. Ninety days, a thousand days . . . how would you feel?"

■ **Theme** (page 91): Look for clues to the theme, or underlying meaning.

"I would want it back," I answered honestly.

She spread her hands out eloquently.

"So?" she asked me.

"That's not fair," I burst out.

"Fair? Who said anything about fair?" She reached up and took off the lavaliere. She fondled it for a moment, and then handed it over to the woman.

"Why should I complain?" she asked no one in particular and shrugged. "For three months I lived in a dream, and for five days I lived like a queen. Is that bad?"

■ **Plot:** Notice that the conflict is resolved in the conclusion of the story.

■ **Characterization:** Mrs. Ostrow looks on the bright side of things.

THINK AND DISCUSS
Understanding
1. What section of the newspaper holds special interest for the narrator's grandmother?
2. What does the grandmother do when she finds a lavaliere?
3. Who is legally entitled to the lavaliere when the owner asks for its return?

Analyzing
4. Why does Mrs. Ostrow ask so many questions of the property clerk?
5. What is the difference between Mrs. Ostrow's feeling about the lavaliere and the owner's feeling about it?
6. What causes Mrs. Ostrow to return the lavaliere?

Extending
7. What do you think might have happened if Mrs. Ostrow had refused to return the lavaliere?

REVIEWING LITERARY TERMS
Plot
1. What is Mrs. Ostrow's inner conflict?
2. What external conflicts does Mrs. Ostrow have?
3. What is the pattern of events in this story?
4. What is the climax, or turning point, of the story?
5. What is the conclusion?

Characterization
6. What kind of person is Mrs. Ostrow? Consider her actions and inner thoughts.
7. What is the owner of the lavaliere like? Consider her actions and words.

Setting
8. What do the details suggest about the place?
9. What general idea do you have about the time of this story?

Theme
10. Does this story have a theme, or underlying meaning? Explain.

■ CONTENT REVIEW
THINKING SKILLS
Classifying

1. List the main conflicts in the following stories: "Cutie Pie," "Raymond's Run," "One Night Stand," "Gentleman of Río en Medio," "Stolen Day," "Rikki-tikki-tavi," and "I'll Give You Law." Classify each as an internal conflict or an external conflict.

Generalizing

2. In which selections in this unit does setting play an important part, beyond serving as background?
3. Which selections in this unit touch on the theme of good versus evil? Explain your choices.

Evaluating

4. Which story in the unit has the greatest suspense for you? Explain what events lead up to the suspense.
5. Which individual from any story comes closest to your personal concept of a hero or heroine? Why?

■ COMPOSITION REVIEW
Writing a Newspaper Account

Pretend that you are a newspaper reporter who has learned the facts about what happened in "The Widow and the Parrot," "Raymond's Run," or "One Night Stand." Choose one of the stories and write a brief account, as it might appear in a newspaper. Before you begin, review the selection. You may want to make up a statement by one of the key characters and quote it in your story to explain the character's reaction to the events.

Writing a Story

Mrs. Wang in "The Old Demon," Ch-tsal in "Cutie Pie," and Keevan in "The Smallest Dragonboy" are just three of the many characters in the stories in this unit who face obstacles or problems. Choose one of the characters in a story in this unit, devise a new obstacle or problem, and write a brief story. Remember to show the conflict and how the character solves the problem. Try to be faithful to the character as presented in the story, and describe the setting and action.

Reviewing Writer's Craft: Be Specific

In this unit you have looked at how writers use details in stories to bring characters to life. Details make Cutie Pie a lovable being and Don Anselmo a man of simple dignity. Sometimes details help you picture an exact scene in your mind. You as reader feel you are right there at the hatching time with Keevan in "The Smallest Dragonboy." Now **try your hand** at creating your own specific details. Write a one- or two-paragraph description of someone your own age. If you prefer, write a description of a place. Be sure to use specific details so that your readers can picture the person or the scene. Skim the pages of the stories and find places where the writers use details. Also consult your **reading/writing log,** if you have been keeping one.

PLAYS

Edward Hopper, *The Sheridan Theatre* (detail), 1937, The Newark Museum

PREVIEW

UNIT 2 PLAYS

The Dying Detective / Michael and Mollie Hardwick
The Monsters Are Due on Maple Street / Rod Serling
Let Me Hear You Whisper / Paul Zindel
from **Teacher, Teacher** / Ellison Carroll

Features
Reading a Play
Comment: The Detective Who
    Wouldn't Die
The Writer's Craft: Use Varied Sentences
Comment: The Twilight Zone

Application of Literary Terms
mood

Reading Literature Skillfully
predicting outcomes

Vocabulary Skills
affixes and roots
synonyms

Thinking Skills
classifying
evaluating
synthesizing

Composition
Writing a Summary
Describing Characters
Writing Dialogue
Writing a Report
Writing as a Character
Supporting an Opinion

Enrichment
Comparing a Story and a Play
Interpreting a Play Orally

Thinking Critically About Literature
Concept Review
Content Review
Composition Review

Reading A PLAY

Unlike other forms of literature, plays are primarily intended to be seen and heard, not read. You will find it easier to imagine what the playwright—the author of the play—intends if you read the dialogue and stage directions carefully.

Dialogue is made up of the lines, or speeches, of the various characters. Stage directions provide the actors with information on how to interpret lines and how to move. They will help you imagine how a play looks and sounds on stage. Often characters are described and **setting** established in the stage directions.

In addition, careful attention to stage directions and dialogue will help you in **predicting outcomes,** or in anticipating how characters may behave in different situations and how conflicts may be resolved as the **plot** develops.

In this book, stage directions are printed in italic type and set off in parentheses. Notice, for example, the stage directions in italics in this excerpt from *The Dying Detective*, the first play in the unit.

> WATSON. Oh, very well.
> (WATSON *goes to the lamp and strikes a match.*)
> HOLMES. I implore you to be careful.
> WATSON (*as though humoring him*). Yes, Holmes. (*He lights the lamp, carefully keeping the flame low. He moves to draw the curtains.*)

The second play in the unit, *The Monsters Are Due on Maple Street*, was written for television. Therefore, directions for use of the camera will occasionally appear in italics. As a reader, you will then have to imagine the scene as viewed through the camera eye.

> NARRATOR. Maple Street, U.S.A., late summer. A tree-lined little world of front porch gliders, hopscotch, the laughter of children, and the bell of an ice cream vendor. (*There is a pause and the camera moves over to a shot of the Good Humor man and two small boys who are standing alongside just buying ice cream.*)

As is true for the short story, **characterization** in a play is developed in several ways. You can learn about a character from what the playwright tells you, from what a person says about himself or herself, from what others say about the person, and from what a person does and the way the person does it.

The plays you are about to read are relatively short. That means that the playwrights quickly had to provide background information and to introduce the major conflict. In each play the conflict builds rapidly to a climax, followed by a brief conclusion. The plays in this unit are strong in atmosphere, or **mood.** As you read, look for details that the playwrights have used to create special feelings such as terror, peacefulness, or tension.

The Dying Detective

Michael and Mollie Hardwick   *from a story by* Sir Arthur Conan Doyle

---

"Yes, Holmes, you are very near your end now. I think I shall sit here and watch you die."

SCENE ONE: *Sherlock Holmes's bedroom, afternoon*
SCENE TWO: *The same, dusk*
SCENE THREE: *The same, evening*

CHARACTERS, *in order of appearance*

MRS. HUDSON

DR. WATSON

SHERLOCK HOLMES

CULVERTON SMITH *"A great yellow face, coarse-grained and greasy, with heavy double chin, and two sullen, menacing grey eyes which glared at me from under tufted and sandy brows . . . "*

INSPECTOR MORTON *Middle-aged, tough, dressed in plain clothes.*

SCENE ONE

SHERLOCK HOLMES's *bedroom at 221B Baker Street. The essential features are: a bed with a large wooden head, placed crosswise on the stage, the head a foot or two from one side wall; a small table near the bed-head, on the audience's side, on which stand a carafe of water and a glass, and a tiny metal or ivory box; a window in the back wall, the curtains parted; and, under the window, a table or chest of drawers, on which stand a green wine bottle, some wine-glasses, a biscuit-barrel,[1] and a lamp. Of course, there may be further lamps and any amount of furnishing and clutter:* HOLMES's *bedroom was adorned with pictures of celebrated criminals and littered with everything from tobacco pipes to revolver cartridges.*

There is daylight outside the window.

---

1. **biscuit-barrel**, in Britain, a cracker barrel.

SHERLOCK HOLMES *lies in the bed on his back, tucked up to the chin and evidently asleep. He is very pale.* MRS. HUDSON *enters followed by* DR. WATSON, *who is wearing his coat and hat and carrying his small medical bag.* MRS. HUDSON *pauses for a moment.*

MRS. HUDSON. He's asleep, sir.

(*They approach the bed.* WATSON *comes round to the audience's side and looks down at* HOLMES *for a moment. He shakes his head gravely, then he and* MRS. HUDSON *move away beyond the foot of the bed.* WATSON *takes off his hat and coat as they talk and she takes them from him.*)

WATSON. This is dreadful, Mrs. Hudson. He was perfectly hale and hearty when I went away only three days ago.

MRS. HUDSON. I know, sir. Oh, Dr. Watson, sir, I'm that glad you've come back. If anyone can save Mr. Holmes, I'm sure you can.

WATSON. I shall have to know what is the matter with him first. Mrs. Hudson, please tell me, as quickly as you can, how it all came about.

MRS. HUDSON. Yes, sir. Mr. Holmes has been working lately on some case down near the river—Rotherhithe,[2] I think.

WATSON. Yes, yes. I know.

MRS. HUDSON. Well, you know what he is for coming in at all hours. I was just taking my lamp to go to my bed on Wednesday night when I heard a faint knocking at the street door. I . . . I found Mr. Holmes there. He could hardly stand. Just muttered to me to help him up to his bed here, and he's barely spoken since.

WATSON. Dear me!

MRS. HUDSON. Won't take food or drink. Just lies there, sleeping or staring in a wild sort of way.

WATSON. But, goodness gracious, Mrs. Hudson, why did you not send for another doctor in my absence?

MRS. HUDSON. Oh, I told him straightaway I was going to do that, sir. But he got so agitated—almost shouted that he wouldn't allow any doctor on the premises. You know how masterful he is, Dr. Watson.

WATSON. Indeed. But you could have telegraphed for me.

(MRS. HUDSON *appears embarrassed.*)

MRS. HUDSON. Well, sir . . .

WATSON. But you didn't. Why, Mrs. Hudson?

MRS. HUDSON. Sir, I don't like to tell you, but . . . well, Mr. Holmes said he wouldn't even have you to see him.

WATSON. What? This is monstrous! I, his oldest friend, and . . . (HOLMES *groans and stirs slightly.*) Ssh! He's waking. You go along, Mrs. Hudson, and leave this to me. Whether he likes it or not, I shall ensure that everything possible is done.

MRS. HUDSON. Thank you, sir. You'll ring if I can be of help.

(*She exits with* WATSON's *things.* HOLMES *groans again and flings out an arm restlessly.* WATSON *comes to the audience's side of the bed and sits on it.*)

WATSON. Holmes? It's I—Watson.

HOLMES (*sighs*). Ahh! Well, Watson? We . . . we seem to have fallen on evil days.

WATSON. My dear fellow!

(*He moves to reach for* HOLMES's *pulse.*)

HOLMES (*urgently*). No, no! Keep back!

---

2. *Rotherhithe* (rŏT͡H'ĕr hīT͡H).

WATSON. Eh?

HOLMES. Mustn't come near.

WATSON. Now, look here, Holmes . . . !

HOLMES. If you come near . . . order you out of the house.

WATSON (*defiantly*). Hah!

HOLMES. For your own sake, Watson. Contracted . . . a coolie disease—from Sumatra.[3] Very little known, except that most deadly. Contagious by touch. So . . . must keep away.

WATSON. Utter rubbish, Holmes! Mrs. Hudson tells me she helped you to your bed. There's nothing the matter with her.

HOLMES. Period of . . . incubation. Only dangerous after two or three days. Deadly by now.

WATSON. Good heavens, do you suppose such a consideration weighs with me? Even if I weren't a doctor, d'you think it would stop me doing my duty to an old friend? Now, let's have a good look at you. (*He moves forward again.*)

HOLMES (*harshly*). I tell you to keep back!

WATSON. See here, Holmes . . .

HOLMES. If you will stay where you are, I will talk to you. If you will not, you can get out.

WATSON. Holmes! (*Recovering*) Holmes, you aren't yourself. You're sick and as helpless as a child. Whether you like it or not, I'm going to examine you and treat you.

HOLMES (*sneering*). If I'm to be forced to have a doctor, let him at least be someone I've some confidence in.

WATSON. Oh! You . . . After all these years, Holmes, you haven't . . . confidence in me?

HOLMES. In your friendship, Watson—yes.

But facts are facts. As a medical man you're a mere general practitioner, of limited experience and mediocre qualifications.

WATSON. Well . . . ! Well, really!

HOLMES. It is painful to say such things, but you leave me no choice.

WATSON (*coldly*). Thank you. I'll tell you this, Holmes. Such a remark, coming from you, merely serves to tell me what state your nerves are in. Still, if you insist that you have no confidence in me, I will not intrude my services. But what I shall do is to summon Sir Jasper Meek or Penrose Fisher, or any of the other best men in London.

HOLMES (*groans*). My . . . dear Watson. You mean well. But do you suppose they—any of them—know of the Tapanuli[4] Fever?

WATSON. The Tap . . . ?

HOLMES. What do you yourself know of the Black Formosa Corruption?

WATSON. Tapanuli Fever? Black Formosa Corruption? I've never heard of either of 'em.

HOLMES. Nor have your colleagues. There are many problems of disease, many pathological possibilities, peculiar to the East. So I've learned during some of my recent researches. It was in the course of one of them that I contracted this complaint. I assure you, Watson, you can do nothing.

WATSON. Can't I? I happen to know, Holmes, that the greatest living authority on tropical disease, Dr. Ainstree, is in London just now.

---

3. **Sumatra** (sù mä′trɔ), a large island in Indonesia. (Holmes is telling Watson that he has become infected with an illness originating in the East Indies.)

4. **Tapanuli** (täp′ə nü′lē).

Cover of *Collier's*, November 22, 1913

HOLMES (*beseeching*). Watson!

WATSON. All remonstrance is useless. I am going this instant to fetch him. (*He gets up.*)

HOLMES (*a great cry*). No!

WATSON. Eh? Holmes . . . my dear fellow . . .

HOLMES. Watson, in the name of our old friendship, do as I ask.

WATSON. But . . .

HOLMES. You have only my own good at heart. Of course, I know that. You . . . you shall have your way. Only . . . give me time to . . . to collect my strength. What is the time now?

(WATSON *sits and consults his watch.*)

WATSON. Four o'clock.

HOLMES. Then at six you can go.

WATSON. This is insanity!

HOLMES. Only two hours, Watson. I promise you may go then.

WATSON. Hang it, this is urgent, man!

HOLMES. I will see no one before six. I will not be examined. I shall resist!

WATSON (*sighing*). Oh, have it your own way, then. But I insist on staying with you in the meantime. You need an eye keeping on you, Holmes.

HOLMES. Very well, Watson. And now I must sleep. I feel exhausted. *(Drowsily)* I wonder how a battery feels when it pours electricity into a non-conductor?

WATSON. Eh?

HOLMES *(yawning)*. At six, Watson, we resume our conversation.

(He lies back and closes his eyes. WATSON *makes as though to move, but thinks better of it. He sits still, watching* HOLMES. *A slow black-out.)*

SCENE TWO

The stage lights up again, though more dimly than before, to disclose the same scene. Twilight is apparent through the window. HOLMES *lies motionless.* WATSON *sits as before, though with his head sagging, half-asleep. His chin drops suddenly and he wakes with a jerk. He glances round, sees the twilight outside, and consults his watch. He yawns, flexes his arms, then proceeds to glance idly about him. His attention is caught by the little box on the bedside table. Stealthily, he reaches over and picks it up.*

HOLMES *(very loudly and urgently)*. No! No, Watson, no!

WATSON *(startled)*. Eh? What?

(HOLMES starts up onto his elbow.)

HOLMES. Put it down! Down this instant! Do as I say, Watson!

WATSON. Oh! All right, then. *(Putting the box down)* Look here, Holmes, I really think . . .

HOLMES. I hate to have my things touched. You know perfectly well I do.

WATSON. Holmes . . . !

HOLMES. You fidget me beyond endurance. You, a doctor—you're enough to drive a patient into an asylum!

WATSON. Really!

HOLMES. Now, for heaven's sake, sit still, and let me have my rest.

WATSON. Holmes, it is almost six o'clock, and I refuse to delay another instant. *(He gets up determinedly.)*

HOLMES. Really? Watson, have you any change in your pocket?

WATSON. Yes.

HOLMES. Any silver?

WATSON *(fishing out his change)*. A good deal.

HOLMES. How many half-crowns?[5]

WATSON. Er, five.

HOLMES *(sighing)*. Ah, too few, too few. However, such as they are, you can put them in your watch-pocket—and all the rest of your money in your left trouser-pocket. It will balance you so much better like that.

WATSON. Balance . . . ? Holmes, you're raving! This has gone too far . . . !

HOLMES. You will now light that lamp by the window, Watson, but you will be very careful that not for one instant shall it be more than at half flame.

WATSON. Oh, very well.

(WATSON goes to the lamp and strikes a match.)

HOLMES. I implore you to be careful.

WATSON *(as though humoring him)*. Yes, Holmes. *(He lights the lamp, carefully keeping the flame low. He moves to draw the curtains.)*

HOLMES. No, you need not draw curtains.

---

5. *half-crown*, a former coin of Great Britain which was equal to 2½ shillings.

(WATSON *leaves them and comes back round the bed.*) So! Good. You may now go and fetch a specialist.

WATSON. Well, thank heaven for that.

HOLMES. His name is Mr. Culverton Smith, of 13 Lower Burke Street.

WATSON (*staring*). Eh?

HOLMES. Well, go on, man. You could hardly wait to fetch someone before.

WATSON. Yes, but . . . Culverton Smith? I've never heard the name!

HOLMES. Possibly not. It may surprise you to know that the one man who knows everything about this disease is not a medical man. He's a planter.

WATSON. A planter!

HOLMES. His plantation is far from medical aid. An outbreak of this disease there caused him to study it intensely. He's a very methodical man, and I asked you not to go before six because I knew you wouldn't find him in his study till then.

WATSON. Holmes, I . . . I never heard such a . . . !

HOLMES. You will tell him exactly how you have left me. A dying man.

WATSON. No, Holmes!

HOLMES. At any rate, delirious. Yes, not dying, delirious. (*Chuckles*) No, I really can't think why the whole ocean bed isn't one solid mass of oysters.

WATSON. Oysters?

HOLMES. They're so prolific, you know.

WATSON. Great Heavens! Now, Holmes, you just lie quiet, and . . .

HOLMES. Strange how the mind controls the brain. Er, what was I saying, Watson?

WATSON. You were . . .

HOLMES. Ah, I remember. Culverton Smith.

My life depends on him, Watson. But you will have to plead with him to come. There is no good feeling between us. He has . . . a grudge. I rely on you to soften him. Beg, Watson. Pray. But get him here by any means.

WATSON. Very well. I'll bring him in a cab, if I have to carry him down to it.

HOLMES. You will do nothing of the sort. You will persuade him to come—and then return before him. (*Deliberately*) Make any excuse so as not to come with him. Don't forget that, Watson. You won't fail me. You never did fail me.

WATSON. That's all very well, Holmes, but . . .

HOLMES (*interrupting*). Then, shall the world be overrun by oysters? No doubt there are natural enemies which limit their increase. And yet . . . No, horrible, horrible!

WATSON (*grimly*). I'm going, Holmes. Say no more, I'm going!

(*He hurries out.* HOLMES *remains propped up for a moment, staring after* WATSON, *then sinks back into a sleeping posture as the stage blacks out.*)

SCENE THREE

The stage lights up on the same scene. HOLMES *lies still. It is now quite dark outside. After a moment* WATSON *bustles in, pulling off his coat. He pauses to hand it to* MRS. HUDSON, *who is behind him.*

WATSON. Thank you, Mrs. Hudson. A gentleman will be calling very shortly. Kindly show him up here immediately.

MRS. HUDSON. Yes, sir.

(*She exits.* WATSON *approaches the bed.*)

HOLMES (*drowsily*). Watson?

WATSON. Yes, Holmes. How are you feeling?

HOLMES. Much the same, I fear. Is Culverton Smith coming?

WATSON. Should be here any minute. It took me some minutes to find a cab, and I almost expected him to have got here first.

HOLMES. Well done, my dear Watson.

WATSON. I must say, Holmes, I'm only doing this to humor you. Frankly, I didn't take to your planter friend at all.

HOLMES. Oh? How so?

WATSON. Rudeness itself. He almost showed me the door before I could give him your message. It wasn't until I mentioned the name, Sherlock Holmes . . .

HOLMES. Ah!

WATSON. Quite changed him—but I wouldn't say it was for the better.

HOLMES. Tell me what he said.

WATSON. Said you'd had some business dealings together, and that he respected your character and talents. Described you as an amateur of crime, in the way that he regards himself as an amateur of disease.

HOLMES. Quite typical—and surely, quite fair?

WATSON. Quite fair—if he hadn't put such sarcasm into saying it. No, Holmes, you said he bears you some grudge. Mark my words, as soon as he has left this house I insist upon calling a recognized specialist.

HOLMES. My dear Watson, you are the best of messengers. Thank you again.

WATSON. Not at all. Holmes, Holmes—let me help you without any of this nonsense. The whole of Great Britain will condemn me otherwise. Why, my cabmen both en-quired anxiously after you; and so did Inspector Morton . . .

HOLMES. Morton?

WATSON. Of the Yard. He was passing our door just now as I came in. Seemed extremely concerned.

HOLMES. Scotland Yard[6] concerned for me? How very touching! And now, Watson, you may disappear from the scene.

WATSON. Disappear! I shall do no such thing. I wish to be present when this Culverton Smith arrives. I wish to hear every word of this so-called medical expert's opinion.

HOLMES (*turning his head*). Yes, of course. Then I think you will just find room behind the head of the bed.

WATSON. What? Hide?

HOLMES. I have reason to suppose that his opinion will be much more frank and valuable if he imagines he is alone with me. (*We hear the murmur of* MRS. HUDSON's *and* CULVERTON SMITH's *voices offstage.*) Listen! I hear him coming. Get behind the bed, Watson, and do not budge, whatever happens. *Whatever* happens, you understand?

WATSON. Oh, all right, Holmes. Anything to please you. But I don't like this. Not at all. (*He goes behind the bed-head and conceals himself.* MRS. HUDSON *enters, looks round the room and then at* HOLMES. SMITH *enters behind her.*)

MRS. HUDSON (*to* SMITH). Oh, Dr. Watson must have let himself out. No doubt he'll be back directly, sir.

SMITH. No matter, my good woman. (MRS. HUDSON *bristles at this form of address.*) You

---

6. *Scotland Yard*, headquarters of the London police.

may leave me alone with your master.

MRS. HUDSON. As you wish—*sir.*

(*She sweeps out.* SMITH *advances slowly to the bed and stands at the foot, staring at the recumbent* HOLMES.)

SMITH (*almost to himself*). So, Holmes. It has come to this, then.

(HOLMES *stirs.* SMITH *chuckles and leans his arms on the bed-foot and his chin on them, continuing to watch* HOLMES.)

HOLMES (*weakly*). Watson? Who . . . ? Smith? Smith, is that you?

(SMITH *chuckles.*)

HOLMES. I . . . I hardly dared hope you would come.

SMITH. I should imagine not. And yet, you see, I'm here. Coals of fire,[7] Holmes— coals of fire!

HOLMES. Noble of you . . .

SMITH. Yes, isn't it?

HOLMES. I appreciate your special knowledge.

SMITH. Then you're the only man in London who does. Do you know what is the matter with you?

HOLMES. The same as young Victor—your cousin.

SMITH. Ah, then you recognize the symptoms. Well, then, it's a bad look-out for you. Victor was a strong, hearty young fellow—but a dead man on the fourth day. As you said at the time, it *was* rather surprising that he should contract an out-of-the-way Asiatic disease in the heart of London—a disease of which *I* have made such a very special study. (*Chuckles*) And now, you, Holmes. Singular coincidence, eh? Or are you going to start making accu-

sations once again—about cause and effect, and so on.

HOLMES. I . . . I knew you caused Victor Savage's death.

(SMITH *comes round the bed.*)

SMITH (*snarling*). Did you? Well, proving it is a different matter, Holmes. But what sort of a game is this, then—spreading lying reports about me one moment, then crawling to me for help the next?

HOLMES (*gasping*). Give . . . give me water. For . . . pity's sake, Smith. Water!

(SMITH *hesitates momentarily, then goes to the table and pours a glass from the carafe.*)

SMITH. You're precious near your end, my friend, but I don't want you to go till I've had a word with you.

(*He holds out the glass to* HOLMES *who struggles up feebly to take it and drinks.*)

HOLMES (*gulping water*). Ah! Thank . . . thank you. Please . . . do what you can for me. Only cure me, and I promise to forget.

SMITH. Forget what?

HOLMES. About Victor Savage's death. You as good as admitted just now that you had done it. I swear I will forget it.

SMITH (*laughs*). Forget it, remember it—do as you like. I don't see you in any witness-box, Holmes. Quite another shape of box, I assure you. But you must hear first how it came about.

HOLMES. Working amongst Chinese sailors. Down at the docks.

SMITH. Proud of your brains, aren't you?

---

7. *Coals of fire,* a reference to the biblical teaching in Proverbs 25: 21-22, "If thine enemy be hungry, give him bread to eat . . . for thou shalt heap coals of fire upon his head, and the Lord shall reward thee."

Think yourself smart? Well, you've met a smarter one this time. (HOLMES *falls back, groaning loudly*.) Getting painful, is it? (HOLMES *cries out, writhing in agony*.)

SMITH. That's the way. Takes you as cramp, I fancy?

HOLMES. Cramp! Cramp!

SMITH. Well, you can still hear me. Now, can't you just remember any unusual incident—just about the time your symptoms began?

HOLMES. I . . . can't think. My mind is gone! Help me, Smith!

SMITH. Did nothing come to you through the post, for instance?

HOLMES. Post? Post?

SMITH. Yes. A little box, perhaps? (HOLMES *emits a shuddering groan*.)

SMITH (*closer; deadly*). Listen! You *shall* hear me! Don't you remember a box—a little ivory box? (*He sees it on the table and holds it up*.) Yes, here it is on your bedside table. It came on Wednesday. You opened it—do you remember?

HOLMES. Box? Opened? Yes, yes! There was . . . sharp spring inside. Pricked my finger. Some sort of joke . . .

SMITH. It was no joke, Holmes. You fool! Who asked you to cross my path? If you'd only left me alone I would never have hurt you.

HOLMES. Box! Yes! Pricked finger. Poison!

SMITH (*triumphantly*). So you do remember. Good, good! I'm glad indeed. Well, the box leaves this room in my pocket, and there's your last shred of evidence gone. (*He pockets it*.) But you have the truth now, Holmes. You can die knowing that I killed you. You knew too much about what happened to Victor Savage, so you must share his fate. Yes, Holmes, you are very near your end now. I think I shall sit here and watch you die. (*He sits on the bed*.)

HOLMES (*almost a whisper*). The . . . shadows . . . falling. Getting . . . so dark. I can't see. Smith! Smith, are you there? The light . . . for charity's sake, turn up the light! (SMITH *laughs, gets up and goes to the light*.)

SMITH. Entering the valley of the shadow,[8] eh, Holmes? Yes, I'll turn up the light for you. I can watch your face more plainly, then. (*He turns the flame up full*.) There! Now, is there any *further* service I can render you?

HOLMES (*in a clear, strong voice*). A match and my pipe, if you please. (*He sits bolt upright*. SMITH *spins round to see him*.)

SMITH. Eh? What the devil's the meaning of this?

HOLMES (*cheerfully*). The best way of successfully acting a part is to *be* it. I give you my word that for three days I have neither tasted food nor drink until you were good enough to pour me out that glass of water. But it's the tobacco I find most irksome. (*We hear the thud of footsteps running upstairs offstage*.) Hello, hello! Do I hear the step of a friend? (INSPECTOR MORTON *hurries in*.)

MORTON. Mr. Holmes?

HOLMES. Inspector Morton, this is your man.

SMITH. What is the meaning of . . . ?

---

8. *valley of the shadow,* a reference to the "valley of the shadow of death" mentioned in Psalm 23.

MORTON. Culverton Smith, I arrest you on the charge of the murder of one Victor Savage, and I must warn you that anything you say . . .

SMITH. You've got nothing on me! It's all a trick! A pack of lies!

(*He makes to escape.* MORTON *restrains him.*)

MORTON. Keep still, or you'll get yourself hurt!

SMITH. Get off me!

MORTON. Hold your hands out! (*They struggle.* MORTON *gets out handcuffs and claps them on* SMITH's *wrists.*) That'll do.

HOLMES. By the way, Inspector, you might add the attempted murder of one Sherlock Holmes to that charge. Oh, and you'll find a small box in the pocket of your prisoner's coat. Pray, leave it on the table, here. Handle it gingerly, though. It may play its part at his trial.

(MORTON *retrieves the box and places it on the table.*)

SMITH. Trial! You'll be the one in the dock,[9] Holmes. Inspector, he asked me to come here. He was ill, and I was sorry for him, so I came. Now he'll pretend I've said anything he cares to invent that will corroborate his insane suspicions. Well, you can lie as you like, Holmes. My word's as good as yours.

HOLMES. Good heavens! I'd completely forgotten him!

MORTON. Forgotten who, sir?

HOLMES. Watson, my dear fellow! Do come out! (WATSON *emerges with cramped groans.*) I owe you a thousand apologies. To think that I should have overlooked you!

WATSON. It's all right, Holmes. Would have come out before, only you said, whatever happened, I wasn't to budge.

SMITH. What's all this about?

HOLMES. I needn't introduce you to my witness, my friend Dr. Watson. I understand you met somewhat earlier in the evening.

SMITH. You . . . you mean you had all this planned?

HOLMES. Of course. To the last detail. I think I may say it worked very well—with your assistance, of course.

SMITH. Mine?

HOLMES. You saved an invalid trouble by giving my signal to Inspector Morton, waiting outside. You turned up the lamp.

(SMITH *and* WATSON *are equally flabbergasted.*)

MORTON. I'd better take him along now, sir. (*To* SMITH) Come on. (*He bundles* SMITH *roughly towards the door.*) We'll see you down at the Yard tomorrow, perhaps, Mr. Holmes?

HOLMES. Very well, Inspector. And many thanks.

WATSON. Goodbye, Inspector. (MORTON *exits with* SMITH.)

WATSON (*chuckles*). Well, Holmes?

HOLMES. Well, Watson, there's a bottle of claret over there—it is uncorked—and some biscuits in the barrel. If you'll be so kind, I'm badly in need of both.

(WATSON *goes to fetch them.*)

WATSON. Certainly. You know, Holmes, all this seems a pretty, well, elaborate way to go about catching that fellow. I mean, tak-

---

9. dock, the place where an accused person stands or sits in a court of law.

ing in Mrs. Hudson—*and me*—like that. Scared us half to death.

HOLMES. It was very essential that I should make Mrs. Hudson believe in my condition. She was to convey it to you, and you to him.

WATSON. Well . . .

HOLMES. Pray do not be offended, my good Watson. You must admit that among your *many* talents, dissimulation scarcely finds a place. If you'd shared my secret, you would never have been able to impress Smith with the urgent necessity of coming to me. It was the vital point of the whole scheme. I knew his vindictive nature, and I was certain he would come to gloat over his handiwork.

(WATSON *returns with the bottle, glasses and barrel.*)

WATSON. But . . . but your appearance, Holmes. Your face! You really do look ghastly.

HOLMES. Three days of absolute fast does not improve one's beauty, Watson. However, as you know, my habits are irregular, and such a feat means less to me than to most men. For the rest, there is nothing that a sponge won't cure. Vaseline to produce the glistening forehead; belladonna for the watering of the eyes; rouge over the cheekbones and crust of beeswax round one's lips . . .

WATSON (*chuckling*). And that babbling about oysters! (*He begins pouring the wine.*)

HOLMES. Yes. I've sometimes thought of writing a monograph on the subject of malingering.[10]

WATSON. But why wouldn't you let me near you? There was no risk of infection.

HOLMES. Whatever I may have said to the contrary in the grip of delirium, do you imagine that I have no respect for your medical talents? Could I imagine that you would be deceived by a dying man with no rise of pulse or temperature? At four yards' distance I *could* deceive you.

(WATSON *reaches for the box.*)

WATSON. This box, then . . .

HOLMES. No, Watson! I wouldn't touch it. You can just see, if you look at it sideways, where the sharp spring emerges as you open it. I dare say it was by some such device that poor young Savage was done to death. He stood between that monster and an inheritance, you know.

WATSON. Then it's true, Holmes! You . . . you might have been killed, too!

HOLMES. As you know, my correspondence is a varied one. I am somewhat on my guard against any packages which reach me. But I saw that by pretending he had succeeded in his design I might be enabled to surprise a confession from him. That pretense I think I may claim to have carried out with the thoroughness of a true artist.

WATSON (*warmly*). You certainly did, Holmes. Er, a biscuit? (*He holds out the barrel.*)

HOLMES. On second thoughts, Watson, no thank you. Let us preserve our appetite. By the time I have shaved and dressed, I fancy it will just be nice time for something nutritious at our little place in the Strand. (*They raise their glasses to one another and drink. The curtain falls.*)

---

10. *monograph on . . . malingering,* a scholarly article on the subject of pretending to be sick in order to escape work or other duties.

Comment

The Detective Who Wouldn't Die

Sherlock Holmes is one of the best-known and best-loved characters in fiction. Sir Arthur Conan Doyle introduced him and the good-natured Dr. Watson in the novel *A Study in Scarlet* in 1887. Holmes and Watson were an instant success with the reading public, prompting Doyle, a physician, to write more stories about the famous pair.

In 1893, hoping to devote his energies elsewhere, Doyle wrote a story in which Holmes falls over a cliff and is presumed to have drowned. This provoked such an outcry from fans that Doyle eventually brought Holmes back to life. In all, he wrote fifty-six stories and four novels featuring the brilliant detective.

Today, thanks in part to movies and television, Holmes is as popular as ever. Millions of people delight in following the master detective as he tracks down evildoers with unerring accuracy. Holmes even has a fan club. The Baker Street Irregulars, founded in 1934, is an American literary society devoted to the study of Sherlock Holmes. It publishes the *Baker Street Journal* and is associated with Holmes societies in other countries.

THINK AND DISCUSS

SCENE ONE

Understanding

1. What is the **setting** of this play?
2. What seems to be Holmes's condition when Watson arrives at 221B Baker Street?
3. What request does Holmes make when Watson insists on summoning a doctor immediately?
4. Why does Holmes make the request?

Analyzing

5. Holmes says he has no faith in Watson's medical ability. What **character** traits in Watson are revealed by his response to this statement?
6. On what grounds does Holmes reject the aid of other doctors?

SCENE TWO

Understanding

1. According to Holmes, why is Culverton Smith qualified to treat his disease?
2. What instructions does Holmes give Watson about Smith?
3. What does Holmes ask Watson to do with the lamp?
4. Point out remarks by Holmes that lead Watson to think Holmes is delirious.

Analyzing

5. What is the effect on Watson of Holmes's delirious remarks?

SCENE THREE

Understanding

1. What reason does Holmes give for wanting Watson to hide behind the bed?

2. What crime does Holmes accuse Culverton Smith of committing?

3. What does Smith do that, unknown to him, triggers his arrest?

Analyzing

4. Smith thinks it unlikely that he will see Holmes in a witness box. What does the planter mean by his reference to another shape of box?

5. Explain Holmes's reasons for the following: (**a**) warning Watson not to touch the ivory box; (**b**) instructing Watson to light the lamp at no more than half flame; (**c**) insisting that Watson return ahead of Smith; (**d**) demanding that Watson hide behind the bed and stay there no matter what happens.

6. How important is the **setting** to the **plot** of *The Dying Detective?* Explain.

7. Is the major conflict in the play external or internal? Explain.

Extending

8. How are short stories and plays alike? How do they differ? If given a choice, which would you prefer to read?

READING LITERATURE SKILLFULLY

Predicting Outcomes

Part of the enjoyment of reading literature comes from trying to **predict** the **outcome** before reading the ending of a selection. With some types of stories, readers can make general predictions even before beginning to read. Usually the good guy will defeat the bad guys in a cowboy story and the sleuth will outwit the criminal in a detective story. Look for clues that will help you predict how conflicts will be resolved.

Finding such clues is not always easy in detective stories. Authors purposely try to mislead, knowing that you will find pleasure at being surprised in the end. Yet authors also need to provide some clues.

1. What is the first clue that Holmes may be pretending to be ill?

2. What clue is given that the little box by Holmes's bedside may be deadly?

3. What clue is provided that Inspector Morton may play an important role in the plot?

VOCABULARY
Affixes and Roots

Recognizing the parts in a word can often help you understand its meaning. The *root* is the main part of a word. *Prefixes* such as *in-*, *ir-*, *dis-*, and *pre-* are added to the beginning of a root to change its meaning. *Suffixes* such as *-ous*, *-ation*, *-ness*, and *-ly* are added to the end of a root. Suffixes can change the meaning, but more importantly, they determine whether a word is used as a noun, adjective, verb, or adverb. The term *affix* refers to both prefixes and suffixes. A word formed from a root plus one or more affixes is a *derivative*. Study the derivatives and answer the questions. Look up any unfamiliar affixes and roots in the Glossary.

dissimulation   irksome
methodical   insane
irregular

1. Which word contains a root, a prefix, and a suffix?

2. Which words are made up only of a root and a prefix?

3. How do the prefixes change the meaning of the words?

4. Which words are made up only of a root and a suffix?

5. Compare the part of speech of each word with a suffix to the part of speech of the word without the suffix.

THINKING SKILLS
Classifying

To classify things is to arrange them into categories or groups according to some system. In *The Dying Detective* much of what happens can be classified into two categories. Some of Holmes's success depends on what he does, such as pretending to be ill. Holmes also depends on what others do; for example, Watson must light the lamp. Make two lists—one of things Holmes must do and a second of things he must get others to do.

COMPOSITION
Writing a Summary

Assume that you are Sherlock Holmes and that Scotland Yard officials have asked you to write a one-paragraph report on the arrest of Culverton Smith. First outline the plans you made beforehand—for example, arranging a signal with Inspector Morton and applying makeup. Next outline the steps you took after you were bedridden— for example, detaining Watson until 6:00 P.M. and sending him to summon Smith to your room. Begin your report, "Catching Culverton Smith was no easy task." See Lesson 5, "Writing to Summarize," in the Writer's Handbook.

Describing Characters

Assume that you are the director of *The Dying Detective.* You need to describe Sherlock Holmes and Dr. Watson for the actors. Write two paragraphs, one for Holmes and one for Watson, in which you describe in detail each individual's physical appearance and way of speaking. Review the play for details, but you will need to read between the lines and use your imagination. Consider each man's costume, facial characteristics, and voice quality. For example, would Watson speak rapidly or slowly? Would his voice be deep or high-pitched?

ENRICHMENT
Comparing a Story and a Play

"The Adventure of the Dying Detective," the story, originally appeared in *His Last Bow* by Arthur Conan Doyle and can be found in various collections. Find the story at your library and compare it to the play you have just read. Make an outline of the changes that were made to adapt the short story for the stage.

BIOGRAPHY
Michael and Mollie Hardwick

Michael and Mollie Hardwick are English authors who make their home in London. Michael began his career as a newspaper reporter; Mollie started hers as a radio announcer. Married since 1961, they became free-lance authors and playwrights in 1963.

Use Varied Sentences

Good writers use different kinds of sentences to establish different types of characters and develop action. By using a variety of statements, questions, commands, and exclamations, writers create dramatic characters and lively dialogue.

In *The Dying Detective,* Michael and Mollie Hardwick emphasize the differences between characters by their choice of sentences. Dr. Watson is upset by the mysterious illness of his friend. Appropriately he speaks in sentences that are short and often end in exclamation marks.

> WATSON. This is insanity!
> HOLMES. Only two hours, Watson.
>   I promise you may go then.
> WATSON. Hang it, this is urgent, man!
>
>   (page 119, column 2)

By comparison, even though Holmes is supposedly sick, notice how he keeps control of the situation by frequently using command sentences.

> HOLMES. You will now light that lamp
>   by the window, Watson, but you will
>   be very careful that not for one instant
>   shall it be more than at half flame.
> WATSON. Oh, very well.
> HOLMES. I implore you to be careful.
> WATSON (*as though humoring him*). *Yes,*
>   Holmes.
> HOLMES. No, you need not draw
>   curtains.   (page 120, column 2)

As you can see, because the authors use sentences that fit each character's personality and situation, the play seems more believable. This doesn't mean, of course, that a character should speak only in one kind of sentence. In real conversations, people ask questions, make statements, exclaim, and sometimes even speak in fragments. In order to reflect the way people actually talk, good writers should also use variety. In the passage below, identify each of the different kinds of sentences the authors use to make the confrontation between Smith and Holmes more realistic.

> SMITH. . . . Did you? Well, proving it is
>   a different matter, Holmes. But what
>   sort of game is this, then—spreading
>   lying reports about me one moment,
>   then crawling to me for help the next?
> HOLMES. . . . Give . . . give me water.
>   For . . . pity's sake, Smith. Water!
>
>   (page 123, column 2)

In your own writing try to use a variety of sentences. One way to do this is to choose the type of sentence that best fits your subject. Another way is to vary the length of sentences you use.

When you read, notice different kinds of sentences.

When you write, use different kinds of sentences.

See MOOD in the Handbook of Literary Terms, page 647.

The Monsters Are Due on Maple Street

Rod Serling

Nothing's working on this street. Nothing.
No lights, no power, no radio. . . . Nothing except one car——

CHARACTERS

NARRATOR	DON MARTIN	TOMMY
FIGURE ONE	STEVE BRAND	SALLY, *Tommy's mother*
FIGURE TWO	MYRA BRAND, *Steve's wife*	LES GOODMAN
	PETE VAN HORN	ETHEL GOODMAN, *Les's wife*
	CHARLIE	MAN ONE
	CHARLIE'S WIFE	MAN TWO
		WOMAN ONE

ACT ONE

Fade in on shot of the night sky. The various heavenly bodies stand out in sharp, sparkling relief. The camera begins a slow pan[1] across the heavens until it passes the horizon and stops on a sign which reads "Maple Street." It is daytime. Then we see the street below. It is a quiet, tree-lined, small-town American street. The houses have front porches on which people sit and swing on gliders, talking across from house to house. STEVE BRAND *is polishing his car, which is parked in front of his house. His neighbor,* DON

---

1. *pan,* movement of the television camera in order to get a wide view or to follow a moving object.

From "The Monsters Are Due on Maple Street" by Rod Serling. Reprinted by permission of International Creative Management. Copyright © 1960 by Rod Serling.

MARTIN, *leans against the fender watching him. A Good Humor man riding a bicycle is just in the process of stopping to sell some ice cream to a couple of kids. Two women gossip on the front lawn. Another man is watering his lawn with a garden hose.*

As we see these various activities, we hear the NARRATOR's *voice.*

NARRATOR. Maple Street, U.S.A., late summer. A tree-lined little world of front porch gliders, hopscotch, the laughter of children, and the bell of an ice cream vendor.

(There is a pause and the camera moves over to a shot of the Good Humor man and two small boys who are standing alongside just buying ice cream.)

NARRATOR. At the sound of the roar and the flash of the light, it will be precisely six-forty-three P.M. on Maple Street.

(At this moment TOMMY, *one of the two boys buying ice cream from the vendor, looks up to listen to a tremendous screeching roar from overhead. A flash of light plays on the faces of both boys and then moves down the street and disappears.*

Various people leave their porches or stop what they are doing to stare up at the sky.

STEVE BRAND, *the man who has been polishing his car, stands there transfixed, staring upwards. He looks at* DON MARTIN, *his neighbor from across the street.)*

STEVE. What was that? A meteor?

DON. That's what it looked like. I didn't hear any crash though, did you?

STEVE. Nope. I didn't hear anything except a roar.

MYRA (*from her porch*). What was that?

STEVE (*raising his voice and looking toward the porch*). Guess it was a meteor, honey. Came awful close, didn't it?

MYRA. Too close for my money! Much too close.

(The camera pans across the various porches to people who stand there watching and talking in low conversing tones.)

NARRATOR. Maple Street. Six-forty-four P.M. on a late September evening. (*A pause*) Maple Street in the last calm and reflective moment . . . before the monsters came!

(The camera takes us across the porches again. A man is replacing a light bulb on a front porch. He gets down off his stool to flick the switch and finds that nothing happens.

Another man is working on an electric power mower. He plugs in the plug, flicks the switch of the mower off and on, but nothing happens.

Through the window we see a woman pushing her finger back and forth on the dial hook of a telephone. Her voice sounds far away.)

WOMAN ONE. Operator, operator, something's wrong on the phone, operator!

*(*MYRA BRAND *comes out on the porch and calls to* STEVE.)*

MYRA (*calling*). Steve, the power's off. I had the soup on the stove and the stove just stopped working.

WOMAN ONE. Same thing over here. I can't get anybody on the phone either. The phone seems to be dead.

(We look down again on the street. Small, mildly disturbed voices creep up from below.)

VOICE ONE. Electricity's off.

VOICE TWO. Phone won't work.

VOICE THREE. Can't get a thing on the radio.

VOICE FOUR. My power mower won't move, won't work at all.

Janis Price, *An Ohio Village* (detail), 1981
Jay Johnson America's Folk Heritage Gallery, N.Y.C.

VOICE FIVE. Radio's gone dead!

(PETE VAN HORN, *a tall, thin man, is seen standing in front of his house.*)

PETE. I'll cut through the back yard . . . see if the power's still on, on Floral Street. I'll be right back!

(*He walks past the side of his house and disappears into the back yard.*

The camera pans down slowly until we are looking at ten or eleven people standing around the street and overflowing to the curb and sidewalk. In the background is STEVE BRAND'*s car.*)

STEVE. Doesn't make sense. Why should the power go off all of a sudden *and* the phone line?

DON. Maybe some kind of an electrical storm or something.

CHARLIE. That don't seem likely. Sky's just as blue as anything. Not a cloud. No lightning. No thunder. No nothing. How could it be a storm?

WOMAN ONE. I can't get a thing on the radio. Not even the portable.

(*The people again murmur softly in wonderment.*)

CHARLIE. Well, why don't you go downtown and check with the police, though they'll probably think we're crazy or something. A little power failure and right away we get all flustered and everything——

STEVE. It isn't just the power failure, Charlie. If it was, we'd still be able to get a broadcast on the portable.

(*There is a murmur of reaction to this.* STEVE *looks from face to face and then over to his car.*)

STEVE. I'll run downtown. We'll get this all straightened out.

(*He walks over to the car, gets in, and turns the key.*

Looking through the open car door, we see the crowd watching STEVE *from the other side. He starts the engine. It turns over sluggishly and then stops dead. He tries it again, and this time he can't get it to turn over. Then very slowly he turns the key back to "off" and gets out of the car.*

The people stare at STEVE. *He stands for a moment by the car and then walks toward them.*)

STEVE. I don't understand it. It was working fine before——

DON. Out of gas?

STEVE (*shakes his head*). I just had it filled up.

WOMAN ONE. What's it mean?

CHARLIE. It's just as if . . . as if everything had stopped. (*Then he turns toward* STEVE.) We'd better *walk* downtown.

(*Another murmur of assent to this.*)

STEVE. The two of us can go, Charlie. (*He turns to look back at the car.*) It couldn't be the meteor. A meteor couldn't do *this*.

(*He and* CHARLIE *exchange a look. Then they start to walk away from the group.*

TOMMY *comes into view. He is a serious-faced young boy in spectacles. He stands halfway between the group and the two men who start to walk down the sidewalk.*)

TOMMY. Mr. Brand . . . you'd better not!

STEVE. Why not?

TOMMY. They don't want you to.

(STEVE *and* CHARLIE *exchange a grin and* STEVE *looks back toward the boy.*)

STEVE. *Who* doesn't want us to?

TOMMY (*jerks his head in the general direction of the distant horizon*). Them!

STEVE. Them?

CHARLIE. Who are *them?*

TOMMY (*intently*). Whoever was in that thing that came by overhead.

(STEVE *knits his brows for a moment, cocking his head questioningly. His voice is intense.*)

STEVE. What?

TOMMY. Whoever was in that thing that came over. I don't think they want us to leave here.

(STEVE *leaves* CHARLIE, *walks over to the boy, and puts his hand on the boy's shoulder. He forces his voice to remain gentle.*)

STEVE. What do you mean? What are you talking about?

TOMMY. They don't want us to leave. That's why they shut everything off.

STEVE. What makes you say that? Whatever gave you *that* idea?

WOMAN ONE (*from the crowd*). Now isn't that the craziest thing you ever heard?

TOMMY (*persistent but a little frightened*). It's always that way, in every story I ever read about a ship landing from outer space.

WOMAN ONE (*to the boy's mother,* SALLY, *who stands on the fringe of the crowd*). From outer space yet! Sally, you better get that boy of yours up to bed. He's been reading too many comic books or seeing too many movies or something!

SALLY. Tommy, come over here and stop that kind of talk.

STEVE. Go ahead, Tommy. We'll be right back. And you'll see. That wasn't any ship or anything like it. That was just a . . . a meteor or something. Likely as not—— (*He turns to the group, now trying very hard to sound more optimistic than he feels.*) No doubt it did have something to do with all this power failure and the rest of it. Mete-ors can do some crazy things. Like sunspots.

DON (*picking up the cue*). Sure. That's the kind of thing—like sunspots. They raise Cain with radio reception all over the world. And this thing being so close— why, there's no telling the sort of stuff it can do. (*He wets his lips, smiles nervously.*) Go ahead, Charlie. You and Steve go into town and see if that isn't what's causing it all.

(STEVE *and* CHARLIE *walk away from the group down the sidewalk as the people watch silently.*

TOMMY *stares at them, biting his lips, and finally calls out again.*)

TOMMY. Mr. Brand!

(*The two men stop.* TOMMY *takes a step toward them.*)

TOMMY. Mr. Brand . . . please don't leave here.

(STEVE *and* CHARLIE *stop once again and turn toward the boy. In the crowd there is a murmur of irritation and concern, as if the boy's words—even though they didn't make sense— were bringing up fears that shouldn't be brought up.*

TOMMY *is partly frightened and partly defiant.*)

TOMMY. You might not even be able to get to town. It was that way in the story. *Nobody* could leave. Nobody except——

STEVE. Except who?

TOMMY. Except the people they sent down ahead of them. They looked just like humans. And it wasn't until the ship landed that——(*The boy suddenly stops, conscious of the people staring at him and his mother and of the sudden hush of the crowd.*)

SALLY (in a whisper, sensing the antagonism of the crowd). Tommy, please son . . . honey, don't talk that way——

MAN ONE. That kid shouldn't talk that way . . . and we shouldn't stand here listening to him. Why this is the craziest thing I ever heard of. The kid tells us a comic book plot and here we stand listening——

(STEVE walks toward the camera, and stops beside the boy.)

STEVE. Go ahead, Tommy. What kind of story was this? What about the people they sent out ahead?

TOMMY. That was the way they prepared things for the landing. They sent four people. A mother and a father and two kids who looked just like humans . . . but they weren't.

(There is another silence as STEVE looks toward the crowd and then toward TOMMY. He wears a tight grin.)

STEVE. Well, I guess what we'd better do then is to run a check on the neighborhood and see which ones of us are really human.

(There is laughter at this, but it's a laughter that comes from a desperate attempt to lighten the atmosphere. The people look at one another in the middle of their laughter.)

CHARLIE (rubs his jaw nervously). I wonder if Floral Street's got the same deal we got. (He looks past the houses.) Where is Pete Van Horn anyway? Didn't he get back yet? (Suddenly there is the sound of a car's engine starting to turn over.

We look across the street toward the driveway of LES GOODMAN's house. He is at the wheel trying to start the car.)

SALLY. Can you get started, Les?

(LES GOODMAN gets out of the car, shaking his head.)

LES. No dice.

(He walks toward the group. He stops suddenly as, behind him, the car engine starts up all by itself. LES whirls around to stare at it.

The car idles roughly, smoke coming from the exhaust, the frame shaking gently.

LES's eyes go wide, and he runs over to his car.

The people stare at the car.)

MAN ONE. He got the car started somehow. He got his car started!

(The people continue to stare, caught up by this revelation and wildly frightened.)

WOMAN ONE. How come his car just up and started like that?

SALLY. All by itself. He wasn't anywheres near it. It started all by itself.

(DON MARTIN approaches the group, stops a few feet away to look toward LES's car and then back toward the group.)

DON. And he never did come out to look at that thing that flew overhead. He wasn't even interested. (He turns to the group, his face taut and serious.) Why? Why didn't he come out with the rest of us to look?

CHARLIE. He always was an oddball. Him and his whole family. Real oddball.

DON. What do you say we ask him?

(The group start toward the house. In this brief fraction of a moment they take the first step toward a metamorphosis that changes people from a group into a mob. They begin to head purposefully across the street toward the house. STEVE stands in front of them. For a moment their fear almost turns their walk into a wild stampede, but STEVE's voice, loud, in-

cisive, and commanding, makes them stop.)

STEVE. Wait a minute . . . *wait a minute!* Let's not be a mob!

(The people stop, pause for a moment, and then much more quietly and slowly start to walk across the street.

LES *stands alone facing the people.)*

LES. I just don't understand it. I tried to start it and it wouldn't start. You saw me. All of you saw me.

(And now, just as suddenly as the engine started, it stops, and there is a long silence that is gradually intruded upon by the frightened murmuring of the people.)

LES. I don't understand. I swear . . . I don't understand. What's happening?

DON. Maybe you better tell us. Nothing's working on this street. Nothing. No lights, no power, no radio. *(Then meaningfully)* Nothing except one car—*yours!*

(The people's murmuring becomes a loud chant filling the air with accusations and demands for action. Two of the men pass DON *and head toward* LES, *who backs away from them against his car. He is cornered.)*

LES. Wait a minute now. You keep your distance—all of you. So I've got a car that starts by itself—well, that's a freak thing— I admit it. But does that make me some kind of a criminal or something? I don't know why the car works—it just does!

(This stops the crowd momentarily and LES, *still backing away, goes toward his front porch. He goes up the steps and then stops, facing the mob.)*

LES. What's it all about, Steve?

STEVE *(quietly).* We're all on a monster kick, Les. Seems that the general impression holds that maybe one family isn't what we think they are. Monsters from outer space or something. Different from us. Fifth columnists[2] from the vast beyond. *(He chuckles.)* You know anybody that might fit that description around here on Maple Street?

LES. What is this, a gag? *(He looks around the group again.)* This a practical joke or something?

(Suddenly the car engine starts all by itself, runs for a moment, and stops. One woman begins to cry. The eyes of the crowd are cold and accusing.)

LES. Now that's supposed to incriminate me, huh? The car engine goes on and off and that really does it, doesn't it? *(He looks around the faces of the people.)* I just don't understand it . . . any more than any of you do! *(He wets his lips, looking from face to face.)* Look, you all know me. We've lived here five years. Right in this house. We're no different from any of the rest of you! We're no different at all. . . . Really . . . this whole thing is just . . . just weird——

WOMAN ONE. Well, if that's the case, Les Goodman, explain why——*(She stops suddenly, clamping her mouth shut.)*

LES *(softly).* Explain what?

STEVE *(interjecting).* Look, let's forget this——

CHARLIE *(overlapping him).* Go ahead, let her talk. What about it? Explain what?

WOMAN ONE *(a little reluctantly).* Well . . . sometimes I go to bed late at night. A couple of times . . . a couple of times I'd come

---

2. **fifth columnists,** people who engage in spying, sabotage, or other secret, treasonous activities within the borders of a nation.

out here on the porch and I'd see Mr. Goodman here in the wee hours of the morning standing out in front of his house . . . looking up at the sky. (*She looks around the circle of faces.*) That's right, looking up at the sky as if . . . as if he were waiting for something. (*A pause*) As if he were looking for something.

(*There's a murmur of reaction from the crowd again as* LES *backs away.*)

LES. She's crazy. Look, I can explain that. Please . . . I can really explain that. . . . She's making it up anyway. (*Then he shouts.*) I tell you she's making it up!

(*He takes a step toward the crowd and they back away from him. He walks down the steps after them and they continue to back away. Suddenly he is left completely alone, and he looks like a man caught in the middle of a menacing circle as the scene slowly fades to black.*)

ACT TWO

SCENE ONE

Fade in on Maple Street at night. On the sidewalk, little knots of people stand around talking in low voices. At the end of each conversation they look toward LES GOODMAN's *house. From the various houses we can see candlelight but no electricity. The quiet which blankets the whole area is disturbed only by the almost whispered voices of the people standing around. In one group* CHARLIE *stands staring across at the* GOODMANS' *house. Two men stand across the street from it in almost sentry-like poses.*

SALLY (*in a small, hesitant voice*). It just doesn't seem right, though, keeping watch on them. Why . . . he was right when he said he was one of our neighbors. Why, I've known Ethel Goodman ever since they moved in. We've been good friends——

CHARLIE. That don't prove a thing. Any guy who'd spend his time lookin' up at the sky early in the morning—well, there's something wrong with that kind of person. There's something that ain't legitimate. Maybe under normal circumstances we could let it go by, but these aren't normal circumstances. Why, look at this street! Nothin' but candles. Why, it's like goin' back into the Dark Ages or somethin'!

(STEVE *walks down the steps of his porch, down the street to the* GOODMANS' *house, and then stops at the foot of the steps.* LES *is standing there;* ETHEL GOODMAN *behind him is very frightened.*)

LES. Just stay right where you are, Steve. We don't want any trouble, but this time if anybody sets foot on my porch—that's what they're going to get—trouble!

STEVE. Look, Les——

LES. I've already explained to you people. I don't sleep very well at night sometimes. I get up and I take a walk and I look up at the sky. I look at the stars!

ETHEL. That's exactly what he does. Why, this whole thing, it's . . . it's some kind of madness or something.

STEVE (*nods grimly*). That's exactly what it is—some kind of madness.

CHARLIE'S VOICE (*shrill, from across the street*). You best watch who you're seen with, Steve! Until we get this all straightened out, you ain't exactly above suspicion yourself.

STEVE (*whirling around toward him*). Or you, Charlie. Or any of us, it seems. From age eight on up!

WOMAN ONE. What I'd like to know is—what are we gonna do? Just stand around here all night?

CHARLIE. There's nothin' else we *can* do! (*He turns back, looking toward* STEVE *and* LES *again.*) One of 'em'll tip their hand. They *got* to.

STEVE (*raising his voice*). There's something you can do, Charlie. You can go home and keep your mouth shut. You can quit strutting around like a self-appointed hanging judge and just climb into bed and forget it.

CHARLIE. You sound real anxious to have that happen, Steve. I think we better keep our eye on you, too!

DON (*as if he were taking the bit in his teeth, takes a hesitant step to the front*). I think everything might as well come out now. (*He turns toward* STEVE.) Your wife's done plenty of talking, Steve, about how odd *you* are!

CHARLIE (*picking this up, his eyes widening*). Go ahead, tell us what she's said.

(STEVE *walks toward them from across the street.*)

STEVE. Go ahead, what's my wife said? Let's get it *all* out. Let's pick out every idiosyncrasy of every single man, woman, and child on the street. And then we might as well set up some kind of kangaroo court.[3] How about a firing squad at dawn, Charlie, so we can get rid of all the suspects. Narrow them down. Make it easier for you.

DON. There's no need gettin' so upset, Steve. It's just that . . . well . . . Myra's talked about how there's been plenty of nights you spent hours down in your basement workin' on some kind of radio or something. Well, none of us have ever *seen* that radio——

(*By this time* STEVE *has reached the group. He stands there defiantly.*)

CHARLIE. Go ahead, Steve. What kind of "radio set" you workin' on? I never seen it. Neither has anyone else. Who do you talk to on that radio set? And who talks to you?

STEVE. I'm surprised at you, Charlie. How come you're so dense all of a sudden? (*A pause*) Who do I talk to? I talk to monsters from outer space. I talk to three-headed green men who fly over here in what look like meteors.

(MYRA BRAND *steps down from the porch, bites her lip, calls out.*)

MYRA. Steve! Steve, please. (*Then looking around, frightened, she walks toward the group.*) It's just a ham radio set, that's all. I bought him a book on it myself. It's just a ham radio set. A lot of people have them. I can show it to you. It's right down in the basement.

STEVE (*whirls around toward her*). Show them nothing! If they want to look inside our house—let them get a search warrant.

CHARLIE. Look, buddy, you can't afford to——

STEVE (*interrupting him*). Charlie, don't start telling me who's dangerous and who isn't and who's safe and who's a menace. (*He turns to the group and shouts.*) And you're with him, too—all of you! You're standing

---

3. **kangaroo court,** an unauthorized, on-the-spot mock trial in which heated emotion replaces reason and justice.

here all set to crucify—all set to find a scapegoat—all desperate to point some kind of a finger at a neighbor! Well now, look, friends, the only thing that's gonna happen is that we'll eat each other up alive——

(*He stops abruptly as* CHARLIE *suddenly grabs his arm.*)

CHARLIE (*in a hushed voice*). That's not the *only* thing that can happen to us.

(*Down the street, a figure has suddenly materialized in the gloom, and in the silence we hear the clickety-clack of slow, measured footsteps on concrete as the figure walks slowly toward them. One of the women lets out a stifled cry.* SALLY *grabs her boy, as do a couple of other mothers.*)

TOMMY (*shouting, frightened*). It's the monster! It's the monster!

(*Another woman lets out a wail and the people fall back in a group staring toward the darkness and the approaching figure.*

The people stand in the shadows watching. DON MARTIN *joins them, carrying a shotgun. He holds it up.*)

DON. We may need this.

STEVE. A shotgun? (*He pulls it out of* DON's *hand.*) No! Will anybody think a thought around here? Will you people wise up? What good would a shotgun do against——

(*The dark figure continues to walk toward them as the people stand there, fearful, mothers clutching children, men standing in front of their wives.*)

CHARLIE (*pulling the gun from* STEVE's *hands*). No more talk, Steve. You're going to talk us into a grave! You'd let whatever's out there walk right over us, wouldn't yuh? Well, some of us won't!

(CHARLIE *swings around, raises the gun, and*

suddenly pulls the trigger. *The sound of the shot explodes in the stillness.*

The figure suddenly lets out a small cry, stumbles forward onto his knees, and then falls forward on his face. DON, CHARLIE, *and* STEVE *race forward to him.* STEVE *is there first and turns the man over. The crowd gathers around them.*)

STEVE (*slowly looks up*). It's Pete Van Horn.

DON (*in a hushed voice*). Pete Van Horn! He was just gonna go over to the next block to see if the power was on——

WOMAN ONE. You killed him, Charlie. You shot him dead!

CHARLIE (*looks around at the circle of faces, his eyes frightened, his face contorted*). But . . . but I didn't know who he was. I certainly didn't know who he was. He comes walkin' out of the darkness—how am I supposed to know who he was? (*He grabs* STEVE.) Steve—you know why I shot! How was I supposed to know he wasn't a monster or something? (*He grabs* DON.) We're all scared of the same thing. I was just tryin' to . . . tryin' to protect my home, that's all! Look, all of you, that's all I was tryin' to do. (*He looks down wildly at the body.*) I didn't know it was somebody we knew! I didn't know——

(*There's a sudden hush and then an intake of breath in the group. Across the street all the lights go on in one of the houses.*)

WOMAN ONE (*in a hushed voice*). Charlie . . . Charlie . . . the lights just went on in your house. Why did the lights just go on?

DON. What about it, Charlie? How come you're the only one with lights now?

LES. That's what I'd like to know.

(*A pause as they all stare toward* CHARLIE.)

LES. You were so quick to kill, Charlie, and

you were so quick to tell us who we had to be careful of. Well, maybe you *had* to kill. Maybe Pete there was trying to tell us something. Maybe he'd found out something and came back to tell us who there was amongst us we should watch out for——

(CHARLIE *backs away from the group, his eyes wide with fright.*)

CHARLIE. No . . . no . . . it's nothing of the sort! I don't know why the lights are on. I swear I don't. Somebody's pulling a gag or something.

(*He bumps against* STEVE *who grabs him and whirls him around.*)

STEVE. A *gag?* A gag? Charlie, there's a dead man on the sidewalk and you killed him! Does this thing look like a gag to you?

(CHARLIE *breaks away and screams as he runs toward his house.*)

CHARLIE. No! No! Please!

(*A man breaks away from the crowd to chase* CHARLIE.

As the man tackles him and lands on top of him, the other people start to run toward them. CHARLIE *gets up, breaks away from the other man's grasp, lands a couple of desperate punches that push the man aside. Then he forces his way, fighting, through the crowd and jumps up on his front porch.*

CHARLIE *is on his porch as a rock thrown from the group smashes a window beside him, the broken glass flying past him. A couple of pieces cut him. He stands there perspiring, rumpled, blood running down from a cut on the cheek. His wife breaks away from the group to throw herself into his arms. He buries his face against her. We can see the crowd converging on the porch.*)

VOICE ONE. It must have been him.

VOICE TWO. He's the one.

VOICE THREE. We got to get Charlie.

(*Another rock lands on the porch.* CHARLIE *pushes his wife behind him, facing the group.*)

CHARLIE. Look, look I swear to you . . . it isn't me . . . but I do know who it is . . . I swear to you, I do know who it is. I know who the monster is here. I know who it is that doesn't belong. I swear to you I know.

DON (*pushing his way to the front of the crowd*). All right, Charlie, let's hear it!

(CHARLIE's *eyes dart around wildly.*)

CHARLIE. It's . . . it's . . .

MAN TWO (*screaming*). Go ahead, Charlie, tell us.

CHARLIE. It's . . . it's the kid. It's Tommy. He's the one!

(*There's a gasp from the crowd as we see* SALLY *holding the boy.* TOMMY *at first doesn't understand and then, realizing the eyes are all on him, buries his face against his mother.*)

SALLY (*backs away*). That's crazy! He's only a boy.

WOMAN ONE. But he knew! He was the only one who knew! He told us all about it. Well, how did he know? How *could* he have known?

(*Various people take this up and repeat the question.*)

VOICE ONE. How could he know?

VOICE TWO. Who told him?

VOICE THREE. Make the kid answer.

(*The crowd starts to converge around the mother, who grabs* TOMMY *and starts to run with him. The crowd starts to follow, at first walking fast, and then running after him.*

Suddenly CHARLIE's *lights go off and the lights in other houses go on, then off.*)

MAN ONE (*shouting*). It isn't the kid . . . it's Bob Weaver's house.

WOMAN ONE. It isn't Bob Weaver's house, it's Don Martin's place.

CHARLIE. I tell you it's the kid.

DON. It's Charlie. He's the one.

(People shout, accuse, and scream as the lights go on and off. Then, slowly, in the middle of this nightmarish confusion of sight and sound the camera starts to pull away until once again we have reached the opening shot looking at the Maple Street sign from high above.)

SCENE TWO

The camera continues to move away while gradually bringing into focus a field. We see the metal side of a spacecraft which sits shrouded in darkness. An open door throws out a beam of light from the illuminated interior. Two figures appear, silhouetted against the bright lights. We get only a vague feeling of form.

FIGURE ONE. Understand the procedure now? Just stop a few of their machines and radios and telephones and lawn mowers . . . throw them into darkness for a few hours, and then just sit back and watch the pattern.

FIGURE TWO. And this pattern is always the same?

FIGURE ONE. With few variations. They pick the most dangerous enemy they can find . . . and it's themselves. And all we need do is sit back . . . and watch.

FIGURE TWO. Then I take it this place . . . this Maple Street . . . is not unique.

FIGURE ONE *(shaking his head)*. By no means. Their world is full of Maple Streets. And we'll go from one to the other and let them destroy themselves. One to the other . . . one to the other . . . one to the other——

SCENE THREE

The camera pans up for a shot of the starry sky, and over this we hear the NARRATOR's voice.

NARRATOR. The tools of conquest do not necessarily come with bombs and explosions and fallout. There are weapons that are simply thoughts, attitudes, prejudices—to be found only in the minds of men. For the record, prejudices can kill and suspicion can destroy and a thoughtless, frightened search for a scapegoat has a fallout all its own for the children . . . and the children yet unborn. *(A pause)* And the pity of it is . . . that these things cannot be confined to . . . The Twilight Zone! *(Fade to black.)*

Comment

The Twilight Zone

The Monsters Are Due on Maple Street appeared in the original series of *The Twilight Zone*, which initially ran on television from October 1959 to September 1965. Since that time the teleplays have often been rerun, particularly for late-night viewers.

In addition to serving as host, Rod

Serling wrote 92 of the 156 episodes in the original series. Although fewer than a third of the episodes can be classified as science fiction, most viewers associated the show with space travel, robots, and alien civilizations.

Science fiction or not, many of the teleplays were offbeat and had surprise endings. In one, for example, a bank teller can never find enough time in which to read. He passes his lunch hour one day reading in a bank vault. While he is absorbed in his book, a nuclear attack kills everyone outside the vault. At last the teller has all the time in the world for reading, with no one to bother him. Unfortunately, however, he trips and breaks his glasses.

Serling's opening narration for each show furnished an appropriate tone.

There is a fifth dimension beyond that which is known to man. It is a dimension as vast as space, and timeless as infinity. It is the middle ground between light and shadow—between science and superstition. And it lies between the pit of man's fears and the summit of his knowledge. This is the dimension of the imagination. It is an area we call the Twilight Zone.

At the end of the show, he would add, ". . . and you, have you been there?"

Not only has the original series been seen by millions of viewers, but the books to which it gave birth have been read by hundreds of thousands of fans. Among them are *Stories from the Twilight Zone*, *More Stories from the Twilight Zone*, and *New Stories from the Twilight Zone*.

THINK AND DISCUSS

Understanding

1. What is the place and time of the play?
2. What happening starts the action of the play?
3. Cite details that make the **setting** seem ordinary and commonplace.

Analyzing

4. Why is it important for the **setting** to be quite ordinary?
5. How does Tommy affect the action?
6. The **plot** centers on external conflicts among the characters. What conflicts develop among neighbors on Maple Street?

7. As the group begins to move toward Les in Act One, a stage direction mentions the "metamorphosis that changes people from a group into a mob." Explain how the people on Maple Street continue the metamorphosis from a group into a mob.
8. What is surprising about Charlie being accused by his neighbors?
9. Which of the following best states the **theme** of the play? (**a**) Prejudice, suspicion, thoughtlessness, and fear cause humans to be their own worst enemies. (**b**) People should be kind to each other, particularly during a time

of crisis. (**c**) Aliens from space invade a town and cause people to distrust and fight one another.

10. The play title is *The Monsters Are Due on Maple Street*. Who are the monsters?

Extending

11. What do you think will happen to the people on Maple Street? Support your answer with evidence from the play.

12. Pretend your block is Maple Street. Would your neighbors have responded in the same way?

APPLYING: Mood H⌀

See Handbook of Literary Terms, p. 647.

Mood is the atmosphere or feeling within a work of art.

1. Reread the stage directions at the beginning of Act One. What words best describe the mood at the outset of the play: (**a**) friendly and serene; (**b**) hateful and angry; (**c**) sad and despairing; (**d**) gloomy and bleak?

2. What alters this mood?

3. Which of the following words seem to capture best the mood throughout the rest of the play: (**a**) peaceful and cheery; (**b**) bleak and lonely; (**c**) sad and mournful; (**d**) fearful and suspicious? Explain.

VOCABULARY

Synonyms

A synonym is a word having a meaning that is the same or nearly the same as that of another word. *Elderly*, for example, is a synonym for *old*. From the list that follows, choose a word that is a synonym for the word in parentheses in each sentence. Write the sentences on paper, substituting the synonym for the word in

the sentence. Consult the Glossary for any listed words you do not know.

transfix	reluctant
assent	illuminate
irritation	legitimate
metamorphosis	idiosyncrasy
purposeful	stifle
incisive	

1. Charlie does not _____ (agree) to Steve's suggestions.

2. Sally seems _____ (unwilling) to have Tommy speak.

3. The pattern created by the aliens is _____ (intentional).

4. Steve doesn't try to _____ (suppress) his anger.

5. His voice is loud and _____ (penetrating).

6. Les's denial is an _____ (annoyance).

7. Charlie does not kill Pete Van Horn for a _____ (lawful) reason.

8. A beam of light is used to _____ (light up) the scene.

THINKING SKILLS

Evaluating

To evaluate is to make a judgment based on some sort of standard. For example, a viewer sees a play on television and, considering all the other TV plays he or she has seen, judges how well the play was written and performed.

Divide into groups of five. Each group is to decide which of the first two plays in this unit is worthy of an award. First decide on five categories on which to evaluate the plays and then make up a rating system for each category. As a group, rate the plays in each category and present your choice for prizewinner to the rest of the class.

COMPOSITION

Reading/Writing Log

Rod Serling uses a variety of sentence types. You will find questions, exclamations, commands, and statements in the examples that follow. In addition, as you would expect in conversational language, you will find a variety in the length of sentences. Copy the examples in your **reading/writing log.** Then find at least five additional examples in which Serling emphasizes meaning by using a variety of sentence types.

> NARRATOR. At the sound of the roar and the flash of the light, it will be precisely six-forty-three P.M. on Maple Street.
>
> STEVE. Wait a minute . . . *wait a minute!* Let's not be a mob!
>
> LES. What's it all about, Steve?

Writing Dialogue

Imagine that you are asking permission to attend a school picnic or basketball game. Write a two-person dialogue in which you begin by quietly asking permission of your parent or guardian, who objects. Give reasons why you should be allowed to go. For example, you might agree to be home early. If you are keeping a **reading/writing log,** refer to the examples of sentence types you copied. Try to use various sentence types when you write your own dialogue. See Lesson 8, "Writing Dialogue," in the Writer's Handbook.

Writing a Report

Imagine that you are Figure One, an alien from outer space. You must inform your superiors in writing of your latest mission. Write a one-paragraph report of what happened on Maple Street. Before you begin, review the play and list the most important events that happen after the electricity goes off. Then use these important events to summarize the neighbors' behavior for your report. See Lesson 5, "Writing to Summarize," in the Writer's Handbook.

BIOGRAPHY

Rod Serling
1924–1975

A native of Syracuse, New York, Rod Serling began his career writing radio plays. In the early 1950s he brought his talent for thoughtful drama to television. A winner of six Emmy awards from the National Academy of Television Arts and Sciences, Serling was once asked whether there was a common theme in his writing. He replied, "I think you'll find that I have an awareness of human conflict—people fighting other people on many levels other than physical. . . . Of the various themes, I've tried to attack prejudice more than any other social evil. I think prejudice is a waste, and its normal end is violence."

Review MOOD in the Handbook of Literary Terms, page 647.

Let Me Hear You Whisper

Paul Zindel

The plans for killing the dolphin had already been made. What could Helen possibly do to save him?

CHARACTERS

HELEN *A little old cleaning lady who lives alone in a one-room apartment and spends most of her spare time feeding stray cats and dogs. She has just been hired to scrub floors in a laboratory that performs rather strange experiments with dolphins.*

MISS MORAY *A briskly efficient custodial supervisor who has to break Helen in to her new duties at the laboratory. She has a face that is so uptight she looks like she either throws stones at pigeons or teaches Latin.*

DR. CROCUS *The dedicated man of science who devises and presides over the weird experiments.*

MR. FRIDGE *Assistant to Dr. Crocus. He is so loyal and uncreative that if Dr. Crocus told him to stick his head in the mouth of a shark, he'd do it.*

DAN *A talky janitor, also under Miss Moray's control, who at every chance ducks out of the Manhattan laboratory for a beer at the corner bar.*

A DOLPHIN *The subject of an experiment being performed by Dr. Crocus.*

SETTING: *The action takes place in the hallway, laboratory and specimen room of a biology experimentation association located in Manhattan near the Hudson River.*

TIME: *The action begins with the night shift on a Monday and ends the following Friday.*

ACT ONE

SCENE ONE

DR. CROCUS *and* MR. FRIDGE *are leaving the laboratory where they have completed their latest experimental tinkering with a dolphin, and they head down a corridor to the elevator. The elevator door opens and* MISS MORAY *emerges with* HELEN.

MISS MORAY. Dr. Crocus. Mr. Fridge. I'm so glad we've run into you. I want you to meet Helen.

HELEN. Hello.

(DR. CROCUS *and* MR. FRIDGE *nod and get on elevator.*)

MISS MORAY. Helen is the newest member of our Custodial Engineering Team.

(MISS MORAY *and* HELEN *start down the hall.*)

MISS MORAY. Dr. Crocus is the guiding heart here at the American Biological Association Development for the Advancement of Brain Analysis. For short, we call it "Abadaba."

HELEN. I guess you have to.

(*They stop at a metal locker at the end of the hall.*)

MISS MORAY. This will be your locker and your key. Your equipment is in this closet.

HELEN. I have to bring in my own hangers, I suppose.

MISS MORAY. Didn't you find Personnel pleasant?

HELEN. They asked a lot of crazy questions.

MISS MORAY. Oh, I'm sorry. (*Pause*) For instance.

HELEN. They wanted to know what went on in my head when I'm watching television in my living room and the audience laughs. They asked if I ever thought the audience was laughing at *me.*

MISS MORAY (*laughing*). My, oh, my! (*Pause*) What did you tell them?

HELEN. I don't have a TV.

MISS MORAY. I'm sorry.

HELEN. I'm not.

MISS MORAY. Yes. Now, it's really quite simple. That's our special soap solution. One tablespoon to a gallon of hot water, if I may suggest.

(HELEN *is busy running water into a pail which fits into a metal stand on wheels.*)

MISS MORAY. I'll start you in the laboratory. We like it done first. The specimen room next, and finally the hallway. By that time we'll be well toward morning, and if there are a few minutes left, you can polish the brass strip. (*She points to brass strip which runs around the corridor, halfway between ceiling and floor.*) Ready? Fine.

(*They start down the hall,* MISS MORAY *thumbing through papers on a clipboard.*)

MISS MORAY. You were with one concern for fourteen years, weren't you? Fourteen years with Metal Climax Building. That's next to the Radio City Music Hall,[1] isn't it, dear?

HELEN. Uh-huh.

MISS MORAY. They sent a marvelous letter of recommendation. My! Fourteen years on the seventeenth floor. You must be very proud. Why did you leave?

HELEN. They put in a rug.

(MISS MORAY *leads* HELEN *into the laboratory, where* DAN *is picking up.*)

MISS MORAY. Dan, Helen will be taking Marguerita's place. Dan is the night porter for the fifth through ninth floors.

DAN. Hiya!

HELEN. Hello. (*She looks around.*)

MISS MORAY. There's a crock on nine you missed, and the technicians on that floor have complained about the odor.

(HELEN *notices what appears to be a large tank of water with a curtain concealing its contents.*)

HELEN. What's that?

MISS MORAY. What? Oh, that's a dolphin, dear. But don't worry about anything except the floor. Dr. Crocus prefers us not to touch either the equipment or the animals.

HELEN. Do you keep him cramped up in that all the time?

MISS MORAY. We have a natatorium for it to exercise in, at Dr. Crocus's discretion.

HELEN. He really looks cramped.

(MISS MORAY *closes a curtain which hides the tank.*)

MISS MORAY. Well, you must be anxious to begin. I'll make myself available at the reception desk in the hall for a few nights in case any questions arise. Coffee break at two and six A.M. Lunch at four A.M. All clear?

HELEN. I don't need a coffee break.

MISS MORAY. Helen, we all need Perk-You-Ups. All of us.

HELEN. I don't want one.

MISS MORAY. They're compulsory. (*Pause*) Oh, Helen, I know you're going to fit right in with our little family. You're such a *nice* person. (*She exits.*)

(HELEN *immediately gets to work, moving her equipment into place and getting down on her hands and knees to scrub the floor.* DAN *exits.* HELEN *gets in a few more rubs, glances at the silhouette of the dolphin's tank behind the curtain, and then continues. After a pause, a record begins to play.*)

RECORD. "Let me call you sweetheart,
I'm in love with you.
Let me hear you whisper
That you love me, too."

---

1. *Radio City Music Hall*, movie theater in New York City, famous for lavish stage shows.

Photo by Russ Kinne

(HELEN's *curiosity makes her open the curtain and look at the dolphin. He looks right back at her. She returns to her work, singing "Let Me Call You Sweetheart" to herself, missing a word here and there; but her eyes return to the dolphin. She becomes uncomfortable under his stare and tries to ease her discomfort by playing peek-a-boo with him. There is no response and she resumes scrubbing and humming. The dolphin then lets out a bubble or two and moves in the tank to bring his blowhole to the surface.*)

DOLPHIN. Youuuuuuuuuuu.

(HELEN *hears the sound, assumes she is mistaken, and goes on with her work.*)

DOLPHIN. Youuuuuuuuuuu.

(HELEN *has heard the sound more clearly this time. She is puzzled, contemplates a moment, and then decides to get up off the floor. She closes the curtain on the dolphin's tank and leaves the laboratory. She walks the length of the hall to* MISS MORAY, *who is sitting at a reception desk near the elevator.*)

MISS MORAY. What is it, Helen?

HELEN. The fish is making some kinda funny noise.

MISS MORAY. Mammal, Helen. It's a mammal.

HELEN. The mammal's making some kinda funny noise.

MISS MORAY. Mammals are supposed to make funny noises.

HELEN. Yes, Miss Moray.

(HELEN *goes back to the lab. She continues scrubbing.*)

DOLPHIN. Youuuuuuuuuuu.

(*She apprehensively approaches the curtain and opens it. Just then* DAN *barges in. He goes to get his reaching pole, and* HELEN *hurriedly returns to scrubbing the floor.*)

DAN. Bulb out on seven.

HELEN. What do they have that thing for?

DAN. What thing?

HELEN. That.

DAN. Yeah, he's something, ain't he? (*Pause*) They're tryin' to get it to talk.

HELEN. Talk?

DAN. Uh-huh, but he don't say nothing. They had one last year that used to laugh. It'd go "heh heh heh heh heh heh heh." Then they got another one that used to say, "Yeah, it's four o'clock." Everybody took pictures of that one. All the magazines and newspapers.

HELEN. It just kept saying "Yeah, it's four o'clock"?

DAN. Until it died of pneumonia. They talk outta their blowholes, when they can talk, that is. Did you see the blowhole?

HELEN. No.

DAN. Come on and take a look.

HELEN. I don't want to look at any blowhole.

DAN. Miss Moray's at the desk. She won't see anything.

(HELEN *and* DAN *go to the tank. Their backs are to the lab door and they don't see* MISS MORAY *open the door and watch them.*)

DAN. This one don't say anything at all. They been playing that record every seven minutes for months, and it can't even learn a single word. Don't even say "Polly want a cracker."

MISS MORAY. Helen?

(HELEN *and* DAN *turn around.*)

MISS MORAY. Helen, would you mind stepping outside a moment?

HELEN. Yes, Miss Moray.

DAN. I was just showing her something.

MISS MORAY. Hadn't we better get on with our duties?

DAN. All right, Miss Moray.

(MISS MORAY *guides* HELEN *out into the hall, and puts her arm around her as though taking her into her confidence.*)

MISS MORAY. Helen, I called you out here because . . . well, frankly, I need your help.

HELEN. He was just showing me . . .

MISS MORAY. Dan is an idle-chatter breeder. How many times we've told him, "Dan, this is a scientific atmosphere you're employed in and we would appreciate a minimum of subjective communication." So— if you can help, Helen—and I'm sure you can, enormously—we'd be so grateful.

HELEN. Yes, Miss Moray.

(MISS MORAY *leads* HELEN *back to the lab.*)

MISS MORAY. Now, we'll just move directly into the specimen room. The working conditions will be ideal for you in here.

(HELEN *looks ready to gag as she looks around the specimen room. It is packed with specimen jars of all sizes. Various animals and parts of animals are visible in their formaldehyde baths.*[2])

MISS MORAY. Now, you will be responsible not only for the floor area but the jars as well. A feather duster—here—is marvelous.

(MISS MORAY *smiles and exits. The sound of music and voice from beyond the walls floats over.*)

RECORD. "Let me call you sweetheart . . . "

(HELEN *gasps as her eyes fall upon one partic-ular jar in which is floating a preserved human brain. The lights go down, ending Act One, Scene One.*)

SCENE TWO

It is the next evening. HELEN *pushes her equipment into the lab. She opens the curtain so she can watch the dolphin as she works. She and the dolphin stare at each other.*

HELEN. Youuuuuuuuuuu. (*She pauses, watches for a response.*) Youuuuuuuuuuu. (*Still no response. She turns her attention to her scrubbing for a moment.*) Polly want a cracker? Polly want a cracker? (*She wrings out a rag and resumes work.*) Yeah, it's four o'clock. Yeah, it's four o'clock. Polly want a cracker at four o'clock?

(*She laughs at her own joke, then goes to the dolphin's tank and notices how sad he looks. She reaches her hand in and just touches the top of his head. He squirms and likes it.*)

HELEN. Heh heh heh heh heh heh heh heh heh.

(MISS MORAY *gets off the elevator and hears the peculiar sounds coming from the laboratory. She puts her ear against the door.*)

HELEN. Heh heh heh heh heh . . .

MISS MORAY (*entering*). Look how nicely the floor's coming along! You must have a special rinsing technique.

HELEN. Just a little vinegar in the rinse water.

MISS MORAY. You brought the vinegar yourself. Just so the floors . . . they are spar-

---

2. *formaldehyde* (fôr mal′də hīd) *baths,* solutions containing the colorless, poisonous gas formaldehyde, used as a preservative.

kling, Helen. Sparkling! *(She pauses— looks at the dolphin, then at* HELEN.*)* It's marvelous, Helen, how well you've adjusted.

HELEN. Thank you, Miss Moray.

MISS MORAY. Helen, the animals here are used for experimentation, and. . . . Well, take Marguerita. She had fallen in love with the mice. All three hundred of them. She seemed shocked when she found out Dr. Crocus was . . . using . . . them at the rate of twenty or so a day in connection with electrode implanting.[3] She noticed them missing after a while and when I told her they'd been decapitated, she seemed terribly upset.

HELEN. What do you want with the fish— mammal?

MISS MORAY. Well, dolphins may have an intelligence equal to our own. And if we can teach them our language—or learn theirs— we'll be able to communicate.

HELEN. I can't understand you.

MISS MORAY *(louder).* Communicate! Wouldn't it be wonderful?

HELEN. Oh, yeah. . . . They chopped the heads off three hundred mice? That's horrible.

MISS MORAY. You're so sensitive, Helen. Every laboratory in the country is doing this type of work. It's quite accepted.

HELEN. Every laboratory cutting off mouse heads!

MISS MORAY. Virtually . . . .

HELEN. How many laboratories are there?

MISS MORAY. I don't know. I suppose at least five thousand.

HELEN. Five thousand times three hundred . . . that's a lot of mouse heads. Can't you just have one lab chop off a couple and then spread the word?

MISS MORAY. Now, Helen—this is exactly what I mean. You will do best not to become fond of the subject animals. When you're here a little longer you'll learn . . . well . . . there are some things you just have to accept on faith.

*(*MISS MORAY *exits, leaving the lab door open for* HELEN *to move her equipment out.)*

DOLPHIN. Whisper. . . . *(*HELEN *pauses a moment.)* Whisper to me. *(She exits as the lights go down, ending the scene.)*

SCENE THREE

It is the next evening. HELEN *goes from her locker to the laboratory.*

DOLPHIN. Hear . . . .

HELEN. What?

DOLPHIN. Hear me . . . .

*(*DAN *barges in with his hamper, almost frightening* HELEN *to death. He goes to dolphin's tank.)*

DAN. Hiya, fella! How are ya? That reminds me. Gotta get some formaldehyde jars set up by Friday. If you want anything just whistle.

(He exits. HELEN *goes to the tank and reaches her hand out to pet the dolphin.)*

HELEN. Hear. *(Pause)* Hear.

DOLPHIN. Hear.

HELEN. Hear me.

DOLPHIN. Hear me.

HELEN. That's a good boy.

DOLPHIN. Hear me . . . .

---

3. *electrode implanting,* the insertion into the mice's heads of devices to measure the electrical activity of their brains.

HELEN. Oh, what a pretty fellow. Such a pretty fellow.

(MISS MORAY *enters.*)

MISS MORAY. What are you doing, Helen?

HELEN. I . . . uh . . . .

MISS MORAY. Never mind. Go on with your work.

(MISS MORAY *surveys everything, then sits on a stool.* DAN *rushes in with large jars on a wheeled table.*)

DAN. Scuse me, but I figure I'll get the formaldehyde set up tonight.

MISS MORAY. Very good, Dan.

HELEN (*noticing the dolphin is stirring*). What's the formaldehyde for?

MISS MORAY. The experiment series on . . . the dolphin will . . . terminate on Friday. That's why it has concerned me that you've apparently grown . . . fond . . . of the mammal.

HELEN. They're gonna kill it?

DAN. Gonna sharpen the handsaws now. Won't have any trouble getting through the skull on this one, no, sir. (*He exits.*)

HELEN. What for? Because it didn't say anything? Is that what they're killing it for?

MISS MORAY. Helen, no matter how lovely our intentions, no matter how lonely we are and how much we want people or animals . . . to like us . . . we have no right to endanger the genius about us. Now, we've spoken about this before.

(HELEN *is dumfounded as* MISS MORAY *exits.* HELEN *gathers her equipment and looks at the dolphin, which is staring desperately at her.*)

DOLPHIN. Help. (*Pause*) Please help me.

(HELEN *is so moved by the cries of the dolphin she looks ready to burst into tears as the lights go down, ending Act One.*)

ACT TWO

The hall. It is the night that the dolphin is to be dissected. Elevator doors open and HELEN *gets off, nods, and starts down the hall.* MISS MORAY *comes to* HELEN *at closet.*

MISS MORAY. I hope you're well this evening.

HELEN. When they gonna kill it?

MISS MORAY. Don't say kill, Helen. You make it sound like murder. Besides, you won't have to go into the laboratory at all this evening.

HELEN. How do they kill it?

MISS MORAY. Nicotine mustard,[4] Helen. It's very humane. They inject it.

HELEN. Maybe he's a mute.

MISS MORAY. Do you have all your paraphernalia?

HELEN. Some human beings are mute, you know. Just because they can't talk we don't kill them.

MISS MORAY. It looks like you're ready to open a new box of steel wool.

HELEN. Maybe he can type with his nose. Did they try that?

MISS MORAY. Now, now, Helen——

HELEN. Miss Moray, I don't mind doing the lab.

MISS MORAY. Absolutely not! I'm placing it off limits for your own good. You're too emotionally involved.

HELEN. I can do the lab, honest. I'm not emotionally involved.

MISS, MORAY (*motioning her to the specimen-room door*). Trust me, Helen. Trust me.

HELEN (*reluctantly disappearing through the door*). Yes, Miss Moray.

---

4. *Nicotine* (nik′ə tēn′) *mustard,* a colorless poison derived from tobacco.

(MISS MORAY *stations herself at the desk near the elevator and begins reading her charts.* HELEN *slips out of the specimen room and into the laboratory without being seen. The lights in the lab are out and moonlight from the window casts eerie shadows.*)

DOLPHIN. Help.

(HELEN *opens the curtain. The dolphin and she look at each other.*)

DOLPHIN. Help me.

HELEN. You don't need me. Just say something to them. Anything. They just need to hear you say something. . . . You want me to tell 'em? I'll tell them. I'll just say I heard you say "Help." (*Pauses, then speaks with feigned cheerfulness*) I'll go tell them.

DOLPHIN. Noooooooooooooooo.

(HELEN *stops. Moves back toward tank.*)

HELEN. They're gonna kill you!

DOLPHIN. Plaaaaan.

HELEN. What?

DOLPHIN. Plaaaaaaaan.

HELEN. Plan? What plan?

(DAN *charges through the door and snaps on the light.*)

DAN. Uh-oh. Miss Moray said she don't want you in here.

(HELEN *goes to* DR. CROCUS'*s desk and begins to look at various books on it.*)

HELEN. Do you know anything about a plan?

DAN. She's gonna be mad. What plan?

HELEN. Something to do with . . . . (*She indicates the dolphin.*)

DAN. Hiya, fella!

HELEN. About the dolphin . . . .

DAN. They got an experiment book they write in.

HELEN. Where?

DAN. I don't know.

HELEN. Find it and bring it to me in the animals' morgue. Please.

DAN. I'll try. I'll try, but I got other things to do, you know.

(HELEN *slips out the door and makes it safely back into the specimen room.* DAN *rummages through the desk and finally finds the folder. He is able to sneak into the specimen room.*)

DAN. Here.

(HELEN *grabs the folder and starts going through it.* DAN *turns and is about to go back out into the hall when he sees that* MISS MORAY *has stopped reading.* HELEN *skims through more of the folder. It is a bulky affair. She stops at a page discussing uses of dolphins.* MISS MORAY *gets up from the desk and heads for the specimen-room door.*)

DAN. She's coming.

HELEN. Maybe you'd better hide. Get behind the table. Here, take the book.

(DAN *ducks down behind one of the specimen tables, and* HELEN *starts scrubbing away.* MISS MORAY *opens the door.*)

MISS MORAY. Perk-You-Up time, Helen. Tell Dan, please. He's in the laboratory.

(HELEN *moves to the lab door, opens it, and calls into the empty room.*)

HELEN. Perk-You-Up time.

MISS MORAY. Tell him we have ladyfingers.

HELEN. We have ladyfingers.

MISS MORAY. Such a strange thing to call a confectionery, isn't it? It's almost macabre.

HELEN. Miss Moray . . . .

MISS MORAY. Yes, Helen?

HELEN. I was wondering why they wanna talk with . . . .

MISS MORAY. Now now now!

HELEN. I mean, supposing dolphins *did* talk?

MISS MORAY. Well, like fishing, Helen. If we could communicate with dolphins, they might be willing to herd fish for us. The fishing industry would be revolutionized.

HELEN. Is that all?

MISS MORAY. All? Heavens, no. They'd be a blessing to the human race. A blessing. They would be worshipped in oceanography. Checking the Gulf Stream . . . taking water temperatures, depth, salinity readings.[5] To say nothing of the contributions they could make in marine biology, navigation, linguistics![6] Oh, Helen, it gives me the chills.

HELEN. It'd be good if they talked?

MISS MORAY. God's own blessing.

(DAN *opens the lab doors and yells over* HELEN's *head to* MISS MORAY.)

DAN. I got everything except the head vise. They can't saw through the skull bone without the head vise.

MISS MORAY. Did you look on five? They had it there last week for . . . what they did to the St. Bernard.

(*From the laboratory, music drifts out. They try to talk over it.*)

DAN. I looked on five.

MISS MORAY. You come with me. It must have been staring you in the face.

(DAN *and* MISS MORAY *get on the elevator.*)

MISS MORAY. We'll be right back, Helen.

(*The doors close and* HELEN *hurries into the laboratory. She stops just inside the door, and it is obvious that she is angry.*)

DOLPHIN. Booooooooook.

HELEN. I looked at your book. I looked at your book all right!

DOLPHIN. Booooooooook.

HELEN. And you want to know what I think?

I don't think much of you, that's what I think.

DOLPHIN. Booooooooook.

HELEN. Oh, shut up. Book book book book book. I'm not interested. You eat yourself silly—but to get a little fish for hungry humans is just too much for you. Well. I'm going to tell 'em you can talk.

(*The dolphin moves in the tank, lets out a few warning bubbles.*)

HELEN. You don't like that, eh? Well, I don't like lazy selfish people, mammals or animals.

(*The dolphin looks increasingly desperate and begins to make loud blatt and beep sounds. He struggles in the tank.*)

HELEN. Cut it out—you're getting water all over the floor.

DOLPHIN. Booooooooook!

(HELEN *looks at the folder on the desk. She picks it up, opens it, closes it, and sets it down again.*)

HELEN. I guess you don't like us. I guess you'd die rather than help us . . . .

DOLPHIN. Hate.

HELEN. I guess you do hate us . . . .

(*She returns to the folder.*)

HELEN (*reading*). Military implications . . . war . . . plant mines in enemy waters . . . deliver atomic warheads . . . war . . . nuclear torpedoes . . . attach bombs to submarines . . . terrorize enemy waters . . .

5. *Gulf Stream . . . salinity readings.* The Gulf Stream is a warm ocean current flowing north along the east coast of the United States. Salinity readings are measurements of salt content of the ocean.

6. *marine biology, navigation, linguistics* (ling gwis'tiks). Marine biology is the scientific study of plant and animal life of the sea. Navigation is the science of finding a ship's or plane's position and course. Linguistics is the science of language.

war . . . . They're already thinking about ways to use you for war. Is that why you can't talk to them? (*Pause*) What did you talk to me for? (*Pause*) You won't talk to them, but you . . . you talk to me because . . . you want something . . . there's something . . . I can do?

DOLPHIN. Hamm . . . .

HELEN. What?

DOLPHIN. Hamm . . . .

HELEN. Ham? I thought you ate fish.

DOLPHIN (*moving with annoyance*). Ham . . . purrrr.

HELEN. Ham . . . purrrr? I don't know what you're talking about.

DOLPHIN (*even more annoyed*). Ham . . . purrrr.

HELEN. Ham . . . purrrr. What's a purrrr? (*Confused and scared, she returns to scrubbing the hall floor just as the doors of the elevator open, revealing* MISS MORAY, DAN, *and* MR. FRIDGE. DAN *pushes a dissection table loaded with shiny instruments toward the lab.*)

MISS MORAY. Is the good doctor in yet?

MR. FRIDGE. He's getting the nicotine mustard on nine. I'll see if he needs assistance.

MISS MORAY. I'll come with you. You'd better leave now, Helen. It's time. (*She smiles and the elevator doors close.*)

DAN (*pushing the dissection table through the lab doors*). I never left a dirty head vise. She's trying to say I left it like that.

HELEN. Would you listen a minute? Ham . . . purrrr. Do you know what a ham . . . purrrr is?

DAN. The only hamper I ever heard of is out in the hall.

(HELEN *darts to the door, opens it, and sees the hamper at the end of the hall.*)

HELEN. The hamper!

DAN. Kazinski left the high-altitude chamber[7] dirty once, and I got blamed for that, too. (*He exits.*)

HELEN (*rushing to the dolphin*). You want me to do something with the hamper. What? To get it? To put . . . you want me to put you in it? But what'll I do with you? Where can I take you?

DOLPHIN. Sea . . . .

HELEN. See? See what?

DOLPHIN. Sea . . . .

HELEN. I don't know what you're talking about. They'll be back in a minute. I don't know what to do!

DOLPHIN. Sea . . . sea . . . .

HELEN. See? . . . The sea! That's what you're talking about! The river . . . to the sea! (*She darts into the hall and heads for the hamper. Quickly she pushes it into the lab, and just as she gets through the doors unseen,* MISS MORAY *gets off the elevator.*)

MISS MORAY. Helen?

(*She starts down the hall. Enters the lab. The curtain is closed in front of the tank.*)

MISS MORAY. Helen? Are you here? Helen? (*She sees nothing and is about to leave when she hears a movement behind the curtain. She looks down and sees* HELEN's *shoes.* MISS MORAY *moves to the curtain and pulls it open. There is* HELEN *with her arms around the front part of the dolphin, lifting it a good part of the way out of the water.*)

MISS MORAY. Helen, what do you think you're hugging?

(HELEN *drops the dolphin back into the tank.*)

---

7. **high-altitude chamber,** a closed container in which air pressure can be varied.

MR. FRIDGE (*entering*). Is anything wrong, Miss Moray?

MISS MORAY. No . . . nothing wrong. Nothing at all. Just a little spilled water.

(HELEN *and* MISS MORAY *grab sponges from the lab sink and begin to wipe up the water around the tank.* DR. CROCUS *enters and begins to fill a hypodermic syringe while* MR. FRIDGE *expertly gets all equipment into place.* DAN *enters.*)

MR. FRIDGE. Would you like to get an encephalogram[8] during the death process, Dr. Crocus?

DR. CROCUS. Why not?

(MR. FRIDGE *begins to implant electrodes in the dolphin's head. The dolphin commences making high-pitched distress signals.*)

MISS MORAY. Come, Helen. I'll see you to the elevator.

(MISS MORAY *leads her out to the hall.* HELEN *gets on her coat and kerchief.*)

MISS MORAY. Frankly, Helen, I'm deeply disappointed. I'd hoped that by being lenient with you—and heaven knows I have been—you'd develop a heightened loyalty to our team.

HELEN (*bursting into tears and going to the elevator*). Leave me alone.

MISS MORAY (*softening as she catches up to her*). You really are a nice person, Helen. A very nice person. But to be simple and nice in a world where great minds are giant-stepping the micro- and macrocosms,[9] well—one would expect you'd have the humility to yield in unquestioning awe. I truly am very fond of you, Helen, but you're fired. Call Personnel after nine A.M. (*As* MISS MORAY *disappears into the laboratory, the record starts to play.*)

RECORD. "Let me call you sweetheart,
　　　I'm in love with you.
　　　Let me hear you whisper. . . . ”

(*The record is roughly interrupted. Instead of getting on the elevator,* HELEN *whirls around and barges into the lab.*)

HELEN. Who do you think you are? (*Pause*) Who do you think you *are?* (*Pause*) I think you're a pack of killers, that's what I think.

MISS MORAY. Doctor. I assure you this is the first psychotic outbreak she's made. She did the entire brass strip . . . .

HELEN. I'm very tired of being a nice person, Miss Moray. I'm going to report you to the ASPCA,[10] or somebody, because . . . I've decided I don't like you cutting the heads off mice and sawing through skulls of St. Bernards . . . and if being a nice person is just not saying anything and letting you pack of butchers run around doing whatever you want, then I don't want to be nice anymore. (*Pause*) You gotta be very stupid people to need an animal to talk before you know just from looking at it that it's saying something . . . that it knows what pain feels like. I'd like to see you all with a few electrodes in your heads. Being nice isn't any good. (*Looking at dolphin*) They just kill you off if you do that. And that's being a coward. You gotta talk back. You gotta speak up against what's wrong and bad, or you can't ever stop it. At least you've gotta try. (*She bursts into tears.*)

---

8. *encephalogram* (en sef′ə lə gram′), a chart measuring the electrical activity of the brain.

9. *great minds . . . macrocosms.* Scientists are making great advances in understanding our world as well as the universe beyond.

10. *ASPCA,* American Society for the Prevention of Cruelty to Animals.

MISS MORAY. Nothing like this has ever happened with a member of the Custodial Engineering . . . . Helen, dear . . . .

HELEN. Get your hands off me. *(Yelling at the dolphin)* You're a coward, that's what you are. I'm going.

DOLPHIN. Loooooooooveeeeeeeee.

(Everyone turns to stare at the dolphin.)

DOLPHIN. Love.

DR. CROCUS. Get the recorder going.

(HELEN pats the dolphin, exits. The laboratory becomes a bustle of activity.)

DOLPHIN. Love . . . .

DR. CROCUS. Is the tape going?

MR. FRIDGE. Yes, Doctor.

DOLPHIN. Love . . . .

DR. CROCUS. I think that woman's got something to do with this. Get her back in here.

MISS MORAY. Oh, I fired her. She was hugging the mammal . . . and . . . .

DOLPHIN. Love . . . .

DR. CROCUS. Just get her. *(To MR. FRIDGE)* You're sure the machine's recording?

MISS MORAY. Doctor, I'm afraid you don't understand. That woman was hugging the mammal . . . .

DR. CROCUS. Try to get another word out of it. One more word . . . .

MISS MORAY. The last thing in the world I want is for our problem in Custodial Engineering to . . . .

DR. CROCUS *(furious)*. Will you shut up and get that washwoman back in here?

MISS MORAY. Immediately, Doctor.

(She hurries out of the lab. HELEN is at the end of the hall waiting for the elevator.)

MISS MORAY. Helen? Oh, Helen? Don't you want to hear what the dolphin has to say? He's so cute! Dr. Crocus thinks that his talking might have something to do with you. Wouldn't that be exciting? *(Pause)* Please, Helen. The doctor . . . .

HELEN. Don't talk to me, do you mind?

MISS MORAY. It was only in the heat of argument that I . . . of course, you won't be discharged. All right? Please, Helen, you'll embarrass me . . . .

(The elevator doors open and HELEN gets on to face MISS MORAY. She looks at her a moment and then lifts her hand to press the button for the ground floor.)

MISS MORAY. Don't you dare . . . Helen, the team needs you, don't you see? You've done so well—the brass strip, the floors. The floors have never looked so good. Ever. Helen, please. What will I do if you leave?

HELEN. Why don't you get a rug?

(HELEN helps slam the elevator doors in MISS MORAY's face as the lights go down, ending the play.)

THINK AND DISCUSS

Understanding

1. What are Helen's responsibilities on her new job?
2. Where did she work before, and why did she leave?
3. How does Helen react upon learning that the dolphin is going to be killed?

Analyzing

4. What do you learn about Helen's **character** from her conversations with Miss Moray?
5. What do you learn about Miss Moray's **character** from these conversations?
6. Explain the conflict between Helen and Miss Moray.
7. Explain the conflict between Helen and the dolphin. Consider how this conflict changes from the beginning to the end of the play.
8. Point out examples of humor in the play. Do you think the humor is intended only to entertain, or does it serve another purpose as well? Explain.
9. Which of the following statements best expresses the **theme** of the play? (**a**) Thoughtful people take a stand against something they think is wrong. (**b**) Fired from her job for trying to aid a dolphin, a cleaning lady refuses her employer's offer to return to work. (**c**) Don't get too involved in your work if you want to stay out of trouble.

Extending

10. After being fired for her actions, Helen accuses the scientists of being a "pack of butchers." Do you agree? Why or why not?
11. What do you think will happen to the dolphin?

REVIEWING: Mood

See Handbook of Literary Terms, p. 647.

Mood is the atmosphere or feeling within a work of art.

1. Which of the following words best describes the mood of the play: (**a**) playful; (**b**) businesslike; (**c**) sinister; (**d**) cheerful? Explain.
2. How would the mood differ at the play's end if the dolphin had been put to death?

THINKING SKILLS

Synthesizing

To synthesize is to put together parts and elements so as to form a whole, a new pattern or structure not evident before. The American scientist Jonas Salk, for example, put together the information he collected about infection and viruses in order to develop a vaccine that would protect against polio.

Suppose you want to learn to communicate with a dolphin. Brainstorm with a group of classmates to devise a better experiment than the one used by Dr. Crocus. Consider the information about dolphins given in the play.

COMPOSITION

Writing as a Character

Pretend that you are the dolphin in the play. You have been put in a pool with several other dolphins in the hope that you will encourage them to talk to the scientists. In two to three paragraphs tell the other dolphins about your experience in the laboratory and advise them what to do if they are taken there. See Lesson 11, "Writing as a Story Character," in the Writer's Handbook.

Supporting an Opinion

Suppose a scientist is conducting laboratory tests on monkeys to determine if a certain new drug is successful in treating heart disease. Assume the role of a representative of an animal-welfare organization and write a letter of protest to the scientist. If you prefer, assume the role of the scientist and write a reply to such a letter, explaining why it is necessary to continue the tests. Whichever role you choose, be sure to give reasons to support your position.

ENRICHMENT
Interpreting a Play Orally

Work with a group of classmates on an oral interpretation of a scene from one of the three plays you have read. First choose the play and a scene. Assign roles and practice reading together, paying attention to the stage directions, which indicate how to say lines and what gestures to make. Note also the punctuation. It shows you when to pause, to exclaim, or to ask a question. Consider the situation and speak in a tone of voice that is appropriate for how your character probably feels. You may want to read your scene aloud for others in the class.

BIOGRAPHY

Paul Zindel
1936–

Paul Zindel is the author of such popular novels as *The Pigman* (1968), *My Darling, My Hamburger* (1969), *I Never Loved Your Mind* (1970), *Pardon Me, You're Stepping on My Eyeball* (1976), *Confessions of a Teenage Baboon* (1977), *The Undertaker's Gone Bananas* (1978), *The Girl Who Wanted a Boy* (1981), and, with Bonnie Zindel, *A Star for the Latecomer* (1985).

About these novels, Zindel has said, "I'm trying to tell all kids that they don't have to consider themselves misfits, that they deserve hopes and dreams and the technique and patience to make those dreams reality."

A multitalented author, Zindel also writes for television, screen, and stage. In 1971 his play *The Effect of Gamma Rays on Man-in-the-Moon Marigolds* won the Pulitzer Prize for drama, the New York Drama Critics Circle Award, and the Drama Desk Award.

UNIT 2 PLAYS

■ CONCEPT REVIEW

The prologue and part of the first act of a three-act television play that follow are designed to review the important ideas and literary elements that you have been studying. The notes in the right-hand margin highlight some of these concepts. Page numbers in the notes refer to an application of a literary skill. A more complete discussion of these terms is in the Handbook of Literary Terms.

from Teacher, Teacher

Ellison Carroll

CAST OF CHARACTERS

HAMILTON CADE

F. NILES PUTNAM

FREDDIE PUTNAM

PROLOGUE

Fade in on gate—day. We are looking through an iron gate from the inside of a driveway of a two-plus acre estate in suburbia. A convertible is just pulling up. It is a somewhat seedy car. Similarly seedy, with the air and the garb of a faded Ivy Leaguer, is the man behind the wheel: HAMILTON

■ Note how the stage directions help establish the setting.

■ **Ivy League:** a group of eight universities in the eastern United States having a reputation for high standards.

CADE. *He blows the horn. Nothing happens. He blows again. Nothing. He climbs out of the car.*

    CADE *checks the gate; it is locked. Shaking it has no effect. He is puzzled. He goes to the gatepost on which is a metal grille, the outlet of an intercom. Above the grille is a plaque:* F. NILES PUTNAM, A.S.A. *Below the nameplate there is a push button with the legend,* TALK. CADE, *with the air of "How dare they do this to me," shrugs, pushes the button. From the grille, a voice:*

■ **A.S.A.**: American Standards Association.

PUTNAM'S VOICE. Putnam here . . .

CADE *(talking into the intercom)*. Hamilton Cade . . .

PUTNAM'S VOICE. Come on up to the house.

    (A buzzer sounds; CADE *pushes the gate: it opens. Then as* CADE *returns to his car:)*

PUTNAM'S VOICE. Close the gate after you.

CADE. Of course . . .

    *(*CADE *drives through, stops, pushes the gate, which swings but does not quite "catch.")*

PUTNAM'S VOICE. All the way, please.

    (Irritated, CADE *climbs out of the car, closes the gate properly, returns to the car, drives off.*

    As CADE'*s car proceeds along the driveway we see a modern but quite modest house. We catch a glimpse of a trampoline. On the trampoline is* FREDDIE, *thirteen, small for his age. He is jumping up and down. No tricks—just going up and down.* CADE *watches the boy as his car passes the area, but* FREDDIE *does not acknowledge his presence.*

    The camera goes in on FREDDIE, *who continues to go up and down. He goes into slow motion . . . a plane is heard overhead.* FREDDIE *jumps off, looks around and up for the plane. As he looks up we notice that the buttons of his shirt are done wrong; that is, he has one buttonhole too many and one button too few. He looks up with a vacant expression. But as the plane sound fades away, he lifts his arms to the sky, his fingers outstretched and grasping hopefully the empty air. But his expression is changeless.)*

■ Notice that Freddie's low intelligence is being implied rather than stated.

ACT ONE

Fade in on PUTNAM'*s study, a combination living room and architect's studio: drawing board, desk, lamp, blueprints, a cork wall on which are architectural projections. As* CADE *comes in,* PUTNAM *is on the phone. His voice is heard off-camera as* CADE *looks around the room.*

PUTNAM'S VOICE. Listen, do you have to call me from London to tell me about this? . . . Well, I knew—I knew all that last week. . . . How can you change it when you haven't even called me to talk about it? . . . Look, the specifications call for pre-stressed concrete—impossible. It's absolutely basic to the total conception. It's not a group of individual structures—it's a completely interrelated complex! . . . Unquestionably. Test borings before the hard weather sets in. Look, we've gone over the logistics a dozen times—now do they want design—or do they want glass boxes? . . . Fine. Fine. Next week— . . . Again? It's the third time you've changed the schedule on me! . . . No, no, I can make it. It's just that—all right. I'll confirm by cable. And I'll expect to hear from you in London. . . . No, no, I'll pick them up at the airport. Goodbye. *(He hangs up. He is tense, edgy. He turns to* CADE.) Well, they've changed the schedule on me again. Now I have to fly the day after tomorrow.

CADE. How long will you be gone?

PUTNAM. A minimum of three weeks . . . more likely a month. I have a commission in the North of England . . . it's an entire community—from the ground up. Designed around a college.

■ The playwright gives a reason for Putnam to be away for a time.

CADE *(indicating a drawing).* Yes, I see you did the science building at Hollenbeck.

PUTNAM *(glancing at* CADE'S *letters in a folder).* I don't really need these . . . what with your letter . . . and some asking around. These recommendations aren't very recent. . . .

CADE. They—ah—do go back a bit, yes. You see, I—I taught Hillsgrove Academy five years . . . then Colebrook. . . .

PUTNAM *(cutting* CADE *off).* Hillsgrove five years, Colebrook three years, Westford Academy six months . . . the schools get less impressive and your stay gets shorter. You're like an actor carrying around old reviews. What happened?

■ Putnam's comments show Cade's background.

CADE. I'm an excellent teacher, Mr. Putnam.

PUTNAM. Ivy Leaguer, Phi Bete, started at the top—worked your way down. Westford Academy six months. Why did they fire you, Mr. Cade?

■ **Phi Bete:** Phi Beta Kappa, an honorary society for those who have ranked high in scholarship.

CADE. I resigned.

PUTNAM. You were *allowed* to resign. Why?

CADE. I had a nervous breakdown.

PUTNAM. You were teaching less and drinking more.

CADE. That's all over now.

PUTNAM. I know, or you wouldn't be here. What I'm really interested in, Mr. Cade, is why you started to reverse your career.

CADE. Oh—I don't know. I—ah—I was depressed by kids from rich homes.

PUTNAM. You were giving them A's and B's to keep your job and they were wiping out on the college boards.

CADE. You've done a very thorough investigation.

PUTNAM. I've designed buildings for two of these schools. I know a few of the Directors.

CADE (*putting the letters back into his case*). Well, yes, you have me at a disadvantage.

PUTNAM. Why did you answer my ad?

CADE. It seemed like an ideal situation for a man with my—history. I need a one-to-one relationship. Away from the pressure of large classes. Prep school boys can be quite cruel, you know.

PUTNAM. I know. I used to be one.

CADE. Yes. I could tell by your approach. (PUTNAM *laughs rather cruelly.*) To answer your question as to why I applied, your ad did say "an exceptional child" . . . and I need the job, Mr. Putnam. But I am also an exceptionally good teacher. I would have liked the challenge of an exceptional child—it would have allowed me to regain a little confidence.

(PUTNAM *motions* CADE *to wait while he pushes a button on the console on his desk. A bell rings outside the house.*)

(*Cut to the trampoline. We see* FREDDIE *jumping. He is not immediately conscious of the bell. It continues to ring.* FREDDIE *stops jumping and heads for the house.*)

(*Cut back to the study.*)

CADE. Where's he been to school?

PUTNAM. Right here. There hasn't been a school invented that's right for him.

(*By now* FREDDIE *has arrived at the house and entered the study. Seeing* CADE, *he comes to* PUTNAM *and leans against him shyly.*)

■ Cade's comments provide insights into his character.

■ **Prep school:** a private school that prepares students for college.

■ **Mood** (page 144): Putnam's behavior contributes to the mood.

■ Putnam's comments help establish Freddie's character.

Martin Gale, *Outsider*, Private Collection

PUTNAM. This is Mr. Cade, Freddie. Shake hands with Mr. Cade, Freddie.

(FREDDIE *goes to* CADE, *puts out his hand.* FREDDIE *does not shake—it is* CADE *doing all the shaking.* CADE *all but knows.* FREDDIE *pulls his hand from* CADE'S *and turns to fiddle with a lamp, making it bend up and down on its elbow joint.* PUTNAM *watches* CADE, *who watches* FREDDIE.)

■ Cade now almost knows for certain why Freddie is an "exceptional" thirteen-year-old.

PUTNAM. All right, Freddie. (FREDDIE *continues playing with the lamp.*) All *right*, Freddie! (*Physically he removes* FREDDIE'S *hand from the lamp and gives him a turn so he is facing him.*) Hey, go wash your hands and face. Use soap.

(FREDDIE *dutifully goes off, but stops in the entranceway.*)

FREDDIE. I saw the airplane. Up up up. Down down down. And it went away. (*He exits.*)

CADE. Your ad said "exceptional child."

PUTNAM. The word "retarded" does not attract many applicants.

CADE. How old is he?

PUTNAM. Freddie's thirteen. As for IQ, he functions somewhere on the seven-year level. But no trouble. No trouble at all. . . . Eats anything you put in front of him. Toilet trained. Dresses himself. Answers the bell. Does what you tell him to do—if he can do it. As for learning—he's a challenge. A real challenge to any teacher——

CADE. Well, how many teachers answered your ad?

PUTNAM. You're the ninth.

CADE. And they all turned you down?

PUTNAM. I turned them down. My son is very precious to me, Mr. Cade.

■ Putnam's remarks reveal his own character.

CADE. I need a job, Mr. Putnam, but I'm not qualified. I've never been trained to work with retarded children.

PUTNAM. Okay, I'm sorry to put you through all this.

CADE. You've only put me through five minutes.

(FREDDIE *enters. He shows his hands to* PUTNAM.)

PUTNAM. Hey, good boy.

(FREDDIE *shows his hands to* CADE.)

CADE. Hmmm. Good and clean.

(CADE *turns to* PUTNAM, *who is now back behind his desk.* FREDDIE *hovers around* CADE. *He examines and fingers the patches on* CADE'S *jacket-sleeve.*)

FREDDIE. What's that?

CADE. That—ah—that's leather . . . . (PUTNAM *watches* CADE *narrowly as* FREDDIE *touches one of two pens in* CADE'S *jacket pocket.* CADE *takes the pen out and hands it to* FREDDIE. FREDDIE *examines it.* CADE *reaches out—it is a push-button ballpoint—and shows* FREDDIE *how it works.*) Here, let me show you—you do it like this. You see, you push it. (FREDDIE *fiddles with the pen and succeeds in making it work. His face lights up.*)

■ Notice how Cade begins to teach Freddie.

FREDDIE. I did it.

(*He sets about pushing the end of the pen, making the point go in and out, in and out.* CADE *shoves a piece of paper toward* FREDDIE.)

CADE. It's for writing. Can you write? (FREDDIE *nods.*) Show me.

(FREDDIE *makes a meaningless scrawl.*)

FREDDIE. See?

PUTNAM. Testing, Professor?

CADE. Teaching.

PUTNAM. He can't write. Or read. And nobody can teach him.

■ Consider that Putnam may be challenging Cade to prove him wrong.

(FREDDIE *scribbles all over the paper. As he does so,* CADE *shakes his head ever so slightly no, and begins to put his papers into his briefcase.*)

PUTNAM (*after a pause*). Say goodbye to Mr. Cade, Freddie. (FREDDIE *turns and dutifully puts out his hand to shake. But he holds the hand with the pen in it behind his back.*) And give Mr. Cade his pen. (FREDDIE *keeps his hand hidden.*)

CADE. That's all right. You can keep it, Freddie.

PUTNAM. Freddie, say thank you to Mr. Cade.

(*But* FREDDIE, *without the automatic prompting, jumps the gun on* PUTNAM.)

FREDDIE. Thank you.

(CADE *is about to rise when* FREDDIE, *without warning, throws his arm around* CADE's *neck and hugs. Thrown off guard,* CADE *responds almost automatically with a hug; then all pretense and aside gone from his face, he kisses* FREDDIE's *forehead.*)

■ Note Cade's behavior.

PUTNAM. I think you ought to take the job.

CADE. Based on what?

PUTNAM. What I just saw.

CADE. I'm not in the habit of kissing children.

PUTNAM. Have you any? (CADE *shakes his head no.*) Will you take the job? Cade, I'm not kidding anybody. I need you. I've built this world for Freddie and it takes everything I can earn to keep it going. I've had five housekeepers in the last seven years. I've just hired a handyman. Who knows if he will stay. (*Pause*) I don't care if all you teach him is C-A-T!

CADE. I won't settle for that.

PUTNAM. I think you will. What do you say?

CADE (*after a pause*). I say *yes*.

(CADE, *briefcase in hand, moves toward the door of the study.* PUTNAM *is with him, stops him.*)

PUTNAM. You come through for me—and I'll pull every string I can to get you back in Hillsgrove. No Shakespeare, no algebra—just the bottom line. You teach him two plus two or how to write his name and you're back in business.

CADE. I don't believe in bottom lines, Mr. Putnam. I'll take him as far as he can go.

PUTNAM. Take him as far as you like—but no farther than that front gate.

CADE. Why not?

PUTNAM. For one thing, he hasn't set foot outside of it since his mother died. For another, this is all the world that Freddie needs.

CADE. Six acres?

PUTNAM. He makes it here or nowhere. Here, nobody laughs at Freddie—and nobody pities him . . . or me.

■ bottom line: only the basic and necessary subjects.

■ Cade's response gives further insight into his character.

■ Note that Putnam seems to realize he is protecting himself as well as his son.

THINK AND DISCUSS
Understanding
1. Putnam has advertised that his child is exceptional. What kind of a child is Freddie?
2. What restriction does Putnam place on Freddie's physical freedom?
3. What is Cade's response when Putnam says Freddie need learn only to write his name and add two and two?

Analyzing
4. When Cade arrives, what kind of child does he expect Freddie to be?
5. Why hasn't Cade sought another job at a preparatory school?
6. During the interview, Cade says that he is an excellent teacher. Does Cade seem to believe this? Explain.
7. What prompts Putnam suddenly to offer Cade the job?

Extending
8. Based on clues given so far, what do you predict will happen next?

REVIEWING LITERARY TERMS
Mood
1. Which word best describes the mood of the scene between Putnam and Cade: (a) relaxed; (b) tense; (c) angry; (d) gloomy? Explain.
2. Give some examples of Cade's behavior or his remarks after meeting Freddie that show the mood has become more hopeful than at the beginning of Act One.

■ CONTENT REVIEW

THINKING SKILLS

Classifying

1. Look over the casts of characters in the four plays in this unit. Which would you classify as likable? Which would you classify as unlikable?
2. Consider the settings of the four plays. When does each take place—in the past, in the present, or in the future?

Generalizing

3. List the characteristics you find in all four plays that set them apart from the other types of literature, such as short stories. Make a general statement about plays.

Synthesizing

4. Choose one of the following themes and devise a plot, characters, and a setting that would illustrate the theme:
   (a) Good actions bring more rewards than evil actions. (b) Sometimes it is better to lose than to win.
   (c) Individuals become stronger when they stand up for their beliefs.

Evaluating

5. Which of the four plays do you think is most effective in creating a mood? Explain.
6. Which play presents the most believable characters? Explain.

■ COMPOSITION REVIEW

Writing a Journal Entry

Assume you are Dr. Watson analyzing the methods used by Sherlock Holmes. Write a one-paragraph journal entry in which your first sentence is "Sherlock Holmes traps Victor Savage's killer through a combination of logic and luck." You might, for example, point out the logic that Holmes uses in planning ahead. On the other hand, you might show that luck plays a part when Culverton Smith agrees to turn up the lamp. Include other examples in which luck or logic seems to play a part.

Writing to Persuade

Imagine that one of your classmates says, "Fantasy is silly; it has nothing to do with the real world." Write a two- to three-paragraph article in reply. Before you begin, review *The Monsters Are Due on Maple Street* and *Let Me Hear You Whisper*. Take notes to support the argument that fantasy can be important to real life. State your opinion at the beginning of your article and then organize the examples from the selections in a way that will convince your classmate that fantasy is not silly.

Reviewing Writer's Craft: Use Varied Sentences

In this unit you have seen how playwrights use different kinds of sentences to emphasize dramatic moments and to reveal character. If you are keeping a **reading/writing log,** you have copied speeches with varied sentences in your log. Now **try your hand** at using varied sentences for emphasis.

Write a brief scene in which Helen is being interviewed for a new job. She will, of course, be asked and will tell about her previous job experiences. In writing speeches for Helen and the interviewer, build in a variety of sentences to show not only what they say and how they say it but also how they react to what each other says. Include any necessary stage directions.

NONFICTION

Frederic Edwin
Church,
The Iceberg, 1861,
Dallas Museum of
Fine Art

PREVIEW

UNIT 3   NONFICTION

Features
Reading Nonfiction
The Writer's Craft: Use a Voice That
     Suits Your Purpose
Comment: Compare the Real Story and
     a Novel

Application of Literary Term
point of view

Reading Literature Skillfully
summarizing
drawing conclusions
author's purpose
main idea and supporting details
fact and opinion

Vocabulary Skills
context
idioms
inflected forms

Thinking Skills
generalizing
synthesizing
evaluating

Composition Assignments Include
Writing as a Story Character
Writing a Feature Story
Writing About a Story Character
Writing a Commendation
Writing to Show Contrast
Writing About a Person
Writing a Letter
Writing About an Experience
Writing a Journal Entry

Enrichment
Learning from Your Classmates
Making Up Dialogue
Using a Map
Doing Research
Researching the Story

Thinking Critically About Literature
Concept Review
Content Review
Composition Review

The Labrador in the Dustbin

James Herriot

The big golden Labrador had many peculiar habits, among them licking the insides of cans that once contained fruit salad, baked beans, or some other kind of food.

n the semidarkness of the surgery passage I thought it was a hideous growth dangling from the side of the dog's face, but as he came closer, I saw that it was only a condensed-milk can. Not that condensed-milk cans are commonly found sprouting from dogs' cheeks, but I was relieved because I knew I was dealing with Brandy again.

I hoisted him onto the table. "Brandy, you've been at the dustbin[1] again."

The big golden Labrador gave me an apologetic grin and did his best to lick my face. He couldn't manage it since his tongue was jammed inside the can, but he made up for it by a furious wagging of tail and rear end.

"Oh, Mr. Herriot, I am sorry to trouble you again." Mrs. Westby, his attractive young mistress, smiled ruefully. "He just won't keep out of that dustbin. Sometimes the children and I can get the cans off ourselves, but this one is stuck fast. His tongue is trapped under the lid."

"Yes . . . yes . . ." I eased my finger along the jagged edge of the metal. "It's a bit tricky, isn't it? We don't want to cut his mouth."

As I reached for a pair of forceps, I thought of the many other occasions when I had done something like this for Brandy. He was one of my patients, a huge, lolloping, slightly goofy animal, but this dustbin raiding was becoming an obsession.

He liked to fish out a can and lick out the tasty remnants, but his licking was carried out with such dedication that he burrowed deeper and deeper until he got stuck. Again and again he had been freed by his family or myself from fruit-salad cans, corned-beef cans, baked-bean cans, soup cans. There didn't seem to be any kind of can he didn't like.

I gripped the edge of the lid with my forceps and gently bent it back along its length till I was able to lift it away from the tongue. An instant later, that tongue was slobbering all over my cheek as Brandy expressed his delight and thanks.

"Get back, you daft dog!" I said, laughing, as I held the panting face away from me.

---

1. *dustbin*, the British word for a trash or garbage can.

"Yes, come down, Brandy." Mrs. Westby hauled him from the table and spoke sharply. "It's all very fine, making a fuss now, but you're becoming a nuisance with this business. It will have to stop."

The scolding had no effect on the lashing tail, and I saw that his mistress was smiling. You just couldn't help liking Brandy because he was a great ball of affection and tolerance, without an ounce of malice in him.

I had seen the Westby children—there were three girls and a boy—carrying him around by the legs, upside down, or pushing him in a pram, sometimes dressed in baby clothes. Those youngsters played all sorts of games with him, but he suffered them all with good humor. In fact, I am sure he enjoyed them.

Brandy had other idiosyncracies, apart from his fondness for dustbins.

I was attending the Westby cat at their home one afternoon when I noticed the dog acting strangely. Mrs. Westby was sitting, knitting in an armchair, while the oldest girl squatted on the hearth rug with me and held the cat's head.

It was when I was searching my pockets for my thermometer that I noticed Brandy slinking into the room. He wore a furtive air as he moved across the carpet and sat down with studied carelessness in front of his mistress. After a few moments he began to work his rear end gradually up the front of the chair towards her knees. Absently, she took a hand away from her knitting and pushed him down, but he immediately restarted his backward ascent. It was an extraordinary mode of progression, his hips moving in a very slow rumba rhythm as he elevated them inch by

inch, and all the time the golden face was blank and innocent, as though nothing at all were happening.

Fascinated, I stopped hunting for my thermometer and watched. Mrs. Westby was absorbed in an intricate part of her knitting and didn't seem to notice that Brandy's bottom was now firmly parked on her shapely knees which were clad in blue jeans. The dog paused, as though acknowledging that phase one had been successfully completed, then ever so gently he began to consolidate his position, pushing his way up the front of the chair with his fore limbs, till at one time he was almost standing on his head.

It was at that moment, just when one final backward heave would have seen the great dog ensconced on her lap, that Mrs. Westby finished the tricky bit of knitting and looked up.

"Oh, really, Brandy, you are silly!" She put a hand on his rump and sent him slithering disconsolately to the carpet, where he lay and looked at her with liquid eyes.

"What was all that about?" I asked.

Mrs. Westby laughed. "Oh, it's these old blue jeans. When Brandy first came here as a tiny puppy, I spent hours nursing him on my knee, and I used to wear the jeans a lot then. Ever since, even though he's a grown dog, the very sight of the things makes him try to get on my knee."

"But he doesn't just jump up?"

"Oh, no," she said. "He's tried it and got ticked off. He knows perfectly well I can't have a huge Labrador in my lap."

"So now it's the stealthy approach, eh?"

She giggled. "That's right. When I'm preoccupied—knitting or reading—sometimes

Andrew Wyeth, *Night Sleeper*, 1979
Private Collection

he manages to get nearly all the way up, and if he's been playing in the mud he makes an awful mess, and I have to go and change. That's when he really does receive a scolding."

A patient like Brandy added color to my daily round. When I was walking my own dog, I often saw him playing in the fields by the river. One particularly hot day many of the dogs were taking to the water, either to chase sticks or just to cool off, but whereas they glided in and swam off sedately, Brandy's approach was quite unique.

I watched as he ran up to the river bank, expecting him to pause before entering. But,

instead, he launched himself outwards, legs splayed in a sort of swallow dive, and hung for a moment in the air rather like a flying fox before splashing thunderously into the depths. To me it was the action of a completely happy extrovert.

On the following day in those same fields I witnessed something even more extraordinary. There is a little children's playground in one corner—a few swings, a roundabout, and a slide. Brandy was disporting himself on the slide.

For this activity he had assumed an uncharacteristic gravity of expression and stood calmly in the queue of children. When his turn came he mounted the steps, slid down the metal slope, all dignity and importance, then took a staid walk round to rejoin the queue.

The little boys and girls who were his companions seemed to take him for granted, but I found it difficult to tear myself away. I could have watched him all day.

I often smiled to myself when I thought of Brandy's antics, but I didn't smile when Mrs. Westby brought him into the surgery a few months later. His bounding ebullience had disappeared, and he dragged himself along the passage to the consulting room.

As I lifted him onto the table, I noticed that he had lost a lot of weight.

"Now, what is the trouble, Mrs. Westby?" I asked.

She looked at me worriedly. "He's been off-color for a few days now, listless and coughing and not eating very well, but this morning he seems quite ill, and you can see he's starting to pant."

"Yes . . . yes . . ." As I inserted the thermometer I watched the rapid rise and fall of the rib cage and noted the gaping mouth and anxious eyes. "He does look very sorry for himself."

Temperature was 104. I took out my stethoscope and auscultated his lungs. I have heard of an old Scottish doctor describing a seriously ill patient's chest as sounding like a "kist o' whustles,"[2] and that just about described Brandy's. Rales, wheezes, squeaks and bubblings—they were all there against a background of labored respiration.

I put the stethoscope back in my pocket. "He's got pneumonia."

"Oh, dear." Mrs. Westby reached out and touched the heaving chest. "That's bad, isn't it?"

"Yes, I'm afraid so."

"But . . ." She gave me an appealing glance. "I understand it isn't so fatal since the new drugs came out."

I hesitated. "Yes, that's quite right. In humans and most animals the sulpha drugs, and now penicillin, have changed the picture completely, but dogs are still very difficult to cure."

Thirty years later it is still the same. Even with all the armory of antibiotics that followed penicillin—streptomycin, the tetracyclines,[3] the synthetics and the new nonantibiotic drugs and steroids—I still hate to see pneumonia in a dog.

"But you don't think it's hopeless?" Mrs. Westby asked.

"No, no, not at all. I'm just warning you that so many dogs don't respond to treatment when they should. But Brandy is young and strong. He must stand a fair chance. I wonder what started this off, anyway."

"Oh, I think I know, Mr. Herriot. He had a swim in the river about a week ago. I try to keep him out of the water in this cold weather, but if he sees a stick floating, he just takes a dive into the middle. You've seen him—it's one of the funny little things he does."

"Yes, I know. And was he shivery afterwards?"

"He was. I walked him straight home, but it was such a freezing-cold day. I could feel

---

2. *kist o' whustles,* British for "chest of whistles."
3. *streptomycin, tetracyclines,* (strep′tō mī′sn, tet′rə sī′klənz).

him trembling as I dried him down."

I nodded. "That would be the cause, all right. Anyway, let's start his treatment. I'm going to give him this injection of penicillin, and I'll call at your house tomorrow to repeat it. He's not well enough to come to the surgery."

"Very well, Mr. Herriot. And is there anything else?"

"Yes, there is. I want you to make him what we call a pneumonia jacket. Cut two holes in an old blanket for his forelegs and stitch him into it along his back. You can use an old sweater if you like, but he must have his chest warmly covered. Only let him out in the garden for necessities."

I called and repeated the injection on the following day. There wasn't much change. I injected him for four more days, and the realization came to me sadly that Brandy was like so many of the others—he wasn't responding. The temperature did drop a little, but he ate hardly anything and grew gradually thinner. I put him on sulphapyridine tablets, but they didn't seem to make any difference.

As the days passed and he continued to cough and pant and to sink deeper into a blank-eyed lethargy, I was forced more and more to a conclusion which, a few weeks ago, would have seemed impossible—that this happy, bounding animal was going to die.

But Brandy didn't die. He survived. You couldn't put it any higher than that. His temperature came down and his appetite improved, and he climbed onto a plateau of twilight existence where he seemed content to stay.

"He isn't Brandy anymore," Mrs. Westby said one morning a few weeks later when I called in. Her eyes filled with tears as she spoke.

I shook my head. "No, I'm afraid he isn't. Are you giving him the halibut liver oil?"

"Yes, every day. But nothing seems to do him any good. Why is he like this, Mr. Herriot?"

"Well, he has recovered from a really virulent pneumonia, but it's left him with a chronic pleurisy, adhesions, and probably other kinds of lung damage. It looks as though he's just stuck there." She dabbed at her eyes. "It breaks my heart to see him like this. He's only five, but he's like an old, old dog. He was so full of life, too." She sniffed and blew her nose. "When I think of how I used to scold him for getting into the dustbins and muddying up my jeans. How I wish he would do some of his funny old tricks now."

I thrust my hands deep into my pockets. "Never does anything like that now, eh?"

"No, no, just hangs about the house. Doesn't even want to go for a walk."

As I watched, Brandy rose from his place in the corner and pottered slowly over to the fire. He stood there for a moment, gaunt and dead-eyed, and he seemed to notice me for the first time because the end of his tail gave a brief twitch before he coughed, groaned, and flopped down on the hearth rug.

Mrs. Westby was right. He was like a very old dog.

"Do you think he'll always be like this?" she asked.

I shrugged. "We can only hope."

But as I got into my car and drove away, I really didn't have much hope. I had seen calves with lung damage after bad pneumonias. They recovered but were called "bad doers" because they remained thin and listless for the rest of their lives. Doctors, too, had plenty of "chesty" people on their books; they were, more or less, in the same predicament.

Weeks and then months went by, and the only time I saw the Labrador was when Mrs. Westby was walking him on his lead. I always had the impression that he was reluctant to move, and his mistress had to stroll along very slowly so that he could keep up with her. The sight of him saddened me when I thought of the lolloping Brandy of old, but I told myself that at least I had saved his life. I could do no more for him now, and I made a determined effort to push him out of my mind.

In fact, I tried to forget Brandy and managed to do so fairly well until one afternoon in February. On the previous night I felt I had been through the fire. I had treated a colicky horse until 4 A.M. and was crawling into bed, comforted by the knowledge that the animal was settled down and free from pain, when I was called to a calving. I had managed to produce a large live calf from a small heifer, but the effort had drained the last of my strength, and when I got home, it was too late to return to bed.

Plowing through the morning round, I was so tired that I felt disembodied.

There were a few dogs in the waiting room at two o'clock, and I dealt with them mechanically, peering through half-closed eyelids.

By the time I reached my last patient, I was almost asleep on my feet. In fact, I had the feeling that I wasn't there at all.

"Next, please," I mumbled as I pushed open the waiting-room door and stood back, expecting the usual sight of a dog being led out to the passage.

But this time there was a big difference. There was a man in the doorway all right, and he had a little poodle with him, but the thing that made my eyes snap wide open was that the dog was walking upright on his hind limbs.

I knew I was half-asleep, but surely I wasn't seeing things. I stared down at the dog, but the picture hadn't changed. The little creature strutted through the doorway, chest out, head up, as erect as a soldier.

"Follow me, please," I said hoarsely and set off over the tiles to the consulting room. Halfway along, I just had to turn round to check the evidence of my eyes, and it was just the same—the poodle, still on his hind legs, marching along unconcernedly at his master's side.

The man must have seen the bewilderment in my face because he burst suddenly into a roar of laughter.

"Don't worry, Mr. Herriot," he said. "This little dog was circus trained before I got him as a pet. I like to show off his little tricks. This one really startles people."

"You can say that again," I said breathlessly. "It nearly gave me heart failure."

The poodle wasn't ill; he just wanted his nails clipped. I smiled as I hoisted him onto the table and began to ply the clippers.

"I suppose he won't want his hind claws doing," I said. "He'll have worn them down himself." I was glad to find I had recovered sufficiently to attempt a little joke.

However, by the time I had finished, the

old lassitude had taken over again, and I felt ready to fall down as I showed man and dog to the front door.

I watched the little animal trotting away down the street—in the orthodox manner this time—and it came to me suddenly that it had been a long time since I had seen a dog doing something unusual and amusing. Like the things Brandy used to do.

A wave of gentle memories flowed through me as I leaned wearily against the doorpost and closed my eyes. When I opened them, I saw Brandy coming round the corner of the street with Mrs. Westby. His nose was entirely obscured by a large, red tomato-soup can, and he strained madly at the leash and whipped his tail when he saw me.

It was certainly a hallucination this time. I was looking into the past. I really ought to go to bed immediately. But I was still rooted to the doorpost when the Labrador bounded up the steps, made an attempt, aborted by the soup can, to lick my face and contented himself with cocking a convivial leg against the bottom step.

I stared into Mrs. Westby's radiant face. "What . . . what . . . ?"

With her sparkling eyes and wide smile, she looked more attractive than ever. "Look, Mr. Herriot, look! He's better, he's better!"

In an instant I was wide awake. "And I . . . I suppose you'll want me to get that can off him?"

"Oh, yes, yes, please!"

It took all my strength to lift him onto the table. He was heavier now than before his illness. I reached for the familiar forceps and began to turn the jagged edges of the can outwards from the nose and mouth. Tomato soup must have been one of his favorites because he was really deeply embedded, and it took some time before I was able to slide the can from his face.

I fought off his slobbering attack. "He's back in the dustbins, I see."

"Yes, he is quite regularly. I've pulled several cans off him myself. And he goes sliding with the children, too." She smiled happily.

Thoughtfully I took my stethoscope from the pocket of my white coat and listened to his lungs. They were wonderfully clear. A slight roughness here and there, but the old cacophony had gone.

I leaned on the table and looked at the great dog with a mixture of thankfulness and incredulity. He was as before, boisterous and full of the joy of living. His tongue lolled in a happy grin, and the sun glinted through the surgery window on his sleek golden coat.

"But Mr. Herriot," Mrs. Westby's eyes were wide, "how on earth has this happened? How has he got better?"

"*Vis medicatrix naturae,*" I replied in tones of deep respect.

"I beg your pardon?"

"The healing power of nature. Something no veterinary surgeon can compete with when it decides to act."

"I see. And you can never tell when this is going to happen?"

"No."

For a few seconds we were silent as we stroked the dog's head and ears and flanks.

"Oh, by the way," I said, "has he shown any renewed interest in the blue jeans?"

"Oh, my word, yes! They're in the washing machine at this very moment. Absolutely covered in mud. Isn't it marvelous!"

THINK AND DISCUSS
Understanding
1. What are some of Brandy's peculiarities, or unusual traits?
2. What is Brandy's illness and how does he get it?
3. What is unusual about the poodle?
4. What is the key to Brandy's full recovery?

Analyzing
5. Why does the narrator seem to enjoy Brandy so much?
6. Why does the poodle remind the narrator of Brandy?
7. The first paragraph brings out the two different **moods** of the selection. What are they? Think about the feelings you get from "In the semidarkness of the surgery passage I thought it was a hideous growth. . . ." and "Not that condensed-milk cans are commonly found sprouting from dogs' cheeks."
8. Which of the following words best describes Brandy at the end of the story: (**a**) pathetic; (**b**) irritating; (**c**) amusing; (**d**) frustrating? Why?

Extending
9. From this account, what are some of the things Herriot does in his job? Would you want to be a veterinarian? Explain why or why not.

READING LITERATURE SKILLFULLY
Summarizing
A **summary** is a short statement—no more than a few sentences—that gives the main ideas of an article or tells what happened in a story. To find these main ideas, it may help if you ask yourself *who* did *what, when,* and *where? Why?* Newspaper reporters use this formula when they summarize events for a news story. Answer the following questions about the selection you have just read.
1. Who is important in the account?
2. Where do the events occur?
3. What happens?
4. Why does it happen?
5. When does the account begin, and when does it end?

Write sentences to answer the above questions and then put the sentences together. You will have a summary of "The Labrador in the Dustbin."

VOCABULARY
Context
Many words common in England, the setting for this selection, are not often heard in the United States. Use the context, or other words in the sentence, to figure out the meaning of each italicized word. Match the word with its meaning.

Meanings
line of people
scolded
doctor's office
merry-go-round
baby carriage
puttered; walked slowly

1. Brandy would try to sit on Mrs. Westby's lap, but she always *ticked* him *off* because of his size.

2. The children pushed Brandy in a *pram,* as if he were an infant.

3. Brandy stood calmly in the *queue* of children, waiting for a turn to go down the slide.

4. The playground had a few swings, a *roundabout,* and a slide.

5. He was not well enough to come to the *surgery.*

6. After his illness, Brandy *pottered* to the fire where he groaned and flopped down on the hearth rug.

COMPOSITION

Writing as a Story Character

Imagine you are one of the Westby children. Write a paragraph describing Brandy to a friend who has never seen him. Tell about Brandy's peculiarities and how you feel about him. Before you begin, review the story to find specific examples to use in your paragraph. List them. Refer to Lesson 11, "Writing as a Story Character," in the Writer's Handbook.

Writing a Feature Story

Imagine you are a local newspaper journalist. Write a four-paragraph feature story about Brandy and his unusual habits. Before you begin, write a list of questions you would want to ask during an interview. Answer these as you expect the Westbys would, and then build your feature story around them. Include a lively headline and the kind of details that would make interesting reading.

ENRICHMENT
Learning from Your Classmates

Work with a small group of your classmates. Discuss the unusual habits of pets you have had or of animals in books or stories you have read. Talk about both lovable habits and irritating behavior. List the various examples suggested in the group. Each group can share ideas with the entire class. In preparation, you might want to read all or parts of other books by James Herriot.

BIOGRAPHY

James Herriot
1916–

James Herriot, whose real name is James Wight, practiced veterinary medicine in rural England for many years before beginning to write books about his experiences. He uses a pseudonym, or false name, because veterinarians in England are not allowed to do any kind of advertising. For this reason he also uses pseudonyms for the people and the places in his stories. The difficult, dirty, and sometimes dangerous work of treating pets and farm animals is described with humor and sensitivity in his books. One of his books, *All Creatures Great and Small,* was made into a popular television series.

Unlike the made-up stories and plays you read in Units 1 and 2 of this book, the selections in Unit 3 are about real people and events. For example, James Herriot, the author of the selection you just finished, is a veterinarian who has written many books about his experiences with people and animals. His books are generally classified as autobiographies.

An **autobiography** is the story of a person's life written by that person. Autobiographies often deal with feelings and observations about the person's experiences. As you read the next selection, think about the experience Richard Wright relates and how it has affected his feelings and life.

Autobiography falls under the general category of nonfiction. In contrast to fiction, which is writing drawn from the imagination of the author rather than history or fact, nonfictional writing is about people who are alive or have lived and events that have taken place. Notice the prefix *non-* meaning "not" in the word *nonfiction*.

Biography, which is the story of a person's life written by another person, is also nonfiction. Through the centuries that literature has been written, biography has meant different things to different people. Today it is seen as a literary form that presents a history of a person's life—a history that is accurate and based on facts. Generally it makes an attempt to interpret the facts about a person in such a way as to present that person's character and mind.

Other kinds of nonfiction include **essays** and **articles.** An essay is a discussion on some specific topic. The **author's purpose** is often to entertain or to express an opinion about something. In this unit you will read about one author's belief in the importance of saying "Thank you."

Articles are usually serious in tone and filled with factual information. News stories are one kind of article, as are feature stories in magazines. In an article the **author's purpose** often is mainly to inform readers.

Certain skills are especially useful in reading nonfiction selections. You will want to look for the main ideas to better understand what you read. A **main idea** is a statement about the topic, and it is supported by details through the selection. In school, you will often find it necessary to **summarize.** Looking for the main ideas and putting them together will help you summarize.

Since accuracy in facts is important in nonfiction, you will want to distinguish between **statements of fact** and **statements of opinion. Drawing conclusions** is important in both fiction and nonfiction. Look at the clues the author gives and draw from them conclusions about the people or events.

See **POINT OF VIEW** in the Handbook of Literary Terms, page 652.

Hunger

Richard Wright

In this true account, Richard Wright tells of the night his mother taught him to stand up and fight for himself.

unger stole upon me so slowly that at first I was not aware of what hunger really meant. Hunger had always been more or less at my elbow when I played, but now I began to wake up at night to find hunger standing at my bedside, staring at me gauntly. The hunger I had known before this had been no grim, hostile stranger; it had been a normal hunger that had made me beg constantly for bread, and when I ate a crust or two I was satisfied. But this new hunger baffled me, scared me, made me angry and insistent. Whenever I begged for food now my mother would pour me a cup of tea which would still the clamor in my stomach for a moment or two; but a little later I would feel hunger nudging my ribs, twisting my empty guts until they ached. I would grow dizzy and my vision would dim. I became less active in my play, and for the first time in my life I had to pause and think of what was happening to me.

"Mama, I'm hungry," I complained one afternoon.

"Jump up and catch a kungry," she said, trying to make me laugh and forget.

"What's a *kungry?*"

"It's what little boys eat when they get hungry," she said.

"What does it taste like?"

"I don't know."

"Then why do you tell me to catch one?"

"Because you said that you were hungry," she said, smiling.

I sensed that she was teasing me and it made me angry.

"But I'm hungry. I want to eat."

"You'll have to wait."

"But I want to eat now."

"But there's nothing to eat," she told me.

"Why?"

From pages 13–16 in *Black Boy* by Richard Wright. Copyright 1937, 1942, 1945 by Richard Wright. Reprinted by permission of Harper & Row, Publishers, Inc., Jonathan Cape Ltd., and Mrs. Ellen Wright.

"Just because there's none," she explained.

"But I want to eat," I said, beginning to cry.

"You'll just have to wait," she said again.

"But why?"

"For God to send some food."

"When is He going to send it?"

"I don't know."

"But I'm hungry!"

She was ironing and she paused and looked at me with tears in her eyes.

"Where's your father?" she asked me.

I stared in bewilderment. Yes, it was true that my father had not come home to sleep for many days now and I could make as much noise as I wanted. Though I had not known why he was absent, I had been glad that he was not there to shout his restrictions at me. But it had never occurred to me that his absence would mean that there would be no food.

"I don't know," I said.

"Who brings food into the house?" my mother asked me.

"Papa," I said. "He always brought food."

"Well, your father isn't here now," she said.

"Where is he?"

"I don't know," she said.

"But I'm hungry," I whimpered, stomping my feet.

"You'll have to wait until I get a job and buy food," she said.

As the days slid past the image of my father became associated with my pangs of hunger, and whenever I felt hunger I thought of him with a deep biological bitterness.

My mother finally went to work as a cook and left me and my brother alone in the flat each day with a loaf of bread and a pot of tea. When she returned at evening she would be tired and dispirited and would cry a lot. Sometimes, when she was in despair, she would call us to her and talk to us for hours, telling us that we now had no father, that our lives would be different from those of other children, that we must learn as soon as possible to take care of ourselves, to dress ourselves, to prepare our own food; that we must take upon ourselves the responsibility of the flat while she worked. Half frightened, we would promise solemnly. We did not understand what had happened between our father and our mother and the most that these long talks did to us was to make us feel a vague dread. Whenever we asked why father had left, she would tell us that we were too young to know.

One evening my mother told me that thereafter I would have to do the shopping for food. She took me to the corner store to show me the way. I was proud; I felt like a grownup. The next afternoon I looped the basket over my arm and went down the pavement toward the store. When I reached the corner, a gang of boys grabbed me, knocked me down, snatched the basket, took the money, and sent me running home in panic. That evening I told my mother what had happened, but she made no comment; she sat down at once, wrote another note, gave me more money, and sent me out to the grocery again. I crept down the steps and saw the same gang of boys playing down the street. I ran back into the house.

"What's the matter?" my mother asked.

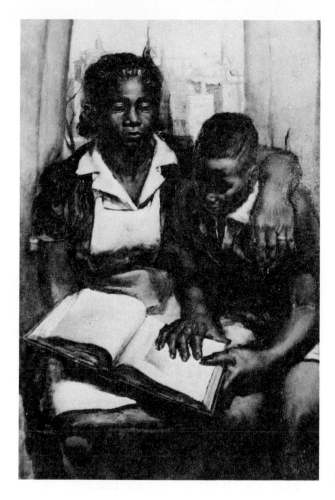

John Wilson, *Mother and Child*, 1943
Private Collection

"It's those same boys," I said. "They'll beat me."

"You've got to get over that," she said. "Now, go on."

"I'm scared," I said.

"Go on and don't pay any attention to them," she said.

I went out of the door and walked briskly down the sidewalk, praying that the gang would not molest me. But when I came abreast of them someone shouted, "There he is!"

They came toward me and I broke into a wild run toward home. They overtook me and flung me to the pavement. I yelled, pleaded, kicked, but they wrenched the money out of my hand. They yanked me to my feet, gave me a few slaps, and sent me home sobbing. My mother met me at the door.

"They b-beat m-me," I gasped. "They t-t-took the m-money."

I started up the steps, seeking the shelter of the house.

"Don't you come in here," my mother warned me.

I froze in my tracks and stared at her.

"But they're coming after me," I said.

"You just stay right where you are," she said in a deadly tone. "I'm going to teach you this night to stand up and fight for yourself."

She went into the house and I waited, terrified, wondering what she was about. Presently she returned with more money and another note; she also had a long heavy stick.

"Take this money, this note, and this stick," she said. "Go to the store and buy those groceries. If those boys bother you, then fight."

I was baffled. My mother was telling me to fight, a thing she had never done before.

"But I'm scared," I said.

"Don't you come into this house until you've gotten those groceries," she said.

"They'll beat me; they'll beat me," I said.

"Then stay in the streets; don't come back here!"

I ran up the steps and tried to force my way past her into the house. A stinging slap came on my jaw. I stood on the sidewalk, crying.

"Please, let me wait until tomorrow," I begged.

"No," she said. "Go now! If you come back into this house without those groceries, I'll whip you!"

She slammed the door and I heard the key turn in the lock. I shook with fright. I was alone upon the dark, hostile streets and gangs were after me. I had the choice of being beaten at home or away from home. I clutched the stick, crying, trying to reason. If I were beaten at home, there was absolutely nothing that I could do about it; but if I were beaten in the streets, I had a chance to fight and defend myself. I walked slowly down the sidewalk, coming closer to the gang of boys, holding the stick tightly. I was so full of fear that I could scarcely breathe. I was almost upon them now.

"There he is again!" the cry went up.

They surrounded me quickly and began to grab for my hand.

"I'll kill you!" I threatened.

They closed in. In blind fear I let the stick fly, feeling it crack against a boy's skull. I swung again, lamming another skull, then another. Realizing that they would retaliate if I let up for but a second, I fought to lay them low, to knock them cold, to kill them so that they could not strike back at me. I flayed with tears in my eyes, teeth clenched, stark fear making me throw every ounce of my strength behind each blow. I hit again and again, dropping the money and the grocery list. The boys scattered, yelling, nursing their heads, staring at me in utter disbelief. They had never seen such frenzy. I stood panting, egging them on, taunting them to come on and fight. When they refused, I ran after them and they tore out for their homes, screaming. The parents of the boys rushed into the streets and threatened me, and for the first time in my life I shouted at grownups, telling them that I would give them the same if they bothered me. I finally found my grocery list and the money and went to the store. On my way back I kept my stick poised for instant use, but there was not a single boy in sight. That night I won the right to the streets of Memphis.

THINK AND DISCUSS
Understanding
1. Why don't the narrator and his family have any food?
2. The narrator compares this new hunger to something else. What is it?
3. Why does the narrator believe it is better to be beaten away from home than to return there?

Analyzing
4. How does the narrator's mother use humor to try to make him forget hunger?
5. What kind of a woman is the narrator's mother?
6. The narrator says he won the right to the streets of Memphis. What else did he win?

Extending
7. How do you think Richard will feel if he needs to fight again?
8. What do you think of the mother's methods of helping her son?

APPLYING: Point of View H☆
See Handbook of Literary Terms, p. 652.

Point of view is the relationship between the narrator and the story. A story may be told from the first-person, third-person limited, or third-person omniscient point of view.
1. From what point of view is "Hunger" narrated? Explain.
2. Do you believe that "Hunger" could have been narrated as well using an all-knowing narrator? Why or why not?

THINKING SKILLS
Generalizing
To generalize is to draw a general conclusion from particular information. With a small group of classmates, discuss the kind of courage it takes to meet each of the following situations. Then write a definition of courage.
1. an illness and long period of recovery
2. the rescue of someone who is drowning
3. school bullies

BIOGRAPHY

Richard Wright
1908–1960

At fifteen Richard Wright discovered the joys of reading and realized he wanted to be a writer. He wrote short stories but refused to show them to anyone for fear of being made fun of. By working at whatever jobs were available, he saved enough money to move to Chicago. It was there that he published his first book and wrote his most important works, including *Black Boy,* an autobiographical account of his early years. "Hunger" is taken from this book. Wright eventually moved to Paris, France, where he continued to write until his death.

Review **POINT OF VIEW** in the Handbook of Literary Terms, page 652.

from Harriet Tubman

Ann Petry

**When they heard the whisper "Moses is back again," the daring
handful of slaves tied up some ashcake and salt herring in their
bandannas and waited for the signal. . . .**

Along the eastern shore of Maryland, in Dorchester County, in Caroline County, the masters kept hearing whispers about the man named Moses, who was running off slaves. At first they did not believe in his existence. The stories about him were fantastic, unbelievable. Yet they watched for him. They offered rewards for his capture.

They never saw him. Now and then they heard whispered rumors to the effect that he was in the neighborhood. The woods were searched. The roads were watched. There was never anything to indicate his whereabouts. But a few days afterward, a goodly number of slaves would be gone from the plantation. Neither the master nor the overseer had heard or seen anything unusual in the quarter. Sometimes one or the other would vaguely remember having heard a whippoorwill call somewhere in the woods, close by, late at night. Though it was the wrong season for whippoorwills.

Sometimes the masters thought they had heard the cry of a hoot owl, repeated, and would remember having thought that the intervals between the low moaning cry were wrong, that it had been repeated four times in succession instead of three. There was never anything more than that to suggest that all was not well in the quarter. Yet when morning came, they invariably discovered that a group of the finest slaves had taken to their heels.

Unfortunately, the discovery was almost always made on a Sunday. Thus a whole day was lost before the machinery of pursuit could be set in motion. The posters offering rewards for the fugitives could not be printed until Monday. The men who made a living hunting for runaway slaves were out of reach, off in the woods with their dogs and their guns, in pursuit of four-footed game, or they were in camp meetings saying their prayers with their wives and families beside them.

Harriet Tubman could have told them that there was far more involved in this matter of running off slaves than signaling the would-be runaways by imitating the call of a whippoorwill, or a hoot owl, far more involved than a matter of waiting for a clear night when the North Star was visible.

In December, 1851, when she started out with the band of fugitives that she planned to take to Canada, she had been in the vicinity of the plantation for days, planning the trip, carefully selecting the slaves that she would take with her.

She had announced her arrival in the quarter by singing the forbidden spiritual—"Go down, Moses, 'way down to Egypt Land"—singing it softly outside the door of a slave cabin, late at night. The husky voice was beautiful even when it was barely more than a murmur borne on the wind.

Once she had made her presence known, word of her coming spread from cabin to cabin. The slaves whispered to each other, ear to mouth, mouth to ear, "Moses is here." "Moses has come." "Get ready. Moses is back again." The ones who had agreed to go North with her put ashcake and salt herring in an old bandanna, hastily tied it into a bundle, and then waited patiently for the signal that meant it was time to start.

There were eleven in this party, including one of her brothers and his wife. It was the largest group that she had ever conducted, but she was determined that more and more slaves should know what freedom was like.

She had to take them all the way to Canada. The Fugitive Slave Law[1] was no longer a great many incomprehensible words written down on the country's lawbooks. The new law had become a reality. It was Thomas Sims, a boy, picked up on the streets of Boston at night and shipped back to Georgia. It was Jerry and Shadrach, arrested and jailed with no warning.

She had never been in Canada. The route beyond Philadelphia was strange to her. But she could not let the runaways who accompanied her know this. As they walked along she told them stories of her own first flight; she kept painting vivid word pictures of what it would be like to be free.

But there were so many of them this time. She knew moments of doubt when she was half-afraid, and kept looking back over her shoulder, imagining that she heard the sound of pursuit. They would certainly be pursued. Eleven of them. Eleven thousand dollars' worth of flesh and bone and muscle that belonged to Maryland planters. If they were caught, the eleven runaways would be whipped and sold South, but she—she would probably be hanged.

They tried to sleep during the day but they never could wholly relax into sleep. She could tell by the positions they assumed, by their restless movements. And they walked at

1. *Fugitive Slave Law.* Between 1793 and 1850, Congress enacted severe laws to provide for the return of escaped slaves. The Underground Railroad was largely a result of public distaste for these laws. Among other harsh measures, the law of 1850 imposed severe penalties upon anyone who helped a slave in his or her escape.

night. Their progress was slow. It took them three nights of walking to reach the first stop. She had told them about the place where they would stay, promising warmth and good food, holding these things out to them as an incentive to keep going.

When she knocked on the door of a farmhouse, a place where she and her parties of runaways had always been welcome, always been given shelter and plenty to eat, there was no answer. She knocked again, softly. A voice from within said, "Who is it?" There was fear in the voice.

She knew instantly from the sound of the voice that there was something wrong. She said, "A friend with friends," the password on the Underground Railroad.

The door opened, slowly. The man who stood in the doorway looked at her coldly, looked with unconcealed astonishment and fear at the eleven disheveled runaways who were standing near her. Then he shouted, "Too many, too many. It's not safe. My place was searched last week. It's not safe!" and slammed the door in her face.

She turned away from the house, frowning. She had promised her passengers food and rest and warmth, and instead of that, there would be hunger and cold and more walking over the frozen ground. Somehow she would have to instill courage into these eleven people, most of them strangers, would have to feed them on hope and bright dreams of freedom instead of the fried pork and corn bread and milk she had promised them.

They stumbled along behind her, half-dead for sleep, and she urged them on, though she was as tired and as discouraged as they were. She had never been in Canada but she kept painting wondrous word pictures of what it would be like. She managed to dispel their fear of pursuit, so that they would not become hysterical, panic-stricken. Then she had to bring some of the fear back, so that they would stay awake and keep walking though they drooped with sleep.

Yet during the day, when they lay down deep in a thicket, they never really slept, because if a twig snapped or the wind sighed in the branches of a pine tree, they jumped to their feet, afraid of their own shadows, shivering and shaking. It was very cold, but they dared not make fires because someone would see the smoke and wonder about it.

She kept thinking, eleven of them. Eleven thousand dollars' worth of slaves. And she had to take them all the way to Canada. Sometimes she told them about Thomas Garrett, in Wilmington. She said he was their friend even though he did not know them. He was the friend of all fugitives. He called them God's poor. He was a Quaker[2] and his speech was a little different from that of other people. His clothing was different, too. He wore the wide-brimmed hat that the Quakers wear.

She said that he had thick white hair, soft, almost like a baby's, and the kindest eyes she had ever seen. He was a big man and strong, but he had never used his strength to harm anyone, always to help people. He would give all of them a new pair of shoes. Everybody. He always did. Once they reached his house in Wilmington, they would be safe. He would see to it that they were.

---

2. **Quaker,** a member of a Christian group called the Society of Friends. The Quakers participated actively in the antislavery effort.

Charles T. Webber, *The Underground Railroad*,
Cincinnati Art Museum

She described the house where he lived, told them about the store where he sold shoes. She said he kept a pail of milk and a loaf of bread in the drawer of his desk so that he would have food ready at hand for any of God's poor who should suddenly appear before him, fainting with hunger. There was a hidden room in the store. A whole wall swung open, and behind it was a room where he could hide fugitives. On the wall there were shelves filled with small boxes—boxes of shoes—so that you would never guess that the wall actually opened.

While she talked, she kept watching them.

They did not believe her. She could tell by their expressions. They were thinking, New shoes, Thomas Garrett, Quaker, Wilmington—what foolishness was this? Who knew if she told the truth? Where was she taking them anyway?

That night they reached the next stop—a farm that belonged to a German. She made the runaways take shelter behind the trees at the edge of the fields before she knocked at the door. She hesitated before she approached the door, thinking, suppose that he, too, should refuse shelter, suppose— Then she thought, Lord, I'm going to hold steady on to You and You've got to see me through—and knocked softly.

She heard the familiar guttural voice say, "Who's there?"

She answered quickly, "A friend with friends."

He opened the door and greeted her warmly. "How many this time?" he asked.

"Eleven," she said and waited, doubting, wondering.

He said, "Good. Bring them in."

He and his wife fed them in the lamplit kitchen, their faces glowing, as they offered food and more food, urging them to eat, saying there was plenty for everybody, have more milk, have more bread, have more meat.

They spent the night in the warm kitchen. They really slept, all that night and until dusk the next day. When they left, it was with reluctance. They had all been warm and safe and well-fed. It was hard to exchange the security offered by that clean warm kitchen for the darkness and the cold of a December night. . . . Harriet had found it hard to leave the warmth and friendliness, too. But she urged them on. For a while, as they walked, they seemed to carry in them a measure of contentment; some of the serenity and the cleanliness of that big warm kitchen lingered on inside them. But as they walked farther and farther away from the warmth and the light, the cold and the darkness entered into them. They fell silent, sullen, suspicious. She waited for the moment when some one of them would turn mutinous. It did not happen that night.

Two nights later she was aware that the feet behind her were moving slower and slower. She heard the irritability in their voices, knew that soon someone would refuse to go on.

She started talking about William Still and the Philadelphia Vigilance Committee.[3] No one commented. No one asked any questions. She told them the story of William and Ellen Craft and how they escaped from Georgia. Ellen was so fair that she looked as though she were white, and so she dressed up in a man's clothing and she looked like a wealthy young planter. Her husband, William, who was dark, played the role of her slave. Thus they traveled from Macon, Georgia, to Philadelphia, riding on the trains, staying at the finest hotels. Ellen pretended to be very ill—her right arm in a sling, and her right hand was bandaged because she was supposed to have rheumatism. Thus she avoided having to sign the register at the hotels, for she could not read or write. They finally arrived safely in Philadelphia, and then went on to Boston.

No one said anything. Not one of them seemed to have heard her.

She told them about Frederick Douglass,[4] the most famous of the escaped slaves, of his eloquence, of his magnificent appearance. Then she told them of her own first vain effort at running away, evoking the memory of that miserable life she had led as a child, reliving it for a moment in the telling.

But they had been tired too long, hungry too long, afraid too long, foot-sore too long. One of them suddenly cried out in despair,

3. *Philadelphia Vigilance Committee,* a group of citizens who guided slaves and helped pay their way to Canada.
4. *Frederick Douglass* (1817–1895), an ex-slave who became a leading figure in the antislavery movement through his eloquent lectures and abolitionist newspaper.

"Let me go back. It is better to be a slave than to suffer like this in order to be free."

She carried a gun with her on these trips. She had never used it—except as a threat. Now as she aimed it, she experienced a feeling of guilt, remembering that time, years ago, when she had prayed for the death of Edward Brodas, the Master, and then not too long afterward had heard that great wailing cry that came from the throats of the field hands, and knew from the sound that the Master was dead.

One of the runaways said, again, "Let me go back. Let me go back," and stood still, and then turned around and said, over his shoulder, "I am going back."

She lifted the gun, aimed it at the despairing slave. She said, "Go on with us or die." The husky low-pitched voice was grim.

He hesitated for a moment and then he joined the others. They started walking again. She tried to explain to them why none of them could go back to the plantation. If a runaway returned, he would turn traitor, the master and the overseer would force him to turn traitor. The returned slave would disclose the stopping places, the hiding places, the cornstacks they had used with the full knowledge of the owner of the farm, the name of the German farmer who had fed them and sheltered them. These people who had risked their own security to help runaways would be ruined, fined, imprisoned.

She said, "We got to go free or die. And freedom's not bought with dust."

This time she told them about the long agony of the Middle Passage[5] on the old slave ships, about the black horror of the holds, about the chains and the whips. They too knew these stories. But she wanted to remind them of the long hard way they had come, about the long hard way they had yet to go. She told them about Thomas Sims, the boy picked up on the streets of Boston and sent back to Georgia. She said when they got him back to Savannah, got him in prison there, they whipped him until a doctor who was standing by watching said, "You will kill him if you strike him again!" His master said, "Let him die!"

Thus she forced them to go on. Sometimes she thought she had become nothing but a voice speaking in the darkness, cajoling, urging, threatening. Sometimes she told them things to make them laugh, sometimes she sang to them, and heard the eleven voices behind her blending softly with hers, and then she knew that for the moment all was well with them.

She gave the impression of being a short, muscular, indomitable woman who could never be defeated. Yet at any moment she was liable to be seized by one of those curious fits of sleep, which might last for a few minutes or for hours.[6]

Even on this trip, she suddenly fell asleep in the woods. The runaways, ragged, dirty, hungry, cold, did not steal the gun as they might have, and set off by themselves, or turn back. They sat on the ground near her and waited patiently until she awakened. They had come to trust her implicitly, totally. They, too, had come to believe her

---

5. **Middle Passage**, the slaves' journey from Africa to America across the Atlantic Ocean.
6. **curious . . . hours.** At thirteen, Harriet Tubman nearly died from an accidental blow on her head. The resulting brain damage caused periodic sleep seizures that troubled her throughout her life.

repeated statement, "We got to go free or die." She was leading them into freedom, and so they waited until she was ready to go on.

Finally, they reached Thomas Garrett's house in Wilmington, Delaware. Just as Harriet had promised, Garrett gave them all new shoes, and provided carriages to take them on to the next stop.

By slow stages they reached Philadelphia, where William Still hastily recorded their names, and the plantations whence they had come, and something of the life they had led in slavery. Then he carefully hid what he had written, for fear it might be discovered. In 1872 he published this record in book form and called it *The Underground Railroad*. In the foreword to his book he said: "While I knew the danger of keeping strict records, and while I did not then dream that in my day slavery would be blotted out, or that the time would come when I could publish these records, it used to afford me great satisfaction to take them down, fresh from the lips of fugitives on the way to freedom, and to preserve them as they had given them."

William Still, who was familiar with all the station stops on the Underground Railroad, supplied Harriet with money and sent her and her eleven fugitives on to Burlington, New Jersey.

Harriet felt safer now, though there were danger spots ahead. But the biggest part of her job was over. As they went farther and farther north, it grew colder; she was aware of the wind on the Jersey ferry and aware of the cold damp in New York. From New York they went on to Syracuse, where the temperature was even lower.

In Syracuse she met the Reverend J. W. Loguen, known as "Jarm" Loguen. This was the beginning of a lifelong friendship. Both Harriet and Jarm Loguen were to become friends and supporters of Old John Brown.[7]

From Syracuse they went north again, into a colder, snowier city—Rochester. Here they almost certainly stayed with Frederick Douglass, for he wrote in his autobiography:

"On one occasion I had eleven fugitives at the same time under my roof, and it was necessary for them to remain with me until I could collect sufficient money to get them to Canada. It was the largest number I ever had at any one time, and I had some difficulty in providing so many with food and shelter, but, as may well be imagined, they were not very fastidious in either direction, and were well content with very plain food, and a strip of carpet on the floor for a bed, or a place on the straw in the barn-loft."

Late in December, 1851, Harriet arrived in St. Catharines, Canada West (now Ontario), with the eleven fugitives. It had taken almost a month to complete this journey; most of the time had been spent getting out of Maryland.

That first winter in St. Catharines was a terrible one. Canada was a strange frozen land, snow everywhere, ice everywhere, and a bone-biting cold the like of which none of them had ever experienced before. Harriet

---

7. *Old John Brown* (1800–1859), a devoted abolitionist who tried to stir up a rebellion among the slaves. He was captured at Harpers Ferry, a town in West Virginia, when he attempted to raid a government arsenal there in 1859.

rented a small frame house in the town and set to work to make a home. The fugitives boarded with her. They worked in the forests, felling trees, and so did she. Sometimes she took other jobs, cooking or cleaning house for people in the town. She cheered on these newly arrived fugitives, working herself, finding work for them, finding food for them, praying for them, sometimes begging for them.

Often she found herself thinking of the beauty of Maryland, the mellowness of the soil, the richness of the plant life there. The climate itself made for an ease of living that could never be duplicated in this bleak, barren countryside.

In spite of the severe cold, the hard work, she came to love St. Catharines, and the other towns and cities in Canada where black men lived. She discovered that freedom meant more than the right to change jobs at will, more than the right to keep the money that one earned. It was the right to vote and to sit on juries. It was the right to be elected to office. In Canada there were black men who were county officials and members of school boards. St. Catharines had a large colony of ex-slaves, and they owned their own homes, kept them neat and clean and in good repair. They lived in whatever part of town they chose and sent their children to the schools.

When spring came she decided that she would make this small Canadian city her home—as much as any place could be said to be home to a woman who traveled from Canada to the Eastern Shore of Maryland as often as she did.

In the spring of 1852, she went back to

Cape May, New Jersey. She spent the summer there, cooking in a hotel. That fall she returned, as usual, to Dorchester County, and brought out nine more slaves, conducting them all the way to St. Catharines, in Canada West, to the bone-biting cold, the snow-covered forests—and freedom.

She continued to live in this fashion, spending the winter in Canada, and the spring and summer working in Cape May, New Jersey, or in Philadelphia. She made two trips a year into slave territory, one in the fall and another in the spring. She now had a definite crystallized purpose, and in carrying it out, her life fell into a pattern which remained unchanged for the next six years.

THINK AND DISCUSS
Understanding
1. What were some of the codes, or passwords, used by Harriet Tubman and the slaves who wanted to escape to freedom?
2. What was the Underground Railroad and its "stops"?
3. Why couldn't runaway slaves ever turn back?

Analyzing
4. Why was Moses an appropriate code name for Harriet Tubman?
5. How did Harriet Tubman help the slaves find the will and the courage to keep going?
6. Why did Harriet Tubman take the slaves all the way to Canada?
7. What did Harriet Tubman mean when she said that freedom couldn't be bought with dust?

Extending
8. Which of Harriet Tubman's qualities do you consider heroic? Why?
9. In your opinion, is Harriet Tubman the only heroic person in the selection, or are there others who could be called heroic as well? Explain.

REVIEWING: Point of View H*T*
See Handbook of Literary Terms, p. 652.

The **point of view** of the narrator of a story can take three forms: first-person personal, third-person limited, and third-person omniscient.
1. What is the point of view in this selection?
2. Would this story be as effective if Harriet Tubman had told it in the first person? Why or why not?

VOCABULARY
Context
In the following sentences you should be able to determine from context clues the meaning of the italicized words. Read each sentence. Then, from the words after the sentence, choose the one closest in meaning to the italicized word.
1. After nights of walking, and days of fitful sleeping on the cold ground, the slaves wore dirty and *disheveled* clothes. (a) bright; (b) fresh; (c) untidy; (d) shrunken
2. Harriet had told them about the place where they would stay, promising warmth, comfortable beds, and good food, holding these things out as an *incentive* to keep on. (a) motive; (b) warning; (c) agreement; (d) threat
3. Despite hardship and difficulty, she was an *indomitable* woman. (a) uneducated; (b) undefeatable; (c) penniless; (d) sick
4. The runaways were not very *fastidious* about the quality of meals and shelter they received from Douglass, since they were used to sleeping on the ground and eating whatever they could find. (a) grateful; (b) hard to please; (c) hasty; (d) interested
5. Harriet spent a great deal of time patiently *cajoling* them into continuing the journey by promises of a better life. (a) beating; (b) coaxing; (c) following; (d) explaining

COMPOSITION
Writing a Commendation

Assume that Harriet Tubman has been chosen to receive a "Show of Courage" award for her service to others. Write a commendation or tribute in which you explain why she deserves the award. Review the selection to decide what information to include. Write as if the commendation were to be read at a gathering. Read it aloud, and then revise it.

Writing About a Story Character

Consider the various character traits Harriet Tubman shows on the trip from Maryland to Canada. Write several paragraphs describing these traits. Each trait should be identified in the first sentence of a paragraph and then supported by examples from the account. If you choose persistence, for example, you might mention that Harriet Tubman continued two trips a year for at least six years. Before you begin, reread the selection to find character traits. Make a list of examples. Consider leadership, flexibility, courage, and similar traits.

ENRICHMENT
Using a Map

Find a map that covers the area from eastern Maryland to St. Catharines, Canada West (now Ontario). Trace the route of the Underground Railroad, as described in this selection. You will probably need to reread parts of the selection and note the stops that are mentioned.

BIOGRAPHY

Ann Petry
1911–

Ann Petry, who worked as a pharmacist before becoming a writer, believes that it is impossible to understand the present—especially relations between people—without a knowledge of the past. She says:

"It seems to me that I have always been fascinated by American history—especially the period which encompasses the African slave trade, the ever-increasing use of slaves in the South, the growing outcry for the abolition of slavery, and ends with the Civil War and the period of reconstruction.

"Slowly, over the years, I have become convinced that the most dramatic material available to the writer in this country is that which deals with the Negro. . . .

"As for Harriet Tubman—I think she is the ideal heroine. When she is first seen, she is defenseless and much abused, [but she] slowly develops into a courageous woman with an impelling desire for freedom."

from The Story of My Life

Helen Keller

At the age of nineteen months, Helen Keller lost her sight and hearing as the result of a fever. Frustrated because she could not communicate with those around her, she turned into an uncontrollable child. Just before her seventh birthday Helen's parents arranged for Anne Sullivan to come to be her teacher. Helen later wrote that the day Anne Sullivan arrived was the most important day of her life.

The most important day I remember in all my life is the one on which my teacher, Anne Mansfield Sullivan, came to me. I am filled with wonder when I consider the immeasurable contrasts between the two lives which it connects. It was the third of March, 1887, three months before I was seven years old.

On the afternoon of that eventful day, I stood on the porch, dumb, expectant. I guessed vaguely from my mother's signs and from the hurrying to and fro in the house that something unusual was about to happen, so I went to the door and waited on the steps. The afternoon sun penetrated the mass of honeysuckle that covered the porch, and fell on my upturned face. My fingers lingered almost unconsciously on the familiar leaves and blossoms which had just come forth to greet the sweet southern spring. I did not know what the future held of marvel or surprise for me.

Anger and bitterness had preyed upon me continually for weeks and a deep languor had succeeded this passionate struggle. . . .

I felt approaching footsteps. I stretched out my hand as I supposed to my mother. Someone took it, and I was caught up and held close in the arms of her who had come to reveal all things to me, and, more than all things else, to love me.

The morning after my teacher came, she led me into her room and gave me a doll. The little blind children at the Perkins Institution[1] had sent it and Laura Bridgman[2] had dressed it; but I did not know this until afterward. When I had played with it a little while, Miss

---

1. *Perkins Institution*, an institution for the blind, located in Boston.
2. *Laura Bridgman*, 1829–1889. Laura Bridgman, like Helen Keller, became blind and deaf as the result of a childhood illness. She was educated at the Perkins Institution, and her life became an inspiration for others.

Helen Keller, *The Story of My Life*, Doubleday & Company, Inc., 1903, pages 34–42.

Sullivan slowly spelled into my hand the word "d-o-l-l." I was at once interested in this finger play and tried to imitate it. When I finally succeeded in making the letters correctly, I was flushed with childish pleasure and pride. Running downstairs to my mother I held up my hand and made the letters for *doll*. I did not know that I was spelling a word or even that words existed. I was simply making my fingers go in monkeylike imitation. In the days that followed I learned to spell in this uncomprehending way a great many words, among them *pin, hat, cup* and a few verbs like *sit, stand* and *walk*. But my teacher had been with me several weeks before I understood that everything has a name.

One day, while I was playing with my new doll, Miss Sullivan put my big rag doll into my lap also, spelled "d-o-l-l" and tried to make me understand that "d-o-l-l" applied to both. Earlier in the day we had had a tussle over the words "m-u-g" and "w-a-t-e-r." Miss Sullivan had tried to impress it upon me that "m-u-g" is *mug* and that "w-a-t-e-r" is *water*, but I persisted in confounding the two. In despair she had dropped the subject for the time, only to renew it at the first opportunity. I became impatient at her repeated attempts and, seizing the new doll, I dashed it upon the floor. I was keenly delighted when I felt the fragments of the broken doll at my feet. Neither sorrow nor regret followed my passionate outburst. I had not loved the doll. In the still, dark world in which I lived there was no strong sentiment or tenderness. I felt my teacher sweep the fragments to one side of the hearth, and I had a sense of satisfaction that the cause of my discomfort was removed. She brought me my hat, and I knew I was going out into the warm sunshine. This thought, if a wordless sensation may be called a thought, made me hop and skip with pleasure.

We walked down the path to the wellhouse, attracted by the fragrance of the honeysuckle with which it was covered. Someone was drawing water, and my teacher placed my hand under the spout. As the cool stream gushed over one hand, she spelled into the other the word *water*, first slowly, then rapidly. I stood still, my whole attention fixed upon the motions of her fingers. Suddenly I felt a misty consciousness as of something forgotten—a thrill of returning thought; and somehow the mystery of language was revealed to me. I knew then that "w-a-t-e-r" meant the wonderful, cool something that was flowing over my hand. That living word awakened my soul, gave it light, hope, joy, set it free! There were barriers still, it is true, but barriers that could in time be swept away.

I left the wellhouse eager to learn. Everything had a name, and each name gave birth to a new thought. As we returned to the house, every object which I touched seemed to quiver with life. That was because I saw everything with the strange, new sight that had come to me. On entering the door, I remembered the doll I had broken. I felt my way to the hearth and picked up the pieces. I tried vainly to put them together. Then my eyes filled with tears; for I realized what I had done, and for the first time I felt repentance and sorrow.

I learned a great many new words that day. I do not remember what they all were; but I do know that *mother, father, sister, teacher* were among them—words that were to make the world blossom for me, "like Aaron's rod,[3] with flowers.". . .

I recall many incidents of the summer of 1887 that followed my soul's sudden awakening. I did nothing but explore with my hands and learn the name of every object that I touched; and the more I handled things and learned their names and uses, the more joyous and confident grew my sense of kinship with the rest of the world.

When the time of daisies and buttercups came, Miss Sullivan took me by the hand across the fields, where men were preparing the earth for the seed, to the banks of the Tennessee River, and there, sitting on the warm grass, I had my first lessons in the beneficence of nature. I learned how the sun and the rain make to grow out of the ground every tree that is pleasant to the sight and good for food, how birds build their nests and live and thrive from land to land, how the squirrel, the deer, the lion, and every other creature finds food and shelter. As my knowledge of things grew I felt more and more the delight of the world I was in. Long before I learned to do a sum in arithmetic or describe the shape of the earth, Miss Sullivan had taught me to find beauty in the fragrant woods, in every blade of grass, and in the curves and dimples of my baby sister's hand. She linked my earliest thoughts with nature and made me feel that "birds and flowers and I were happy peers."

But about this time I had an experience which taught me that nature is not always kind. One day my teacher and I were returning from a long ramble. The morning had been fine, but it was growing warm and sultry when at last we turned our faces homeward. Two or three times we stopped to rest under a tree by the wayside. Our last halt was under a wild cherry tree a short distance from the house. The shade was grateful, and the tree was so easy to climb that with my teacher's assistance I was able to scramble to a seat in the branches. It was so cool up in the tree that Miss Sullivan proposed that we have our luncheon there. I promised to keep still while she went to the house to fetch it.

Suddenly a change passed over the tree. All the sun's warmth left the air. I knew the sky was black, because all the heat, which meant light to me, had died out of the atmosphere. A strange odor came up from the earth. I knew it; it was the odor that always precedes a thunderstorm, and a nameless fear clutched at my heart. I felt absolutely alone, cut off from my friends and the firm earth. The immense, the unknown, enfolded me. I remained still and expectant; a chilling terror crept over me. I longed for my teacher's return; but above all things I wanted to get down from that tree.

There was a moment of sinister silence, then a multitudinous stirring of the leaves. A shiver ran through the tree, and the wind sent forth a blast that would have knocked me off had I not clung to the branch with might and main. The tree swayed and strained. The small twigs snapped and fell about me in showers. A wild impulse to jump seized me, but terror held me fast. I crouched

---

3. Aaron's rod, any of various tall plants with long flower-bearing stems. In the Bible, Aaron performed miracles with a rod that turned into a serpent and later blossomed and bore almonds.

Helen Keller and Anne Sullivan
Courtesy of the American Foundation for the Blind

down in the fork of the tree. The branches lashed about me. I felt the intermittent jarring that came now and then, as if something heavy had fallen and the shock had traveled up till it reached the limb I sat on. It worked my suspense up to the highest point, and just as I was thinking the tree and I should fall together, my teacher seized my hand and helped me down. I clung to her, trembling with joy to feel the earth under my feet once more. I had learned a new lesson—that nature "wages open war against her children, and under softest touch hides treacherous claws."

After this experience it was a long time before I climbed another tree. The mere thought filled me with terror. It was the sweet allurement of the mimosa tree in full bloom that finally overcame my fears. One beautiful spring morning when I was alone in the summerhouse, reading, I became aware of a wonderful subtle fragrance in the air. I started up and instinctively stretched out my hands. It seemed as if the spirit of spring had passed through the summerhouse. "What is it?" I asked, and the next minute I recognized the odor of the mimosa blossoms. I felt my way to the end of the garden, knowing that the mimosa tree was near the fence, at the turn of the path. Yes, there it was, all quivering in the warm sunshine, its blossom-laden branches almost touching the long grass. Was there ever anything so exquisitely beautiful in the world before! Its delicate blossoms shrank from the slightest earthly touch; it seemed as if a tree of paradise had been transplanted to earth. I made my way through a shower of petals to the great trunk and for one minute stood irresolute; then,

putting my foot in the broad space between the forked branches, I pulled myself up into the tree. I had some difficulty in holding on, for the branches were very large and the bark hurt my hands. But I had a delicious sense that I was doing something unusual and wonderful, so I kept on climbing higher and higher, until I reached a little seat which somebody had built there so long ago that it had grown part of the tree itself. I sat there for a long, long time, feeling like a fairy on a rosy cloud. After that I spent many happy hours in my tree of paradise, thinking fair thoughts and dreaming bright dreams.

I had now the key to all language, and I was eager to learn to use it. Children who hear acquire language without any particular effort; the words that fall from others' lips they catch on the wing, as it were, delightedly, while the little deaf child must trap them by a slow and often painful process. But whatever the process, the result is wonderful. . . .

At first, when my teacher told me about a new thing I asked very few questions. My ideas were vague, and my vocabulary was inadequate; but as my knowledge of things grew, and I learned more and more words, my field of inquiry broadened, and I would return again and again to the same subject, eager for further information. Sometimes a new word revived an image that some earlier experience had engraved on my brain.

I remember the morning that I first asked the meaning of the word, "love." This was before I knew many words. I had found a few early violets in the garden and brought them to my teacher. She tried to kiss me: but at that time I did not like to have anyone kiss me except my mother. Miss Sullivan put her arm gently round me and spelled into my hand, "I love Helen."

"What is love?" I asked.

She drew me closer to her and said, "It is here," pointing to my heart, whose beats I was conscious of for the first time. Her words puzzled me very much because I did not then understand anything unless I touched it.

I smelt the violets in her hand and asked, half in words, half in signs, a question which meant, "Is love the sweetness of flowers?"

"No," said my teacher.

Again I thought. The warm sun was shining on us.

"Is this not love?" I asked, pointing in the direction from which the heat came. "Is this not love?"

It seemed to me that there could be nothing more beautiful than the sun, whose warmth makes all things grow. But Miss Sullivan shook her head, and I was greatly puzzled and disappointed. I thought it strange that my teacher could not show me love.

A day or two afterward I was stringing beads of different sizes in symmetrical groups—two large beads, three small ones, and so on. I had made many mistakes, and Miss Sullivan had pointed them out again and again with gentle patience. Finally I noticed a very obvious error in the sequence and for an instant I concentrated my attention on the lesson and tried to think how I should have arranged the beads. Miss Sullivan touched my forehead and spelled with decided emphasis, "Think."

In a flash I knew that the word was the name of the process that was going on in my head. This was my first conscious perception of an abstract idea.

For a long time I was still—I was not thinking of the beads in my lap, but trying to find a meaning for "love" in the light of this new idea. The sun had been under a cloud all day, and there had been brief showers; but suddenly the sun broke forth in all its southern splendor.

Again I asked my teacher, "Is this not love?"

"Love is something like the clouds that were in the sky before the sun came out," she replied. Then in simpler words than these, which at that time I could not have understood, she explained: "You cannot touch the clouds, you know; but you feel the rain and know how glad the flowers and the thirsty earth are to have it after a hot day. You cannot touch love either; but you feel the sweetness that it pours into everything. Without love you would not be happy or want to play."

The beautiful truth burst upon my mind—I felt that there were invisible lines stretched between my spirit and the spirits of others.

From the beginning of my education Miss Sullivan made it a practice to speak to me as she would speak to any hearing child; the only difference was that she spelled the sentences into my hand instead of speaking them. If I did not know the words and idioms necessary to express my thoughts, she supplied them, even suggesting conversation when I was unable to keep up my end of the dialogue.

This process was continued for several years; for the deaf child does not learn in a month, or even in two or three years, the numberless idioms and expressions used in the simplest daily intercourse. The little hearing child learns these from constant repetition and imitation. The conversation he hears in his home stimulates his mind and suggests topics and calls forth the spontaneous expression of his own thoughts. This natural exchange of ideas is denied to the deaf child. My teacher, realizing this, determined to supply the kinds of stimulus I lacked. This she did by repeating to me as far as possible, verbatim, what she heard, and by showing me how I could take part in the conversation. But it was a long time before I ventured to take the initiative, and still longer before I could find something appropriate to say at the right time.

THINK AND DISCUSS

Understanding

1. How old was Helen Keller when Anne Sullivan came to be her teacher?
2. When was the first time Helen felt sorrow, or sadness about doing wrong?
3. When and how was the mystery of language finally revealed to Helen?
4. How did Helen learn what the word *think* means?
5. How did Helen define love after her discussion with Anne Sullivan?

Analyzing

6. Describe the qualities of Helen Keller's **character** that are revealed in these few pages from her autobiography.
7. Which **point of view** does this account illustrate?

Extending

8. Helen says that hearing children catch words "on the wing." This is an idiom because the words don't have their usual meanings in the phrase. If a deaf student entered your school, what idioms that you and your friends use might give this person difficulty?

VOCABULARY

Idioms

Helen Keller points out that she had trouble learning idioms that the hearing child picks up naturally through imitation and repetition. An idiom is an expression that can't be understood from the usual meanings of the words in it. For example, to "be all thumbs" means to "be very clumsy or awkward."

Tell the meaning for each of the idioms below. If necessary, look up in the Glossary the most important word in the phrase.

1. play by ear
2. out on a limb
3. the game is up
4. a frog in the throat
5. in the same boat

THINKING SKILLS

Synthesizing

To synthesize is to put together parts and elements so as to form a whole, a new pattern or structure not evident before. Synthesis can involve personal experience and imagination. For example, with Anne Sullivan's help Helen Keller came to understand that every object had a name and that by learning these words she could communicate.

Study for yourself how young children learn to communicate through words. If you can observe a young child learning language, do so. If you don't have this opportunity, interview at least one person who has or knows a young child learning to speak. Make notes on what words are said first. Do babies first say words or sentences? Do they make sounds that seem to have no meaning, or do they imitate what others say? Compare what you discover with the findings of others in your class.

COMPOSITION
Writing to Show Contrast
Recall that Helen climbed both a cherry tree and a mimosa tree. Write two paragraphs contrasting Helen's experiences in these trees. Before you begin, list details about each tree under columns headed *cherry tree* and *mimosa tree*. Include what Helen learned from each experience.

Writing About a Person
Anne Sullivan was a gifted teacher. Write a two- to four-paragraph composition about her titled "A Gifted Teacher." Before you begin, read through the story to find examples that show her traits as a teacher. Look for descriptive words, such as *patient, loving,* and *persistent.* Write one paragraph about each quality you choose, and be sure to back up your choices with examples from the account.

BIOGRAPHY

Helen Keller
1880–1968

After Helen Keller was stricken with a fever that destroyed her sight and her hearing, she became a bad-tempered, hostile, and unmanageable youngster who would lock doors, hide keys, and pull tablecloths with dishes onto the floor.

Through the efforts of her gifted and determined teacher, Anne Sullivan, Helen learned sign language and Braille. *The Story of My Life* was first published in 1903, the year before her graduation with honors from Radcliffe College. During her life she wrote, traveled, and lectured for the handicapped. She also supported the women's suffrage movement and the peace movement. She met many well-known people during her lifetime: Mark Twain (Samuel Clemens), Franklin Roosevelt, Albert Einstein, and Alexander Graham Bell, among others. Her life has been an inspiration to all people, handicapped and nonhandicapped alike.

The Green Mamba

Roald Dahl

There was a green flash as the snake darted forward at least ten feet and struck at the snake-man's leg. Nobody could have got out of the way of that one. I heard the snake's head strike against the thick cowhide boot with a sharp little *crack*. . . .

Oh, those snakes! How I hated them! They were the only fearful thing about Tanganyika,[1] and a newcomer very quickly learnt to identify most of them and to know which were deadly and which were simply poisonous. The killers, apart from the black mambas, were the green mambas, the cobras, and the tiny little puff adders that looked very much like small sticks lying motionless in the middle of a dusty path, and so easy to step on.

One Sunday evening I was invited to go and have a sundowner[2] at the house of an Englishman called Fuller who worked in the Customs office in Dar es Salaam.[3] He lived with his wife and two small children in a plain white wooden house that stood alone some way back from the road in a rough grassy piece of ground with coconut trees scattered about. I was walking across the grass towards the house and was about twenty yards away when I saw a large green snake go gliding straight up the veranda steps of Fuller's house and in through the open front door. The brilliant yellowy-green skin and its great size made me certain it was a green mamba, a creature almost as deadly as the black mamba, and for a few seconds I was so startled and dumbfounded and horrified that I froze to the spot. Then I pulled myself together and ran round to the back of the house shouting. "Mr. Fuller! Mr. Fuller!"

Mrs. Fuller popped her head out of an upstairs window. "What on earth's the matter?" she said.

"You've got a large green mamba in your front room!" I shouted. "I saw it go up the veranda steps and right in through the door!"

"Fred!" Mrs. Fuller shouted, turning round. "Fred! Come here!"

Freddy Fuller's round red face appeared at the window beside his wife. "What's up?" he asked.

---

1. *Tanganyika* (tang′gə nyē′kə), former British trust territory and later country in eastern Africa, now part of Tanzania.
2. *sundowner,* something to drink at the end of the day.
3. *Dar es Salaam* (där es sə läm′), seaport in eastern Tanzania, formerly the capital of Tanganyika.

Illustration by Dougal MacDougal

"There's a green mamba in your living room!" I shouted.

Without hesitation and without wasting time with more questions, he said to me, "Stay there. I'm going to lower the children down to you one at a time." He was com-pletely cool and unruffled. He didn't even raise his voice.

A small girl was lowered down to me by her wrists, and I was able to catch her easily by the legs. Then came a small boy. Then Freddy Fuller lowered his wife, and I caught her by the waist and put her on the ground. Then came Fuller himself. He hung by his hands from the windowsill and when he let go he landed neatly on his two feet.

We stood in a little group on the grass at the back of the house, and I told Fuller exactly what I had seen.

The mother was holding the two children by the hand, one on each side of her. They didn't seem to be particularly alarmed.

"What happens now?" I asked.

"Go down to the road, all of you," Fuller said. "I'm off to fetch the snake-man." He trotted away and got into his small ancient black car and drove off. Mrs. Fuller and the two small children and I went down to the road and sat in the shade of a large mango tree.

"Who is this snake-man?" I asked Mrs. Fuller.

"He is an old Englishman who has been out here for years," Mrs. Fuller said. "He actually *likes* snakes. He understands them and never kills them. He catches them and sells them to zoos and laboratories all over the world. Every native for miles around knows about him and whenever one of them sees a snake, he marks its hiding place and runs, often for great distances, to tell the snake-man. Then the snake-man comes along and captures it. The snake-man's strict rule is that he will never buy a captured snake from the natives."

"Why not?" I asked.

"To discourage them from trying to catch snakes themselves," Mrs. Fuller said. "In his early days he used to buy caught snakes, but so many natives got bitten trying to catch them, and so many died, that he decided to put a stop to it. Now any native who brings in a caught snake, no matter how rare, gets turned away."

"That's good," I said.

"What is the snake-man's name?" I asked.

"Donald Macfarlane," she said. "I believe he's Scottish."

"Is the snake in the house, Mummy?" the small girl asked.

"Yes, darling. But the snake-man is going to get it out."

"He'll bite Jack," the girl said.

"Oh!" Mrs. Fuller cried, jumping to her feet. "I forgot about Jack!" She began calling out, "Jack! Come here, Jack! Jack! . . . Jack! . . . Jack!"

The children jumped up as well, and all of them started calling to the dog. But no dog came out of the open front door.

"He's bitten Jack!" the small girl cried out. "He must have bitten him!" She began to cry and so did her brother, who was a year or so younger than she was. Mrs. Fuller looked grim.

"Jack's probably hiding upstairs," she said. "You know how clever he is."

Mrs. Fuller and I seated ourselves again on the grass, but the children remained standing. In between their tears they went on calling to the dog.

"Would you like me to take you down to the Maddens' house?" their mother asked.

"No!" they cried. "No, no, no! We want Jack!"

"Here's Daddy!" Mrs. Fuller cried, pointing at the tiny black car coming up the road in a swirl of dust. I noticed a long wooden pole sticking out through one of the car windows.

The children ran to meet the car. "Jack's inside the house and he's been bitten by the snake!" they wailed. "We know he's been bitten! He doesn't come when we call him!"

Mr. Fuller and the snake-man got out of the car. The snake-man was small and very old, probably over seventy. He wore leather boots made of thick cowhide, and he had long gauntlet-type gloves on his hands made of the same stuff. The gloves reached above his elbows. In his right hand he carried an extraordinary implement, an eight-foot-long wooden pole with a forked end. The two prongs of the fork were made, so it seemed, of black rubber, about an inch thick and quite flexible, and it was clear that if the fork was pressed against the ground the two prongs would bend outwards, allowing the neck of the fork to go down as close to the ground as necessary. In his left hand he carried an ordinary brown sack.

Donald Macfarlane, the snake-man, may have been old and small but he was an impressive-looking character. His eyes were pale blue, deep-set in a face round and dark and wrinkled as a walnut. Above the blue eyes, the eyebrows were thick and startlingly white, but the hair on his head was almost black. In spite of the thick leather boots, he moved like a leopard, with soft slow catlike strides, and he came straight up to me and said, "Who are you?"

"He's with the oil company," Fuller said. "He hasn't been here long."

"You want to watch?" the snake-man said to me.

"Watch?" I said, wavering. "Watch? How do you mean watch? I mean where from? Not in the house?"

"You can stand out on the veranda and look through the window," the snake-man said.

"Come on," Fuller said. "We'll both watch."

"Now don't do anything silly," Mrs. Fuller said.

The two children stood there forlorn and miserable, with tears all over their cheeks.

The snake-man and Fuller and I walked over the grass towards the house, and as we approached the veranda steps the snake-man whispered, "Tread softly on the wooden boards or he'll pick up the vibration. Wait until I've gone in, then walk up quietly and stand by the window."

The snake-man went up the steps first and he made absolutely no sound at all with his feet. He moved soft and catlike onto the veranda and straight through the front door, and then he quickly but very quietly closed the door behind him.

I felt better with the door closed. What I mean is I felt better for myself. I certainly didn't feel better for the snake-man. I figured he was committing suicide. I followed Fuller onto the veranda and we both crept over to the window. The window was open, but it had a fine mesh mosquito netting all over it. That made me feel better still. We peered through the netting.

The living room was simple and ordinary, coconut matting on the floor, a red sofa, a coffee table, and a couple of armchairs. The dog was sprawled on the matting under the coffee table, a large Airedale with curly brown and black hair. He was stone dead.

The snake-man was standing absolutely still just inside the door of the living room.

The brown sack was now slung over his left shoulder, and he was grasping the long pole with both hands, holding it out in front of him, parallel to the ground. I couldn't see the snake. I didn't think the snake-man had seen it yet either.

A minute went by . . . two minutes . . . three . . . four . . . five. Nobody moved. There was death in that room. The air was heavy with death and the snake-man stood as motionless as a pillar of stone, with the long rod held out in front of him.

And still he waited. Another minute . . . and another . . . and another.

And now I saw the snake-man beginning to bend his knees. Very slowly he bent his knees until he was almost squatting on the floor, and from that position he tried to peer under the sofa and the armchairs.

And still it didn't look as though he was seeing anything.

Slowly he straightened his legs again, and then his head began to swivel around the room. Over to the right, in the far corner, a staircase led up to the floor above. The snake-man looked at the stairs, and I knew very well what was going through his head. Quite abruptly, he took one step forward and stopped.

Nothing happened.

A moment later I caught sight of the snake. It was lying full-length along the skirting of the right-hand wall, but hidden from the snake-man's view by the back of the sofa. It lay there like a long, beautiful, deadly shaft of green glass, quite motionless, perhaps asleep. It was facing away from us who were at the window, with its small triangular head resting on the matting near the foot of the stairs.

I nudged Fuller and whispered, "It's over there against the wall." I pointed and Fuller saw the snake. At once, he started waving both hands, palms outward, back and forth across the window, hoping to get the snake-man's attention. The snake-man didn't see him. Very softly, Fuller said, "Pssst!" and the snake-man looked up sharply. Fuller pointed. The snake-man understood and gave a nod.

Now the snake-man began working his way very, very slowly to the back wall of the room so as to get a view of the snake behind the sofa. He never walked on his toes as you or I would have done. His feet remained flat on the ground all the time. The cowhide boots were like moccasins, with neither soles nor heels. Gradually, he worked his way over to the back wall, and from there he was able to see at least the head and two or three feet of the snake itself.

But the snake also saw him. With a movement so fast it was invisible, the snake's head came up about two feet off the floor, and the front of the body arched backwards, ready to strike. Almost simultaneously, it bunched its whole body into a series of curves, ready to flash forward.

The snake-man was just a bit too far away from the snake to reach it with the end of his pole. He waited, staring at the snake, and the snake stared back at him with two small malevolent black eyes.

Then the snake-man started speaking to the snake. "Come along, my pretty," he whispered in a soft wheedling voice.

"There's a good boy. Nobody's going to hurt you. Nobody's going to harm you, my pretty little thing. Just lie still and relax . . ." He took a step forward towards the snake, holding the pole out in front of him.

What the snake did next was so fast that the whole movement couldn't have taken more than a hundredth of a second, like the flick of a camera shutter. There was a green flash as the snake darted forward at least ten feet and struck at the snake-man's leg. Nobody could have got out of the way of that one. I heard the snake's head strike against the thick cowhide boot with a sharp little *crack*, and then at once the head was back in that same deadly backward-curving position, ready to strike again.

"There's a good boy," the snake-man said softly. "There's a clever boy. There's a lovely fellow. You mustn't get excited. Keep calm and everything's going to be all right." As he was speaking, he was slowly lowering the end of the pole until the forked prongs were about twelve inches above the middle of the snake's body. "There's a lovely fellow," he whispered. "There's a good kind little chap. Keep still now, my beauty. Keep still, my pretty. Keep quite still. Daddy's not going to hurt you."

I could see a thin dark trickle of venom running down the snake-man's right boot where the snake had struck.

The snake, head raised and arcing backwards, was as tense as a tight-wound spring and ready to strike again. "Keep still, my lovely," the snake-man whispered. "Don't move now. Keep still. No one's going to hurt you."

Then *wham*, the rubber prongs came down right across the snake's body, about midway along its length, and pinned it to the floor. All I could see was a green blur as the snake thrashed around furiously in an effort to free itself. But the snake-man kept up the pressure on the prongs and the snake was trapped.

What happens next? I wondered. There was no way he could catch hold of that madly twisting flailing length of green muscle with his hands, and even if he could have done so, the head would surely have flashed around and bitten him in the face.

Holding the very end of the eight-foot pole, the snake-man began to work his way round the room until he was at the tail end of the snake. Then, in spite of the flailing and the thrashing, he started pushing the prongs forward along the snake's body towards the head. Very very slowly he did it, pushing the rubber prongs forward over the snake's flailing body, keeping the snake pinned down all the time and pushing, pushing, pushing the long wooden rod forward millimeter by millimeter. It was a fascinating and frightening thing to watch, the little man with white eyebrows and black hair carefully manipulating his long implement and sliding the fork ever so slowly along the length of the twisting snake towards the head. The snake's body was thumping against the coconut matting with such a noise that if you had been upstairs you might have thought two big men were wrestling on the floor.

Then at last the prongs were right behind the head itself, pinning it down, and at that point the snake-man reached forward with one gloved hand and grasped the snake very firmly by the neck. He threw away the pole. He took the sack off his shoulder with his free hand. He lifted the great, still twisting length of the deadly green snake and pushed the head into the sack. Then he let go the head and bundled the rest of the creature in and closed the sack. The sack started jumping about as though there were fifty angry rats inside it, but the snake-man was now totally relaxed, and he held the sack casually in one hand as if it contained no more than a few pounds of potatoes. He stooped and picked up his pole from the floor, then he turned and looked towards the window where we were peering in.

"Pity about the dog," he said. "You'd better get it out of the way before the children see it."

THINK AND DISCUSS
Understanding
1. Who is Jack and what happens to him?
2. Why does Donald Macfarlane refuse to buy captured snakes from the natives?
3. Describe the extraordinary implement Macfarlane uses.

Analyzing
4. What are the two ways that the narrator helps the Fullers?
5. Describe Macfarlane's **character**. Tell about his appearance and his actions.
6. Why does Macfarlane keep talking to the snake?
7. From what **point of view** is this story told?
8. Is the narrator's choice of **point of view** effective in this account? Why or why not?

Extending
9. Do you think that the narrator's reaction upon seeing the snake is a typical human reaction to snakes? Explain.

READING LITERATURE SKILLFULLY
Drawing Conclusions
A **conclusion** is a decision or opinion reached after thinking about the facts and details that are given. When you read, you must draw conclusions about characters, setting, and events based on facts and details given by the author.

Consider that Mr. Fuller gets his family out of the house as soon as he learns about the green mamba in the living room. You, as reader, can conclude that he fears the snake will harm someone in the family.
1. After reading "The Green Mamba," can you conclude that Macfarlane is knowledgeable about snakes and courageous, or that he is ill-informed about snakes and foolhardy? Use details to back up your conclusion.
2. What conclusion can you make about Macfarlane's previous experience with snakes?
3. What conclusion can you make about

thc narrator's ability to observe what was happening around him? Give examples to support your conclusion.

COMPOSITION
Writing a Letter

Imagine that you are with the narrator and able to watch the battle between Macfarlane and the snake through the window. Write a short letter to a friend in which you describe the scene. Before you begin, review the selection and write the movements of Macfarlane in one column and the movements of the snake in another column. Use these details to create suspense in your account of the scene.

Writing About an Experience

Think of a time when you had a frightening encounter of some kind. Write two to four paragraphs about the experience. Before you begin, make a list of details you remember. Include what you felt, saw, heard, tasted, or were thinking.

ENRICHMENT
Doing Research

Snakes both fascinate and repel us. Do some research to learn about the snakes found in your state or local area. Some information can be found in books and encyclopedias in the library. If your community has a zoo, a herpetologist, someone who studies snakes, may be on the staff. Try to arrange an interview with that person. Among the things you will want to find out are the number of varieties of snakes native to your area and the coloring, size, and habits of these snakes. You will also want to know if there are any poisonous snakes in the area and if any of the varieties are endangered species.

BIOGRAPHY

Roald Dahl
1916–1990

Roald Dahl was born in Wales, a division of Great Britain, west of England. *Going Solo*, the autobiography in which this story appears, includes many of his other experiences while a member of the staff of an oil company in Tanzania.

Dahl once admitted he hadn't planned a writing career. It happened because he was interviewed by a famous writer over lunch. The writer had difficulty eating and taking notes at the same time, so Dahl offered to help. When he got the notes together to send to the interviewer, he discovered he had written a story. The interviewer sent it to the magazine, and Dahl was paid a thousand dollars for it.

Dahl is known as a master of horror and the surprise ending. Twenty-two of his short stories were dramatized for television under the series *Tales of the Unexpected*.

Use a Voice That Suits Your Purpose

When people talk, it's easy to hear different tones of voice. You can also notice different tones of voice in writing. Good writing will always have a distinct voice that suits the author's purpose. For example, if an author is writing an instruction manual, the voice will probably be logical and matter-of-fact. On the other hand, if an author wants to describe a beautiful sunset, a tone of awe and wonder is more appropriate.

In the selections you are now reading, each character speaks in a voice that suits his or her own particular personality. Read how frightened the stammering boy sounds in the following passage from Richard Wright's "Hunger." Notice too the determined tone of his mother's voice as she insists that he learn to defend himself.

> "They b-beat m-me," I gasped. "They t-t-took the m-money." . . .
>
> (page 185, column 2)

> "Don't you come in here," my mother warned me. . . . "You just stay right where you are," she said in a deadly tone. "I'm going to teach you this night to stand up and fight for yourself."
>
> (page 186, column 1)

Whatever a character thinks, feels, or experiences will be reflected in the tone of voice. In *The Story of My Life*, listen to the adventurous and daring way Helen Keller describes climbing a tree.

> But I had a delicious sense that I was doing something unusual and wonderful, so I kept on climbing higher and higher, until I reached a little seat which somebody had built there so long ago that it had grown part of the tree itself.
>
> (page 202, column 2)

Tone of voice is important whether a character is speaking, or whether the author is speaking directly to the reader. Whatever the situation, the tone should be clear and appropriate. Consider the methodical way that Ann Petry describes the process of looking for runaway slaves in the selection about Harriet Tubman.

> Unfortunately, the discovery was almost always made on a Sunday. Thus a whole day was lost before the machinery of pursuit could be set in motion.
>
> (page 188, column 2)

Similarly, in "The Green Mamba," Roald Dahl makes the snake-man's instrument easy to imagine by describing it in a detailed and precise tone.

> In his right hand he carried an extraordinary implement, an eight-foot-long wooden pole with a forked end. The two prongs of the fork were made, so it seemed, of black rubber, about an inch thick and quite flexible. . . .
>
> (page 209, column 1)

When you read, listen to voice.
When you write, choose a voice that
  suits your purpose.

Thank You

Alex Haley

We yearn to receive praise. But we forget that for someone to receive it, someone must first give it.

t was 1943, during World War II, and I was a young U.S. coastguardsman, serial number 212-548, a number we never seem to forget. My ship, the USS *Murzim,* had been underway for several days. Most of her holds contained thousands of cartons of canned or dried foods. The other holds were loaded with 500-pound bombs packed delicately in padded racks. Our destination was a big base on the Island of Tulagi in the South Pacific.

I was one of the *Murzim*'s several cooks and, quite the same as for folk ashore, this Thanksgiving morning had seen us busily preparing a traditional dinner featuring roast turkey.

Well, as any cook knows, it's a lot of hard work to cook and serve a big meal, and clean up and put everything away. But finally, around sundown, with our whole galley crew just bushed, we finished at last and were free to go flop into our bunks in the fo'c'sle.[1]

But I decided first to go out on the *Murzim*'s afterdeck for a breath of open air. I made my way out there, breathing in great, deep draughts while walking slowly about, still wearing my white cook's hat and the long apron, my feet sensing the big ship's vibrations from the deep-set, turbine diesels[2] and my ears hearing that slightly hissing sound the sea makes in resisting the skin of a ship.

I got to thinking about Thanksgiving. In reflex, my thoughts registered the historic imagery of the Pilgrims, Indians, wild turkeys, pumpkins, corn on the cob, and the rest.

Yet my mind seemed to be questing for something else—some way that I could personally apply to the waning Thanksgiving. It must have taken me a half-hour to sense that maybe some key to an answer could result from reversing the word "Thanksgiving"—at least that suggested a verbal direction, "Giving Thanks."

Giving thanks—as in praying, thanking God, I thought. Yes, of course. Certainly.

---

1. *fo'c'sle* (fōk'səl), the *forecastle* or sailors' quarters in the forward part of a cargo ship.
2. *turbine diesels* (tėr'bən dē'zəlz), the ship's engines.

"Thank You" by Alex Haley, published in *Parade Magazine,* November 21, 1982. Copyright © 1982 by Alex Haley. Reprinted by permission of John Hawkins & Associates, Inc., 71 W. 23rd St., N.Y., 10010.

Yet my mind continued nagging me. Fine. But something else.

After a while, like a dawn's brightening, a further answer did come—that there were *people* to thank, people who had done so much for me that I could never possibly repay them. The embarrassing truth was I'd always just accepted what they'd done, taken all of it for granted. Not one time had I ever bothered to express to any of them so much as a simple, sincere "Thank you."

At least seven people had been particularly and indelibly helpful to me. I realized, with a gulp, that about half of them had since died— so they were forever beyond any possible expression of gratitude from me. The more I thought about it, the more ashamed I became. Then I pictured the three who were still alive and, within minutes, I was down in the fo'c'sle.

Sitting at a mess table with writing paper and memories of things each had done, I tried composing genuine statements of heart-felt appreciation and gratitude to my dad, Simon A. Haley, a professor at the old AMNC (Agricultural Mechanical Normal College) in Pine Bluff, Arkansas, now a branch of the University of Arkansas; to my grandma, Cynthia Palmer, back in our little hometown of Henning, Tennessee; and to the Rev. Lonual Nelson, my grammar school principal, retired and living in Ripley, six miles north of Henning.

I couldn't even be certain if they would recall some of their acts of years past, acts that I vividly remembered and saw now as having given me vital training, or inspiration, or directions, if not all of these desirables rolled into one.

The texts of my letters began something like, "Here, this Thanksgiving at sea, I find my thoughts upon how much you have done for me, but I have never stopped and said to you how much I feel the need to thank you—" And briefly I recalled for each of them specific acts performed in my behalf.

For instance, something uppermost about my father was how he had impressed upon me from boyhood to love books and reading. In fact, this graduated into a family habit of after-dinner quizzes at the table about books read most recently and new words learned. My love of books never diminished and later led me toward writing books myself. So many times I have felt a sadness when exposed to modern children so immersed in the electronic media that they have little to no awareness of the wondrous world to be discovered in books.

I reminded the Reverend Nelson how each morning he would open our little country town's grammar school with a prayer over his assembled students. I told him that whatever positive things I had done since had been influenced at least in part by his morning school prayers.

In the letter to my grandmother, I reminded her of a dozen ways she used to teach me how to tell the truth, to be thrifty, to share, and to be forgiving and considerate of others. (My reminders included how she'd make me pull switches from a peach tree for my needed lesson.) I thanked her for the years of eating her good cooking, the equal of which I had not found since. (By now, though, I've reflected that those peerless dishes are most gloriously flavored with a pinch of nostalgia.) Finally, I thanked her simply for having sprinkled my life with stardust.

Before I slept, my three letters went into our ship's office mail sack. They got mailed when we reached Tulagi Island.

We unloaded cargo, reloaded with something else, then again we put to sea in the routine familiar to us, and as the days became weeks, my little personal experience receded. Sometimes, when we were at sea, a mail ship would rendezvous and bring us mail from home, which, of course, we accorded topmost priority.

Every time the ship's loudspeaker rasped, "Attention! Mail call!" 200-odd shipmates came pounding up on deck and clustered about the raised hatch atop which two yeomen, standing by those precious bulging gray sacks, were alternately pulling out fistfuls of letters and barking successive names of sailors who were, in turn, hollering "Here! Here!" amid the jostling.

One "Mail Call" brought me responses from Grandma, Dad and the Reverend Nelson—and my reading of their letters left me not only astounded, but more humbled than before.

Rather than saying they would forgive that I hadn't previously thanked them, instead, for Pete's sake, they were thanking *me*—for having remembered, for having considered they had done anything so exceptional.

Always the college professor, my dad had carefully avoided anything he considered too sentimental, so I knew how moved he was to write me that, after having helped educate many young people, he now felt that his best results included his own son.

The Reverend Nelson wrote that his decades as a "simple, old-fashioned principal" had ended with grammar schools undergoing such swift changes that he had retired in self-doubt. "I heard more of what I had done wrong than what I did right," he said, adding that my letter had brought him welcome reassurance that his career had been appreciated.

A glance at Grandma's familiar handwriting brought back, in a flash, memories of standing alongside her white wicker rocking chair, watching her "settin' down" some letter to relatives. Frequently touching her pencil's tip to pursed lips, character by character, each between a short, soft grunt, Grandma would slowly accomplish one word, then the next, so that a finished single page would consume hours. I wept over the page representing my Grandma's recent hours invested in expressing her loving gratefulness to *me*—whom she used to diaper!

Much later, retired from the Coast Guard and trying to make a living as a writer, I never forgot how those three "thank you" letters gave me an insight into something nigh mystical[3] in human beings, most of whom go about yearning in secret for more of their fellows to express appreciation for their efforts.

I discovered in time that, even in the business world, probably no two words are more valued than "thank you," especially among people at stores, airlines, utilities and others that directly serve the public.

Late one night, I was one of a half-dozen passengers who straggled weary and grumbling off a plane that had been forced to land

---

3. **nigh mystical**, nearly impossible for a person to understand through intellectual processes alone.

Alex Haley, right, with his brothers Julius, left, and George, center, looks at a news story about the special Pulitzer Prize he was awarded for his book *Roots*. (See the biography.)

at the huge Dallas/Fort Worth Airport. Suddenly, a buoyant, cheerful, red-jacketed airline man waved us away from the regular waiting room seats, saying, "You sure look bushed. I know a big empty office where you can stretch out while you wait." And we surely did. When the weather improved enough for us to leave, "Gene Erickson" was in my notebook and, back home, I wrote the president of that airline describing his sensitivity and his courtesy. And I received a thank you!

I travel a good deal on lecture tours and I urge students especially to tell their parents, grandparents, and other living elders simply "Thank you" for all they have done to make possible the lives they now enjoy. Many students have told me they found themselves moved by the response. It is not really surprising, if one only reflects how it must feel to be thanked after you have given for years.

Now, approaching Thanksgiving of 1982, I have asked myself what will I wish for all who are reading this, for our nation, indeed for our whole world—since, quoting a good and wise friend of mine, "In the end we are mightily and merely people, each with similar needs." First, I wish for us, of course, the simple common sense to achieve world peace, that being paramount for the very survival of our kind.

And there is something else I wish—so strongly that I have had this line printed across the bottom of all my stationery: *"Find the good—and praise it."*

THINK AND DISCUSS
Understanding
1. Where is Alex Haley on Thanksgiving Day in 1943?
2. Why does Haley decide to write the thank-you letters?
3. For what specific actions does he thank his dad, Reverend Nelson, and his grandmother?

Analyzing
4. What do the letters Haley receives from his dad, Reverend Nelson, and his grandmother have in common?
5. What does Haley learn about human beings as a result of the three letters?
6. Does Haley live up to the line "Find the good—and praise it"? Explain.

Extending
7. Do you agree with Haley that most human beings secretly yearn for more of their fellows to express appreciation for their efforts? Why or why not?

READING LITERATURE SKILLFULLY
Author's Purpose
The **author's purpose** is the reason or reasons the author has for writing. Three common purposes are (**1**) to inform—to explain or to give information; (**2**) to persuade—to convince the reader to think or act in a certain way; and (**3**) to entertain—to amuse, scare, or make the reader feel sadness or triumph.
1. Which of the three purposes do you think was the most important reason for Alex Haley as he wrote "Thank You"?

2. Does Haley succeed in this purpose, at least with you as reader?
3. To what extent do the other two purposes apply to this selection?

VOCABULARY
Inflected Forms
Inflected forms of words are regularly formed by adding *-ed*, *-ing*, *-s*, *-es*, *-er*, and *-est* to the root word. Not all words, however, have regularly inflected forms. The plural of *priority* is *priorities*. The comparative and superlative forms of *weary* are *wearier* and *weariest*. The past tense of *commit* is spelled with two *t*'s: *committed*. Irregularly spelled inflected forms can be found in a dictionary. They often are listed near the beginning of an entry, after the part-of-speech label.

Study the sentences below. On your paper, write the correct inflected form of each italicized word. Use your Glossary for any unfamiliar words.
1. I (*immerse*, past tense) myself in the book and forgot about my problem.
2. The volunteers displayed a wide range of (*sensitivity*, plural).
3. Of the two, Max had the (*surly*, comparative) personality.
4. Our last three (*rendezvous*, plural) took place in the park.
5. Sue aided and (*abet*, past tense) the protesters.

COMPOSITION
Reading/Writing Log
In this selection, Alex Haley explains his belief that most people appreciate hearing

"thank you" for something they have done. To convince readers of his own belief, Haley gives specific examples in a matter-of-fact tone of voice. Notice the examples listed below and add at least three others from the selection.

> After a while . . . a further answer did come—that there were *people* to thank. . . .

> For instance, something uppermost about my father was how he had impressed upon me from boyhood to love books and reading.

Writing as a Story Character

Suppose that Mrs. Westby were to write a thank-you letter to James Herriot, or that Richard Wright were to write a thank-you letter to his mother. Helen Keller might write to her teacher, Anne Sullivan. Write a letter as one of the characters in this unit might have written it. Before you begin, review the selection and determine the voice that character would use. If you are keeping a **reading/writing log,** refer to the examples of Haley's voice that you copied earlier.

Writing a Personal Letter

Follow Alex Haley's example by expressing thanks to someone who has helped you in some way. Write a letter to that person, who might be a parent, a relative, a friend, a teacher, or a casual acquaintance. Before you write the letter, jot down a list of the specific ways the person helped you. In the letter, review what the individual did, under what circumstances, and with what consequences.

BIOGRAPHY

Alex Haley

1921–

During a twenty-year career in the U.S. Coast Guard (1939–1959), Alex Haley taught himself good writing. Upon retiring as the first Chief Journalist, Haley became a magazine writer, interviewer, and biographer, publishing *The Autobiography of Malcolm X* in 1965. For twelve years he researched and wrote *Roots,* a highly acclaimed account of his search for his African origins.

About *Roots,* which Haley calls "faction" (a combination of *fact* and *fiction*), he has said, "All the major incidents are true . . . the names and dates are real, but obviously when it comes to dialogue, and people's emotions and thoughts, I had to make things up. It's heightened history, or fiction based on real people's lives." In 1977 *Roots* won a special Pulitzer Prize. *Roots* has been translated into twenty-four languages, and it is a best seller in many countries throughout the world.

Captain of His Ship

Bob Greene

This attitude of his—this pride in the work he was doing—was the very thing we have for so long been told has vanished from the American work force.

---

ometimes, when you're not looking for anything, something comes up and strikes you as clear as daybreak. I had been traveling by bus through corn-and-soybean country for several days; my reasons were personal ones, and I had found what I was looking for, and now I was on my way back to Chicago.

I seldom ride interstate buses, but these few days had been enough to convince me that there is little romance to them. As a traveler who usually finds himself in airports, I had become numbed by this week's endless hours in dank, musty buses, heading slowly between places that no other form of public transportation serves.

My fellow passengers were not inflation-fighters; they were on the buses because buses are the lowest common denominator of American transportation. There is nothing cheaper; the low price was the only reason that the people were aboard. They were the bottom social stratum of the country's travelers; they needed to get someplace, and the bus was all they could afford.

Now I was on the last leg of my journey; the bus I was on had started the trip in St. Louis, and was on a nine-hour run through Missouri and Illinois. Several hours into the ride, I began to notice something.

It was the driver. He was a young man with a mustache and sideburns; I would have to guess he was in his early thirties. What struck me was the manner of crispness and precision he brought to his job. He was dressed neatly, and he addressed his passengers politely, and at the rest stops he timed his schedule exactly with his wristwatch.

When a passenger approached him with a question along the way, the driver did not act as if he were annoyed; he took time to answer in a friendly, informed way. It was, frankly, a lousy route; instead of heading directly to Chicago, the schedule called for him to stop at any number of tiny towns along the way: Clinton, Fullerton, Farmer City, Gibson.

Usually there was no bus station in these cities; the driver would pull the coach into a gas station parking lot, or stop in front of a restaurant. One person might get off, or two

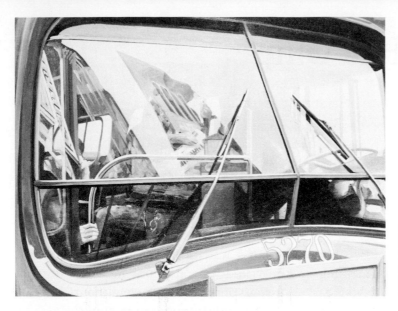

Richard Estes, *Bus Front*, 1967
Private Collection
This is an example of photorealism,
a technique in which the painter
strives to make the painting look
like a photograph.

might get on. It hardly seemed worth his
time to be making the detours to serve so few
passengers.

And yet he carried out his job with class.
He welcomed each passenger to the bus; hurried out the door to assist with baggage; made
a fresh count of travelers for his logbook at
every stop. I got the impression that he was
memorizing all of our faces; we might be with
him only for one gray autumn day, but we
were his passengers and he seemed to be
making an effort to take a personal interest in
that.

He was just a long-haul bus driver heading
up some forgotten route in the middle of the
country, but for his attitude, this might have
been a Boeing 747 on its way to Paris. I found
myself wondering what struck me so oddly
about this man, and in a second the realization came. This attitude of his—this pride in
the work he was doing—was the very thing
we have for so long been told has vanished
from the American work force.

Had the driver taken a lazy and slovenly
approach, no one would have ever known;
the passengers on an interstate bus aren't the
kind of people who have the pull to make
trouble. They have no alternative; if they
don't like the bus, there's no cheaper way for
them to go. Certainly there was no prestige
built into the driver's work.

But on this ride, it was as if the idea of not
doing his job well had never crossed the driver's mind. And a funny thing was happening;
because the driver found dignity in his own
work, he instilled his load of passengers with
a small feeling of dignity, too. Oh, they knew
they were riding on an uncomfortable bus
with men and women who probably couldn't
afford any other means of transportation; but
because the driver had pride, the passengers
seemed to feel a little better, too.

At one toll booth the driver paid the attendant, then leaned out the window to say
something. I listened. The driver had seen a
car stalled on the side of the highway several

miles back, and was advising the toll-booth man to telephone the state police to inform them that there was a traveler in trouble. I hadn't noticed the stalled car, but the driver had, and he obviously considered this part of his job.

When we pulled into the station in Chicago's Loop, the driver stood at the bottom of the steps leading out of the bus, helping each passenger depart, saying good-bye to each of us. He stayed there until the bus was empty.

It was something to see. Most of the passengers had no one to greet them; they wandered out of the station one by one. In a bus station there is none of that sense of drama you're always getting at a big airport; here the feeling was not of an adventure beginning, but of dreary, uneventful life continuing.

And yet, because of his attitude—the way he feels about his work—the driver had, for a few hours, made things different. When I arrived home, I realized something inexcusable: for all the driver's impressiveness, I hadn't even bothered to learn his name. So I called the dispatcher and found out. It is Ted Litt.

THINK AND DISCUSS
Understanding
1. What is important about the fact that the bus driver is on a nine-hour run through Missouri and Illinois?
2. Judging by the bus driver's attitude, what might the route be?
3. What are some of the words the narrator uses to describe the bus driver?
4. Because the driver has dignity in his work, how does he affect the passengers?

Analyzing
5. Judging by the driver's actions, how do you think he feels about himself?
6. Do you think that the **author's** main **purpose** was to inform, to persuade, or to entertain? Explain.

Extending
7. In what ways might the narrator's phone call to the dispatcher help Ted Litt in the future?

READING LITERATURE SKILLFULLY
Main Idea and Supporting Details
Suppose you are talking to some classmates after taking a test. Undoubtedly, the **topic** of your conversation is the test. Usually there is a **main idea** about that test, such as "That was the hardest test we've had this year!" Next, some people will probably give examples of questions— or **details**—that support the idea that the test was difficult.

Similarly, nonfiction writing will have a topic, a main idea, and supporting details. The topic of "Captain of His Ship" is the bus driver, Ted Litt.
1. What main idea about the bus driver is expressed by the narrator?

2. What are some of the details that support the main idea?
3. Most often the main idea of an article is not directly stated by the author, but occasionally there is a sentence that states it. Reread the last paragraph. Which sentence best states the main idea?

THINKING SKILLS
Evaluating

To evaluate is to make a judgment based on some sort of standard. For example, the narrator judges the bus driver, Ted Litt, to have an unusually good attitude toward his job.

Work with a small group of classmates to establish a set of standards for evaluating a student's attitude toward school. Make a list of attitudes that show pride in being a student. Consider such things as dress, treatment of others, schedules, and homework.

COMPOSITION
Writing a Thank-You Letter

Suppose that the narrator of this selection takes a lesson from Alex Haley and decides to write a letter to the bus driver. Imagine you are Bob Greene. Write a letter to Ted Litt thanking him for a job well done. Be sure to list specific details that impressed you. You may want to make a list of things to mention before you write the letter.

Writing About Someone You Know

Think about someone who has helped you in such a way that afterwards you felt you had more dignity because of that person's attitude. Write two or three paragraphs that describe the person and the situation. You might choose to write about a family member, a friend, a store clerk, or a teacher. Your purpose should be to inform others about someone who has made life a little better for you.

BIOGRAPHY

Robert Greene
1947–

Robert Greene writes a column under the name Bob Greene. It appears in more than two hundred newspapers. Greene is also a contributing editor to *Esquire* magazine, where his monthly column is called "American Beat." This selection comes from one of those columns. In an interview he said that his favorite columns are those he finds while traveling around the country; they are usually stories about people who would not otherwise make the news. In 1977 Greene won the National Headliner award for best newspaper column in the United States. He has eight books to his credit. The most recent, *Be True to Your School*, was published in 1987 and is based on diaries that he kept during his junior and senior years in high school.

Disaster at Sea

Walter R. Brown
Norman D. Anderson

The luxury liner *Titanic* set sail from England to America on April 10, 1912, its first voyage. The design of the ship was expected to become the model for shipbuilding in the years to come.

ifeboats?" Mrs. Astor's voice showed surprise. "I thought the *Titanic* was supposed to be un-sinkable."

First Officer William Murdoch had just led Colonel and Mrs. John Jacob Astor on a brief tour of the first-class section of the huge ship. He had met them as they boarded the passenger liner. They had then taken a quick look at the first-class dining room in the middle of D Deck. An elevator had carried them to the boat deck, where they now stood.

"She is unsinkable, Madam." First Officer Murdoch let his hand brush lightly against one of the sixteen lifeboats that lined the deck. "The *Titanic* is the world's largest and safest ship."

"He is correct, Mrs. Astor."

At the sound of the deep voice, the couple turned. Here was the man they had come to the boat deck to meet.

Captain Edward L. Smith looked like the captain of a huge passenger liner. He was nearly sixty, and his heavy beard and mustache were flecked deeply with gray. He was not very tall, but he was slim. He wore a dress-white uniform. The brim of his cap, that he touched as he bowed slightly, was trimmed with gold braid.

"She is as nearly unsinkable as can be built. She has two hulls, one inside the other." The Captain led them inside the wheelhouse at the front of the boat deck. It was from here that the ship was steered.

"Fifteen thick, steel walls divide the lower deck into sixteen compartments," he explained to Mrs. Astor. "At the push of this button," he continued, pointing to a red button near the wheel, "electric motors close and seal steel doors. That makes each compartment completely watertight.

"The engineers who designed the ship figure that the worst that could happen to her would be a collision with another ship. An accident like that might puncture both hulls and flood the compartment inside. There is a slight chance, of course, that such a hole might be made at the point where a crosswall joins the hulls. If that happened, *two* compartments might flood. The engineers' figures show that the ship will float easily with two compartments flooded. She would even survive with as many as three compartments filled with water. A worse accident than that is impossible."

He shook hands again with Astor and again welcomed the two aboard the *Titanic*. As he watched them leave, he saw Murdoch again brush his hand lightly against one of the lifeboats. Neither of the men had mentioned to their passengers that the *Titanic* carried only enough lifeboats for about half of the people on board.

The *Titanic* left Southampton, England, at noon on Wednesday, April 10, 1912. The first part of the voyage went well. Sunday, April 14, found the *Titanic* in the middle of the North Atlantic. After church services, most of the passengers read, played card games or squash, wrote letters, or worked out in the gym. Only a few tried to walk the open decks. The air was quite chilly and, as the sun went down, the temperature dropped to near freezing.

The ship's two radio operators were too busy to relax and enjoy the trip. Their radio shack was a jumble of batteries, wires, and keys. They were proud to be in charge of the most modern wireless telegraph equipment in the world. By tapping out Morse code on their key, they could send messages hundreds of miles across the ocean. The passengers had asked that dozens and dozens of messages be sent ahead to New York.

Messages came to the *Titanic*'s radio room from other ships too. Several of these told of icebergs and sheets of ice in the water near the course of the big liner. These warnings were written out and taken to the wheelhouse. At 9:25 in the evening, Captain Smith gave the ice warnings to the officer in charge and went to bed. According to the messages from other ships, the *Titanic* would not reach the danger area for several hours.

Fifteen minutes later, a radio message was received warning of "icebergs and pack ice" between Latitude 42° N to 41°25′ N; Longitude 49° to 50°30′ W. Radio Operator John Phillips was busy trying to get the passengers' messages out. He wrote the location of the ice on a scrap of paper, but did not bother to take it to the wheelhouse. He did not realize that the *Titanic* had just entered the area described in the radio message.

At 10 P.M. First Officer William Murdoch took over command of the ship. He was given the old warnings about ice ahead. He passed these on to the two men on watch in the crow's nest, high above the ship's boat deck. Seamen Fleet and Lee reported that they could see fairly well in spite of there being no moon, since the stars were shining brightly. They told Murdoch that from where they were the sea was so calm it looked "slick." Murdoch replied, "I would be happier if there were a little wind." Ice lying in the water would be easier to see if the wind were pushing waves against it.

Radio Operator Phillips stayed busy sending messages ahead to New York. Suddenly, his headphone crackled with a signal so strong it hurt his ears. It was a steamer named *California* calling. "We are stopped and surrounded by ice," the message said.

Phillips was the type of person who liked to do his job well. But he was not able to

Chris Mayger, *The Maiden Voyage of the Titanic*, 1975
New English Library

think very carefully about a new situation. He felt that he had to get the messages off to New York for the important passengers on board the *Titanic*. The loudness of the signal from the *California* should have warned him that the steamer was nearby and that the *Titanic* was heading for the ice field that surrounded the other ship. Instead, he radioed back, "Shut up! Shut up! I'm busy!" and pulled the headphones from his ears.

From the wheelhouse, Murdoch watched the water ahead carefully. He ordered a hatch cover closed because the light bothered his eyes. High above him, Fleet and Lee searched the night quietly. At 11:40, Fleet saw something in the water ahead. He pulled the alarm chain three times and yelled into the telephone. "ICEBERG—RIGHT AHEAD!"

Murdoch acted instantly. He ordered a quick turn to the left and reached for the engine room telegraph. FULL STOP, he signaled to the engine room. Then FULL REVERSE.

For half a minute, that seemed like hours, the men watched as they rushed through the darkness. As they neared it, the iceberg seemed to grow and grow until it towered above the boat deck.

In the dining rooms, the stewards' talking was interrupted by the rattling of the dishes and silverware they had put in place for breakfast. A card game was interrupted briefly by the sight of a mountain of glistening white ice sliding past the windows.

On the lower decks of the ship, it was a different story. The crewmen on duty in the boiler rooms had jumped into action when the signal from Murdoch arrived. As they worked, turning valves and shoveling coal, they felt a terrible shock. Coal was thrown from the bins and men were thrown off their feet.

Murdoch had felt only a slight jar as they passed the iceberg, but he knew what that shock meant. He quickly pressed the button that controlled the watertight doors. Red lights flashed and bells rang their warning throughout the sixteen compartments of the lowest deck. Fifteen steel doors slid shut and sealed tightly. Just then, the sea broke through. The greenish water swirled around the pipes and machinery. Firemen, stokers, and engineers in boiler rooms 5 and 6 scrambled up safety ladders as the water rose behind them. Ahead of the boiler rooms were a baggage compartment, two cargo holds, and a chain locker. Each was sealed off by the watertight doors, but each was rapidly filling with water.

The third-class passengers were only one deck above the boiler rooms and felt the shock nearly as strongly as did the crewmen below. Those in the front of the ship knew that something was terribly wrong. One of these was an Irish girl, Katherine Gilnagh. She felt that she had to get out of those cramped spaces that were so near the water. But she had no idea where she should go. There had been no boat drills and no one had told any of the passengers where the lifeboat deck was or how to get there. Katherine began to climb the stairs. All she knew was she wanted to go up.

Captain Smith had taken command of the ship from First Officer Murdoch. The ship's carpenter quickly arrived in the wheelhouse.

"She's hurt bad," he reported. "There's a gash below the water line, running from the bow to boiler room 5. We're taking water into six compartments!"

Smith, along with one of the engineers who had helped design the ship, made a quick trip below. With six compartments damaged, they decided, there was nothing they could do to save the ship.

It was now 12:05 in the morning—twenty-five minutes after the iceberg had brushed the ship. Captain Smith ordered the lifeboats uncovered. Stewards were sent through the ship to tell the passengers to put on lifejackets and move to the boat deck. Radio Operator Phillips was ordered to send a call for help. Over and over he tapped the message "CQD-MGY 41°46′N; 50°14′W."

"CQD" was, in 1912, the universal call for help. The signal "SOS" that we use today had only recently been suggested because it was easier to send and to understand. Later that night, Phillips switched to the SOS signal. This was the first time this signal had been used by a ship in need of help.

The frantic CQD signal was heard immediately by many ships. The German steamer *Frankfort* signaled "OK" at 12:18. The Canadian ship *Mt. Temple*, the American liner *Virginian*, the Russian steamer *Birma*, and the *Titanic*'s sister ship, the *Olympia*, all heard the distress signal and changed course, heading for the crippled ship. Messages of encouragement flew through the air. But all of these ships were 150 or more miles away. It would be hours and hours before any of them reached the *Titanic*'s position.

There was a ship much closer to the damaged *Titanic*. In fact, the *California* was so close Captain Smith could see her lights. This was the ship that had warned the *Titanic* of the ice field where she still lay, just ten miles north of the sinking ship. But no one on the *California* realized the *Titanic* was in trouble. Shortly after being told to "Shut up" by the liner's radio operator, the only radioman on the *California* had shut his equipment off and gone to bed. A signal light was used to try to get the attention of the men on the *California*, but it was not answered.

The passenger liner *Carpathia* was only sixty miles away, but she too carried only one radio operator. His name was Harold Cottom. At the time the first calls for help went out from the *Titanic*, Cottom was not at his radio. He had gone to the bridge to deliver a message and to chat over a cup of coffee with the men on watch. At 12:25, he returned to his post. Hearing the CQD signal, he tapped out the message, CARPATHIA—COMING HARD, and ran for the wheelhouse. Even at top speed, the liner was nearly four hours away.

The lights of the *California* still twinkled dimly in the distance. A man was sent to the stern of the *Titanic* to fire off signal rockets to try to attract the attention of the other ship. On board the *California*, Seaman James Gibson saw the rockets. He studied the lights of the liner through binoculars. He pointed out the rockets to Second Officer Herbert Stone.

Neither man guessed that the fireworks were a last, desperate call for help.

The *Titanic* had now begun to settle heavily in its bow. The officers and crewmen were trying to get the passengers into the boats. The passengers were confused. They had not been given a boat drill and did not know what to do. The ship's crew were not even certain to which boats they had been assigned. "Women and children first!" they shouted. They tried to allow men in the boats only after as many women as possible were already in.

Some of the passengers fought to get into the boats. Others refused to leave at all. Mrs. Isidor Straud did not want to leave her husband, and he would not go until everyone else was safe. So, hand and hand, the elderly couple sat quietly in deck chairs until the water claimed them.

Lifeboat #4 had been lowered until it was level with A Deck. Windows were broken out and deck chairs were placed against the rail. Colonel Astor lifted his wife up in his arms and passed her over the windowsill and into the boat. He then leaned through the window and kissed her lightly.

"I'll see you later, Dearie," he said calmly. He then turned and walked slowly down the slanting deck.

Katherine Gilnagh had found her way to A Deck, but could not find the stairs that led to the boat deck. As she ran down the slanting deck, she saw a man—the only person she had seen on the entire deck. He was standing by the railing, watching Lifeboat #4 pull away from the ship.

"Sir! Sir! Can you help me?" the crying girl pleaded. "I can't find the stairs."

Colonel Astor knew how crowded the boat deck was, and how few of these people were going to get into the last few boats. Instead of taking the girl to the stairs, he led her to the rail.

"Climb up on my shoulders," he ordered. "One of the seamen on the deck above will pull you into a lifeboat."

This was quickly done. As the lifeboat was lowered into the sea, Katherine saw the man for the last time, leaning against the rail, calmly watching the boats pull away into the night.

Engineers, firemen, and stokers worked at keeping the boilers going to give the ship the electricity it needed for the radio signals and for lights. They died at their posts, 122 feet below the boat deck.

The band leader had called his seven musicians to the boat deck. There they played happy Ragtime music as the boats were being filled. As the last boat pulled away and the water began to lap around their ankles, they began playing hymns. One by one, they slipped down the slanting deck and into the dark, cold water.

Radioman Phillips continued to tap out a steady call for help. Radioman Cottom on the Carpathia listened helplessly as his big liner smashed its way northward. At 2:17 the signal sputtered "CQ . . ." and stopped. The Titanic was gone. The Carpathia was still more than two hours away.

On board the California, only ten miles away, Seaman Gibson reported that he could no longer see lights from the liner. "She must have turned and moved farther south," he reported.

There were sixteen lifeboats and two rubber life rafts in the water when the Titanic finally stood straight up on her bow and slipped into the ocean. The lifeboats were not completely full, but even if they had been there would not have been enough room in them for more than half of the people on board the ship.

The temperature of the water was 28°F. A person can live for only a short while in water at that temperature. When the Carpathia arrived two hours later, everyone who was still in the water was dead.

The rescue liner picked up a total of only 705 survivors. Nearly 1,500 people had died along with the "world's largest and safest ship."

Comment

Compare the Real Story and a Novel

Is it possible to predict the future? Morgan Robertson's novel *Futility* was published in 1898, fourteen years before the *Titanic* sank in history's most famous sea disaster. It told of a great "unsinkable" luxury liner named the *Titan* that sank on its first voyage. Like the *Titanic*, the *Titan* hit an iceberg, and almost all passengers were lost because there were not enough lifeboats. Consider these other similarities between the novel and the true story.

	Titan	*Titanic*
Ship length	800 feet	882.5 feet
Ship tonnage	75,000	66,000
Propellers	3	3
Speed at impact	25 knots	23 knots
Passengers	3,000	2,207
Month of disaster	April	April

From *The Literary Life and Other Curiosities* by Robert Hendrickson. Copyright © 1981 by Robert Hendrickson. Reprinted by permission of the author.

THINK AND DISCUSS

Understanding

1. Why did Radio Operator John Phillips twice fail to relay the messages warning of ice ahead?
2. Why did First Officer Murdoch say he would be happier if there were a little wind instead of the calm?
3. Who spotted the ice first, and what was done?
4. How much damage did the iceberg do to the ship?

Analyzing

5. Why do you think Captain Smith had not had any lifeboat drills?

6. People remained on board the sinking *Titanic* for different reasons. What were some of these reasons? Who do you think were the heroes? Explain your choices.
7. Many circumstances combined to produce this sea disaster. What were some of the things that could have been done to prevent it?
8. What is the **point of view** from which this account is told?

Extending

9. The *California* was only ten miles away, but it was surrounded by ice. Do you think it could have moved

enough to rescue the passengers from the *Titanic?*

10. Suppose you were the age you are now and a passenger on the *Titanic.* How do you think you would have reacted to the situation?

READING LITERATURE SKILLFULLY
Fact and Opinion

A **statement of fact** is a statement that can be proved true or false. If a friend tells you that there are fewer ship disasters today than airplane disasters, you can check the facts in a reference book or by talking with an authority on the subject. If you find out the statement is correct, then you have a statement of fact that is true. If the statement is not correct, then you have a statement of fact that is false.

Statements of opinion express attitudes, personal feelings, and judgments. "We should make all ships safe for travel before we build huge ocean liners" is an opinion. Many people would agree, but some would not. Words that are clues to opinions are *should, ought, best, worst, ugly, beautiful, funny,* and *strange.* Some opinions are more valid than others in that they can be supported or explained.

Identify each of the following as a statement of fact or a statement of opinion.
1. The *Titanic* is the world's safest ship.
2. Fifteen thick, steel walls divided the lower deck into sixteen compartments.
3. The worst that could happen would be a collision with another ship.
4. The *Titanic* left Southampton, England, at noon on Wednesday, April 10, 1912.
5. Phillips was the type of person who liked to do his job well.
6. Phillips must have thought he should send the passengers' messages first.
7. "CQD" was, in 1912, the universal call for help.
8. The rescue liner picked up a total of only 705 survivors.

COMPOSITION
Reading/Writing Log

The authors of this account tell the true story in a factual way to inform readers about the sinking of the *Titanic.* Yet they also use dialogue between the people aboard ship to keep the story moving and to entertain readers. Notice the examples of both factual information and dialogue below. The words spoken by people show various feelings, such as surprise, awe, and fear. If you are keeping a **reading/writing log,** add at least four more examples of your own.

"Lifeboats?" Mrs. Astor's voice showed surprise. "I thought the *Titanic* was supposed to be unsinkable."

Sunday, April 14, found the *Titanic* in the middle of the North Atlantic.

Messages came to the *Titanic*'s radio room from other ships too.

Writing a Journal Entry

Write a journal entry as Mrs. Astor, Katherine Gilnagh, or any other man, woman, or child who survived the disaster might have done on the day after the rescue efforts. Include details about the rescue, what happened during the last hour aboard ship, and how the person probably felt. Refer to your **reading/writing log,** if you are keeping one, for details. You will probably want to add more examples before you write the journal entry.

Writing as a Story Character

Imagine yourself in Katherine Gilnagh's place. After the rescue, you feel you want to write to Mrs. John Astor to let her know how her husband helped you escape from the sinking ship, saving you instead of himself. Write a letter as you think Katherine would have written it. Remember that Mrs. Astor would need to know what happened as much as Katherine would need to write about it.

ENRICHMENT
Researching the Story

Many books and newspaper articles have been written about the sinking of the *Titanic,* including efforts to salvage items from the sunken ship in the summer of 1987. Do some reading about the *Titanic,* and then with a small group of classmates choose an interesting aspect of the story to report to the entire class. One group might draw the ship and label its parts on a large poster board, showing the placement of the boat deck, the wheelhouse, and the crow's nest. Another group might compare the sinking of the *Titanic* with other sea disasters, some of which resulted in a greater loss of life.

 BIOGRAPHIES

Walter Reed Brown   1929–

Walter Reed Brown has taught science at the university, high school and junior high school levels, and he has served as coordinator for science and mathematics programs. He has contributed to and written many books, especially the "Historical Catastrophies" series on subjects such as volcanoes, tornadoes, earthquakes, floods, famines, snowstorms, and avalanches.

Norman Dean Anderson   1928–

Norman Dean Anderson has been a junior high and high school teacher. He has also won awards for distinguished teaching at the university level and contributed to or written many books in science. He says that his contact with young people and science—as a father of six, former junior high science teacher, and university professor of science education—has given him more ideas than he could write about in a lifetime.

THINKING CRITICALLY
ABOUT LITERATURE

UNIT 3 NONFICTION

■ CONCEPT REVIEW

The selection that follows contains many of the important ideas found in the selections in this unit. It includes notes and questions designed to help you think critically about your reading. Page numbers in the notes refer to an application. A more complete discussion of the term is in the Handbook of Literary Terms.

Nobody's Better Off Dead

Quentin Reynolds

In a veterans' hospital in New York lay a young Air Force pilot. His face was turned to the wall. He was bitter and angry. A plane crash had left his body paralyzed. He could not move from his neck down. He wanted to die.

He wouldn't even listen to the doctors. They spoke of a plan that might teach him to live with his handicap.

"Let's get Junius Kellogg to talk to him," one of the doctors said. "He's helped other men take hold of life again; maybe he can do it now. This young pilot was a college athlete. It should mean a lot to him to know that Junius once played basketball with the Harlem Globetrotters."

Six-foot-nine-inch Junius Kellogg had been there for three years. He roomed with seven other men who, like him, were paralyzed. In that room Junius read the pilot's record. Then he wheeled himself down the corridor and into the young vet's room. But the pilot wasn't

■ As you read, note how the mood changes from the beginning to the end of the selection.

■ Note the doctor's reasons for wanting Junius Kellogg to talk with the pilot.

■ **Harlem Globetrotters:** World-famous basketball team whose members each have a distinctive style of playing or a comedy routine.

interested in what Junius had to say. "You're talking to a vegetable," he said.

"I was a vegetable myself," Kellogg laughed. "I was worse off than you."

"Stop wasting your time," the boy told him. "I'd be better off dead."

"Nobody's better off dead," Kellogg said sharply.

That was the first of many visits. The pilot began to look forward to seeing Kellogg. Kellogg has a soft voice. He spent his childhood in Virginia. Like so many big men, he was gentle. He took over the job of feeding the young man.

One day the pilot said: "I just found out who you are. Don't you miss playing basketball?"

"I'm too busy," Kellogg grinned. "I coach a wheel-chair basketball team. I exercise about five hours a day. I can't just lie in bed. My muscles must be made to work again. Why don't you get with this exercise deal like the rest of us?"

Four months later I saw the young pilot swinging on parallel bars. I saw him swimming in the pool. And I heard him laughing. Kellogg had started him on the road back.

■ Note the change that has occurred in the pilot's attitude.

As a young man, Junius Kellogg already had been tested more than most men are in a lifetime. He is the oldest of eleven children. His family was very poor. Even as a child he was big. When he went to high school, he found he was a natural athlete. He was a star in football, track, and basketball. He served for three and a half years in the army. Then he won a scholarship to a New York College.

■ tested: put through trials

By his senior year, Kellogg was among the country's top basketball stars. Offers began to come in for him to play for money after graduation.

■ The narrator gives information about Kellogg's background.

One day a gambler offered him $1000 if he'd play poorly so his team would lose. Kellogg knew how unfair this would be. Such a deal would hurt honest players and the game itself. After asking for time to think it over, he went to his coach. College officials took Kellogg to the authorities.

Junius was asked to play along with the gamblers. He was to try to get more evidence. This would be a dangerous trick if the gamblers found out. He played his part well, though. The police were able to

■ Note this example of Kellogg's courage.

catch the leaders of the mob. The basketball scandals of 1951 hit the front pages.

Kellogg was praised by the newspapers. At his college he was a hero. When school was finished, he signed with the famous Harlem Globetrotters. He felt he could play for at least ten years. He would make more money each year. He also planned to study for a higher degree in physical education.

"I thought I had life licked," Kellogg says now. "Then the roof fell in on me."

On April 2, 1954, Kellogg and four friends were driving to a game. A tire blew, and the car turned over.

■ **Point of view** (page 187): Note the point of view used by the narrator of this selection.

Five days later, Kellogg woke up in a hospital. His body was smashed, it seemed, beyond help. His friends were not badly hurt. Kellogg's neck was broken. His spinal cord was injured, too. To help him breathe, a hole was made in his windpipe. Then he could get air through a tube. Holes were also drilled in his head; put in them were tongs attached to weights. The weights were used to stretch his neck. Kellogg, in a state of coma nearly two weeks, didn't know about it.

When he finally came to, he found he had no feeling in his arms or his legs, and he could not move them. But as he says now, "Every day a wonderful woman therapist came to work with me. She kept telling me, 'Move your thumb.' And darned if one day I didn't move it! That was a really big thrill for me. It was even better than scoring thirty-two points in one game!"

■ Kellogg mentions three people who helped him. The first is described here.

Months later Kellogg could feed himself and shave. At last he had gained enough strength to be sent to another veterans' hospital. Now he faced harder tasks. Before, he had been fighting just to stay alive. But this would begin a fight toward a *way* to live.

"I had a great worker called Brownie," Kellogg recalls. "He had me do exercises on a special table. I got so I could sit up without falling off. Often my hand would start to shake. 'Fight it!' Brownie would yell. 'Close your fist until it passes. Do you want to lie down all your life?'"

■ Note how the second individual helped Kellogg.

"He kept at it for eight or nine hours a day. Sometimes I thought I hated him. Today I'm grateful."

It was a big day when Kellogg went to another class. Only his legs were helpless now. He could move his wheelchair around the hospital.

Saul Welger (18) of the New York Pan Am Jets, and Frank Barlowski (11) of the New Jersey Wheelers, grapple for the ball during a National Wheelchair championship game.

Next Brownie made him drop into the pool. He sank like a stone. When he came to the surface, he found he could still swim.

A few months later he met Saul Welger. Saul had been a polio victim since he was a small child. Saul was one of the stars of a wheelchair basketball team. He played for Pan American Airways. Saul asked Kellogg to come over and watch his team practice. Kellogg had a friend drive him out there the next night.

■ Note the third person who helped Kellogg.

Kellogg was amazed at what he saw. The Pan Am Jets shot baskets and moved around the floor in wheelchairs. All of these men held full-time jobs with Pan American. Kellogg found that there were about fifty such teams in the country.

In the fall of 1956 Kellogg was called to Pan Am. He was asked to take the place of their coach. "It's a job without pay," he was told. "But when you get in better shape, you may want to work for us."

"You got yourself a deal," Kellogg said. With him, the Pan Am Jets were a great team. They became about the best wheelchair players in the country.

Kellogg drives a car. A gift, the car was made just for his use. He doesn't know who gave him the car. It came from someone who had read about Kellogg and wanted to do something to help him.

I drove to New Jersey with Kellogg one night. His team was playing the New Jersey Wheelers, a great team, too.

The game ended in an overtime win for the Jets, 46-45. As we went back to the hospital, I said, "That was one of the most exciting games I ever saw. Disability doesn't seem to bother your boys."

The big man laughed. "We've got a saying in some of our groups: 'Ability, not disability, is what counts.' That about sums it up."

I noticed that he didn't say anything about courage. But, I suppose, to a man like Junius Kellogg courage is something you take for granted.

■ **car was made . . . use:** try to imagine the special kind of car.

■ Consider how this saying sums up Kellogg's attitude.

THINK AND DISCUSS
Understanding
1. Why do the doctors want Junius Kellogg to talk to the young Air Force pilot?
2. Why is Kellogg successful with the young pilot?
3. Who are the three people Kellogg credits for his own recovery, and what did each do for Kellogg?

Analyzing
4. Which of the purposes for writing—to persuade, to inform, or to entertain— seems to apply to this selection?
5. Which of the following best states the main idea of the selection?
   (a) Six-foot nine-inch Junius Kellogg had been there for three years.
   (b) "Nobody's better off dead," Kellogg said sharply.
   (c) Four months later the young pilot was swinging on parallel bars.
6. What conclusions can you draw about Kellogg's car?

7. Identify each of the following as a statement of fact or a statement of opinion.
   (a) Junius Kellogg is a courageous person.
   (b) The game ended in an overtime win for the Jets, 46–45.
   (c) "That was one of the most exciting games I ever saw."
8. Summarize this selection by telling who did what, when, where, and why.

Extending
9. Name some other well-known people who, like Junius Kellogg, overcame serious problems to make a mark in the world.

REVIEWING LITERARY TERMS
Point of View
1. From what point of view is this account told?
2. Which of the following words best describes the narrator's point of view?
   (a) admiring; (b) sad; (c) angry; (d) unconcerned

■ CONTENT REVIEW
THINKING SKILLS
Classifying
1. Use *First Person* and *Third Person* as headings for two columns. List each selection in the unit under one of these headings.
2. Which of the statements below are statements of fact? Which are statements of opinion?
   (a) Richard Wright showed more courage than any other person in a selection in this unit.
   (b) Harriet Tubman and the runaways stopped at Thomas Garrett's house in Wilmington, Delaware.
   (c) Some snakes are deadly.

Generalizing
3. Consider the various people in the selections in this unit. Can you make any general conclusions about why an individual's life will be of interest to others? What do readers enjoy in selections about real people and events?

Synthesizing
4. Choose one of the following projects:
   (a) Make up a code of hand signals that a deaf and blind person could use to communicate words and ideas.
   (b) Make up a code that could be used by modern-day computers to sound distress signals from one ship to another.
   (c) Devise an instrument or instruments for trapping dangerous snakes.

Evaluating
5. Suppose you could go back in time and talk to someone no longer living. Which of the people described in this unit would you most want to meet? What questions would you ask that person?

■ COMPOSITION REVIEW
Writing About Courage
The Carnegie Commission concluded that the following answers might be given to the question of "What makes a hero?" Choose one of the three statements and use it as your first sentence in a paragraph about one of the people in this unit.
1. "It is not the individual altogether but the inspired moment that accounts for the deed."
2. "Perhaps all of us are eligible for acts of heroism if the spark comes at the right time."
3. "Heroism is not made; some tragedy finds it out. Like gold, it is uncovered."

Writing About a Person
Consider your friends, people in your family, teachers, and members of the staff at your school. Which person do you admire most? You might choose someone who has done something special for others or someone whose qualities you admire. Write two to four paragraphs about that person. The facts you include should be true, as in a biography. You may want to interview the person first, making notes to be sure your information is accurate.

Reviewing Writer's Craft:
Use a Voice That Suits Your Purpose
In this unit you have seen how writers use a voice to suit a purpose. Now **try your hand** at creating a voice that suits your own purpose. Choose two people from selections in the unit. Write a dialogue that might take place between these two people. For example, what might Alex Haley say to the bus driver in "Captain of His Ship"?

POETRY

By Quiltmaker Mary Jane Reese Findley, *Indian Teepee Quilt* (detail), c. 1885, Private Collection

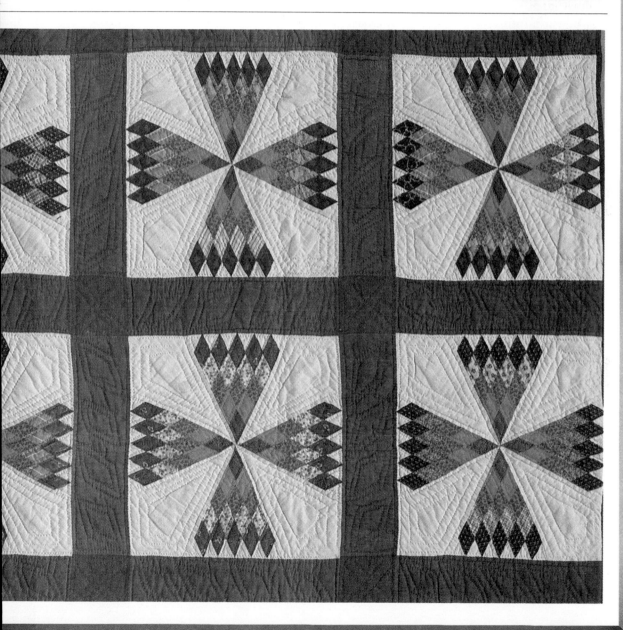

PREVIEW

UNIT 4   POETRY

Poets in This Unit Include

John Ciardi	Gary Soto
E. E. Cummings	Richard Wright
Shel Silverstein	Rachel Field
T. S. Eliot	Theodore Roethke
Arthur Guiterman	Victor Hernández Cruz
Ogden Nash	Emily Dickinson
Lewis Carroll	Carl Sandburg
Countee Cullen	Robert Frost

Features
Reading Poetry: Part One
Comment: Macavity on Broadway
Reading Poetry: Part Two
The Writer's Craft: Use Comparisons
Comment: Glossary of Jabberwocky Terms
Comment: Too "Modern" for Her Time

Application of Literary Terms
rhythm
rhyme
imagery
connotation/denotation
simile
metaphor
alliteration
personification
tone

Reading Literature Skillfully
comparison/contrast

Vocabulary Skills
context
dictionary and usage

Thinking Skills
classifying
generalizing
evaluating

Composition Assignments Include
Writing About a Character
Writing a Poem
Writing About an Imaginary Creature
Writing to Teach a Lesson
Writing an Invitation
Writing to Summarize

Enrichment
Interpreting a Poem Orally
Researching and Reporting
Reading a Humorous Poem Aloud
Describing an Incident
Doing Research

Thinking Critically About Literature
Concept Review
Content Review
Composition Review

The Builders

Sara Henderson Hay

I told them a thousand times if I told them once:
Stop fooling around, I said, with straw and sticks;
They won't hold up; you're taking an awful chance.
Brick is the stuff to build with, solid bricks.
5 You want to be impractical, go ahead.
But just remember, I told them; wait and see.
You're making a big mistake. Awright, I said,
But when the wolf comes, don't come running to me.

The funny thing is, they didn't. There they sat,
10 One in his crummy yellow shack, and one
Under his roof of twigs, and the wolf ate
Them, hair and hide. Well, what is done is done.
But I'd been willing to help them, all along,
If only they'd once admitted they were wrong.

THINK AND DISCUSS

Understanding
1. Who is the speaker in the poem? What is the first clue to his identity?

Analyzing
2. What do the words "what is done is done" indicate about the speaker's attitude toward his brothers and toward what happened to them?
3. Why is the speaker telling this story?
4. Which of the following **characteristics** describe the speaker: (**a**) concern for others; (**b**) self-righteousness; (**c**) selfishness; (**d**) practicality; (**e**) guilt? Explain.
5. Do you believe that the speaker would really have helped his brothers?
6. How does this version of the story differ from the original?

Extending
7. In what ways does the behavior of the pigs remind you of people's behavior?

Speed Adjustments

John Ciardi

A man stopped by and he wanted to know
Why my son John had become so slow.

I looked out the window and there was John
Running so fast he had been and gone
5 Before I saw him. "Look at him go!"
I said to the man. "Do you call *that* slow?"

"He seems to be fast when he wants to be,"
The man said. "He appears to be
One of those two-speed boys. You know—
10 Sometimes fast, and sometimes slow,
He can run a mile in nothing flat.
He can run right out from under his hat
When there's nowhere, really, to go.
    And yet
That very same boy that's as fast as a jet
15 Will take all day—and sometimes two—
To get to school. I'm sure that you
Send him to school. But yesterday
He didn't arrive. And all he would say
Was, yes, he started at half-past eight
20 But it took so long he got there late."

"How late?" said I.
                    Said the man, "A day."

"I see," said I, "and I think I can say
He won't be late again. He needs
A little adjustment of his speeds,
25 And I'm sure I know the place to adjust."

"Well, then," said he, "that's that, and
    I must
Be on my way."

                "Thank you," said I.
"If you see John as you go by
Would you be so good as to send him in?
30 There is never a better time to begin
A speed adjustment than right away."

"Agreed, and I will," said the man.
    "Good day."

And just a few minutes after that
In came John and down he sat:
35 "You wanted to see me, I understand?"

"I did and I do. But you'll have to stand—
At least at first—for what I need.
I'm going to have to adjust your speed
And when I'm through adjusting it,
40 I think you won't much care to sit.
Do you know what I mean?"
                         "Oh, oh," said he,
"I'm afraid I do. Is it going to be
Terribly long before you're through?"

"Why, not at all," said I. "Like you,
45 I can be speedy sometimes, too."

And soon after that his speed was adjusted.
And also the seat of his pants was dusted.
It was busy work, but it didn't take long,
Though I double-checked as I went along
50 Just to make sure there was nothing wrong.
And whatever *was* wrong, I set it straight,
For since that time he hasn't been late.

John Ciardi (chär′dē).

"Speed Adjustments" from *The Monster Den* by John Ciardi.
Copyright © 1963, 1964, 1966 by John Ciardi. Reprinted by
permission of the Estate of John Ciardi.

Norman Rockwell, *Day in the Life of a Boy*, 1952

THINK AND DISCUSS
Understanding
1. In analyzing any poem, it is important not to confuse the speaker—the person telling the poem—with the poet, who may or may not agree with what the poet says. Who is the speaker in this poem?

Analyzing
2. Is the **point of view** in this poem first person or third person?
3. Who do you think is the man who "stopped by"?
4. When is John fast and when is he slow?
5. How is his speed adjusted?

Extending
6. Do you think the method used by John's parent is the best one? Explain.

COMPOSITION
Describing Different Speeds
Like John, you probably do some things fast and some things slow. Write two paragraphs to share with classmates, the first in which you describe those things you do quickly, the second in which you describe those things you do slowly.

ENRICHMENT
Interpreting a Poem Orally
In groups of three, practice reading "Speed Adjustments" aloud. One student can assume the role of the speaker, another that of the man who "stopped by," and the third that of John. As you read, do not stop at the end of each line; instead, be guided by punctuation marks and the sense of what is being said.

Song of the Sky Loom

Tewa Indian

Oh our Mother the Earth, oh our Father the Sky,
Your children are we, and with tired backs
We bring you the gifts that you love.

Then weave for us a garment of brightness;
5 May the warp be the white light of morning,
May the weft be the red light of evening,
May the fringes be the falling rain,
May the border be the standing rainbow.

Thus weave for us a garment of brightness
10 That we may walk fittingly where birds sing,
That we may walk fittingly where grass is green,

Oh our Mother the Earth, oh our Father the Sky!

Herbert J. Spinden, translator. "Song of the Sky Loom" from *Songs of the Tewa*. Published under the auspices of The Exposition of Indian Tribal Arts, Inc., New York, 1933.

THINK AND DISCUSS

Understanding

1. The Tewa Indians live in the dry Southwest region of the United States. "Song of the Sky Loom" is a Tewa prayer for well-being. To whom or what is the song addressed?
2. What request do the speakers make?
3. Describe the four items that would make up the garment of brightness.
4. What do the speakers offer in return?

Analyzing

5. What do you think the speakers' gifts might be?
6. What do you think the garment of brightness is meant to represent?
7. What word or words would you use to describe the **mood** of this poem?

Extending

8. What reasons can you give for being thankful for rainfall in your own community?

Tony Da, *Coming of Spring*, c. 1976
Private Collection

COMPOSITION
Writing About a Crisis

Assume that your area has been experiencing a severe drought and that water has been sharply rationed. Write a three- to four-paragraph letter to a relative or friend in which you describe the effects of the drought on life about you. For example, you might describe its effects on plant life, on people's moods, or on your own day-to-day living.

Before you write, first make and then organize detailed notes on what you intend to describe. For your final draft, review the checklist at the end of Lesson 1 in the Writer's Handbook.

Common Dust

Georgia Douglas Johnson

And who shall separate the dust
Which later we shall be:
Whose keen discerning eye will scan
And solve the mystery?

5 The high, the low, the rich, the poor,
The black, the white, the red,
And all the chromatique[1] between,
Of whom shall it be said:

Here lies the dust of Africa;
10 Here are the sons of Rome;
Here lies one unlabeled
The world at large his home!

Can one then separate the dust,
Will mankind lie apart,
15 When life has settled back again
The same as from the start?

---

1. *chromatique* (krō mä tēk′), French for *chromatics*, the science of colors, meaning in this context "shades of color" or "hues."

"Common Dust" by Georgia Douglas Johnson.

THINK AND DISCUSS
Understanding
1. To whom does "we" refer in the first stanza?
2. What will happen in time to "we"?
3. To what does "the mystery" in line 4 refer?
4. According to the speaker, into what various groups are human beings separated when they are alive?

Analyzing
5. What does the speaker seem to believe happens to people after death?
6. What do you think is the **theme**, or underlying meaning, of the poem?

Poetry is the oldest form of literary expression. It dates back to the beginning of human communities, to a time long before print. Ancient peoples first used poetic forms in their tribal ceremonies. Later they were to tell stories in verse so that these stories might be memorized and passed down from one generation to the next.

Early poems illustrate various techniques that make memorization easier. Two of these are **rhythm,** which is the arrangement of stressed and unstressed sounds into regular patterns, and **rhyme,** which is the repetition of syllable sounds. For example, note the rhythm and rhyme in the first four lines of "The Demon of the Gibbet," a ballad that you will read next.

> There was no west, there was no east,
>   No star abroad for eyes to see;
> And Norman spurred his jaded beast
>   Hard by the terrible gallows tree.

The above lines comprise one **stanza** in the poem. A stanza is a group of a certain number of lines, usually four or more, forming a division in the poem.

Concrete words or details were used by early poets to create **imagery,** the means by which they appealed to their listeners' senses and feelings. Note the images that appeal to sight, sound, and touch in the following two lines from "The Demon of the Gibbet."

> The wind is bold, my bones are old,
>   And I am cold on the gallows tree.

Many of the techniques that were first used long ago are still being used by poets today, but not all poems are written in regular patterns of rhyme and rhythm. Some poets create an effect by making the form of the poem fit a particular idea or feeling. One well-known poet, E. E. Cummings, ignores the usual rules of spacing and punctuation. Note the strong visual image created by the first four lines of a poem by him that you will read later in this unit.

> old age sticks
> up Keep
> Off
> signs)&

As you read "old age sticks," look for **comparisons** and **contrasts** between youth and old age. How are young people and elderly people alike? In what ways are they different?

In the poems ahead, you will find many different pleasures awaiting you, pleasures to be found both in what poetry says and in the ways that it says it. You will meet memorable characters, participate in a wide range of experiences, and observe masterful uses of language. Read the poems, then, to understand, to appreciate, and, of course, to enjoy.

The Demon of the Gibbet

Fitz-James O'Brien

There was no west, there was no east,
  No star abroad for eyes to see;
And Norman spurred his jaded beast
  Hard by the terrible gallows tree.

5 "O, Norman, haste across this waste—
  For something seems to follow me!"
"Cheer up, dear Maud, for, thanked be God,
  We nigh have passed the gallows tree!"

He kissed her lip: then—spur and whip
10   And fast they fled across the lea.
But vain the heel, and rowel steel—
  For something leaped from the gallows tree!

"Give me your cloak, your knightly cloak,
  That wrapped you oft beyond the sea!
15 *The wind is bold, my bones are old,*
  And I am cold on the gallows tree."

"O holy God! O dearest Maud,
  Quick, quick, some prayers—the best that be!
A bony hand my neck has spanned,
20   And tears my knightly cloak from me!"

"Give me your wine, the red, red wine,
  That in the flask hangs by your knee!
Ten summers burst on me accurst,
  And I'm athirst on the gallows tree!"

Charles Burchfield, *An April Mood* (detail), 1946–55
Collection of the Whitney Museum of American Art

"The Demon of the Gibbet" by Fitz-James O'Brien. *Dark of the Moon; Poems of Fantasy and the Macabre*, August Derleth, ed. (Sauk City, Wis.: Arkham House), 1947.

₂₅ "O Maud, my life, my loving wife!
    Have you no prayer to set us free?
My belt unclasps—a demon grasps,
    And drags my wine flask from my knee!"

"Give me your bride, your bonnie bride,
₃₀ *   That left her nest with you to flee!*
O she hath flown to be my own,
    For I'm alone on the gallows tree!"

"Cling closer, Maud, and trust in God!
    Cling close—Ah, heaven, she slips from me!"
₃₅ A prayer, a groan, and he alone
    Rode on that night from the gallows tree.

THINK AND DISCUSS
Understanding
1. Describe the **setting** of the first stanza.
2. What **character** is introduced in the first stanza?
3. A new **character** is introduced in the second stanza. What concern does she express, and what response does she receive?
4. Where in the poem do you learn the relationship between the speakers in the second stanza?
5. In stanza three why are Norman's efforts to speed his horse of no use?

Analyzing
6. Who do you think speaks in the lines set in italics?

7. Remember that you can summarize by telling who did what, when, where, and why. Summarize the story told in this poem.
8. Describe the **mood** created by this poem.

ENRICHMENT
Researching and Reporting
In the school or local library, locate reference materials on ballads. Be prepared to give a brief report to the class on the history of folk ballads and on the differences between folk and literary ballads. Illustrate your report with examples of old English, Scottish, and American ballads.

old age sticks

E. E. Cummings

old age sticks
up Keep
Off
signs)&

5 youth yanks them
down(old
age
cries No

Tres)&(pas)
10 youth laughs
(sing
old age

scolds Forbid
den Stop
15 Must
n't Don't

&)youth goes
right on
gr
20 owing old

Rembrandt van Rijn, *Self-Portrait* (detail), 1660
The Metropolitan Museum of Art

Rembrandt van Rijn, *Titus at His Desk*, 1655
Rotterdam, Museum Boymans-van Beuningen

THINK AND DISCUSS

Understanding

1. According to the speaker, what are some of the things that older people say to youth?
2. How do young people react to their elders' advice?

Analyzing

3. From the poem, what seems to be the basic difference between the attitudes of youth and their elders?
4. What is suggested by lines 17–20?
5. What are some unusual features in the form of this poem?

Extending

6. Why do you think the poet chose this form?
7. Is a change in outlook a necessary part of aging? Explain.

READING LITERATURE SKILLFULLY

Comparison and Contrast

Comparisons and **contrasts** are basic to life. As human beings we are much alike, yet each of us is different. One day may seem much like the next, but each is nonetheless unique.

Writers can draw comparisons between persons, objects, and events, or they may choose to show contrasts. Note the following examples:

My brother and I are much alike.

New York differs markedly from Los Angeles.

The two plays are alike in setting but very different in plot.

Recall the contrast shown in "Speed Adjustments," in which John is sometimes fast and sometimes slow.

1. What groups are contrasted in "old age sticks"?
2. Give examples that show the differences between the actions of youth and age.
3. In what way is youth like age?

THINKING SKILLS

Evaluating

To evaluate is to make a judgment based on some sort of standard. Think about this poem and compare it to others you have read in the past. Consider such questions as these: Did I enjoy reading "old age sticks" more or less than other poems I have read? Does it create a mood more or less effectively than other poems? Did I understand the poem easily, or did I need to reread it several times in order to figure out what it means? Would I recommend the poem to a friend?

BIOGRAPHIES

Sara Henderson Hay   1906–1987

Born in Pittsburgh, Sara Henderson Hay attended Brenau College and Columbia University. Subjects for her poetry are often provided by daily events and familiar scenes on which she sheds a special light. In *Story Hour*, she reconsiders fairy tales and legends as if their events and characters were real.

About "The Builders" Hay said, "I was primarily trying . . . to illustrate the age-old conflict between the practical businessman and his frequently impractical artist brother, neither of whom understands the other."

John Ciardi   1916–1986

No truant officer actually came to check on John Ciardi's son. Instead, Ciardi said that he began this poem "as a joke about him, and probably to remind him that he is fast about what he likes to do and slow about what I want him to do, and that I intend to speed him up a bit about what I want him to do."

The Boston-born Ciardi was a leading American poet and lecturer on poetry. He also translated into English major works of the Italian poet Dante, wrote books introducing students to poetry, and explored the origin of American words and phrases in his own dictionaries for "browsers" and on National Public Radio.

Georgia Douglas Johnson   1886–1966

Although she referred to herself as a writer and a housewife in a listing of famous black Americans published during her lifetime, Georgia Douglas Johnson also was a teacher and, for a time, a government employee. But foremost she was a playwright and poet, counting among her publications five plays and four volumes of poetry. A graduate of Atlanta University and the Oberlin Conservatory of Music, she converted her home in Washington, D.C., into a center for literary gatherings.

Fitz-James O'Brien 1828–1862

Fitz-James O'Brien was born in County Limerick, Ireland. As a young man, he wasted his entire inheritance during four years in London and Paris. Broke when he arrived in New York in 1852, he soon established himself as a writer of essays, poems, stories, and articles. When the Civil War began, he enlisted in the New York National Guard. He was wounded and died of tetanus shortly after having received special mention for gallantry at the Battle of Bloomery Gap.

E. E. Cummings 1894–1962

Edward Estlin Cummings (or e. e. cummings, as he signed his poems) drove an ambulance for the French during World War I. But through a series of misunderstandings, he was mistakenly accused of treason and thrown into a French prison for several months. From this experience came his first book, *The Enormous Room* (1922).

Cummings was a daring experimenter in modern poetry. Searching for new ways to convey sounds and movement in verse, he often ignored conventional spacing and punctuation. Sometimes he ran words together to suggest speed, or separated them, one to a line, for a slower pace. To give commonplace words new meanings, he often divided them in unusual ways. His poems are sprightly and forceful in their originality, not because they look different, but because he succeeded in making the form of his poems fit the particular idea and feeling he wished to express.

See **RHYTHM** in the Handbook of Literary Terms, page 655.

Almost Perfect

Shel Silverstein

"Almost perfect . . . but not quite."
Those were the words of Mary Hume
At her seventh birthday party,
Looking 'round the ribboned room.
5 "This tablecloth is *pink* not *white*—
Almost perfect . . . but not quite."

"Almost perfect . . . but not quite."
Those were the words of grown-up Mary
Talking about her handsome beau,
10 The one she wasn't gonna marry.
"Squeezes me a bit too tight—
Almost perfect . . . but not quite."

"Almost perfect . . . but not quite."
Those were the words of ol' Miss Hume
15 Teaching in the seventh grade,
Grading papers in the gloom
Late at night up in her room.
"They never cross their t's just right—
Almost perfect . . . but not quite."

20 Ninety-eight the day she died
Complainin' 'bout the spotless floor.
People shook their heads and sighed,
"Guess that she'll like heaven more."
Up went her soul on feathered wings,
25 Out the door, up out of sight.
Another voice from heaven came—
"Almost perfect . . . but not quite."

THINK AND DISCUSS
Understanding
1. The speaker presents four examples of times when Mary Hume found things less than perfect. List these examples. Describe them.
2. What happens to Mary when she gets to heaven?

Analyzing
3. Who do you think is speaking in the last line?
4. Is the **mood** of this poem serious, frightening, humorous, or sad?
5. Which of the following best states the **theme** of the poem? (**a**) Mary Hume, who is never completely satisfied with anything in her life, dies, goes to heaven, and learns that she is less than perfect. (**b**) People who are overly critical sometimes are unaware of their own imperfections. (**c**) People who live in glass houses should not throw stones.

Extending
6. Can anything in life be perfect? Explain.

APPLYING: Rhythm H⊅
See Handbook of Literary Terms, p. 655.

Rhythm is the arrangement of stressed and unstressed sounds. The rhythm in a poem may have a regular beat, or it may be varied to fit different moods or to emphasize certain words.
1. Reread "Almost Perfect." Which words or syllables do you stress in each line?
2. Does the poem have a regular or a varied rhythm?
3. Does the rhythm of the poem fit the mood? Why or why not?

COMPOSITION ◆➡
Writing About a Character
Assume that you had Ms. Hume as a teacher this year. Write a three- to four-paragraph letter to a friend in another state about your experiences in her class. Before you write, take notes on these questions and others you think of: What does Ms. Hume look like? What are her mannerisms and habits? her outlook on life? her assignments and grading policy? Begin your letter:

"Dear _____,

What a teacher I've had this year!"

Review RHYTHM in the Handbook of Literary Terms, page 655.

Macavity: The Mystery Cat

T. S. Eliot

Macavity's a Mystery Cat: he's called the Hidden Paw—
For he's the master criminal who can defy the Law.
He's the bafflement of Scotland Yard, the Flying Squad's despair:[1]
For when they reach the scene of crime—*Macavity's not there!*

5 Macavity, Macavity, there's no one like Macavity,
He's broken every human law, he breaks the law of gravity.
His powers of levitation would make a fakir stare,[2]
And when you reach the scene of crime—*Macavity's not there!*
You may seek him in the basement, you may look up in the air—
10 But I tell you once and once again, *Macavity's not there!*

Macavity's a ginger cat, he's very tall and thin;
You would know him if you saw him, for his eyes are sunken in.
His brow is deeply lined with thought, his head is highly domed;
His coat is dusty from neglect, his whiskers are uncombed.
15 He sways his head from side to side, with movements like a snake;
And when you think he's half asleep, he's always wide awake.

Macavity (mə kav′ə tē)

1. *Scotland Yard . . . Flying Squad's despair.* The Flying Squad, a group prepared to travel anywhere on short notice, is a section of the criminal investigation department of Scotland Yard, the headquarters of the London police.
2. *His powers . . . would make a fakir stare.* His ability to rise and float in the air (*levitate*) would surprise even a *fakir* (fə kir′ *or* fā′kər), a Hindu religious man said to possess such powers.

Macavity, Macavity, there's no one like Macavity,
For he's a fiend in feline shape, a monster of depravity.
You may meet him in a by-street, you may see him in the square—
20 But when a crime's discovered, then *Macavity's not there!*

He's outwardly respectable. (They say he cheats at cards.)
And his footprints are not found in any file of Scotland Yard's.
And when the larder's looted, or the jewel-case is rifled,
Or when the milk is missing, or another Peke's[3] been stifled,
25 Or the greenhouse glass is broken, and the trellis past repair—
Ay, there's the wonder of the thing! *Macavity's not there!*

And when the Foreign Office[4] finds a Treaty's gone astray,
Or the Admiralty[5] loses some plans and drawings by the way,
There may be a scrap of paper in the hall or on the stair—
30 But it's useless to investigate—*Macavity's not there!*
And when the loss has been disclosed, the Secret Service say:
"It *must* have been Macavity!"—but he's a mile away.
You'll be sure to find him resting, or a-licking of his thumbs,
Or engaged in doing complicated long division sums.

35 Macavity, Macavity, there's no one like Macavity,
There never was a cat of such deceitfulness and suavity.
He always has an alibi, and one or two to spare:
At whatever time the deed took place—MACAVITY WASN'T THERE!
And they say that all the Cats whose wicked deeds are widely known
40 (I might mention Mungojerrie, I might mention Griddlebone[6])
Are nothing more than agents for the Cat who all the time
Just controls their operations: the Napoleon[7] of Crime!

---

3. *Peke's.* A Pekingese is a tiny, Oriental breed of dog.
4. *Foreign Office,* the department of the government that deals with foreign affairs. It is comparable to the U.S. State Department.
5. *Admiralty,* the government department that handles commerce and shipping affairs.
6. *Mungojerrie, Griddlebone,* characters in *Old Possum's Book of Practical Cats,* in which "Macavity" is included.
7. *Napoleon* (nə pō′lē ən). Napoleon Bonaparte (1769–1821) was a French general who made himself emperor of France in 1804 and conquered a large part of Europe before being defeated at Waterloo in 1815.

THINK AND DISCUSS

Understanding

1. What is Macavity called in line 1?
2. Why is it impossible to prosecute him for his deeds?
3. Point out details in the poem that suggest Macavity's importance as a criminal.

Analyzing

4. How do Macavity's crimes vary in degrees of importance? Give examples.
5. What is suggested by the phrase "the Napoleon of Crime" in line 42?
6. What is the **mood** of the poem? Cite details that illustrate the mood.

Extending

7. What "Macavity-like" behavior have you witnessed in cats you have known?

REVIEWING: Rhythm HⱫ
See Handbook of Literary Terms, p. 655.

Rhythm is the arrangement of stressed and unstressed sounds. The rhythm in a poem may have a regular beat, or it may be varied to fit different moods or to emphasize certain words.

1. Pronounce the name *Macavity*. Which syllable do you stress?
2. Find and read lines that illustrate how the rhythm of the whole poem resembles the rhythm of the name *Macavity*.
3. Do you think the rhythm of the poem fits the overall mood? Explain.

COMPOSITION ◆━

Writing a Report

Assume that you are a detective from Scotland Yard and that you finally catch Macavity. You have to file a three- to four-paragraph report for your captain in which you tell how you caught the "Mystery Cat." Before writing your report, make notes on these questions: What exactly happened? When and where did it happen? How did it happen? Who was involved? How did the criminal behave upon being arrested?

ENRICHMENT

Interpreting a Poem Orally

Select three of your classmates to read aloud stanzas one, three, and five of "Macavity: The Mystery Cat." The rest of the class will do a choral reading of stanzas two, four, and six.

When reading aloud, stand so that your voice can project. Read the lines dramatically, paying close attention to the sense and mood of the poem. Note punctuation, which provides clues to interpretation.

After you have practiced a number of times, you may wish to interpret the poem for other classes.

Comment

Macavity on Broadway

Shortly after "Macavity: The Mystery Cat" was written, poet T. S. Eliot revealed in a letter that he had modeled the mysterious cat after Professor Moriarty, the master criminal and enemy of Sherlock Holmes, Sir Arthur Conan Doyle's fictional detective.

Macavity and several other feline characters created by Eliot have been widely loved both in the poet's original book, *Old Possum's Book of Practical Cats*, and in the stage musical *Cats*.

In the musical, the stage was designed to resemble a huge junkyard, built to scale so that the actors playing the cats would seem as small in their environment as real cats appear in theirs. In order to capture the graceful, fluid movement of felines, the cast performed dance numbers that became perhaps the most important part of the show. The costumes were designed to be flexible, allowing the actors to move freely. Their freedom of movement permitted the staging of Macavity's realistic catfight in the play.

Edward Gorey

Cats was an instant success on Broadway. In 1983 it was voted best musical of the year and was honored with six other Antoinette Perry ("Tony") Awards, including one to the late T. S. Eliot for *Old Possum's Book of Practical Cats*. Still popular with audiences, the musical continues to be produced from time to time.

Dorlan's Home Walk

Arthur Guiterman

The ninth; last half; the score was tied,
    The hour was big with fate,
For Neal had fanned and Kling had flied
    When Dorlan toed the plate.

5 And every rooter drew a breath
    And rose from where he sat,
For weal or woe, or life or death
    Now hung on Dorlan's bat.

The pitcher scowled; the pitcher flung
10   An inshoot,[1] swift and queer;
But Dorlan whirled his wagon-tongue[2]
    And smote the leathern sphere.

He smote the ball with might and main,
    He drove it long and low,
15 And firstward like a railway train
    He sped to beat the throw.

He reached first base with time to spare
    (The throw went high and wide),
But what a tumult rent the air
20   When "Safe!" the umpire cried.

"What!" shrieked the pitcher, lean
    and tall,
    "What!" roared the catcher stout,
"Wha-at!" yelled the basemen one
    and all,
    "Ye're off! the man is out!"

25 The shortstop swore, the catcher pled,
    They waved their arms around.
The umpire shook his bullet-head
    And sternly held his ground,

Though in the wild-eyed fielders ran
30   To tear him limb from limb
Or else to tell that erring man
    Just what they thought of *him*.

The basemen left the bases clear
    And came to urge their case—
35 So Dorlan yawned and scratched his ear
    And strolled to second base.

"Safe? Safe?" the pitcher hissed. "Ye're
    blind!"
    And breathed a naughty word;
While Dorlan hitched his belt behind
40   And rambled on to third.

And throats were hoarse and words ran
    high
    And lips were flecked with foam,
As Dorlan scanned the azure sky
    And ambled on toward home.

---

1. *inshoot,* a pitched baseball that curves toward the batter.
2. *wagon-tongue,* normally, the pole of a two-horse carriage; here, a bat.

Thomas Eakins, *Baseball Players Practicing* (detail)
Museum of Art, Rhode Island School of Design

45 And still he heard in dreamy bliss,
   As down the line he came,
The umpire growl, "Enough o' this!
   He's safe. Now play the game!"

"All right. Come, boys," the pitcher
      bawled,
50   "Two out; now make it three!"
When Dorlan touched the plate and
      drawled,
   "Hey! score that run fer me!"

What wrath was there, what bitter talk,
   What joy and wild acclaim!
55 For Dorlan's peaceful homeward walk
   Had won the doubtful game.

Aye, thus the game was lost and won;
   So, athletes, great and small,
If like mischance ye fain would shun[3]
60   Keep cool, don't kick, play ball.

3. *If like mischance ye fain would shun,* if you would
like to avoid a similar misfortune.

THINK AND DISCUSS

Understanding

1. What is the situation in the ball game when Dorlan comes to bat?

Analyzing

2. Briefly summarize the story told, in which Dorlan scores the winning run.

3. The speaker in the poem uses a number of uncommon words for more common ones: *weal* for *prosperity*, *wagon-tongue* for *bat*, and *smote* for *hit*. Locate at least three other unusual words and indicate what commonplace words might substitute for them.

4. Do the uncommon words make events in the poem seem more or less serious than they otherwise would?

5. Does the poem conclude with (**a**) a **theme,** (**b**) a summary, or (**c**) a moral that tells the reader to act in a certain way? Explain.

6. Reread the first three stanzas of "Dorlan's Home Walk." Which words or syllables do you stress in each line? Would you call the **rhythm** regular or irregular?

7. Does the **rhythm** seem fast, slow, or a mix of the two? Explain.

THINKING SKILLS

Classifying

To classify things is to arrange them into groups or categories according to some system. Think about the characters or situations in the poems you have read so far in this unit. Which could be classified as real? Which could be classified as not real? Make two lists.

COMPOSITION ✑

Interviewing a Character

You are a TV sportscaster who has been allotted two minutes to interview Dorlan immediately after the game. Carefully compose the questions you wish to ask, as well as the responses you think Dorlan would make. See Lesson 8 in the Writer's Handbook, "Writing Dialogue."

By this time you have read enough poetry to realize that poets choose their words carefully. They call forth emotional and intellectual responses using the fewest possible words.

To make comparisons of basically unlike things, poets use **simile** and **metaphor.** A simile is a figure of speech that compares two things with the word *like* or the word *as*. A metaphor is a figure of speech that makes an implied comparison and does not use *like* or *as*. For example, "He ate like a wolf" is a simile, but "He wolfed down his food" is a metaphor. In both cases, a comparison is made in just a few words. For the comparison to be effective, readers need to be familiar with how wolves consume food. At the same time, readers need to be aware that humans and wolves are more unlike than they are similar.

The repeating of sounds, called **alliteration,** gives rhythm and melody to poetry, and it stirs emotions in readers. Notice the repetition of the sound of the letter *m* in the following lines from a poem by Alfred, Lord Tennyson.

The moan of doves in immemorial elms,
And murmuring of innumerable bees.

To help humans relate to that which is not human, poets frequently use **personification.** Notice how spring takes on human characteristics in the following line from "Four Little Foxes," which you will read in this unit.

Speak gently, Spring, and make no
    sudden sound;

All of the elements of poetry, including rhythm, rhyme, imagery, simile, metaphor, alliteration, and personification, contribute to **tone,** an author's expressed attitude toward the subject. Tone in a poem is communicated through the particular choice of words and details that the poet uses in describing setting, portraying characters, and presenting events. Compare the tone used by a poet to tone of voice as it refers to the way people speak to each other.

Because poets cut away needless words and pack those they use with multiple meanings and a range of emotions, you should read a poem slowly and carefully, perhaps a number of times. To understand the poem fully, you need to be sensitive to the various poetic devices that the poet is using. In addition, you need to be aware of the **denotation,** the usual dictionary meaning, and the **connotations,** what is suggested beyond the literal dictionary meaning, of each word. To develop that awareness, keep a dictionary at hand, not only to check the meanings of unfamiliar words but also to discover at times unfamiliar meanings for familiar words.

The more you understand and appreciate a poet's varied uses of language, the greater will be your pleasure in reading poetry.

The Listeners

Walter de la Mare

"Is there anybody there?" said the Traveler,
    Knocking on the moonlit door;
And his horse in the silence champed the grasses
    Of the forest's ferny floor:
5 And a bird flew up out of the turret,
    Above the Traveler's head:
And he smote upon the door again a second time;
    "Is there anybody there?" he said.
But no one descended to the Traveler;
10   No head from the leaf-fringed sill
Leaned over and looked into his grey eyes,
    Where he stood perplexed and still.
But only a host of phantom listeners
    That dwelt in the lone house then
15 Stood listening in the quiet of the moonlight
    To that voice from the world of men:
Stood thronging the faint moonbeams on the dark stair,
    That goes down to the empty hall,
Hearkening in an air stirred and shaken
20   By the lonely Traveler's call.
And he felt in his heart their strangeness,
    Their stillness answering his cry,
While his horse moved, cropping the dark turf,
    'Neath the starred and leafy sky;
25 For he suddenly smote on the door, even
    Louder, and lifted his head:—
"Tell them I came, and no one answered,
    That I kept my word," he said.

Tom Adams

Never the least stir made the listeners,
30 Though every word he spake
Fell echoing through the shadowiness of the still house
    From the one man left awake:
Ay, they heard his foot upon the stirrup,
    And the sound of iron on stone,
35 And how the silence surged softly backward,
    When the plunging hoofs were gone.

THINK AND DISCUSS

Understanding

1. What question does the Traveler ask?
2. What response does he receive?
3. Briefly describe the **setting** as it is presented in the first eight lines of the poem.

Analyzing

4. What do you learn from lines 27–28 that helps explain why the Traveler was puzzled when no one responded to his knock on the door?
5. Reread lines 13–16. If the word *then* in line 14 is interpreted to mean "some time in the past," what does *then* suggest about the "phantom listeners"?
6. Do you think that the Traveler is or is not himself a phantom? Point out a line or lines in the poem to support your answer.
7. Which one of these words best describes the **mood** of the poem: *light-hearted, mysterious, angry, joyful?*

8. Is the **rhythm** of the poem fast or slow?
9. Is the **rhythm** appropriate to the **mood?** Explain.

Extending

10. Do you think the **mood** of the poem would be different if the Traveler were identified by name? Explain.

COMPOSITION

Describing an Emotional Experience

Describe for classmates in two to three paragraphs a situation in which you felt something mysterious or frighteningly strange. The feeling may have been evoked by a visit to an abandoned building, the viewing of a scary movie, the sense that a stranger was following you, or by some other situation.

In your paper, try to include precise details about where and when the experience occurred, who was there, what happened, and how and why it happened.

BIOGRAPHIES

Shel Silverstein 1932–

Shel Silverstein keeps in touch with the modern scene. His songs—for which he writes both words and music—have made a hit with country/ western and pop singers and their vast audiences. Before turning to writing songs and poetry, he was already widely known as a cartoonist and as a writer and illustrator of children's books. Two of his volumes of poetry, *Where the Sidewalk Ends* and *A Light in the Attic*, have been immensely popular with both children and adults.

Silverstein travels all over the world, but when he is not wandering, he lives on a houseboat off Sausalito, California, where he keeps a piano, a guitar, a saxophone, a trombone, and a camera. He experiments with all these things "just to see if I can come up with anything." He feels the houseboat allows him the freedom to go wherever he pleases and do whatever he wants.

T. S. Eliot 1888–1965

T. S. Eliot was born in St. Louis, but spent most of his life in England. In 1926 he became a British citizen. The author of some of the most influential poems of the twentieth century, among them *The Wasteland* and *Four Quartets*, Eliot won the Nobel Prize for literature in 1948. A serious scholar, playwright, and poet, he nonetheless had a delightful sense of humor, which he reveals in *Old Possum's Book of Practical Cats*.

Arthur Guiterman 1871–1943

Arthur Guiterman was a New York poet, journalist, and librettist for both light and grand operas. Best known for his humorous verse and ballads dealing with American history and legends, he wrote, among other works, *The Laughing Muse, The Mirthful Lyre, Ballads of Old New York, I Sing the Pioneer, Song and Laughter*, and *Brave Laughter*.

Walter de la Mare 1873–1956

Born in Chariton, Kent, in England, Walter de la Mare became a bookkeeper for a London branch of Standard Oil, a post he held for eighteen years. In 1908 he was granted a pension from the government, enabling him to devote full time to writing. In 1912 his book *The Listeners and Other Poems* brought him fame. He continued throughout his life to write verse and prose, including five novels. He also edited anthologies of poetry, including *Come Hither*, "for the young of all ages."

Writer's Craft

Use Comparisons

Often writers will use a comparison to help the reader understand a difficult idea. Sometimes the comparison is between something you can't see, like an idea or feeling, and something you can see, like an object. Consider the sentence: "Katy's love of music was like a magnet, drawing her to the piano." Because you can readily imagine how powerful a magnet is, you are better able to understand how Katy feels.

> Oh our Mother the Earth, oh our Father
>   the Sky,
> Your children are we . . .
>
> (page 246)

Since they compare nature to their family, you immediately understand that the Tewa Indians feel very close to it. This feeling of warmth and protection is made even more clear by the next comparison in the poem.

> Then weave for us a garment of
>   brightness;
> May the warp be the white light of
>   morning,
> May the weft be the red light of
>   evening,
> May the fringes be the falling rain,
> May the border be the standing
>   rainbow.
>
> (page 246)

Notice how in the above lines elements of nature are compared to a beautiful garment.

Similarly, in the poem "Macavity: The Mystery Cat," T. S. Eliot uses an unusual comparison to show us a particular cat's personality.

> Macavity's a Mystery Cat: he's called
>   the Hidden Paw—
> For he's the master criminal who can
>   defy the Law.
> He's the bafflement of Scotland Yard,
>   the Flying Squad's despair:
> For when they reach the scene of
>   crime—*Macavity's not there!*
>
> (page 258)

Of course, the author could simply have said that Macavity was sly and clever, but by comparing him to a criminal, he paints a more original and entertaining picture of the cat's behavior.

Another example of the way a writer uses comparisons to explain personality traits is found in "Speed Adjustments." In this poem, John Ciardi describes the boy's character by telling us:

> He appears to be
> One of those two-speed boys. You know—
> Sometimes fast, and sometimes slow,
>
> (page 244)

If you want to help your readers understand a difficult idea, or show them something in a fresh, unique way, try using more comparisons in your own writing.

Notice comparisons in your reading.
Use comparisons in your writing.

See RHYME in the Handbook of Literary Terms, page 653.

The Hunter

Ogden Nash

The hunter crouches in his blind
'Neath camouflage of every kind,
And conjures up a quacking noise
To lend allure to his decoys.
5 This grown-up man, with pluck and luck,
Is hoping to outwit a duck.

John J. Audubon, *Mallard,* Courtesy the Newberry Library, Chicago

THINK AND DISCUSS
Understanding
1. What has the hunter done to try to "outwit" his prey?

Analyzing
2. What is the speaker's attitude toward the hunter's behavior? How do you know?
3. Is the **rhythm** of the poem fast or slow?
4. Would the same **rhythm** be suitable for a poem describing the actions of a person seriously weakened by illness? Why or why not?

APPLYING: Rhyme H𝐙
See Handbook of Literary Terms, p. 653.

Rhyme is the repetition of syllable sounds. End words that share a particular sound are called **end rhymes.** The pattern of end rhymes in a poem is called a **rhyme scheme.**
1. What words rhyme at the ends of lines in this poem?
2. You can chart a rhyme scheme with letters of the alphabet by using the same letter for end words that rhyme. Chart the rhyme scheme in this poem.
3. Would the rhyme scheme for the poem be suitable for a serious poem? Explain your opinion.

VOCABULARY
Context
Words often have more than one meaning. In "The Hunter," the word *kind* means "sort or type," but it can also mean "friendly." The word *duck* refers to a bird, but it can also mean "avoid."

Use the Glossary to determine the appropriate meaning for each italicized word. On your paper, write the meaning after the sentence number. Then, for each word, write a sentence in which the word is used with a different meaning.
1. Because of the thick clouds, the pilot had to fly *blind.*
2. Rebecca has plenty of *ginger;* she's never still a moment.
3. My parents offered to *board* John until he finds a place of his own.
4. The young women put on *clogs* but then found it difficult to dance.
5. Ms. Strand warned Sandy not to *pluck* the guitar strings too hard.

COMPOSITION
Reading/Writing Log
In this poem, Ogden Nash creates humor by effectively comparing the hunter's behavior to that of the hunted duck. An example is given below. Copy the example in your **reading/writing log.** Then find two additional examples in the poem and add them to the log.

crouches in his blind

Writing a Poem
Readers see the behavior of the hunter and understand the speaker's attitude through Ogden Nash's careful choice of words to show comparison. Write a short poem of four to six lines in which you use words to show a comparison between a person and something else. For example, you might write about someone who likes to fish, play the violin, or watch TV.

Review RHYME in the Handbook of Literary Terms, page 653.

Jabberwocky

Lewis Carroll

'Twas brillig, and the slithy toves
  Did gyre and gimble in the wabe;
All mimsy were the borogoves,
  And the mome raths outgrabe.

5 "Beware the Jabberwock, my son!
  The jaws that bite, the claws that catch!
Beware the Jubjub bird, and shun
  The frumious Bandersnatch!"

He took his vorpal sword in hand;
10 Long time the manxome foe he sought—
So rested he by the Tumtum tree,
  And stood awhile in thought.

And, as in uffish thought he stood,
  The Jabberwock, with eyes of flame,
15 Came whiffling through the tulgey wood,
  And burbled as it came!

One, two! One, two! And through and through
  The vorpal blade went snicker-snack!
He left it dead, and with its head
20 He went galumphing back.

Henri Rousseau, *The Snake Charmer* (detail)
The Louvre, Paris

"Jabberwocky" by Lewis Carroll. *Through the Looking Glass*, 1871.

"And hast thou slain the Jabberwock?
    Come to my arms, my beamish boy!
O frabjous day! Callooh! Callay!"
    He chortled in his joy.

25 'Twas brillig and the slithy toves
    Did gyre and gimble in the wabe;
All mimsy were the borogoves,
    And the mome raths outgrabe.

Comment

Glossary of Jabberwocky Terms

The following glossary of the invented words in "Jabberwocky" is compiled from ingenious definitions given by Humpty Dumpty in Lewis Carroll's *Through the Looking Glass*. The last definition is found in the *Preface* to *The Hunting of the Snark*.

Brillig, four o'clock in the afternoon—the time to begin broiling things for dinner.
Slithy, both lithe (bending easily) and slimy. Humpty Dumpty calls *slithy* a portmanteau (pôrt man'tō) word because, like the suitcase of that name, there are two or more meanings packed up into one word.
Toves, animals something like badgers—they're something like lizards—and they're something like corkscrews. They nest under sundials and live on cheese.
Gyre, to go round like a gyroscope.

Gimble, to make holes like a gimlet.
Wabe, a grass-plot round a sundial; so called because it goes a long way before it, a long way behind it, and a long way beyond it on each side.
Mimsy, flimsy and miserable; another portmanteau word.
Borogove, a thin, shabby-looking bird with its feathers sticking out all around—something like a live mop.
Mome. Humpty is uncertain of the meaning; he thinks it's "short for *from home*—meaning that they'd lost their way."
Rath, a sort of green pig.
Outgrabe, past tense of *outgribe*, meaning to make a noise like something between bellowing and whistling, with a kind of sneeze in the middle.
Frumious, another portmanteau word meaning fuming and furious.

THINK AND DISCUSS

Understanding

1. What does the father advise his son to do?
2. Does the son take the father's advice?
3. How does the father feel about the son's action?

Analyzing

4. The nonsense words in the poem can spark the imagination and make you laugh. The "Glossary of Jabberwocky Terms" defines several of the words. Two other words invented for this poem have become accepted words in the English language: *galumph* and *chortle*. Of what two common words might *chortle* be a blend? Check your guess in the Glossary.
5. An unusual contrast is created when some words are nonsense and others are formal. Point out as many examples as you can of formal language.

Extending

6. Some nonsense words are not defined in the "Jabberwocky" glossary. Find them and make up origins and meanings.
7. Give examples of playful or nonsense language you have heard, such as jump-rope rhymes or tongue twisters.

REVIEWING: Rhyme HↃ
See Handbook of Literary Terms, p. 653.

Rhyme is the repetition of syllable sounds. End words that share a particular sound are called **end rhymes.** The pattern of end rhymes in a poem is called a **rhyme scheme.**

1. Chart the rhyme scheme in the first three stanzas of "Jabberwocky."
2. In addition to a pattern of end rhymes, the poem contains internal rhymes— rhymes within a line. Find as many of these as you can.
3. In "Jabberwocky," the rhyme scheme can help you pronounce words that were invented for this poem. Point out nonsense words you can pronounce because they rhyme with real words.

COMPOSITION
Writing About an Imaginary Creature

Not much information is given about the Jabberwock. Plan a "Wanted" poster for this creature. On the poster, write two or more paragraphs in which you describe the creature and tell where it likes to hide, why it is dangerous, how it might be trapped, and what reward you are offering. Draw a picture of the Jabberwock or paste one up using parts of animal pictures cut from magazines.

Under the Mistletoe

Countee Cullen

I did not know she'd take it so,
   Or else I'd never dared;
Although the bliss was worth the blow,
I did not know she'd take it so.
5 She stood beneath the mistletoe
So long I thought she cared;
I did not know she'd take it so,
Or else I'd never dared.

Marilena Pistoia

THINK AND DISCUSS
Understanding
1. What examples of repetition can you find in the poem?
2. What might the repetition reveal about the state of the speaker's mind?

Analyzing
3. From what the speaker says, what do you think has happened?
4. Is the **point of view** first person, third-person limited, or third-person omniscient? Explain.
5. Would you describe the **rhythm** of the lines as familiar or unusual?
6. Is the **rhyme scheme** of the poem regular or irregular? Explain.

Extending
7. Do you think the speaker would be willing to undergo the same experience again? Explain.

THINKING SKILLS
Generalizing
To generalize is to draw a general conclusion from particular information. Work with a small group of classmates. List at least two poems you have read so far in this unit that support the following generalization: A poem can be humorous and still make a point about something. Give reasons for your choice of poems.

Rebecca, Who Slammed Doors for Fun and Perished Miserably

Hilaire Belloc

A trick that everyone abhors
In Little Girls is slamming Doors,
A Wealthy Banker's Little Daughter
Who lived in Palace Green, Bayswater
5 (By name Rebecca Offendort),
Was given to this Furious Sport.

She would deliberately go
And Slam the door like Billy-Ho!
To make her Uncle Jacob start.
10 She was not really bad at heart,
But only rather rude and wild:
She was an aggravating child . . .

It happened that a Marble Bust
Of Abraham was standing just
15 Above the Door this little Lamb
Had carefully prepared to Slam,
And Down it came! It knocked her flat!
It laid her out! She looked like that.

Mary Cassatt, *Little Girl in a Blue Armchair* (detail), 1878
National Gallery of Art

Her funeral Sermon (which was long
20 And followed by a Sacred Song)
Mentioned her Virtues, it is true,
But dwelt upon her Vices too,
And showed the Dreadful End of One
Who goes and slams the door for Fun.

25 The children who were brought to hear
The awful Tale from far and near
Were much impressed, and inly swore
They never more would slam the Door.
—As often they had done before.

THINK AND DISCUSS

Understanding

1. Who is Rebecca?
2. Why does she deliberately slam doors?
3. What happens to her?
4. What effect does the sermon at her funeral have on other children?

Analyzing

5. Read the poem aloud. Is the **rhythm** slow or fast, regular or irregular?
6. Is the **rhythm** appropriate? Explain.
7. What is the **rhyme scheme** of the poem?

Extending

8. Compare Rebecca to someone you have known who might be described as aggravating. You might choose a sister or brother, a neighbor, or even yourself at a younger age.

COMPOSITION ◁━●

Writing to Teach a Lesson

Assume that you are asked to give the sermon at Rebecca's funeral. A sermon is often thought of as a talk for religious instruction, but it can be any serious talk about morals or conduct. Write three to four paragraphs in which you try to impress upon your young listeners the serious consequences of slamming doors. As the poem indicates, in your sermon you will need to mention Rebecca's virtues, most of which you will have to invent, but mainly you will want to dwell upon her vices. Your purpose is to convince youngsters that Rebecca's behavior is not a model to follow. See Lesson 12 in the Writer's Handbook, "Writing to Persuade."

ENRICHMENT

Reading a Humorous Poem Aloud

With the help of the school or local librarian, select a humorous poem that you would be willing to share orally in a group of three or four. The selection should not take more than three minutes to read aloud. Each group will select the most humorous poem read by one of its members. These selections could then be shared orally with the entire class.

BIOGRAPHIES

Ogden Nash 1902–1971

Ogden Nash poked fun at our way of life, our social customs, and his own pet peeves. He used rhymes that were never meant to be and may never be again. He misspelled and mispronounced words to make them rhyme with other words. He distorted meanings and invented new ones.

In 1931 Nash published his first volume of light verse, *Free Wheeling.* Over four hundred of his poems are collected in *I Wouldn't Have Missed It: Selected Poems of Ogden Nash.*

Lewis Carroll 1832–1898

Charles Lutwidge Dodgson, better known by his pen name of Lewis Carroll, was a mathematician. Shy with adults, Dodgson felt more at home with young people. To amuse a young girl named Alice Liddell, he wrote *Alice in Wonderland.* It was so successful that he continued the story in *Through the Looking Glass.* These two classics are Dodgson's best-known works.

Dodgson loved poetry and took delight in writing nonsense. "Jabberwocky" well represents its author's humor and imagination.

Countee Cullen 1903–1946

Though he wrote drama and prose as well as poetry, Countee Cullen is best remembered for his powerful lyrics, which explore the attitudes of people toward one another and the world about them, and often reveal both the joyous and sorrowful aspects of black American heritage.

Raised in New York City, Cullen attended New York University and Harvard. Considered one of the foremost lyric poets of this century, he once remarked about his poetry, "Most things I write I do for the sheer joy of music in them."

Hilaire Belloc 1870–1953

Hilaire Belloc was born in France and educated in England. A practicing journalist for much of his life, he was also a versatile writer of essays, novels, verse, biographies, travels, history, and literary criticism. His light and comic verses appear in *The Bad Child's Book of Beasts* (1896) and in *The Verse of Hilaire Belloc* (1954), published after his death.

See **IMAGERY** in the Handbook of Literary Terms, page 641.

Oranges

Gary Soto

The first time I walked
With a girl, I was twelve,
Cold, and weighted down
With two oranges in my jacket.
5 December. Frost cracking
Beneath my steps, my breath
Before me, then gone,
As I walked toward
Her house, the one whose
10 Porchlight burned yellow
Night and day, in any weather.
A dog barked at me, until
She came out pulling
At her gloves, face bright
15 With rouge. I smiled,
Touched her shoulder, and led
Her down the street, across
A used car lot and a line
Of newly planted trees,
20 Until we were breathing
Before a drugstore. We
Entered, the tiny bell
Bringing a saleslady
Down a narrow aisle of goods.
25 I turned to the candies
Tiered like bleachers,
And asked what she wanted—
Light in her eyes, a smile
Starting at the corners

30 Of her mouth. I fingered
A nickel in my pocket,
And when she lifted a chocolate
That cost a dime,
I didn't say anything.
35 I took the nickel from
My pocket, then an orange,
And set them quietly on
The counter. When I looked up,
The lady's eyes met mine,
40 And held them, knowing
Very well what it was all
About.
        Outside,
A few cars hissing past,
45 Fog hanging like old
Coats between the trees.
I took my girl's hand
In mine for two blocks,
Then released it to let
50 Her unwrap the chocolate.
I peeled my orange
That was so bright against
The gray of December
That, from some distance,
55 Someone might have thought
I was making a fire in my hands.

THINK AND DISCUSS

Understanding

1. Where is the speaker going at the beginning of the poem?
2. Where does the speaker take his companion?

Analyzing

3. Describe the speaker.
4. Describe the speaker's companion.
5. What creates a momentary crisis for the speaker? How does he handle the situation?
6. Explain the meaning of lines 38–42.

Extending

7. Would the poem be equally effective if the events described took place in the summer, or if the speaker and his companion were each twenty-two? Explain.
8. Would the poem be as effective if it were titled "The Drugstore"?

APPLYING: Imagery
See Handbook of Literary Terms, p. 641.

Imagery consists of concrete words or details that appeal to the senses of sight, sound, touch, smell, and taste, or to internal feelings.

1. What is the first image that occurs in "Oranges," and to what sense does it appeal?
2. What word in the first five lines appeals to the reader's sense of feeling?
3. What is the first image in the poem that appeals to the senses of sight and sound at the same time?
4. What other images appeal to both sight and sound at the same time?

COMPOSITION

Reading/Writing Log

In this poem Gary Soto uses images that show both comparisons and contrasts. Two of these are given below. Copy them in your **reading/writing log.** Then add several examples of your own.

> Porchlight burned yellow
> Night and day, in any weather.

> . . . the candies
> Tiered like bleachers,

Writing a Poem

Try your hand at writing a short poem that begins, "The first time I walked . . ." Use images that show comparisons and contrasts, as in "Oranges." If you are keeping a **reading/writing log,** you may want to add more examples before you begin to write. Also make a list of things to compare and contrast in your own poem. Tell about an experience you remember from the first, second, or third grade. See Lesson 10, "Writing a Poem," in the Writer's Handbook.

Writing a Letter

Assume that you are the saleslady who helped the speaker in "Oranges." Write a one- to two-paragraph letter to a friend in which you relate the incident in the poem. You will want to use specific details to help your friend visualize how the young people looked and acted. In addition, you will want your friend to understand how and why you behaved as you did. Before writing the letter, make notes and organize them. When you are ready, begin your letter with this sentence: Today something unusual happened in the drugstore!

Review IMAGERY in the Handbook of Literary Terms, page 641.

Three Hokku Poems

Richard Wright

The spring lingers on
In the scent of a damp log
Rotting in the sun

      The crow flew so fast
      That he left his lonely caw
      Behind in the fields

In the falling snow
A laughing boy holds out his palms
Until they are white

THINK AND DISCUSS
Understanding
1. What objects are mentioned in the poems?

Analyzing
2. Substitute *sitting* for *rotting* in the first hokku, *friendly* for *lonely* in the second, and *grinning* for *laughing* in the third. How is the poem altered in each instance?
3. The hokku form allows a poet to create vivid "snapshots" out of a few words. Which hokku above could be captured most fully in a photograph? Explain your choice.

Extending
4. What two-word titles would you suggest for each hokku? Why?

REVIEWING: Imagery
See Handbook of Literary Terms, p. 641.
  Imagery consists of concrete words or details that appeal to the senses of sight, sound, touch, smell, and taste, or to internal feelings. Name the sense or senses to which each hokku appeals.

Something Told the Wild Geese

Rachel Field

Something told the wild geese
   It was time to go.
Though the fields lay golden
   Something whispered,—"Snow."
5 Leaves were green and stirring,
   Berries, luster-glossed,
But beneath warm feathers
   Something cautioned,—"Frost."
All the sagging orchards
10   Steamed with amber spice,
But each wild breast stiffened
   At remembered ice.
Something told the wild geese
   It was time to fly,—
15 Summer sun was on their wings,
   Winter in their cry.

"Something Told the Wild Geese" reprinted by permission of Macmillan Publishing Company from *Poems* by Rachel Field. Copyright 1934 by Macmillan Publishing Company, renewed © 1962 by Arthur S. Pederson.

THINK AND DISCUSS
Understanding
1. What fear leads the geese to fly away?

Analyzing
2. What do you think the "something" is that tells the geese to go?
3. In what season is the poem set? What makes you think so?
4. Chart the **rhyme scheme** for the poem.

Does it seem regular, irregular, or somewhere in between?
5. Read the poem aloud. Is the **rhythm** fast or slow?
6. To what sense does the **image** "warm feathers" appeal?
7. To what does the following image appeal: ". . . each wild breast stiffened/ At remembered ice"?

James Lockhart, *Canada Goose*, Private Collection

Cleaning the Well

Paul Ruffin

Each spring there was the well to be cleaned.
On a day my grandfather would say,
"It's got to be done. Let's go." This time
I dropped bat and glove, submitted to the rope,
5 and he lowered me into the dark and cold
water of the well. The sun
slid off at a crazy cant and I
was there, thirty feet down, waist deep
in icy water, grappling for whatever
10 was not pure and wet and cold.
The sky hovered like some pale moon
above, eclipsed by his heavy red face
bellowing down to me not to dally,
to feel deep and load the bucket.
15 My feet rasped against cold stone,
toes selecting unnatural shapes, curling
and gripping, raising them to my fingers,
then into the bucket and up to him:
a rubber ball, pine cones, leather glove,
20 beer can, fruit jars, an indefinable bone.
It was a time of fears: suppose he
should die or forget me, the rope break,
the water rise, a snake strike, the
bottom give way, the slick sides crumble?

John R. Koser, *Well Bucket*, Collection of Katherine Knox

---

25 The last bucket filled, my grandfather
assured, the rope loop dropped to me
and I was delivered by him who
sent me down, drawn slowly to sun
and sky and his fiercely grinning face.
30 "There was something else down there:
a cat or possum skeleton, but it
broke up, I couldn't pick it up."

He dropped his yellow hand on my head.
"There's always something down there

35 you can't quite get in your hands.
You'd know that if it wasn't your first
trip down. You'll know from now on."

"But what about the water?
Can we keep on drinking it?"

40 "You've drunk all that cat
you're likely to drink. Forget it
and don't tell the others. It's just
one more secret you got to live with."

THINK AND DISCUSS
Understanding
1. When and why is the speaker lowered into the well?
2. What things does the speaker discover once at the bottom?
3. How does the speaker pick up the objects?
4. What fears does the speaker experience after being lowered?

Analyzing
5. Do the fears the speaker experiences seem realistic or unrealistic?
6. What does the grandfather say about the broken skeleton in the well?
7. When the speaker expresses concern about the drinking water, what advice does the grandfather offer?
8. Which of the following methods does the poet use to develop the **character** of the speaker: (**a**) physical description; (**b**) speech; (**c**) action; (**d**) inner thoughts; (**e**) other characters' attitudes and reactions?

9. To what senses does the following **image** appeal: "My feet rasped against cold stone"?
10. Do you think that the grandfather's final advice to the speaker is sound? Explain.

COMPOSITION
Writing About Lessons
Like the speaker in "Cleaning the Well," all of us have learned lessons from childhood. In two to four paragraphs, write about a lesson learned from your childhood—perhaps that fire burns, that sharp rocks hurt, that not everyone is to be trusted, or that some problems are not easily solved. In your paper, relate where and when the incident occurred, who was involved, how and why it happened, and what you learned as a consequence.

Before submitting your final draft, review the checklist on revision at the end of Lesson 1 in the Writer's Handbook.

The Bat

Theodore Roethke

By day the bat is cousin to the mouse.
He likes the attic of an aging house.

His fingers make a hat about his head.
His pulse beat is so slow we think him dead.

5 He loops in crazy figures half the night
Among the trees that face the corner light.

But when he brushes up against a screen,
We are afraid of what our eyes have seen:

For something is amiss or out of place
10 When mice with wings can wear a human face.

THINK AND DISCUSS
Understanding
1. In the poem, what comparison is made between a bat and a mouse?

Analyzing
2. To what sense does the **image** in line 3 appeal?
3. Why does the speaker express fear in line 8?
4. What is the **rhyme scheme** of the poem?
5. Read the poem aloud. Is the **rhythm** fast or slow?

ENRICHMENT
Describing an Incident
Think of an occurrence that involved you and an animal. Then pair with another student and take turns describing the incidents. In your account, tell where and when the incident took place, who was involved, what happened, and how you felt as a consequence. To test how carefully you listen, write down what you remember after you both have finished your oral presentations. Do not turn your paper in until your partner has initialed it for accuracy.

BIOGRAPHIES

Gary Soto 1952–

A former worker in the fields of the San Joaquin Valley in California, Gary Soto was raised in Fresno, California. His first book of poems, *The Elements of San Joaquin*, won the United States Award of the International Poetry Forum. Since that time he has published *The Tale of Sunlight*, *Where Sparrows Work Hard*, *Black Hair*, and *Living Up the Street*, which won an American Book Award in 1985.

Rachel Field 1894–1942

Rachel Field could write before she could read, because rather than read childish books herself, she preferred the more mature books her mother read to her. At school a teacher read aloud poetry and Field learned to memorize a poem after hearing it once. Field wrote plays, children's stories, and novels as well as poems. *All This and Heaven Too* was a national best seller for months and was then made into a very successful movie. Field was the first woman to win a Newbery Medal, awarded to her book *Hitty: Her First Hundred Years*.

Paul Ruffin 1942–

Paul Ruffin, editor of *Texas Review*, enjoys teaching poetry to young people and giving readings. His poetry has appeared in various magazines including the *Michigan Quarterly Review*, *Kansas Quarterly*, *New Orleans Review*, and *South Carolina Review*. "Cleaning the Well" appears in his book *Lighting the Furnace Pilot*. Ruffin has published two other books, *Our Women* and *The Storm Cellar*.

Theodore Roethke 1908–1963

Theodore Roethke grew up in Saginaw, Michigan, and was educated at the University of Michigan and Harvard. He was noted for using rhyme and rhythm so skillfully that the reader is often involved in a poem before understanding its meaning. In 1954 Roethke's collection *The Waking* won the National Book Award and the Pulitzer Prize for poetry. At the time of his death, he was professor of English and poet in residence at the University of Washington in Seattle.

H⃝ See **CONNOTATION/DENOTATION**
in the Handbook of Literary Terms, page 637.

Business

Victor Hernández Cruz

Don Arturo says:
There was a man
who sold puppets and whistles
for a living
5 He also played guitar
He used to go
to the shopping areas
and draw huge crowds
They bought his whistles
10 and puppets
They threw money into
his guitar
This was against the law
So he was arrested at
15 least three times a week
When his turn came up
in the courtroom
He took a puppet out
and put a show on
20 All the detectives
and court clerks
rolled on the floor
When he finished
they all bought puppets
25 and whistles from him

Edouard Manet, *The Spanish Singer,* 1860
The Metropolitan Museum of Art

The judge got angry
and yelled:
What kind of business
is this
30 And the man said
I am the monkey man
and the
Monkey man sells
Monkey business.

Victor Hernández (er nän′des) **Cruz** (krüs).

"Business" from *Mainland* by Victor Hernández Cruz. Copyright © 1973 by Victor Hernández Cruz.
Reprinted by permission of Random House, Inc.

THINK AND DISCUSS
Understanding
1. Why was the man who sold puppets and whistles arrested?
2. How did the man behave when his turn came up in the courtroom?
3. How did the people in the courtroom respond to his behavior?

Analyzing
4. The arrested man referred to himself as the monkey man, yet he had no monkey. Why might he have identified himself as he did?
5. What, if anything, do you think the **theme** of the poem is?
6. Why do you think the poem begins as it does with the line "Don Arturo says"?

APPLYING: Connotation/Denotation H∕
See Handbook of Literary Terms, p. 637.

Connotation refers to the emotional and cultural associations and added meanings that affect how we respond to words. **Denotation** is the exact dictionary meaning of a word. The denotation of *school* is "a place for teaching and learning," but the word *school* has many connotations, including different ones for students, teachers, and parents.

1. For you, what is the connotation of the word *business?*
2. What kind of business does the title of the poem lead you to expect the poem will be about?

3. Does the word *business* as it is used in the last line of this poem have the same connotation that it ordinarily has? Explain.

VOCABULARY
Dictionary and Usage
A dictionary or glossary uses the label INFORMAL before definitions of words that are used in informal speech or writing. For example, the phrase *monkey business* is used informally in the poem "Business." You would not use it in a term paper for a business-management class. Look up the following words in the Glossary. Write two sentences for each word, using the word in an informal and then in a formal context.

1. broke
2. clout
3. ginger

COMPOSITION
Reporting an Event
Assume that you are a reporter on a school newspaper and that you have been asked to write a two- to three-paragraph story on the monkey man. In your report, discuss his performance. Include the size of the crowd he draws, his age and appearance, the kinds of music he plays, what his puppets and whistles look like, what he does with them, and how the crowd responds. Before you write, review Lesson 3, "Writing a Clear Description," in the Writer's Handbook.

Review CONNOTATION/DENOTATION
in the Handbook of Literary Terms, page 637.

Words

Pauli Murray

We are spendthrifts with words,
We squander them,
Toss them like pennies in the air—
Arrogant words,
5 Angry words,
Cruel words,
Comradely words,
Shy words tiptoeing from mouth to ear.

But the slowly wrought words of love
10 And the thunderous words of heartbreak—
These we hoard.

THINK AND DISCUSS
Understanding
1. According to the speaker, how do we
   behave toward most words?
2. What words do we save and store away?

Analyzing
3. What comparison is implied in lines 1
   and 2?
4. How would you explain the difference
   between "angry words" and "cruel
   words"?
5. Name three words you think are
   "comradely words."

Extending
6. Do the **comparisons** in lines 1 and 2
   and lines 9–11 seem appropriate or
   farfetched? Explain.

Connotation refers to the emotional and cultural associations and added meanings that affect how we respond to words. **Denotation** is the exact dictionary meaning of a word.

1. What is the denotation of *spendthrift?*
2. What are the connotations of *spendthrift?*
3. Point out the differences between the denotation and connotation of other words in the poem.

THINKING SKILLS
Classifying

To classify means to put things into groups according to some system. Classify the following words as arrogant words, angry words, cruel words, or comradely words. Add words of your own to each of your groups.

love	biting	sharp	warm
solid	baleful	proud	cold
conceited	friendly	jagged	united

COMPOSITION
Writing About Words

If you were given a choice of five words to keep in the English language, what five would you choose? In two to three paragraphs, specify your choices and your reasons for making them. It may be that you associate particular personal experiences with some of your choices, or it may be that you select a word just because you enjoy its sound.

Before writing your first draft, see Lesson 2 in the Writer's Handbook, "Supporting Your Ideas."

BIOGRAPHIES

Victor Hernández Cruz   1949–

Cruz was born in Aguas Buenas, Puerto Rico, and moved with his family to New York City in 1954. There he attended Benjamin Franklin High School. His first collection of poetry, *Snaps*, was published in 1968. Since 1973, Cruz has been a lecturer at San Francisco State University, San Francisco, California, and has published other collections of his work.

Pauli Murray   1910–1986

Born in Baltimore, Maryland, Pauli Murray spent most of her life as a poet, civil-rights activist, and attorney-at-law. At age 74, she became an Episcopal clergywoman. Murray, whose poems have appeared in numerous periodicals and anthologies, is the author of *The Dark Testament and Other Poems*.

See SIMILE in the Handbook of Literary Terms, page 658.

I'm Nobody

Emily Dickinson

I'm nobody! Who are you?
Are you nobody, too?
Then there's a pair of us—don't tell!
They'd banish us, you know.

5 How dreary to be somebody!
How public, like a frog
To tell your name the livelong day
To an admiring bog.

"I'm Nobody" from *Poems of Emily Dickinson*, Second Series, edited by T. W. Higginson and Mabel Loomis Todd. (Boston: Roberts Brothers), 1891.

Winslow Homer, *Mink Pond*, 1891
Fogg Art Museum, Harvard University, Cambridge, MA

THINK AND DISCUSS

Understanding
1. Who is the "pair" in line 3?

Analyzing
2. In line 4, to whom do you think *they* refers?
3. How would "they" be likely to react to this pair of nobodies?
4. How does the speaker feel about being "somebody"?
5. What **theme** is implied in the poem?

Extending
6. Do you agree or disagree with the speaker in this poem?

7. To what extent might a person who chooses to be a nobody be regarded as an outsider—one who doesn't belong?

APPLYING: Simile HŻ
See Handbook of Literary Terms, p. 658.

A **simile** is a comparison in which the word *like* or *as* is used to point out a similarity between two basically unlike things.
1. What is the simile in "I'm Nobody"?
2. What two things are compared in the simile?

Comment

Too "Modern" for Her Time

Emily Dickinson and her poetry never fully belonged to their own time. Born in 1830, she was an individualist who never conformed to "what was expected," and her poetry reflected her individuality.

Dickinson wrote her poems secretly on scraps of paper—used envelopes, backs of recipes. Some poems she copied into little booklets; the rest she tied up with thread and stuffed in drawers. There are hints in her letters that she recognized the quality and possible importance of her work; yet— like the speaker in "I'm Nobody"—she maintained that she had no wish for recognition in her own time.

The first of her poems to appear in print was published without her permission, and the publisher had changed the poem without her consent. Dickinson was greatly disturbed. From that point on she insisted that her poems not be published rather than be tampered with. Only seven of her 1,775 poems were published during her lifetime. After her death in 1886, relatives gathered her manuscripts for publication.

Today more than ever, Dickinson's poetry seems to be greatly appreciated. Her popularity increased when actress Julie Harris toured the country in a one-woman show based on Dickinson's life and works. Harris won Broadway's Tony award for her characterization of Emily Dickinson, *The Belle of Amherst.*

HLT Review SIMILE in the Handbook of Literary Terms, page 658.

Hilaire Germain Edgar Degas, *A Woman with Chrysanthemums*, 1865
The Metropolitan Museum of Art

My Aunt

Ted Hughes

You've heard how a green thumb
Makes flowers come
Quite without toil
Out of any old soil.

5 Well, my Aunt's thumbs were green.
At a touch, she had blooms
Of prize Chrysanthemums—
The grandest ever seen.

People from miles around
10 Came to see those flowers
And were truly astounded
By her unusual powers.

One day a little weed
Pushed up to drink and feed
15 Among the pampered flowers
At her water-can showers.

Day by day it grew
With ragged leaves and bristles
Till it was tall as me or you—
20 It was a King of Thistles.

"Prizes for flowers are easy,"
My Aunt said in her pride.
"But was there ever such a weed
The whole world wide?"

25 She watered it, she tended it,
It grew alarmingly.
As if I had offended it,
It bristled over me.

"Oh Aunt!" I cried. "Beware of that!
30 I saw it eat a bird."
She went on polishing its points
As if she hadn't heard.

"Oh Aunt!" I cried. "It has a flower
Like a lion's beard—"
35 Too late! It was devouring her
Just as I had feared!

Her feet were waving in the air
But I shall not proceed.
Here ends the story of my Aunt
40 And her ungrateful weed.

THINK AND DISCUSS

Understanding

1. How does the speaker's aunt spend her days?
2. What happens to change the course of her life?

Analyzing

3. Describe the **character** of the aunt.
4. What clues does the speaker notice that reveal the danger of the weed?
5. How do the **rhythm** and **rhyme scheme** contribute to the humor in the poem?
6. How does exaggeration contribute to the humor?

Extending

7. If you could, would you eliminate all weeds from life? Why or why not?

REVIEWING: Simile HZ

See Handbook of Literary Terms, p. 658.

A **simile** is a comparison in which the word *like* or *as* is used to point out a similarity between two basically unlike things.

Reread line 34. Is this an appropriate simile? Why or why not?

The Chipmunk's Day

Randall Jarrell

James J. Audubon, *Eastern Chipmunk*
Courtesy the Newberry Library, Chicago

In and out the bushes, up the ivy,
Into the hole
By the old oak stump, the chipmunk flashes.
Up the pole

5 To the feeder full of seeds he dashes,
Stuffs his cheeks,
The chickadee and titmouse scold him.
Down he streaks.

Red as the leaves the wind blows off the maple,
10 Red as a fox,
Striped like a skunk, the chipmunk whistles
Past the love seat, past the mailbox,

Down the path,
Home to his warm hole stuffed with sweet
15 Things to eat.
Neat and slight and shining, his front feet

Curled at his breast, he sits there while the sun
Stripes the red west
With its last light: the chipmunk
20 Dives to his rest.

THINK AND DISCUSS

Understanding

1. What words suggest the speed of the chipmunk and the direction in which he moves?

Analyzing

2. Note that the poet uses the word *and* only once. Where else might he have used it?

3. How does the absence of *and* affect the **rhythm** of the poem?

4. Work out the **rhyme scheme.** What is unusual about stanza four, lines 13–16?

5. Writers sometimes use inversion, or reverse the usual order of words in a sentence to achieve emphasis or for a certain poetic effect. In lines 1–3, the word order is inverted to help make the reader aware of how fast the chipmunk moves. Point out the inversion in lines 4–5. How does it help you get a picture of the way the chipmunk moves?

6. Locate another inversion in the poem. What effect do you think the poet intended?

Extending

7. Would the last line be improved if it read "Curls to his rest"? Explain.

BIOGRAPHIES

Ted Hughes   1930–

Ted Hughes is one of England's best-known poets. He has received many awards and honors for his poetry and also writes plays, short stories, and novels. Most of his work deals with the natural world of animals—farm, zoo, wild, domestic, and imaginary animals. In 1984 Hughes was named poet laureate of England.

Randall Jarrell   1914–1965

Randall Jarrell once said a good poet was one "who manages, in a lifetime of standing out in thunderstorms, to be struck by lightning five or six times; a dozen or two dozen times and he is great." Jarrell spent his life writing poems, novels, and critical books and articles on poetry. He also taught English and creative writing.

See METAPHOR in the Handbook of Literary Terms, page 646.

Fog

Carl Sandburg

The fog comes
on little cat feet.

It sits looking
over harbor and city
5 on silent haunches
and then moves on.

James McNeill Whistler, *Old Battersea Bridge: Nocturne in Blue and Gold* c. 1865 Tate Gallery

THINK AND DISCUSS

Understanding

1. To what is the fog being compared?

Analyzing

2. How would the poem differ if line 2 read "on big cat feet"? if line 6 read "and then shuffles off"?

Extending

3. Do you think a photograph could express the same idea? Why or why not?

APPLYING: Metaphor H𝕋
See Handbook of Literary Terms, p. 646.

A **metaphor** is a comparison that does not use *like* or *as*. Unlike a simile, a metaphor involves an implied comparison between two things that are basically unlike.

1. What is the metaphor in "Fog"?
2. How effective is the metaphor in helping you to see something in a new way?

COMPOSITION ⬤═

Writing Similes and Metaphors

Complete the following phrases by creating fresh and vivid **similes** and **metaphors.** For example, you might write "The moon is like a silver dollar afloat in a black sea" or "The moon is a silent watchman guarding the long night."

Similes

The noonday sun is like ...

Daytime television is like ...

Third grade is like ...

A rainy day is like ...

A new book is like ...

Summer vacation is like ...

Homework is like ...

Metaphors

The noonday sun is ...

Daytime television is ...

Third grade is ...

A rainy day is ...

A new book is ...

Summer vacation is ...

Homework is ...

Review METAPHOR in the Handbook of Literary Terms, page 646.

Nancy Hanks   1784–1818

Rosemary and Stephen Vincent Benét

If Nancy Hanks
Came back as a ghost,
Seeking news
Of what she loved most,
5 She'd ask first
"Where's my son?
What's happened to Abe?
What's he done?

"Poor little Abe,
10 Left all alone
Except for Tom,
Who's a rolling stone;
He was only nine
The year I died.
15 I remember still
How hard he cried.

"Scraping along
In a little shack
With hardly a shirt
20 To cover his back,
And a prairie wind
To blow him down,
Or pinching times
If he went to town.

25 "You wouldn't know
About my son?
Did he grow tall?
Did he have fun?
Did he learn to read?
30 Did he get to town?
Do you know his name?
Did he get on?"

Eastman Johnson, *Boyhood of Lincoln*, 1868
The University of Michigan Museum of Art

THINK AND DISCUSS
Understanding
1. According to the poem, what would be Nancy Hanks's major concern if she came back as a ghost?
2. How old was Abraham Lincoln when his mother died?
3. What does Abe's mother remember about his life the year she died?

Analyzing
4. What do you think "pinching times" in line 23 means?
5. What lines **rhyme** in the first three stanzas? What is unusual about the last stanza?

Extending
6. Of the questions Nancy Hanks asks, which two do you consider most important? Why?

REVIEWING: Metaphor HT
See Handbook of Literary Terms, p. 646.
   A **metaphor** is a comparison that does not use *like* or *as*.
1. What is the metaphor in the second stanza?
2. What does the comparison mean?

ENRICHMENT
Doing Research
   In your school or local library, learn about the life of Abraham Lincoln. After taking notes on his major activities and accomplishments, write a friendly letter to Nancy Hanks in which you respond to many, if not all, of her questions. Your letter might begin as follows: Yes, your son Abe got on.

See ALLITERATION in the Handbook of Literary Terms, page 634.

Sarah Cynthia Sylvia Stout
Would Not Take the Garbage Out

Shel Silverstein

Sarah Cynthia Sylvia Stout
Would not take the garbage out!
She'd scour the pots and scrape the pans,
Candy the yams and spice the hams,
5 And though her daddy would scream and shout,
She simply would not take the garbage out.
And so it piled up to the ceilings:
Coffee grounds, potato peelings,
Brown bananas, rotten peas,
10 Chunks of sour cottage cheese.
It filled the can, it covered the floor,
It cracked the window and blocked the door
With bacon rinds and chicken bones,
Drippy ends of ice cream cones,
15 Prune pits, peach pits, orange peel,
Gloppy glumps of cold oatmeal,
Pizza crusts and withered greens,
Soggy beans and tangerines,
Crusts of black burned buttered toast,
20 Gristly bits of beefy roasts . . .
The garbage rolled on down the hall,
It raised the roof, it broke the wall . . .
Greasy napkins, cookie crumbs,
Globs of gooey bubble gum,
25 Cellophane from green baloney,
Rubbery blubbery macaroni,
Peanut butter, caked and dry,
Curdled milk and crusts of pie,

Moldy melons, dried-up mustard,
30 Eggshells mixed with lemon custard,
Cold french fries and rancid meat,
Yellow lumps of Cream of Wheat.
At last the garbage reached so high
That finally it touched the sky.
35 And all the neighbors moved away,
And none of her friends would come to play.
And finally Sarah Cynthia Stout said,
"OK, I'll take the garbage out!"
But then, of course, it was too late . . .
40 The garbage reached across the state,
From New York to the Golden Gate.
And there, in the garbage she did hate,
Poor Sarah met an awful fate,
That I cannot right now relate
45 Because the hour is much too late.
But children, remember Sarah Stout
And always take the garbage out!

THINK AND DISCUSS
Understanding
1. What happens because Sarah refuses to take out the garbage?

Analyzing
2. Give examples of exaggeration in the poem. What effect does it create?
3. Years ago, stories written for children frequently showed "bad" or "naughty" boys and girls coming to horrible ends. Such stories always had a moral, or lesson, to teach young children how they should or should not behave. Find a moral in "Sarah Cynthia Sylvia Stout."
4. Is the moral in the poem to be taken seriously, or not? Explain.

APPLYING: Alliteration HandbookΖ
See Handbook of Literary Terms, p. 634.

The repetition of identical consonant or vowel sounds at the beginning of words or within words is **alliteration.** For example, the sound of the letter *s* is repeated in "She sells sea shells by the sea shore." The sound of the letter *i* is repeated in "I like ice cream at night."
1. Silverstein uses alliteration frequently with such word pairs as "potato peelings" and "brown bananas." List at least five more word combinations that show alliteration.
2. Do you think alliteration adds to or detracts from the humor? Explain.

Review ALLITERATION in the Handbook of Literary Terms, page 634.

The Sidewalk Racer or On the Skateboard

Lillian Morrison

Skimming
an asphalt sea
I swerve, I curve, I
sway; I speed to whirring
5 sound an inch above the
ground; I'm the sailor
and the sail, I'm the
driver and the wheel
I'm the one and only
10 single engine
human auto
mobile.

THINK AND DISCUSS
Understanding
1. What **images** describe the **setting** and the action of the poem?

Analyzing
2. Read the poem aloud and feel its **rhythm.** Do you find that you speed up, slow down, or maintain a steady pace as you read? If you alter your pace, why do you do so?

3. Why do you think the poet makes two words out of *automobile?* (Think of the meanings of *auto* and *mobile.*)

4. The speaker claims to be both "the sailor and the sail," and "the driver and the wheel." What feelings do these combined **images** suggest?

Peter Berg, *Threshold* (detail), 1986
Oxford Gallery, New York

Extending

5. Is the sidewalk racer really "one and only"? If not, why do you suppose the speaker makes this claim in lines 9–12?

REVIEWING: Alliteration

See Handbook of Literary Terms, p. 634.

The repetition of identical consonant or vowel sounds at the beginning of words or within words is **alliteration.**

1. What consonant sound is repeated in "The Sidewalk Racer"?

2. What effect does the repeated sound have in the poem?

COMPOSITION

Reading/Writing Log

Lillian Morrison uses comparisons to show how the sidewalk racer feels on the skateboard. One of these is given below. Copy the example in your **reading/writing log.** Then add at least two examples.

I'm the sailor / and the sail

Writing a Poem

Notice how the poet compares the skateboarder to a sailor and a sail to show how the sidewalk racer feels. Write a short poem in which you use comparisons to express feelings. Choose something you have experienced, such as riding a bicycle. Think of comparisons that will show your feelings. It may help you to write two or three word combinations that repeat sounds before you begin to write. If you are keeping a **reading/writing log,** refer to it for ideas.

See PERSONIFICATION in the Handbook of Literary Terms, page 648.

Four Little Foxes

Lew Sarett

Speak gently, Spring, and make no sudden sound;
For in my windy valley, yesterday I found
New-born foxes squirming on the ground—
         Speak gently.

5 Walk softly, March, forbear the bitter blow;
Her feet within a trap, her blood upon the snow,
The four little foxes saw their mother go—
         Walk softly.

Go lightly, Spring, oh, give them no alarm;
10 When I covered them with boughs to shelter them from harm,
The thin blue foxes suckled at my arm—
         Go lightly.

Step softly, March, with your rampant hurricane;
Nuzzling one another, and whimpering with pain,
15 The new little foxes are shivering in the rain—
         Step softly.

Glen Loates, *Red Fox*, 1969
Private Collection

THINK AND DISCUSS
Understanding
1. What has happened to the mother fox?
2. What does the speaker do to protect the young animals?

Analyzing
3. Describe the **setting** of the poem.
4. Why does the speaker urge March to "walk softly" and "step softly"?
5. Read the poem aloud. Is the **rhythm** fast or slow? Explain.
6. Is the **rhyme scheme** regular or irregular? Explain.

APPLYING: Personification   H⌖
See Handbook of Literary Terms, p. 648.

   Personification is a figure of speech that gives human form, action, or feeling to animals, ideas, objects, or even abstract things such as seasons of the year. For example, the moon is personified in, "The moon pulled a cover of clouds over herself and peacefully slept." A rabbit is personified in, "The rabbit thought to himself, 'I know how to hop out of this predicament!'"

1. Find two examples of personification in "Four Little Foxes."
2. What effect does personification have upon the poem? How would the poem be different without it?

COMPOSITION   ✎
Describing a Responsibility

   Almost everyone has had the responsibility of taking care of something or someone at some time. In two or three paragraphs, describe to classmates a time when you had to take care of an animal, a plant, a younger brother or sister, or the children of others. Before writing your first draft, take notes of the circumstances surrounding your responsibility: Who gave you this responsibility? When? Where? Why? What specifically were you to do?

Review **PERSONIFICATION** in the Handbook of Literary Terms, page 648.

Street Window

Carl Sandburg

The pawn-shop man knows hunger,
And how far hunger has eaten the heart
Of one who comes with an old keepsake.
Here are wedding rings and baby bracelets,
5 Scarf pins and shoe buckles, jeweled garters,
Old-fashioned knives with inlaid handles,
Watches of old gold and silver,
Old coins worn with finger-marks.
They tell stories.

Audrey Flack, *Jolie Madam* (detail), 1973
Australian National Gallery, Canberra

"Street Window" from *Cornhuskers* by Carl Sandburg, copyright 1918 by Holt, Rinehart and Winston, Inc.; renewed 1946 by Carl Sandburg. Reprinted by permission of Harcourt Brace Jovanovich, Inc.

THINK AND DISCUSS

Understanding

1. What kinds of things are brought to the pawnshop and why?

Analyzing

2. What word besides *and* is used four times in the poem? Why do you think the poet repeated this word so often?
3. Read the poem aloud. Do the words make you want to read slowly or quickly? Explain.

REVIEWING: Personification H🖋

See Handbook of Literary Terms, p. 648.

Personification gives human form, character, feelings, or actions to animals, ideas, abstractions, or objects.

1. In what lines does personification occur in "Street Window"?
2. What is personified in each example?
3. What effect does personification have on the poem?

BIOGRAPHIES

Carl Sandburg 1878–1967

Because his family was poor, Carl Sandburg left school at thirteen to drive a milk truck. While still in his teens he traveled around the country in boxcars, making friends with hobos and working when he needed money. Later he worked his way through college and finally took a job in Chicago. That city and its people are the subject of many of his poems.

Sandburg's talents were not limited to poetry; he was also a noted collector of folklore who did much to popularize folk music. He won recognition as a historian with his six-volume biography of Abraham Lincoln.

Rosemary Benét 1898–1962
Stephen Vincent Benét 1898–1943

Rosemary Benét and her husband Stephen Vincent Benét wrote *A Book of Americans*, a book of poems about America's heroes. A graduate of the University of Chicago, Rosemary was the Paris correspondent for *The London Daily Mail* and the *Chicago Tribune*.

A graduate of Yale University, Stephen Benét won the Pulitzer Prize in 1928 for *John Brown's Body*, a long narrative poem about the Civil War. He also wrote radio scripts and plays and American folk tales.

Lillian Morrison 1917–

Of "The Sidewalk Racer," Lillian Morrison says, "I love rhythms, the body movement implicit in poetry, explicit in sports. And there are emotions connected with sports, sometimes a kind of transcendence and beauty one wants to catch. One turns naturally to poetry to express these things." Morrison has published several volumes of poetry, including collections of sports poems and a book of "sciencepoems."

Lew Sarett 1888–1954

Lew Sarett was born in Chicago. After working his way through college and law school, Sarett taught at Northwestern University. A lover of nature, he spent much of his free time in the Rocky Mountains and northern Canada. This rugged country furnishes background for many of Sarett's poems.

BIOGRAPHY

Robert Frost

1874–1963

A descendant of nine generations of New Englanders, Robert Frost was a New England poet who loved the earth and the things close to it. Rocky farms, lush woodlands, old houses, stone fences, and the rugged people who work the soil are the stuff of his poems.

Born in San Francisco, Frost moved to Massachusetts at the age of eleven. He married at twenty, studied at Harvard for two years, and then held a number of odd jobs before settling down on a New Hampshire farm. But after eleven years of farming and writing poetry, Frost moved to England, his farm a failure and his poetry unrecognized. In London he offered some of his poems to a publisher. When published as *A Boy's Will* in 1913, they were immediately recognized as fresh and original. Frost quickly followed this collection with *North of Boston* (1914).

In 1915 Frost returned home famous. He maintained that fame throughout his life by the quality of his poems, by his often quotable remarks to the press, and by his frequent poetry readings. Four times a winner of the Pulitzer Prize in poetry, Frost, like most New Englanders, was restrained in both emotion and language. He once wrote to a friend, "A poem . . . begins as a lump in the throat, a sense of wrong, a lovesickness. . . . It finds the thought and the thought finds the words." On another occasion, he wrote that a poem should "begin in delight and end in wisdom."

H T See **TONE** in the Handbook of Literary Terms, page 663.

Jean-François Millet, *Bringing Home the New-Born Calf* (detail)
c. 1864 The Art Institute of Chicago

The Pasture

I'm going out to clean the pasture spring;
I'll only stop to rake the leaves away
(And wait to watch the water clear, I may):
I shan't be gone long.—You come too.

5 I'm going out to fetch the little calf
That's standing by the mother. It's so young
It totters when she licks it with her tongue.
I shan't be gone long.—You come too.

THINK AND DISCUSS
Understanding
1. What two purposes does the speaker have for going out to the pasture?

Analyzing
2. What can you tell about the occupation and the personality of the speaker from the poem?
3. How do you interpret the invitation to come along?
4. What does it suggest about the speaker's feelings toward the person addressed?
5. Find the phrases that are repeated. What purpose does each serve?

Extending
6. Robert Frost put "The Pasture" at the beginning of several collections of his poetry. Why might he have done this?

APPLYING: Tone   H⫯
See Handbook of Literary Terms, p. 663.

Tone is an author's attitude toward his or her subject. The tone of a work may be informal, formal, intimate, distant, playful, serious, carefree, somber, forthright, ironic, or any of many other possibilities.

1. Does the tone of "The Pasture" appear to be formal or informal, friendly or unfriendly?
2. Which words in particular seem to contribute to the tone?

COMPOSITION ◄━●
Writing an Invitation
Think of a place you might like to invite a friend. Write a letter describing the place and giving reasons why you think your friend would enjoy going also. The purpose of the letter is to persuade your friend to accompany you.

The place you choose might be a movie theater where a particular film is being shown, a sports event, a resort, a dance, a shopping mall, your own home, or some other place. In your letter, use specific details. Keep the tone of the letter informal and friendly. You might begin as follows:

Dear _____,
I think you'd really enjoy going with me to _____.

Review TONE in the Handbook of Literary Terms, page 663.

A Time to Talk

When a friend calls to me from the road
And slows his horse to a meaning walk,
I don't stand still and look around
On all the hills I haven't hoed,
5 And shout from where I am, "What is it?"
No, not as there is a time to talk.
I thrust my hoe in the mellow ground,
Blade-end up and five feet tall,
And plod: I go up to the stone wall
10 For a friendly visit.

"A Time to Talk" from *The Poetry of Robert Frost* edited by Edward Connery Lathem. Copyright 1916, 1939, © 1967, © 1969 by Holt, Rinehart and Winston. Copyright 1944 by Robert Frost. Reprinted by permission of Henry Holt and Company, Inc., the Estate of Robert Frost and Jonathan Cape Ltd.

THINK AND DISCUSS

Understanding

1. When called by a friend, what does the speaker do?

Analyzing

2. Do you think that the speaker wishes to avoid work? Explain.
3. Do you think the two friends see each other often? Why do you think so?
4. What reasons might the farmer have for standing the hoe upright in the ground?
5. Robert Frost once said, "Every time a poem is written, it is written not by cunning, but by belief." What do you think Frost's belief about time is as shown by this poem?

REVIEWING: Tone
See Handbook of Literary Terms, p. 663.

Tone is the author's attitude toward the subject. Is the tone of this poem formal and ironic, tense and angry, or casual and friendly? Explain.

The Runaway

Once when the snow of the year was beginning to fall,
We stopped by a mountain pasture to say "Whose colt?"
A little Morgan[1] had one forefoot on the wall,
The other curled at his breast. He dipped his head
5 And snorted at us. And then he had to bolt.
We heard the miniature thunder where he fled,
And we saw him, or thought we saw him, dim and gray,
Like a shadow against the curtain of falling flakes.
"I think the little fellow's afraid of the snow.
10 He isn't winter-broken. It isn't play
With the little fellow at all. He's running away.
I doubt if even his mother could tell him, 'Sakes,
It's only weather.' He'd think she didn't know!
Where is his mother? He can't be out alone."
15 And now he comes again with clatter of stone,
And mounts the wall again with whited eyes
And all his tail that isn't hair up straight.
He shudders his coat as if to throw off flies.
"Whoever it is that leaves him out so late,
20 When other creatures have gone to stall and bin,
Ought to be told to come and take him in."

---

1. *Morgan,* any of an American breed of sturdy, light horses that originated in Vermont in the late eighteenth century; used for work on farms.

THINK AND DISCUSS
Understanding
  1. Describe the time and place of the poem.
  2. Describe the behavior of the colt.
  3. How does the speaker explain the colt's behavior?
  4. What does the speaker think should be done with the colt?

Paulus Potter, *Horses in a Field* (detail), 1649, Rijksmuseum, Amsterdam

Analyzing

5. Who is the "we" in line 2? What effect does the use of "we" and "us" have upon the poem?
6. Find the **metaphor** in line 8.
7. What is the **simile** in line 8?
8. Do you think the figures of speech in line 8 are effective? Explain.
9. Reread the poem. Is the **rhythm** fast or slow?
10. Does the **tone** of "The Runaway" seem to be one of concern, indifference, amusement, or despair? Explain your idea using words from the poem.

Extending

11. Do you think the speaker in the poem has an obligation to try to locate the colt's owner and find shelter for the animal?

THINKING SKILLS
Generalizing

To generalize is to draw a general conclusion from particular information.

1. What impression of Frost the person do you get from reading "The Pasture," "A Time to Talk," and "The Runaway"?
2. What generalizations could you make about the way Frost felt about people? animals? work?

COMPOSITION
Writing to Summarize

Choose one of the poems by Robert Frost and write a summary of the event described. Consider who, what, when, where, and why in your summary. Before you write, review Lesson 5, "Writing to Summarize," in the Writer's Handbook.

THINKING CRITICALLY
ABOUT LITERATURE

UNIT 4   POETRY

■ CONCEPT REVIEW

The poems that follow review the important ideas and literary elements you have just studied. The notes in the right-hand margin highlight some of these concepts. Page numbers in the notes refer you to an application. A more extensive discussion of these ideas and elements appears in the Handbook of Literary Terms. Each of the following poems focuses on a person who comforts the speaker in some way or ways.

While I Slept

Robert Francis

While I slept, while I slept and the night grew colder
She would come to my bedroom stepping softly
And draw a blanket about my shoulder
While I slept.

5 While I slept, while I slept in the dark still heat
She would come to my bedside stepping coolly
And smooth the twisted troubled sheet
While I slept.

Now she sleeps, sleeps under quiet rain
10 While nights grow warm or nights grow colder
And I wake and sleep and wake again
While she sleeps.

■ **Alliteration** (page 303): Look for the sound that is repeated in every line.

■ **Rhythm** (page 257): Notice how repetition affects the rhythm.

■ **Rhyme** (page 271): Note the rhyme scheme.

■ **Tone** (page 312): Note how there is a shift of tone between stanzas two and three.

■ **Imagery** (page 280): Note the words that appeal to the senses.

■ **Connotation** (page 289): The word *sleeps* is being used in a special way in stanza three.

George W. Delaney, *Naschimento*, Private Collection. This watercolor won the bronze medal of honor in the American Watercolor Society 118th Annual Exhibition in 1985.

Mama Is a Sunrise

Evelyn Tooley Hunt

When she comes slip-footing through the door,
  she kindles us
  like lump coal lighted,
  and we wake up glowing.
5 She puts a spark even in Papa's eyes
and turns out all our darkness.

When she comes sweet-talking in the room,
  she warms us
  like grits and gravy,
10   and we rise up shining.
Even at night-time Mama is a sunrise
that promises tomorrow and tomorrow.

■ **Simile** (page 293): Note the similes in lines 3 and 9.

■ **Connotation**: *Darkness* takes on a special meaning in line 6.
■ **Rhyme**: Notice whether the poet employs a rhyme scheme.
■ **Tone**: Try to figure out the poet's attitude toward *mama*.
■ **Metaphor** (page 299): Note the metaphor in line 11.

"Mama Is a Sunrise" from *The Lyric* (1972). Reprinted by permission of the author.

THINK AND DISCUSS
Understanding
1. Who is the "she" in "While I Slept"?
2. Who is the "she" in "Mama Is a Sunrise"?

Analyzing
3. In each poem, what is the relationship of the speaker to the "she"?
4. In the first two stanzas of "While I Slept," what actions does "she" perform?
5. From her actions, what kind of person is Mama?
6. In the third stanza of "While I Slept," what has taken place to change the focus of the poem?
7. How does Mama affect the other family members? How do you know?

Extending
8. At what times do people become aware of the loving acts others have performed for them?

REVIEWING LITERARY TERMS
Alliteration
1. Identify two lines in which alliteration occurs in "While I Slept."

Rhythm
2. "While I Slept" is repeated six times in stanzas one and two. Does the repetition quicken the rhythm or slow it? Explain.

Rhyme
3. Compare the rhyme schemes of the two poems. Are they regular, irregular, or a combination of the two?

Tone
4. The tone expressed in the first two stanzas of "While I Slept"—that of

grateful appreciation—changes in stanza three. Would you characterize the tone in the last stanza as one of angry resentment, quiet mourning, deep despair, or happy acceptance? Explain.
5. How would you describe the tone of "Mama Is a Sunrise"?

Imagery
6. To what senses do the images in the first stanza of "While I Slept" appeal? Explain.

Connotation/Denotation
7. What is the denotation of *sleep*? What is its connotation in line 12 of "While I Slept"?
8. What are the denotation and connotation of *darkness* in "Mama Is a Sunrise"?

Simile
9. Identify the simile in the first stanza of "Mama Is a Sunrise."
10. Is this simile effective? Explain.

Metaphor
11. What impression of Mama do you get from the metaphor "Mama Is a Sunrise"?

■ CONTENT REVIEW
THINKING SKILLS
Classifying
1. Classify the poems in Unit 4 according to subject. Use at least three groups.
2. Make a list of humorous poems and a list of serious poems. You won't use all of the poems in Unit 4.

Generalizing
3. To what sense do poets seem to refer

most often? Use examples from the poems to support your idea.

Synthesizing

4. Suppose you must think of a title for this unit other than "Poetry." What would you suggest?

Evaluating

5. Evaluate the following statement: Story poems like "The Demon of the Gibbet" and "Dorlan's Home Walk" are more interesting than descriptive poems like "Fog" and "Hokku Poems." Tell whether you agree or disagree and why.

6. Complete the following sentence and explain why: I would like to read more poems by _____ .

■ COMPOSITION REVIEW

Writing Poetry

In the first stanza of "Mama Is a Sunrise," the speaker suggests that Mama's mere presence in a room can light up the people around her. In the second stanza the speaker suggests that Mama's words can warm others. Write a third stanza that tells other qualities Mama might have. For example, you might write about the effects on others of Mama's laughter, her cooking, or her manner of dress. Or you might wish to change the mood and tone in the poem by describing how Mama's crying affects others. Whatever quality you choose, keep the language and imagery consistent with the first two stanzas.

Describing Behavior

"Four Little Foxes," "Something Told the Wild Geese," "The Bat," and "The Chipmunk's Day" are all based on close observation of animals. Write a two- to three-paragraph description of a creature you have observed closely—the family dog or cat, an ant, a bird at a feeder, a bear cub at the zoo. In your description, include what the creature does and your reactions to its behavior.

As preparation for the assignment, you might reread the poems mentioned above, taking particular notice of the authors' attention to detail.

Reviewing Writer's Craft: Use Comparisons

In this unit you have seen how poets use comparisons and contrasts. You may have read examples, copied some, and found examples on your own. Now **try your hand** at creating your own comparisons and contrasts. Write a short poem about any subject. Think of an animal, a person, or an experience. Think of a way to compare it to something. You may want your poem to tell a story in verse. Decide whether your poem will be serious or humorous. It may use such techniques as rhyme, alliteration, and imagery or not, but be sure to include comparisons. First review how poets in this unit use comparisons. Consult your **reading/writing log,** if you have been keeping one. Then make a list of things to compare or contrast in your own poem.

Winslow Homer, *Three Boys on the Shore*, 1873, Daniel J. Terra Collection,

Terra Museum of American Art, Chicago

PREVIEW

UNIT 5   SHORT STORY 2

President Cleveland, Where Are You? /
    Robert Cormier
A Man Who Had No Eyes /
    MacKinlay Kantor
A Haircut / I. S. Nakata
Nancy / Elizabeth Enright
Adolf / D. H. Lawrence
The Gift / Ray Bradbury

The Hundredth Dove / Jane Yolen
**The Hummingbird That Lived Through
    Winter** / William Saroyan
The Storyteller / H. H. Munro
The Day the Sun Came Out /
    Dorothy M. Johnson
Last Cover / Paul Annixter
Key Item / Isaac Asimov

Features
The Writer's Craft: Use Words That
    Appeal to the Senses
Reading Fantasy
Comment: The Red Fox

Application of Literary Terms
irony   stereotype
figurative language   inference
symbol   flashback

Reading Literature Skillfully
author's purpose

Vocabulary Skills
synonyms
roots and suffixes
dictionary and glossary
context
antonyms

Thinking Skills
classifying   synthesizing
generalizing   evaluating

Composition Assignments Include
Describing a Collection
Writing About a Story Character
Contrasting Story Characters
Writing Dialogue
Writing Your Own Story
Describing Two Homes
Describing a Pet
Imagining a Trip into Space
Being a Story Character
Writing a Story Ending
Writing a Journal Entry
Writing a Diary Entry
Writing About Plot
Writing a Report

Enrichment
Doing Research
Reading Dialogue Aloud
Making a Booklet

Thinking Critically About Literature
Concept Review
Content Review
Composition Review

President Cleveland, Where Are You?

Robert Cormier

Jerry was half sick with longing. The prize was an official imitation major league baseball glove, and he was one card away from winning it.

hat was the autumn of the cowboy cards—Buck Jones and Tom Tyler and Hoot Gibson and especially Ken Maynard. The cards were available in those five-cent packages of gum: pink sticks, three together, covered with a sweet white powder. You couldn't blow bubbles with that particular gum, but it couldn't have mattered less. The cowboy cards were important—the pictures of those rock-faced men with eyes of blue steel.

On those wind-swept, leaf-tumbling afternoons we gathered after school on the sidewalk in front of Lemire's Drugstore, across from St. Jude's Parochial School, and we swapped and bargained and matched for the cards. Because a Ken Maynard serial was playing at the Globe every Saturday afternoon, he was the most popular cowboy of all, and one of his cards was worth at least ten of any other kind. Rollie Tremaine had a treasure of thirty or so, and he guarded them jealously. He'd match you for the other cards, but he risked his Ken Maynards only when the other kids threatened to leave him out of the competition altogether.

You could almost hate Rollie Tremaine. In the first place, he was the only son of Auguste Tremaine, who operated the Uptown Dry Goods Store, and he did not live in a tenement but in a big white birthday cake of a house on Laurel Street. He was too fat to be effective in the football games between the Frenchtown Tigers and the North Side Knights, and he made us constantly aware of the jingle of coins in his pockets. He was able to stroll into Lemire's and casually select a quarter's worth of cowboy cards while the rest of us watched, aching with envy.

Once in a while I earned a nickel or dime by running errands or washing windows for blind old Mrs. Belander, or by finding pieces of copper, brass, and other valuable metals at the dump and selling them to the junkman.

Robert Cormier (kôr mē ā′).

"President Cleveland, Where Are You?" from *Eight Plus One* by Robert Cormier. Copyright © 1965 by Robert Cormier. First appeared in *Redbook*. Reprinted by permission of Pantheon Books, a Division of Random House, Inc. and Curtis Brown, Ltd.

The coins clutched in my hand, I would race to Lemire's to buy a cowboy card or two, hoping that Ken Maynard would stare boldly out at me as I opened the pack. At one time, before a disastrous matching session with Roger Lussier (my best friend, except where the cards were involved), I owned five Ken Maynards and considered myself a millionaire, of sorts.

One week I was particularly lucky; I had spent two afternoons washing floors for Mrs. Belander and received a quarter. Because my father had worked a full week at the shop, where a rush order for fancy combs had been received, he allotted my brothers and sisters and me an extra dime along with the usual ten cents for the Saturday-afternoon movie. Setting aside the movie fare, I found myself with a bonus of thirty-five cents, and I then planned to put Rollie Tremaine to shame the following Monday afternoon.

Monday was the best day to buy the cards because the candy man stopped at Lemire's every Monday morning to deliver the new assortments. There was nothing more exciting in the world than a fresh batch of card boxes. I rushed home from school that day and hurriedly changed my clothes, eager to set off for the store. As I burst through the doorway, letting the screen door slam behind me, my brother Armand blocked my way.

He was fourteen, three years older than I, and a freshman at Monument High School. He had recently become a stranger to me in many ways—indifferent to such matters as cowboy cards and the Frenchtown Tigers—and he carried himself with a mysterious dignity that was fractured now and then when his voice began shooting off in all directions

like some kind of vocal fireworks.

"Wait a minute, Jerry," he said. "I want to talk to you." He motioned me out of earshot of my mother, who was busy supervising the usual after-school skirmish in the kitchen.

I sighed with impatience. In recent months Armand had become a figure of authority, siding with my father and mother occasionally. As the oldest son he sometimes took advantage of his age and experience to issue rules and regulations.

"How much money have you got?" he whispered.

"You in some kind of trouble?" I asked, excitement rising in me as I remembered the blackmail plot of a movie at the Globe a month before.

He shook his head in annoyance. "Look," he said, "it's Pa's birthday tomorrow. I think we ought to chip in and buy him something . . ."

I reached into my pocket and caressed the coins. "Here," I said carefully, pulling out a nickel. "If we all give a nickel we should have enough to buy him something pretty nice."

He regarded me with contempt. "Rita already gave me fifteen cents, and I'm throwing in a quarter. Albert handed over a dime—all that's left of his birthday money. Is that all you can do—a nickel?"

"Aw, come on," I protested. "I haven't got a single Ken Maynard left, and I was going to buy some cards this afternoon."

"Ken Maynard!" he snorted. "Who's more important—him or your father?"

His question was unfair because he knew that there was no possible choice—"my father" had to be the only answer. My father was a huge man who believed in the things of the spirit, although my mother often maintained that the spirits he believed in came in bottles. He had worked at the Monument Comb Shop since the age of fourteen; his booming laugh—or grumble—greeted us each night when he returned from the factory. A steady worker when the shop had enough work, he quickened with gaiety on Friday nights and weekends, a bottle of beer at his elbow, and he was fond of making long speeches about the good things in life. In the middle of the Depression,[1] for instance, he paid cash for a piano, of all things, and insisted that my twin sisters, Yolande and Yvette, take lessons once a week.

I took a dime from my pocket and handed it to Armand.

"Thanks, Jerry," he said. "I hate to take your last cent."

"That's all right," I replied, turning away and consoling myself with the thought that twenty cents was better than nothing at all.

When I arrived at Lemire's I sensed disaster in the air. Roger Lussier was kicking disconsolately at a tin can in the gutter, and Rollie Tremaine sat sullenly on the steps in front of the store.

"Save your money," Roger said. He had known about my plans to splurge on the cards.

"What's the matter?" I asked.

"There's no more cowboy cards," Rollie Tremaine said. "The company's not making any more."

"They're going to have President cards," Roger said, his face twisting with disgust. He pointed to the store window. "Look!"

A placard in the window announced: "Attention, Boys. Watch for the New Series.

Presidents of the United States. Free in Each 5-Cent Package of Caramel Chew."

"President cards?" I asked, dismayed.

I read on: "Collect a Complete Set and Receive an Official Imitation Major League Baseball Glove, Embossed with Lefty Grove's Autograph."

Glove or no glove, who could become excited about Presidents, of all things?

Rollie Tremaine stared at the sign. "Benjamin Harrison, for crying out loud," he said. "Why would I want Benjamin Harrison when I've got twenty-two Ken Maynards?"

I felt the warmth of guilt creep over me. I jingled the coins in my pocket, but the sound was hollow. No more Ken Maynards to buy.

"I'm going to buy a Mr. Goodbar," Rollie Tremaine decided.

I was without appetite, indifferent even to a Baby Ruth, which was my favorite. I thought of how I had betrayed Armand and, worst of all, my father.

"I'll see you after supper," I called over my shoulder to Roger as I hurried away toward home. I took the shortcut behind the church, although it involved leaping over a tall wooden fence, and I zigzagged recklessly through Mr. Thibodeau's garden, trying to outrace my guilt. I pounded up the steps and into the house, only to learn that Armand had already taken Yolande and Yvette uptown to shop for the birthday present.

I pedaled my bike furiously through the streets, ignoring the indignant horns of automobiles as I sliced through the traffic. Finally

---

1. *the Depression,* a reference to the Great Depression, a period of the 1930s marked by a serious reduction of business activity, widespread unemployment, and low wages.

I saw Armand and my sisters emerge from the Monument Men's Shop. My heart sank when I spied the long, slim package that Armand was holding.

"Did you buy the present yet?" I asked, although I knew it was too late.

"Just now. A blue tie," Armand said. "What's the matter?"

"Nothing," I replied, my chest hurting.

He looked at me for a long moment. At first his eyes were hard, but then they softened. He smiled at me, almost sadly, and touched my arm. I turned away from him because I felt naked and exposed.

"It's all right," he said gently. "Maybe you've learned something." The words were gentle, but they held a curious dignity, the dignity remaining even when his voice suddenly cracked on the last syllable.

I wondered what was happening to me, because I did not know whether to laugh or cry.

Sister Angela was amazed when, a week before Christmas vacation, everybody in the class submitted a history essay worthy of a high mark—in some cases as high as A-minus. (Sister Angela did not believe that anyone in the world ever deserved an A.) She never learned—or at least she never let on that she knew—we all had become experts on the Presidents because of the cards we purchased at Lemire's. Each card contained a picture of a President, and on the reverse side, a summary of his career. We looked at those cards so often that the biographies imprinted themselves on our minds without effort. Even our street-corner conversations were filled with such information as the fact that James Madison was called "The Father of the Constitution," or that John Adams had intended to become a minister.

The President cards were a roaring success and the cowboy cards were quickly forgotten. In the first place we did not receive gum with the cards, but a kind of chewy caramel. The caramel could be tucked into a corner of your mouth, bulging your cheek in much the same manner as wads of tobacco bulged the mouths of baseball stars. In the second place the competition for collecting the cards was fierce and frustrating—fierce because everyone was intent on being the first to send away for a baseball glove and frustrating because although there were only thirty-two Presidents, including Franklin Delano Roosevelt, the variety at Lemire's was at a minimum. When the deliveryman left the boxes of cards at the store each Monday, we often discovered that one entire box was devoted to a single President—two weeks in a row the boxes contained nothing but Abraham Lincolns. One week Roger Lussier and I were the heroes of Frenchtown. We journeyed on our bicycles to the North Side, engaged three boys in a matching bout and returned with five new Presidents, including Chester Alan Arthur, who up to that time had been missing.

Perhaps to sharpen our desire, the card company sent a sample glove to Mr. Lemire, and it dangled, orange and sleek, in the window. I was half sick with longing, thinking of my old glove at home, which I had inherited from Armand. But Rollie Tremaine's desire for the glove outdistanced my own. He even got Mr. Lemire to agree to give the glove in the window to the first person to get a complete set of cards, so that precious time

HOOT GIBSON

BUCK JONES

GROVER CLEVELAND

KEN MAYNARD

TOM TYLER

wouldn't be wasted waiting for the postman.

We were delighted at Rollie Tremaine's frustration, especially since he was only a substitute player for the Tigers. Once after spending fifty cents on cards—all of which turned out to be Calvin Coolidge—he threw them to the ground, pulled some dollar bills out of his pocket and said, "The heck with it. I'm going to buy a glove!"

"Not that glove," Roger Lussier said. "Not a glove with Lefty Grove's autograph. Look what it says at the bottom of the sign."

We all looked, although we knew the words by heart: "This Glove Is Not For Sale Anywhere."

Rollie Tremaine scrambled to pick up the cards from the sidewalk, pouting more than ever. After that he was quietly obsessed with the Presidents, hugging the cards close to his chest and refusing to tell us how many more he needed to complete his set.

I too was obsessed with the cards, because they had become things of comfort in a world that had suddenly grown dismal. After Christmas a layoff at the shop had thrown my father out of work. He received no paycheck for four weeks, and the only income we had was from Armand's after-school job at the Blue and White Grocery Store—a job he lost finally when business dwindled as the layoff continued.

Although we had enough food and clothing—my father's credit had always been good, a matter of pride with him—the inactivity made my father restless and irritable. He did not drink any beer at all, and laughed loudly, but not convincingly, after gulping down a glass of water and saying, "Lent[2] came early this year." The twins fell sick and

went to the hospital to have their tonsils removed. My father was confident that he would return to work eventually and pay off his debts, but he seemed to age before our eyes.

When orders again were received at the comb shop and he returned to work, another disaster occurred, although I was the only one aware of it. Armand fell in love.

I discovered his situation by accident, when I happened to pick up a piece of paper that had fallen to the floor in the bedroom he and I shared. I frowned at the paper, puzzled.

"Dear Sally, When I look into your eyes the world stands still . . ."

The letter was snatched from my hands before I finished reading it.

"What's the big idea, snooping around?" Armand asked, his face crimson. "Can't a guy have any privacy?"

He had never mentioned privacy before. "It was on the floor," I said. "I didn't know it was a letter. Who's Sally?"

He flung himself across the bed. "You tell anybody and I'll muckalize you," he threatened. "Sally Knowlton."

Nobody in Frenchtown had a name like Knowlton.

"A girl from the North Side?" I asked, incredulous.

He rolled over and faced me, anger in his eyes, and a kind of despair too.

"What's the matter with that? Think she's too good for me?" he asked. "I'm warning you, Jerry, if you tell anybody . . ."

"Don't worry," I said. Love had no partic-

---

2. *Lent,* the forty weekdays between Ash Wednesday and Easter, observed in many Christian churches.

ular place in my life; it seemed an unnecessary waste of time. And a girl from the North Side was so remote that for all practical purposes she did not exist. But I was curious. "What are you writing her a letter for? Did she leave town, or something?"

"She hasn't left town," he answered. "I wasn't going to send it. I just felt like writing to her."

I was glad that I had never become involved with love—love that brought desperation to your eyes, that caused you to write letters you did not plan to send. Shrugging with indifference, I began to search in the closet for the old baseball glove. I found it on the shelf, under some old sneakers. The webbing was torn and the padding gone. I thought of the sting I would feel when a sharp grounder slapped into the glove, and I winced.

"You tell anybody about me and Sally and I'll——"

"I know. You'll muckalize me."

I did not divulge his secret and often shared his agony, particularly when he sat at the supper table and left my mother's special butterscotch pie untouched. I had never realized before how terrible love could be. But my compassion was short-lived because I had other things to worry about: report cards due at Eastertime; the loss of income from old Mrs. Belander, who had gone to live with a daughter in Boston; and, of course, the Presidents.

Because a stalemate had been reached, the President cards were the dominant force in our lives—mine, Roger Lussier's and Rollie Tremaine's. For three weeks, as the baseball season approached, each of us had a complete set—complete except for one President, Grover Cleveland. Each time a box of cards arrived at the store we hurriedly bought them (as hurriedly as our funds allowed) and tore off the wrappers, only to be confronted by James Monroe or Martin Van Buren or someone else. But never Grover Cleveland, never the man who had been the twenty-second *and* the twenty-fourth President of the United States. We argued about Grover Cleveland. Should he be placed between Chester Alan Arthur and Benjamin Harrison as the twenty-second President or did he belong between Benjamin Harrison and William McKinley as the twenty-fourth President? Was the card company playing fair? Roger Lussier brought up a horrifying possibility—did we need *two* Grover Clevelands to complete the set?

Indignant, we stormed Lemire's and protested to the harassed storeowner, who had long since vowed never to stock a new series. Muttering angrily, he searched his bills and receipts for a list of rules.

"All right," he announced. "Says here you only need one Grover Cleveland to finish the set. Now get out, all of you, unless you've got money to spend."

Outside the store, Rollie Tremaine picked up an empty tobacco tin and scaled it across the street. "Boy," he said. "I'd give five dollars for a Grover Cleveland."

When I returned home I found Armand sitting on the piazza steps, his chin in his hands. His mood of dejection mirrored my own, and I sat down beside him. We did not say anything for a while.

"Want to throw the ball around?" I asked.

He sighed, not bothering to answer.

"You sick?" I asked.

He stood up and hitched up his trousers, pulled at his ear and finally told me what the matter was—there was a big dance next week at the high school, the Spring Promenade, and Sally had asked him to be her escort.

I shook my head at the folly of love. "Well, what's so bad about that?"

"How can I take Sally to a fancy dance?" he asked desperately. "I'd have to buy her a corsage. . . . And my shoes are practically falling apart. Pa's got too many worries now to buy me new shoes or give me money for flowers for a girl."

I nodded in sympathy. "Yeah," I said. "Look at me. Baseball time is almost here, and all I've got is that old glove. And no Grover Cleveland card yet . . ."

"Grover Cleveland?" he asked. "They've got some of those up on the North Side. Some kid was telling me there's a store that's got them. He says they're looking for Warren G. Harding."

"Holy Smoke!" I said. "I've got an extra Warren G. Harding!" Pure joy sang in my veins. I ran to my bicycle, swung into the seat—and found that the front tire was flat.

"I'll help you fix it," Armand said.

Within half an hour I was at the North Side Drugstore, where several boys were matching cards on the sidewalk. Silently but blissfully I shouted: President Grover Cleveland, here I come!

After Armand had left for the dance, all dressed up as if it were Sunday, the small green box containing the corsage under his arm, I sat on the railing of the piazza, letting my feet dangle. The neighborhood was quiet because the Frenchtown Tigers were at Daggett's Field, practicing for the first baseball game of the season.

I thought of Armand and the ridiculous expression on his face when he'd stood before the mirror in the bedroom. I'd avoided looking at his new black shoes. "Love," I muttered.

Spring had arrived in a sudden stampede of apple blossoms and fragrant breezes. Windows had been thrown open and dust mops had banged on the sills all day long as the women busied themselves with housecleaning. I was puzzled by my lethargy. Wasn't spring supposed to make everything bright and gay?

I turned at the sound of footsteps on the stairs. Roger Lussier greeted me with a sour face.

"I thought you were practicing with the Tigers," I said.

"Rollie Tremaine," he said. "I just couldn't stand him." He slammed his fist against the railing. "Jeez, why did *he* have to be the one to get a Grover Cleveland? You should see him showing off. He won't let anybody even touch that glove . . ."

I felt like Benedict Arnold[3] and knew that I had to confess what I had done.

"Roger," I said, "I got a Grover Cleveland card up on the North Side. I sold it to Rollie Tremaine for five dollars."

"Are you crazy?" he asked.

"I needed that five dollars. It was an—emergency."

"Boy!" he said, looking down at the ground and shaking his head. "What did you

---

3. **Benedict Arnold** (1741–1801), American general in the Revolutionary War who became a traitor.

have to do a thing like that for?"

I watched him as he turned away and began walking down the stairs.

"Hey, Roger!" I called.

He squinted up at me as if I were a stranger, someone he'd never seen before.

"What?" he asked, his voice flat.

"I had to do it," I said. "Honest."

He didn't answer. He headed toward the fence, searching for the board we had loosened to give us a secret passage.

I thought of my father and Armand and Rollie Tremaine and Grover Cleveland and wished that I could go away someplace far away. But there was no place to go.

Roger found the loose slat in the fence and slipped through. I felt betrayed: weren't you supposed to feel good when you did something fine and noble?

A moment later two hands gripped the top of the fence and Roger's face appeared. "Was it a real emergency?" he yelled.

"A real one!" I called. "Something important!"

His face dropped from sight and his voice reached me across the yard: "All right."

"See you tomorrow!" I yelled.

I swung my legs over the railing again. The gathering dusk began to soften the sharp edges of the fence, the rooftops, the distant church steeple. I sat there a long time, waiting for the good feeling to come.

THINK AND DISCUSS
Understanding
1. Why do many of the boys dislike Rollie Tremaine?
2. How does collecting President cards help the boys in school?
3. Although the President cards are not greeted with enthusiasm, why do they become a roaring success?

Analyzing
4. What clues are given to the **setting**— the time and place—of this story?
5. How does Armand show that he cares about Jerry and his interests?
6. Why does Jerry sell Rollie Tremaine the Grover Cleveland card?
7. What is the difference between the first and second times that Jerry gives money to Armand?

8. What do you think the last line of the story means?
9. Is the author's **tone** in this story formal and serious or informal and lighthearted?

Extending
10. If cowboy cards were collected today, whose pictures might be on the cards?

THINKING SKILLS
Classifying
To classify things is to arrange them into categories or groups according to some system.

The words *competition* and *cooperation* are antonyms; that is, they have opposite meanings. This story is about both competition and cooperation. Your class will be divided into groups. Each group is to find examples of competition and examples of cooperation in the story. For example, under "competition" you might list collecting cowboy cards. Under "cooperation" you might list the example of Armand helping Jerry fix the bicycle. Compare your lists with those of other groups in the class.

COMPOSITION
Describing a Collection
Think about something you or someone you know has collected such as stamps, coins, records, or baseball caps. Write a paragraph or two describing the collection. Tell about why the collection was started and describe in detail some of the special items it includes. Before you begin, review the story and note the specific details the author uses to describe the cards. Be just as specific in describing the collection about which you have chosen to write.

Writing About a Story Character
What behavior reveals that Jerry is growing up? Write a paragraph or two describing Jerry. Include examples of his thoughts and his actions that show how he is maturing. Before you begin, review the story and note at least two examples of his thoughts and two examples of his actions to use in your composition. Refer to Lesson 7, "Writing About Characters," in the Writer's Handbook for help.

ENRICHMENT
Doing Research
Write the names of all of the Presidents of the United States on separate pieces of paper. Put these in a box. Each member of the class draws a name to research. The task is to find three interesting facts about the President to report to the class. Whoever draws Grover Cleveland should explain why he was both the twenty-second and the twenty-fourth President.

BIOGRAPHY

Robert Cormier
1925–

Like many writers of fiction, Robert Cormier began his career as a journalist. He wrote for radio news broadcasts and for newspapers, receiving top honors and awards for his columns. Today he devotes full time to free-lance writing.

Reading is one of Cormier's greatest pleasures. "Books are a lot like people," he says. "We don't get to know them all at once, and some are more interesting than others." He prefers stories reflecting modern life and showing characters challenged by circumstances that demand the most from them. Cormier feels that he writes such stories. His work includes the award-winning novels *The Chocolate War* and *I Am the Cheese*. His recent books include *Beyond the Chocolate War* and *The Bumblebee Flies Away*.

See IRONY in the Handbook of Literary Terms, page 644.

A Man Who Had No Eyes

MacKinlay Kantor

"But I'm blind! I'm blind, and you've been standing here . . . laughing at me . . . ."

A beggar was coming down the avenue just as Mr. Parsons emerged from his hotel.

He was a blind beggar, carrying the traditional battered cane, and thumping his way before him with the cautious, half-furtive effort of the sightless. He was a shaggy, thicknecked fellow; his coat was greasy about the lapels and pockets, and his hand splayed over the cane's crook with a futile sort of clinging. He wore a black pouch slung over his shoulder. Apparently he had something to sell.

The air was rich with spring; sun was warm and yellowed on the asphalt. Mr. Parsons, standing there in front of his hotel and noting the *clack-clack* approach of the sightless man, felt a sudden and foolish sort of pity for all blind creatures.

And, thought Mr. Parsons, he was very glad to be alive. A few years ago he had been little more than a skilled laborer; now he was successful, respected, admired. . . . Insurance. . . . And he had done it alone, unaided, struggling beneath handicaps. . . . And he was still young. The blue air of spring, fresh from its memories of windy pools and lush shrubbery, could thrill him with eagerness.

He took a step forward just as the tapping blind man passed him by. Quickly the shabby fellow turned.

"Listen, guv'nor. Just a minute of your time."

Mr. Parsons said, "It's late. I have an appointment. Do you want me to give you something?"

"I ain't no beggar, guv'nor. You bet I ain't. I got a handy little article here"—he fumbled until he could press a small object into Mr. Parsons' hand—"that I sell. One buck. Best cigarette lighter made."

Mr. Parsons stood there, somewhat annoyed and embarrassed. He was a handsome figure with his immaculate gray suit and gray hat and malacca stick. Of course the man with the cigarette lighters could not see him. . . . "But I don't smoke," he said.

"Listen. I bet you know plenty people who smoke. Nice little present," wheedled the man. "And, mister, you wouldn't mind helping a poor guy out?" He clung to Mr. Parsons' sleeve.

Mr. Parsons sighed and felt in his vest pocket. He brought out two half dollars and pressed them into the man's hand. "Certainly. I'll help you out. As you say, I can give it to someone. Maybe the elevator boy would——" He hesitated, not wishing to be boorish and inquisitive, even with a blind peddler. "Have you lost your sight entirely?"

The shabby man pocketed the two half dollars. "Fourteen years, guv'nor." Then he added with an insane sort of pride: "Westbury, sir. I was one of 'em."

"Westbury," repeated Mr. Parsons. "Ah, yes. The chemical explosion. . . . The papers haven't mentioned it for years. But at the time it was supposed to be one of the greatest disasters in——"

"They've all forgot about it." The fellow shifted his feet wearily. "I tell you, guv'nor, a man who was in it don't forget about it. Last thing I ever saw was C shop going up in one grand smudge, and gas pouring in all the busted windows."

Mr. Parsons coughed. But the blind peddler was caught up with the train of his one dramatic reminiscence. And, also, he was thinking that there might be more half dollars in Mr. Parsons' pocket.

"Just think about it, guv'nor. There was a hundred and eight people killed, about two hundred injured, and over fifty of them lost their eyes. Blind as bats——" He groped forward until his dirty hand rested against Mr. Parsons' coat. "I tell you, sir, there wasn't nothing worse than that in the war. If I had lost my eyes in the war, okay. I would have been well took care of. But I was just a workman, working for what was in it. And I got it. You're darn right I got it, while the capitalists were making their dough! They was insured, don't worry about that. They——"

"Insured," repeated his listener. "Yes. That's what I sell——"

"You want to know how I lost my eyes?" cried the man. "Well here it is!" His words fell with the bitter and studied drama of a story often told, and told for money. "I was there in C shop, last of all the folks rushing out. Out in the air there was a chance, even with buildings exploding right and left. A lot of guys made it safe out the door and got away. And just when I was about there, crawling along between those big vats, a guy behind me grabs my leg. He says, 'Let me past, you——!' Maybe he was nuts. I dunno. I try to forgive him in my heart, guv'nor. But he was bigger than me. He hauls me back and climbs right over me! Tramples me into the dirt. And he gets out, and I lie there with all that poison gas pouring down on all sides of me, and flame and stuff. . . ." He swallowed—a studied sob—and stood dumbly

Reginald Marsh, *View of Manhattan*, 1929
Worcester Art Museum

expectant. He could imagine the next words: *Tough luck, my man. Now, I want to——*

"That's the story, guv'nor."

The spring wind shrilled past them, damp and quivering.

"Not quite," said Mr. Parsons.

The blind peddler shivered crazily. "Not quite? What do you mean, you——"

"The story is true," Mr. Parsons said, "except that it was the other way around."

"Other way around?" He croaked unamiably. "Say, guv'nor——"

"I was in C shop," said Mr. Parsons. "It was the other way around. You were the fellow who hauled back on me and climbed over me. You were bigger than I was, Markwardt."

The blind man stood for a long time, swallowing hoarsely. He gulped: "Parsons. I thought you——" And then he screamed fiendishly: "Yes. Maybe so. Maybe so. But I'm blind! I'm blind, and you've been standing here letting me spout to you, and laughing at me every minute! I'm blind."

People in the street turned to stare at him.

"You got away, but I'm blind! Do you hear? I'm——"

"Well," said Mr. Parsons, "don't make such a row about it, Markwardt. . . . So am I."

THINK AND DISCUSS
Understanding
1. What brings the two men together at the beginning of this story?
2. For what reason does Markwardt tell Parsons the story about the explosion?

Analyzing
3. What hints do you find early in the story to suggest that Parsons is also blind?
4. Describe the **character** of the beggar. Look for words and phrases in the story that tell about his physical appearance, speech, and actions.
5. Find words and phrases that develop the **character** of Parsons.
6. Is Parsons bitter about what happened to him in the explosion? Give examples to support your answer.

Extending
7. Markwardt has many times told his story about being trampled by a man who was rushing out of C shop. Do you think that after telling a lie over and over people begin to believe it is true? Explain.

APPLYING: Irony H▨
See Handbook of Literary Terms, p. 644.

   Irony is a contrast between what appears to be and what really is. The word *ironic* is often used to describe any statement or situation contrary to what is expected or the opposite of what is intended.

   Think about the ending of this story and how the real situation is different from what you expect.

1. What is ironic about the ending?
2. Name the three types of irony discussed in the Handbook of Literary Terms.
3. Which of the three types occurs at the end of "A Man Who Had No Eyes"?
4. Does the title contain a trace of irony? Explain.

VOCABULARY
Synonyms
   The second paragraph of the story begins "He was a blind beggar. . . ." Later the narrator refers to the beggar as "the sightless man." *Sightless* and *blind* are synonyms. A synonym is a word whose meaning is the same or nearly the same as another word.

   On your paper, copy the words from the left column below. Then, after each word, write the word in the right column that has the same or nearly the same meaning. You will not use one word. Refer to the Glossary for the meanings of any unfamiliar words.

1. inquisitive   (a) coax
2. emerge   (b) rude
3. boorish   (c) curious
4. wheedle   (d) flatter
5. furtive   (e) issue
                 (f) sly

THINKING SKILLS
Generalizing
   To generalize is to draw a general conclusion from particular information. Discuss with your classmates famous people in sports, government, entertainment, and business who have

overcome physical handicaps to become successful. List the traits shown by these individuals and then decide which traits seem to be common to most of the people. As a group, make two or three generalizations about what it takes to become successful in spite of a handicap.

COMPOSITION

Contrasting Story Characters

Although Markwardt and Parsons share one experience, they afterwards live very different lives. Write three to four paragraphs in which you contrast the two men. Before you begin, make notes using the exact descriptions found in the story. You might put these notes in columns headed "Markwardt" and "Parsons." Include physical descriptions as well as the words and attitudes of the men. See Lesson 4, "Writing to Compare and Contrast," in the Writer's Handbook.

Writing Dialogue

Imagine a situation in which Mr. Parsons is applying for a new job. Write a dialogue that might occur during the job interview. Consider that an interviewer would ask questions about how Parsons got into the insurance business and how he overcame his handicap. What other questions would likely be asked in a job interview? Answer these as Parsons would. Base your answers on information given or make up answers based on the kind of person Parsons is shown to be in the story. Refer to Lesson 8, "Writing Dialogue," in the Writer's Handbook.

BIOGRAPHY

MacKinlay Kantor
1904–1977

Newspaper reporter, columnist, free-lance writer, and author of forty-three books, MacKinlay Kantor once offered the harsh opinion that although his stories had appeared in many magazines, they had little value except as entertaining reading. He added, however, that the discipline involved in producing such a large amount of writing helped him refine his craft—particularly his command of plot and construction. The tight plot of "A Man Who Had No Eyes" provides an early example of the success he achieved through such discipline.

During World War II, Kantor served in Britain as a war correspondent for *The Saturday Evening Post* and *Esquire*. His novel *Glory for Me* was adapted into the award-winning movie *The Best Years of Our Lives*. *Andersonville*, a novel of life in a Confederate prisoner-of-war camp during the Civil War, won the Pulitzer Prize for fiction in 1956.

Review IRONY in the Handbook of Literary Terms, page 644.

A Haircut

I. S. Nakata

He looked slyly around and then lowered his voice. "You running away from there, Chief? Maybe from the police?"

"I AM NOT RUNNING AWAY FROM THE POLICE," I told him.

---

eople have trouble deciding what I am. Indians mistake me for one of their own; in Chinatown they give me a menu written in Chinese; and once even a Japanese kid asked me if I was Korean. My ancestors are full-blooded Japanese, but I have had to get used to people thinking I'm something else.

Like that time I went to the barber college on North Clark Street for my cut-rate haircut. It's a place where student-barbers get on-the-job training, and that's where I met this guy. He was last in line, and he kept staring at me as I walked in. I just stared back.

Finally he smiled and said with a southern drawl straight out of Alabama, "Say, you're Indian, aren't you?"

I looked into the long mirror on the opposite wall. "No," I told the guy, "I'm not an Indian."

"Not an Indian?" Alabama said. "I would have sworn you were."

"I'm not."

Alabama shook his head and said, "You can't fool me. I've been all over the country. Seen all kinds of Indians. Cherokees in the Carolinas and Georgia and Alabama. Navajos in Arizona and New Mexico. Winnebagos in Wisconsin, and even some Shastas once in the mountains of California. I know you're some kind of Indian."

I shook my head, crossed my arms in front of my chest, and took a deep breath. "No."

"Cherokee?"

"No, not Cherokee."

"Not Sioux, are you?"

"Never been in North or South Dakota," I said.

"Winnebago?"

I didn't answer. I knew a lot about the Winnebagos. After World War II at an army

I. S. Nakata. "A Haircut" from *The Husk* (March 1966), Vol. XLV, No. 3.

Edward Hopper, *Early Sunday Morning*, 1930
Collection of Whitney Museum of American Art

post just outside Paris, I had met a Winnebago Indian from Black River Falls, Wisconsin. Jameson, I think his name was. A medic. And in the week or so that we were at the army post we spent a lot of time talking and eating. Every night we would go and buy a couple of long loaves of bread fresh from the baker's oven, and we would eat and talk for hours. He made me promise to visit him in Wisconsin when I got back to the States.

"That's God's country—where the Winnebagos live," I told Alabama. "Plenty of hunting and fishing, especially for muskellunge."

"Muskellunge, huh?" Alabama said. He looked impressed.

"Yeah, muskellunge. Most people call them muskies. Good eating, too. Salted, fried, or broiled in the ashes of hickory wood."

"Wish you was there, huh, Chief?"

"Yeah, nice place," I said.

"So, you're a Winnebago?" he said with a happy nod.

"I never said that. I am not a Winnebago." I turned away.

"Now, now, Chief. Don't get mad," Alabama said. "I'm your friend. Yes, sir, I'm truly your friend. I've worked with Indians and helped lots of them working for Standard Oil. The reason I thought you were Winnebago is because you know so much about them."

"I don't know so much."

"You do. You sure do, Chief." He looked slyly around and then lowered his voice.

"You running away from there, Chief? Maybe from the police?"

"I AM NOT RUNNING AWAY FROM THE POLICE," I told him.

"OK, Chief," he said quickly. "I didn't mean no harm."

For a long time Alabama didn't say anything. Some of the guys ahead of us moved up in line and we moved along, too. Soon Alabama had a choice of sitting or standing. He sat down on the bench and slid over to make room for me. Then he began again.

"So you're not a Winnebago, huh?"

I didn't answer him.

"Crow?"

"No, I am not a Crow," I said very sharply, although I had nothing against that tribe.

He rubbed his chin with his left hand and thought hard. "Arapaho?"

I shook my head.

"Navajo, then?"

I smiled. The Navajos were a tribe that I'd be proud to be part of. Great weavers, great in handicrafts, and among the best when it came to farming. I'd once gone to an art school in Kansas City with Custer Begay—a Navajo and a fine artist. I started thinking about Custer and his beautiful drawings of Indians on horseback. Then I remembered some of the great times we'd had and I began to laugh.

Alabama slapped his knee and said, "You're a Navajo! From Arizona."

This guy would not give up!

"Well," I said with a sigh, "I *was* once on a reservation in Arizona."

I really had been, too. I'd been sent to Arizona to live in a relocation camp for Japanese-Americans during World War II,[1] before I volunteered for the army.

Alabama's eyes lit up. "I knew it! You couldn't fool me. What reservation was it, Chief?"

"Poston, Arizona," I said, remembering the wartime internment camp. "On the Colorado River."

"I mean," Alabama moaned, "what tribe was it?"

"Nipponese.[2] We were scattered a bit until Uncle Sam gathered us up and put us all together again."

Alabama nodded a couple of times. "Well, I sure do think that was the best thing to do, having the government look after you all. Nipponese, eh? That must be a very small tribe. Never heard of it, Chief."

I had enjoyed my joke. Alabama wanted me to be something else, but I wasn't going to be anyone else but myself.

"A Nipponese is a Japanese. I am Japanese." I spoke slowly, feeling a little self-conscious as I wondered how I am supposed to say I am what I am.

Alabama rubbed his chin and looked puzzled. "Jap, eh? Wouldn't think it to look at you. You could pass for Indian any day."

"Japanese," I said.

"Sure, sure, Jap-a-nees. Japanese. But you were born in the USA, weren't you? You can't talk American like that without your being born here."

"I was born in Hawaii."

---

1. *relocation camp . . . World War II.* After Japanese planes attacked Pearl Harbor on December 7, 1941, the United States government evacuated from their homes persons of Japanese ancestry on the West Coast. The government relocated these people to inland detention camps.

2. *Nipponese* (nip′ə nēz′).

"Well, you're American like the rest of us, then. A man should be proud of what he is. Aren't you?"

Did I sense a threatening tone in his voice?

"I am pleased that I am who I am, Alabama," I told him. "It's good to be alive."

"Sure is, all right," he said. "But you're wrong about me. I don't come from Alabama."

"No?"

"No!" He stood up because it was finally his turn to get a haircut. "I'm from Georgia," he said in a loud voice, "and proud of it."

"Sorry I made the mistake," I told him. Then I shrugged. For the life of me I couldn't see what difference it made if he came from Georgia or Alabama.

THINK AND DISCUSS
Understanding
1. What is the narrator's ancestry?
2. With what groups has the narrator been mistakenly identified?

Analyzing
3. Explain the joke the narrator plays on Alabama with the word *Nipponese*.
4. What does the narrator reveal about himself when he admits that he does not see the difference it makes whether Alabama came from Georgia or Alabama?
5. What is the **theme,** or underlying meaning, of this story?

Extending
6. Do you think the barbershop conversation will change the attitudes of Alabama and the narrator? Why or why not?

REVIEWING: Irony H𝕋
See Handbook of Literary Terms, p. 644.
   Irony is a contrast between what appears to be and what really is. Reread the last paragraph of the story.
1. Why doesn't it matter to the narrator whether Alabama comes from Georgia or Alabama?
2. Explain the irony in the last sentence of the story.

COMPOSITION
Writing Your Own Story
   Perhaps you or someone you know has had a conversation with a person met by chance while waiting in line. Write a brief story of several paragraphs about the experience. Be sure to include dialogue, as in the story "A Haircut." If you don't recall exactly what was said, make up conversation based on your memory of the encounter.

ENRICHMENT
Reading Dialogue Aloud
   With a partner, read aloud the dialogue between the narrator and Alabama. Remember to read only the words enclosed in quotation marks. Pay attention to punctuation such as commas and question marks. Also let your tone of voice show how you believe the character would be saying the words.

Use Words That Appeal to the Senses

Authors use words that appeal to the senses to make their writing more vivid. By including details of sight, sound, taste, smell, and touch, good writers involve their readers. For example, "an icy, blue lake whose waves slap against the shore" is more appealing than "a blue lake" because it tells you not only how the lake looks but also how it feels and sounds.

In "President Cleveland, Where Are You?" Robert Cormier uses words that appeal to the senses to help you visualize the trading cards Jerry collects.

> The cards were available in those five-cent packages of gum: pink sticks, three together, covered with a sweet white powder. You couldn't blow bubbles with that particular gum, but it couldn't have mattered less. The cowboy cards were important—the pictures of those rock-faced men with eyes of blue steel.
>
> (page 323, column 1)

Notice how words like *pink, sweet, powder, rock-faced,* and *steel* make it possible for you to almost taste the gum and see the cowboys' stern expressions.

It's not only objects, however, that can be made to come alive through words that appeal to the senses. By skillfully using words, an author can also make the characters and events more real. In the next example, it's easy to understand why Jerry dislikes Rollie Tremaine.

> . . . he did not live in a tenement but in a big white birthday cake of a house on Laurel Street. He was too fat to be effective in the football games . . . and he made us constantly aware of the jingle of coins in his pockets.
>
> (page 323, column 2)

Instead of just telling you that Rollie was richer than the other boys, note how the author lets you learn this through your senses of sight and hearing.

By using words that appeal to the senses, an author can also heighten the most exciting moments in a story. In the following passage from "A Man Who Had No Eyes," the beggar's description of his accident is more dramatic because MacKinlay Kantor allows you to see, hear, and feel it.

> "I was there in C shop, last of all the folks rushing out. Out in the air there was a chance, even with buildings exploding right and left. . . And just when I was about there, crawling along between those big vats, a guy behind me grabs my leg."   (page 334, column 2)

As you continue reading, pay attention to the way words that appeal to the senses make each story livelier and clearer than it would be without those words.

Notice what appeals to the senses when
   you read.
Use what appeals to the senses when you
   write.

See **FIGURATIVE LANGUAGE** in the Handbook of Literary Terms, page 638.

Nancy

Elizabeth Enright

Fiona Farmer discovers a world she never knew existed—and is given a new name, besides.

iona Farmer was seven years old. Her mother was forty-six, her father was fifty-five, her nurse was sixty-one, and her grandmother and grandfather with whom they were all spending the summer had reached such altitudes of age that no one remembered what they were. From these great heights Fiona was loved and directed.

She wore her hair as her mother had worn it in 1914, braided tight and tied back in pretzel loops with big stiff ribbons. In winter she was the only girl at school to wear a flannel petticoat and underwear with sleeves. Her mother read her all the books she had loved in her childhood: *Rebecca of Sunnybrook Farm*, and *The Five Little Peppers*, and *Under the Lilacs*. Her grandmother read her the books *she* had loved as a child: Macé's *Fairy Tales*, and Grimm's *Fairy Tales*, and *The Princess and Curdie*. On this mixed diet of decorum and brutality Fiona was rapidly turning into a "quaint little creature." She was a pensive child with large attentive eyes and rather elderly manners; all her play was quiet, accompanied at times by nothing noisier than a low continuous murmuring, so it was strange that the ranks of dolls on her nursery shelves were scalped, and eyeless, like the victims of a Sioux massacre.

"What on earth does she do to them?" her mother said to Nana, the nurse. "Why, when I was little my dollies were really like babies to me. I took such *care* of them, I *loved* them so. . . ."

"I honestly don't know, Mrs. Farmer," Nana said. "She'll be as quiet as a mouse in here for hours at a time, and then I'll come in and find all this—this destruction! It seems so unlike her!"

Fiona's grandmother reproached her quietly. "How would you like it if your dear mother pulled all your hair out of your head and broke your arms and legs? Your dolls are your little responsibilities, your *children* in a way. . . . "

Her admonishments though frequent were always mild. When Fiona scratched her head, or picked her nose, she would say: "That's not very pretty, dear, is it? We don't do those things, do we?" . . . She was a lofty, dignified, conventional lady, and she smelled like an old dictionary among whose pages many flowers had been dried and pressed. She taught Fiona how to make a sachet and a pomander ball and play parcheesi.

Fiona liked her grandfather the best. He was a man of wonderful patience and politeness, deaf as a post. Every morning she followed him out to the vegetable garden where, in his old loose button-down-the-front sweater and his white canvas golf hat that sagged in a ruffle around his head, he worked along the rows of beets and cabbages with his hoe and rake. Fiona followed at his heels, speaking ceaselessly; it did not matter to her that he never heard a word she said, she told him everything. Now and then he would stop, resting on his hoe handle, and look down at her appreciatively. "Well," he would say. "You're a pleasant little companion, aren't you?" Then he would reach out his old parched hand (he was so old that he never sweated any more) and give her a brittle tap or two on the shoulder or head, and he and Fiona would smile at each other out of a mutual feeling of benevolence.

Sooner or later, though, Nana's voice would begin to caw: "Fee-ona! Fee-ona!"

and she would have to go back to the house to pick up her toys or change her dress or eat a meal, or some other dull thing.

Her grandparents' house was big and cool inside. All the rooms were full of greenish light reflected from the maple trees outdoors; the floors were dark and gleaming, the carpets had been taken up for the summer and the furniture had linen dresses on. There was no dust anywhere, not even in the corners of the empty fireplaces, for Cora and Mary, the maids who had been there for thirty years, spent their lives seeing that there was not.

Cora had arthritis, and on Sundays when Fiona had noon dinner with the whole family she marveled at the extreme slowness with which the maid moved about the table, like a running-down toy. Her face looked very still and concentrated then, relaxing only when she served Fiona, whispering: "Eat it all up now, dear, every bit, so I can tell Mary."

Oh food! People were always speaking of food to Fiona; the Sunday dinners were a trial to toil through. "Eat it all up, dear," and "Clean your plate" were phrases that were ugly in her ears.

After Sunday dinner everyone went to sleep for a while and the house droned with different pitches of snoring. Wearing nothing but a pink wrapper Fiona would lie on the big white bed while Nana sat in an armchair by the window rattling the Sunday paper. Out of doors the cicadas sounded hot as drills; the lazy air coming in the window brought a smell of grass, and Fiona wished that Nana would fall asleep so that she could get up and find something to play with, but Nana would not fall asleep.

But once she did.

Pierre-Auguste Renoir, *Children's Afternoon at Wargemont* (detail), 1884
Nationalgalerie, Staatliche, Museen, Preussischer Kulturbesitz, Berlin

Once on Sunday after the usual slow massive dinner, as Fiona lay in the extremity of boredom counting mosquito bites and listening to herself yawn, she heard another sound; a new one that might promise much. Quietly she raised herself to her elbows, hardly daring to believe, and saw that the impossible had happened at last. Nana lay in the armchair, abandoned, with her head thrown back and her hair coming down and her mouth wide open like that of a fish; a faint guttural sound came out of it each time she breathed.

A great light seemed to flood the room, and a voice from on high addressed Fiona: "Get up and dress, but do not put on your shoes. Carry them in your hand till you get outside, and close the front door quietly behind you."

Fiona got up at once, dressed with the silence and speed of light, and departed. The upstairs hall hummed and trumpeted with the noises of sleeping; no one heard her running down the stairs.

Out of doors it was bright and hot; she sat on the front step and put on her sandals with her heart galloping in her chest. Though old, the members of her family were tall, their legs were long as ladders, and if they came after her they would surely catch her. Leaving the sandal straps unbuckled, Fiona ran out of the gate and down the street, terrified and exhilarated. She ran till she was giddy and breathless, but when at last she stopped and looked behind her the street on which she found herself was still and empty; steeped in Sunday.

She walked for a long time. Her heart stopped racing and her breathing became comfortable again. Her fear, too, gave way to pleasure and pride. It was a beautiful afternoon. The street was very high with elms. The light that came through their roof of leaves was green and trembling like light through water. Fiona became a little crab crawling among the roots of seaweed. The parked cars were fishes which would eat her up, danger was everywhere. . . . She walked sideways, made claws out of her thumbs, hid behind trees, and felt that her eyes grew out on stems. But not for long. Suddenly, as

sometimes happened, the fancy collapsed, betrayed her completely. There was no danger; the cars were cars only. Nothing was any better than real; in the end somebody would catch her and take her home or she would return of her own accord, driven by hunger or conscience, and everything would be as it had always been.

The houses sat back from their green laps of lawn, silent and substantial, regarding her like people wearing glasses. There was a smell of privet and hot asphalt in the still air; a boring smell. . . . Intolerable boredom amounting to anguish drove Fiona to turn abruptly and kick the iron palings of a fence that she was passing; a kick that hurt right through her shoe.

The big street came to an end finally at a small Civil War monument and branched out beyond it in three roads. She chose the right-hand one because there was a dog asleep on the sidewalk there, but when she got to him she saw the flies strolling up and down his face and he looked up at her balefully with a low ripple of sound in his throat and she hurried on.

This street had few trees; it was broader, and the houses, while farther apart, were shabbier. The afternoon sun was in her eyes, drawing her along the gilded road. The wind had sprung up, too, warm and lively, blowing from the west.

On the outskirts of the town she came upon her destination, though at first she did not realize it. For some time the wind had been bringing her great blasts of radio music; and she saw now that these had their source in a gray frame house that fairly trembled with melody. Though not small, this was the seediest of all the houses. It stood in the middle of a yard as full of tall grass as a field. There were paths through the field and bald patches where people had stamped and trampled, and many souvenirs abandoned and half grown over: a rusted little wagon with no wheels, somebody's shoe, an old tire . . .

The house had a queer shape, fancy, but with everything coming off or breaking. Some of the shutters hung by one hinge only; the cupola on top was crooked and so was the porch from which half the palings were gone. The fence, too, had lost many of its pickets and stood propped against the tangle like a large comb with teeth missing; but it had kept its gate and hanging onto this and swinging slowly back and forth were three little girls. Fiona walked more slowly.

One of the girls had a bandanna tied tightly around her head but the other two regarded her from under untrimmed dusty bangs, like animals peering out from under ferns. The gate gave a long snarl of sound as they pushed it forward. "Where are you going?" said the tallest one.

Fiona could not be sure of the tone of this question: was it a friendly or a hostile challenge? She moved still more slowly touching each picket with her forefinger.

"No place," she said guardedly.

"What's your name?" demanded the girl with the bandanna. She smelled of kerosene.

"Fiona Farmer," said Fiona.

"That's a funny name. My name's Darlene, and hers is Pearl, and *hers* is Merle. Nancy is a nice name."

Fiona saw that all of them were wearing red nail polish and asked a question of her own.

"Are you all three sisters?"

"Yes, and there's more of us. *Them*," said

Pearl, the tallest girl, jerking her head. "In the swing."

Beyond the house Fiona now saw for the first time an old double-rocker swing full of boys.

"There's Norman and Stanley and Earl," Darlene said. "And in the house we got a baby sister named Marilyn, and down to the picture theater we got a big sister named Deanna. Come on in."

"Will they let me swing in the swing?" said Fiona.

"Sure they will. *What* did you say your name was?"

"Fiona," she admitted. "Fiona Farmer."

"Gee," said Pearl.

"We'll call her Nancy," said Darlene, who, though younger, seemed to be a leader in her way. "Come on, Nancy, you wanna swing on the gate? Get off, Merle."

Merle got off obediently, sucking her thumb.

"I would like to swing in the *swing*," Fiona said.

She came into the yard gazing up at the tipsy cupola. "Can you get up there into that kind of little tower?"

"Sure," said Darlene. "Come on up and we'll show you."

Fiona followed them through the interesting grass in which she now saw a broken doll, somebody's garter, somebody's hat, and many weathered corncobs and beer cans.

On the porch which swayed when they walked on it there were a tough-looking baby buggy, two sleds, a bent tricycle, a lot of chairs and boxes and bushel baskets and peck baskets and a baby pen and a wagon wheel and some kindling wood. The screen door was full of holes and instead of a doorknob there was a wooden thread spool to turn.

The noise of music was stunning as they went indoors; it kept the Mason jars[1] ringing on the shelves. They walked right into it, into the thrilling heart of noise which was the kitchen, where a woman was sitting nursing a baby and shouting random conversation at an old, old woman with a beak nose.

The music ceased with a flourish and the radio announcer's tremendous tones replaced it, but this did not stop the shouted discourse of the woman with the baby. As the girls crossed the kitchen she turned for a moment to look at them, saw Fiona and said, "Who's she?"

"She's Nancy," called Darlene, against the radio.

"Who?"

"Nancy! She dropped in."

"That's Mom," Pearl said.

Fiona went over to the lady to shake her hand. She made her usual curtsy and said, "How do you do?"

Mom's hand felt limp and rather damp and startled. She was a big woman with a wide face and tired blue eyes.

"The old one's Gramma," Darlene said, so Fiona curtsied to the old lady too, and shook her hand which felt like a few twigs in a glove.

"And that's my father," Darlene added, a few seconds later when they had gone up the loud bare stairs to the next floor; Fiona peeked in the doorway of the dim strong-smelling room but all she saw of *him* was the soles of his socks and she heard him snoring.

"Just like at home," she said. "Sunday afternoon they all sleep."

"Heck, he sleeps all *day* on Sundays,"
Darlene said, and Fiona felt a little humiliated for her own father.

"This is Gramma's room." Pearl threw open the door. "She likes flowers."

The room was a jungle steeped in musky twilight. A vine of some kind had crawled all over the window and parts of the wall, and on the sill, the sash, the floor below, were pots and jars and coffee tins in which stout lusty plants were growing and flowering.

"How does she open the window at night?" Fiona wondered.

"*She* don't open no windows day or night," Darlene said. "Heck, she's *old*, she's gotta stay *warm*."

They went up another flight of stairs, narrow steep ones, crowded with magazines and articles of clothing and decayed toys. "Up here's where we sleep," Darlene said. "Us girls, all of us except Marilyn. Pearl and me and Merle sleep in the big bed and Deanna she sleeps in the cot. This is the attic like."

The big bed was made of iron with the post knobs missing. It dipped in the middle like a hammock and there, Fiona knew, the little girls would lie at night, dumped together in a tangle, quarreling or giggling in whispers.

"Look at all the comic books!" she cried, and indeed they lay everywhere in tattered profusion, a drift of stained, disordered leaves.

"We got about a hundred or a thousand of 'em, I guess," Pearl said. "You want some?"

"Could I really, Pearl? Could you spare them?"

"*Atom Annie's* a good one," Pearl said.

---

1. **Mason jars,** wide-mouthed, glass jars used for canning fruits and vegetables. Mason is a brand name.

"We got a lot about her, and here's one called *Hellray* that's real good, real scary. Take these."

Fiona looked at them longingly.

"I don't know if my mother—she doesn't like for me to have comics."

"Heck, why not?"

"Well, maybe this time she won't mind," Fiona said, taking the books, determined that everything would be all right for once. "Thank you very, very much, Darlene and Pearl."

"Here's the stairs to the lookout," Darlene said. "Get out of the way, Merle, you wait till last."

They climbed the ladder steps in the middle of the room. Pearl pushed open the trap door and one by one they ascended into the tiny chamber.

It was a tipped little cubicle like a ship's cabin in stiff weather, and stiflingly hot. It seemed remote, high, cozy, and its four soiled windows showed four different views of the town faded and reduced as pictures in an old book. Flies buzzed and butted at the hot glass. Fiona felt disappointed when she saw the steeple of the church that stood across the street from her grandfather's house. She had not thought it was so near.

"Jump!" cried Darlene. They all began to jump, and the cupola jarred and trembled under the pounding.

"Won't it break?" cried Fiona, pounding with the rest. "Won't it fall off?"

"Naw, it won't break," Darlene called back. "It never did yet."

"But it might some day, though," shouted Pearl encouragingly.

It was fun to jump riotously and yell, as the

tiny tower rocked and resounded.

There was an interruption from below.

"Get out of there!" bawled Mom up the stairs. "How many times I told you kids to stay down out of there! You want to get your backs broke? You want to get killed? You scram down!"

"Get out of the way, Merle, let Nancy go first," Pearl said.

Mom stood at the foot of the steps wearing the baby around her neck. Anxiety had made her furious. "That place ain't safe, you know that!" she cried. "How many times have I told you?" She gave Pearl a slap on the cheek and would have given one to Darlene, too, if Darlene had not bent her neck adroitly.

"You let me catch you up there one more time and I'll get your father to lick you good!"

"Aw, climb a tree," said Darlene.

Fiona was aghast. What would happen now?

But nothing happened. Merle still quietly sucked her thumb, Darlene and Pearl seemed cool and jaunty, and as they descended through the house Mom's anger dried up like dew.

"You kids want a snack?" she said. "You didn't eat since breakfast."

"Can Nancy stay?"

"Why sure, I guess. Why not?"

"Oh, thank you very, very much. . . . "

The kitchen, like the rest of the house, had a rich bold musty smell. It smelled of constant usage and memories of usage. It was crowded and crusted with objects: pots, pans, kettles, boxes, jars, cans, buckets, dippers. There were two alarm clocks, one lying on its side, and each asserting a different hour, and four big Coca-Cola calendars on the wall, none for the current year. The radio was still thundering music, and close beside it warming herself at the noise sat Gramma, dark as a crow, chewing and chewing on her empty gums.

The stove was named Ebony Gem, and behind it in a cardboard box there was something alive; something moved. . . .

"It's kittens," said Merle, removing her thumb from her mouth and speaking for the first time. "Our cat had kittens."

"Oh, let me see!" Fiona knelt by the box. There inside it lay a bland and happy group: mother cat with her yellow eyes half closed and her paws splayed out in pleasure; kittens lined up all along her, sucking.

Merle put out her little forefinger with its chipped red nail polish, stroking first one infant, then the next. "The black one's name is Blackie and the white one's name is Whitey and we call *this* one Butch because he's so . . ."

"My father usually drowns them, all but one," Darlene interrupted. She bent her kerchiefed head close to Fiona's, so that there was a blinding smell of kerosene. "Tomorrow probably," she whispered. "We don't tell Merle, it makes her feel so bad." Then she raised her voice. "She knows it's going to happen but she don't know when, huh, Merle?"

"You could take one, Nancy," Merle said, still gazing at the kittens. "You could keep it and be good to it."

"Do you mean honestly and truly?" Fiona's joy was suffocating.

"Any one? Any one at all?"

"Except Butch," Darlene said. "We're going to keep him to help with the rats."

"Could I have Blackie? Really for keeps?"

Merle plucked the dark little thing from the mother as if she were plucking off a burr and gave it to Fiona.

"I can feel its little tiny heart," Fiona said. "I'll give it milk all the time and brush its fur and it can sleep in the doll cradle. Oh look at its ears, oh Merle, oh thank you!"

Shamed by gratitude Merle put her thumb back in her mouth and looked away.

"You kids get out from under my feet," Mom said. "Sit up to the table now, it's all ready. Come on Mama, come on *boys!*" She opened the screen door and put her head out, shouting so hard that great cords stood out on her neck.

They sat around the big table with its oil-cloth cover, everything in easy reach: cereal in paper boxes, sugar, catsup. . . . They had cornflakes and milk, Swiss cheese sandwiches with catsup, cream soda in bottles, and little cakes out of a box with pink and green beads on them. Fiona ate everything.

"Nancy eats good, don't she, Mom?" Darlene said.

"I never had catsup before," said Fiona. "My, it certainly is delicious, isn't it?"

The table was a family battlefield. Fiona had never seen anything like it in her life. Stanley and Norman threw pieces of sandwich at each other, Earl took one of Merle's cakes and Merle cried and Mom slapped Earl; Darlene stole big swigs from Pearl's soda bottle, was loudly accused and loudly defended herself.

"You kids shut up," Mom said, eating over Marilyn's head and giving her occasional bits of cake dipped in tea. Gramma was the only quiet one; she sat bent over, all wrapped and absorbed in her old age, gazing into her cup as she drank from it with a long purring sound. Blackie was quiet, too, asleep in Fiona's lap. She kept one hand on his little velvet back. Mom pointed at Fiona with her spoon. "Looks like Margaret O'Brien[2] used to, don't she? The ribbons and all."

"Margaret who?" said Fiona.

"O'Brien, *you* know, the kid in the movies," Darlene said.

"Oh, I never go to movies," said Fiona. "I'm not allowed."

"Not allowed!" cried Darlene incredulously. "Heck, we go all the time, don't we, Mom? Even Deanna goes. We could take Nancy with us sometimes, couldn't we, Mom?"

"Maybe, if her folks say yes."

"Oh, if I went with *you* it would be all right, I'm sure," cried Fiona joyously. Drunk with noise, strange flavors, gifts, and new friendship, she really believed this.

Afterward, still with catsup on their upper lips, they went outdoors to play hide-and-seek.

"You be her partner, Stanley," ordered Darlene, who was "it." "You kind of look after her, she don't know our places to hide."

Then she hid her eyes with her arm, cast herself against a tree like a girl in grief, and began to count out loud.

"The cellar," hissed Stanley, grabbing Fiona's hand. He was a big eight-year-old boy, and still clutching the kitten Fiona ran with him willingly, hesitating only for a second at sight of the dark abyss. On the steps were many cans and beer crates, but Stanley led her safely down among these and into the

black deep tunnel beyond. Fiona could feel that there were solid things all around them; probably more boxes, more beer crates, but she could see nothing. Stanley's hand was warm and firm, it just fitted hers, and she liked having him lead her.

"We can stop now," he said, "but keep quiet."

Darlene could still be heard, faintly. Her counting voice sounded deserted and defiant: "*Ninety*-five, *ninety*-six, *ninety*-seven" . . . The blackness throbbed and shimmered and the air had a dense aged smell.

"Coming, ready or not!" called the faraway defiant voice.

"We're safe here anyways," Stanley said. "She won't come down *here*, she's scared to." He laughed silently and gave Fiona's hand a squeeze. "There's rats down here."

"Oh no, oh no! Oh, Stanley, let's go up again," cried Fiona, tears of panic in her voice.

But Stanley held onto her hand. "You going to be a sissy too?" he demanded. "We got the *cat*, ain't we?"

Fiona strained the tiny kitten to her chest. Her heart was banging terribly and she wanted to cry but she would not. All around the rats were closing in, large as dogs and smiling strangely; smiling like people. She almost sobbed when Stanley said, "Now we can go, hurry up, and keep still!"

They were the first ones back.

For a long time they played and Stanley always was her partner. He knew the best places to hide: up in the boughs of a pear

---

2. *Margaret O'Brien*, a child movie star, popular in the late 1940s and early 1950s.

tree, under the porch steps, in the fearful little dark privy with its different-sized "family
accommodations," and flat on their stomachs
under the folded-back cellar door. Darlene
was "it" till she caught Merle and Merle was
"it" for hours. Fiona got spider webs in her
mouth and gnats up her nose, tore her dress,
scraped her knee, lost one hair ribbon, and
gave the other to Merle, who had admired it.

When they were through with hide-and-
seek they all got into the rocker swing and
played gangsters. The swing leapt to and fro,
to and fro, screaming wildly at the joints;
surely it would break, and soon! That was the
thrilling thing about this place: so many features of it—the tower, the swing, the porch—
trembled at the edge of ruin, hung by a
thread above the fatal plunge. Earl and Stanley and Norman leaned over the back of one
of the seats firing at the enemy. "Step on it,
you guys," yelled Stanley, "they got a gat!"

"They got a rod!" yelled Norman. "They
got a lotta rods!"

"What's a rod?" cried Fiona. "What's a
gat?"

"Guns he means," Darlene told her.
"Rods and gats is guns."

"Shoot 'em, Stanley," yelled Fiona. "With
your gat, shoot the eyes out of 'em!"

Clutching the clawing kitten to her col-
larbone, her hair in her open mouth, she
bawled encouragement to them. The swing
accelerated ever more wildly: soon it would
take off entirely, depart from its hinges, fly
through the air, burn a hole through the
sky! . . .

"Fee-ona Farmer!"

The cry was loud enough to be heard above
all sounds of war and wind and radio music.

Beside the swing stood Nana, so tall, so
highly charged with hurry and emotion, that
the children stopped their play at once.

"Who's she?" Stanley asked.

"She's my nurse," Fiona murmured.

"Your nurse! What's the matter, are you
sick?"

"No . . . she just—takes care of me."

"Takes *care* of you!"

"You get out of that swing and come this
in-stant!"

Having struck the bottom of disgrace,
Fiona stepped down and slowly went to
Nana. From the swing the others watched as
still as children posing for a photograph.

"Put down that cat and come at once."

"Oh no!" Fiona said. "It's mine, they gave
it to me."

"Put. Down. That. Cat."

Darlene came to stand beside Fiona. "But
we did give it to her, we want for her to
have it."

Nana struck the kitten from Fiona's arms.
"You will not take that creature home! It's
filthy, it has fleas!"

"Oh my kitty!" shrieked Fiona, diving
after Blackie, but Nana caught her wrist.

"You come!"

Fiona pulled, struggled, cast a glare of anguish at all the rapt photograph-faces in the
swing.

"You should be punished. You should be
whipped. Whipped!" Nana whistled the
cruel words; Nana, who was never cruel! Her
fingers on Fiona's wrist were hard.

"Let me say good-by to them, Nana, let
me say good-by to their *mother!* You said I
should *always* say good-by to the mother!"

"Not this time, this time it doesn't matter," Nana said. "You're going straight home and into the tub. Heaven knows what you will have caught!" Upon Fiona's friends she turned a single brilliant glance like one cold flash from a lighthouse.

There was nothing to commend Fiona's departure; dragged by the hand, whimpering, she looked back at her friends in desperation. "Oh, Darlene!"

But it was easy to see that Darlene had detached herself. "Good-by, Nancy," she said, not without a certain pride. She did not smile or say anything else, but her attitude showed Fiona and Nana that she had no need for either of them, could not be hurt by them, and would not think of them again. As they went out the gate she turned her back and skipped away, and Fiona heard the rocker swing resume its screaming tempo.

Halfway home Nana's recriminations began to modify, gradually becoming reproaches: "How could you have, Fiona, run away like that, why it's only by the grace of God I ever found you at all! And all the time I was half sick with worry I never said a word to your father and mother! I didn't want *them* to worry!"

Somewhere deep inside her Fiona understood exactly why Nana had said nothing to her parents, but she just kept on saying: "I want my kitty, I want my kitty."

Finally Nana said: "If you're a good girl maybe we'll get you another kitten."

"I don't want another, I want that one."

"Oh for pity's sakes, it had fleas, or worse. Anything belonging to the Fadgins would be bound to have——"

"Do *you* know them?"

"I know *about* them, everybody does.

They're the dirtiest, the shiftlessest, the most down-at-the-heel tribe in this whole town!"

"They are not, they're nice, I love them!"

Nana relented a little. "Maybe it's hard not to be shiftless when you're that poor."

"*They* aren't poor. You should see all the things they've got! More than Grandmother's got in her whole house!"

"All right now, dearie, all right. We'll forget about it, shall we? It will be our secret and we'll never tell anyone because we don't want them to worry, do we? But you must promise me never, never to do such a thing again, hear?"

"I want my kitty," droned Fiona.

Her grandparents' house smelled cool and sweetish. There was a bowl of white and pink stock on the hall table and her grandmother's green linen parasol leaned in a corner among the pearly company of her grandfather's canes.

In the shaded living room Fiona saw her mother knitting and her grandmother at the piano playing the same kind of music she always played, with the loose rings clicking on her fingers.

"Is that my baby?" called her mother—but Nana answered hastily, "I'm getting her right into her bath, Mrs. Farmer. She's simply fil-thy."

Upstairs Nana went in to run the water in the tub. Fiona kicked off one sandal, then the other. A terrible pain took hold of her; it began in her mind and spread down to her stomach. She had never been homesick before and did not know what ailed her: she knew only that she wanted to sleep at night in a big twanging bed full of children and to eat meals at a crowded table where people threw bread at each other and drank pop. She wanted Stanley's hand to guide her and Darlene's voice to teach her and Blackie's purr to throb against her chest. . . .

Beyond the window she saw her grandfather's wilted golf hat bobbing among the cornstalks and escaped again, running on bare feet down the back stairs and out of doors across the billowing lawn which seemed to be colliding with the trees and sky and shadows, all flooded and dazzled with tears. Blindly she flung open the garden gate and pushed her way through the green-paper corn forest to her grandfather who dropped his hoe and held out his arms when he saw her face.

"Come here now," he said in his gentle deaf voice. "Well, well, this won't do, no it won't, not at all. Come sit here with Grandpa, sit here in the arbor. Did you hurt yourself?"

He led her to the seat under the green grape trellis where he sometimes rested from the hot sun. He put his arm around her shoulders, offering himself as a support for grief, and Fiona howled against his waistcoat till the wet tweed chapped her cheek and there was not a tear left in her. He did not interrupt or ask questions but kept patting her shoulder in a sort of sympathetic accompaniment to her sobs, which he could not hear but which he felt. What's the cause of it all, he wondered. A broken toy? A scolding? Children's tragedies, he thought, children's little tragedies: there are bigger ones in store for you, Fiona, a world of them. The thought did not move him deeply; everyone must suf-

fer, but for an instant he was not sorry to be old.

Fiona leaned against him and after a while between the hiccups left from sobbing she could hear the ancient heart inside his chest tick-tocking steadily, as tranquil and unhurried as he was himself. All the wild performance of her sorrow had not quickened its tempo by a single beat, and this for some reason was a comfort.

The sound of her grandmother's music, sugary and elegant, came sparkling from the house, and upstairs in the bedroom or the hall Nana began to call. "Fee-ona?" she cried. "Oh, Fee-*ona?*"

There was a hint of panic in her voice, now, but no response came from under the green trellis: Fiona's grandfather could not hear the calling, and Fiona, for the time being, did not choose to answer.

THINK AND DISCUSS
Understanding
1. With whom does Fiona live in the summer of this story?
2. Who is her favorite family member? Why?
3. What new experiences does Fiona enjoy at the Fadgins' home?

Analyzing
4. Describe the **character** of Fiona. Tell her age, her physical appearance, and what her actions show about her.
5. Contrast the two families in this story.

6. Why do you think Darlene acts the way she does when Fiona must leave?

7. Why do you suppose Fiona is so impressed with the Fadgins that she tells her nurse, "I love them"?

8. What is the meaning of the last line of the story, in which Fiona chooses not to answer when she is called?

9. Is "Nancy" an appropriate title for this story? Why or why not?

Extending

10. If you had to choose between living with the Farmers or with the Fadgins, which family would you choose? Why?

APPLYING:
Figurative language H*
See Handbook of Literary Terms, p. 638.

Figurative language is language expanded beyond its ordinary literal meaning. In figurative language, comparisons achieve new effects, provide fresh insights, or express a fitting relationship between things essentially unlike.

For example, the author of this story chose to compare the fence with lost pickets to a large comb with teeth missing instead of writing "The fence had lost some of its pickets."

Find the figurative expressions in the following lines from the story and explain in your own words what each means.

1. Cora . . . moved about the table, like a running-down toy.

2. Fiona became a little crab crawling among the roots of seaweed.

3. The houses sat back from their green laps of lawn, silent and substantial, regarding her like people wearing glasses.

4. Mom stood at the foot of the steps wearing the baby around her neck.

5. Fiona . . . shook her hand which felt like a few twigs in a glove.

VOCABULARY
Roots and Suffixes

Words that are at first unfamiliar often turn out to be simple root words with one or more suffixes added. When you are trying to figure out the meaning of an unfamiliar word, look first for the root. For example, in *joyously* the root word is *joy*, and the suffixes *-ous* and *-ly* have been added.

It is important to keep in mind that spelling changes may occur when suffixes are added. Some of the most common changes include dropping the final *e*, changing final *y* to *i*, and doubling the final consonant. Note the examples: *desperat(e)* + *-ion*, *accompan(y)i* + *-ment*, and *wrap(p)* + *-er*.

Copy the following words on your paper. After each, write the root word. If there is a spelling change, indicate it in parentheses.

1. departure
2. massive
3. ceaselessly
4. boredom
5. extremity
6. appreciative
7. defiant
8. musky
9. brutality
10. stiflingly

THINKING SKILLS
Synthesizing

To synthesize is to put together parts and elements so as to form a whole, a new pattern or structure not evident before.

Consider what might happen if Darlene visited the Farmers. Discuss with a small group of classmates what the Farmers might say and do. What would impress Darlene? One person in the group could list the ideas suggested. Turn the ideas into a short play with various members taking the roles of Darlene, Fiona, and the other people in Fiona's family.

COMPOSITION
Reading/Writing Log

Elizabeth Enright, the author of "Nancy," uses many details that appeal to the senses of sight, hearing, taste, smell, and touch. Several are listed below. Copy the examples in your **reading/writing log.** Then find at least four more examples in the story and add them to the log.

Her grandparents' house was big and cool inside.

greenish light reflected from the maple trees outdoors

the wind had been bringing her great blasts of radio music

Describing Two Homes

The homes of the Farmers and the Fadgins are very different. Write two or three paragraphs in which you contrast the homes by using descriptions that appeal to the senses. Before you begin, list examples to use in your descriptions. If you are keeping a **reading/writing log,** note the words that appeal to the senses that you recorded earlier. You may want to add to your log first. Keep your list with you as you write.

Writing About Being Seven

Think back to when you were seven years old. What did you like to do? How important was your imagination? Write one paragraph in which you use words that appeal to the senses to describe what it is like to be seven years old. If you prefer, use the experiences of Fiona to show what being seven is like. Before you begin, make a list of things you enjoyed doing and imagining, or review "Nancy" and note similar things about Fiona.

BIOGRAPHY

Elizabeth Enright
1909–1968

Because Elizabeth Enright's mother was an artist and her father a cartoonist, it seemed natural that she should be interested in art. After studying at the School of Applied Art in Paris, Enright began illustrating children's books. Only after she had done the artwork for several books written by other people did she attempt to write one of her own. Her first book, *Kintu,* which she wrote and illustrated, was honored for its literary content as well as its art. Her second, *Thimble Summer,* won the Newbery Medal.

Review **FIGURATIVE LANGUAGE** in the Handbook of Literary Terms, page 638.

Adolf

D. H. Lawrence

We couldn't really love him, because he was wild and loveless to the end. But he was an unmixed delight.

hen we were children our father often worked on the night-shift. Once it was spring-time, and he used to arrive home, black and tired, just as we were downstairs in our nightdresses. Then night met morning face to face, and the contact was not always happy. Perhaps it was painful to my father to see us gaily entering upon the day into which he dragged himself soiled and weary. He didn't like going to bed in the spring morning sunshine.

But sometimes he was happy, because of his long walk through the dewy fields in the first daybreak. He loved the open morning, the crystal and the space, after a night down pit.[1] He watched every bird, every stir in the trembling grass, answered the whinnying of the peewits and tweeted to the wrens. If he could, he also would have whinnied and tweeted and whistled in a native language that was not human. He liked non-human things best.

One sunny morning we were all sitting at table when we heard his heavy slurring walk up the entry. We became uneasy. His was always a disturbing presence, trammelling. He passed the window darkly, and we heard him go into the scullery and put down his tin bottle. But directly he came into the kitchen. We felt at once that he had something to communicate. No one spoke. We watched his black face for a second.

"Give me a drink," he said.

My mother hastily poured out his tea. He went to pour it out into his saucer. But instead of drinking he suddenly put something on the table among the teacups. A tiny brown rabbit! A small rabbit, a mere morsel, sitting against the bread as still as if it were a made thing.

---

1. **down pit,** down in the coal mine.

"Adolf" from *Phoenix* by D. H. Lawrence. Reprinted by permission of Laurence Pollinger Ltd. and the Estate of Mrs. Frieda Lawrence Ravagli.

"A rabbit! A young one! Who gave it you, Father?"

But he laughed enigmatically, with a sliding motion of his yellow-grey eyes, and went to take off his coat. We pounced on the rabbit.

"Is it alive? Can you feel its heart beat?"

My father came back and sat down heavily in his armchair. He dragged his saucer to him, and blew his tea, pushing out his red lips under his black moustache.

"Where did you get it, Father?"

"I picked it up," he said, wiping his naked forearm over his mouth and beard.

"Where?"

"It is a wild one!" came my mother's quick voice.

"Yes it is."

"Then why did you bring it?" cried my mother.

"Oh, we wanted it," came our cry.

"Yes, I've no doubt you did——" retorted my mother. But she was drowned in our clamor of questions.

On the field path my father had found a dead mother rabbit and three dead little ones—this one alive, but unmoving.

"But what had killed them, Daddy?"

"I couldn't say, my child. I s'd think she'd aten something."

"Why did you bring it!" again my mother's voice of condemnation. "You know what it will be."

My father made no answer, but we were loud in protest.

"He must bring it. It's not big enough to live by itself. It would die," we shouted.

"Yes, and it will die now. And then there'll be *another* outcry."

My mother set her face against the tragedy of dead pets. Our hearts sank.

"It won't die, Father, will it? Why will it? It won't."

"I s'd think not," said my father.

"You know well enough it will. Haven't we had it all before!" said my mother.

"They dunna always pine,"[2] replied my father testily.

But my mother reminded him of other little wild animals he had brought, which had sulked and refused to live, and brought storms of tears and trouble in our house of lunatics.

Trouble fell on us. The little rabbit sat on our lap, unmoving, its eye wide and dark. We brought it milk, warm milk, and held it to its nose. It sat still as if it was far away, retreated down some deep burrow, hidden, oblivious. We wetted its mouth and whiskers with drops of milk. It gave no sign, did not even shake off the wet white drops. Somebody began to shed a few secret tears.

"What did I say?" cried my mother. "Take it and put it down in the field."

Her command was in vain. We were driven to get dressed for school. There sat the rabbit. It was like a tiny obscure cloud. Watching it, the emotions died out of our breast. Useless to love it, to yearn over it. Its little feelings were all ambushed. They must be circumvented. Love and affection were a trespass upon it. A little wild thing, it became more mute and asphyxiated still in its own arrest, when we approached with love. We

---

2. *They dunna always pine,* they don't always waste away with hunger, grief, and homesickness.

Glen Loates, *Cottontail Bunny*, 1975, Private Collection

must not love it. We must circumvent it, for its own existence.

So I passed the order to my sister and my mother. The rabbit was not to be spoken to, nor even looked at. Wrapping it in a piece of flannel I put it in an obscure corner of the cold parlor, and put a saucer of milk before its nose. My mother was forbidden to enter the parlor while we were at school.

"As if I should take any notice of your nonsense," she cried affronted. Yet I doubt if she ventured into the parlor.

At midday, after school, creeping into the front room, there we saw the rabbit still and unmoving in the piece of flannel. Strange grey-brown neutralization of life, still living! It was a sore problem to us.

"Why won't it drink its milk, Mother?" we whispered. Our father was asleep.

"It prefers to sulk its life away, silly little thing." A profound problem. Prefers to sulk

its life away! We put young dandelion leaves to its nose. The sphinx was not more oblivious. Yet its eye was bright.

At tea-time, however, it had hopped a few inches, out of its flannel, and there it sat again, uncovered, a little solid cloud of muteness, brown, with unmoving whiskers. Only its side palpitated slightly with life.

Darkness came; my father set off to work. The rabbit was still unmoving. Dumb despair was coming over the sisters, a threat of tears before bed-time. Clouds of my mother's anger gathered as she muttered against my father's wantonness.

Once more the rabbit was wrapped in the old pit-singlet.[3] But now it was carried into the scullery and put under the copper fireplace, that it might imagine itself inside a

---

3. pit-singlet, a woolen (or, in this case, flannel) undershirt or jersey worn by coal miners.

burrow. The saucers were placed about, four or five, here and there on the floor, so that if the little creature *should* chance to hop abroad, it could not fail to come upon some food. After this my mother was allowed to take from the scullery what she wanted and then she was forbidden to open the door.

When morning came and it was light, I went downstairs. Opening the scullery door, I heard a slight scuffle. Then I saw dabbles of milk all over the floor and tiny rabbit droppings in the saucers. And there the miscreant, the tips of his ears showing behind a pair of boots. I peeped at him. He sat bright-eyed and askance, twitching his nose and looking at me while not looking at me.

He was alive—very much alive. But still we were afraid to trespass much on his confidence.

"Father!" My father was arrested at the door. "Father, the rabbit's alive."

"Back your life it is," said my father.

"Mind how you go in."

By evening, however, the little creature was tame, quite tame. He was christened Adolf. We were enchanted by him. We couldn't really love him, because he was wild and loveless to the end. But he was an unmixed delight.

We decided he was too small to live in a hutch—he must live at large in the house. My mother protested, but in vain. He was so tiny. So we had him upstairs, and he dropped his tiny pills on the bed and we were enchanted.

Adolf made himself instantly at home. He had the run of the house, and was perfectly happy, with his tunnels and his holes behind the furniture.

We loved him to take meals with us. He would sit on the table humping his back, sipping his milk, shaking his whiskers and his tender ears, hopping off and hobbling back to his saucer, with an air of supreme unconcern. Suddenly he was alert. He hobbled a few tiny paces, and reared himself up inquisitively at the sugar basin. He fluttered his tiny fore-paws, and then reached and laid them on the edge of the basin, while he craned his thin neck and peeped in. He trembled his whiskers at the sugar, then he did the best to lift down a lump.

"*Do* you think I will have it! Animals in the sugar pot!" cried my mother, with a rap of her hand on the table.

Which so delighted the electric Adolf that he flung his hind-quarters and knocked over a cup.

"It's your own fault, Mother. If you left him alone——"

He continued to take tea with us. He rather liked warm tea. And he loved sugar. Having nibbled a lump, he would turn to the butter. There he was shooed off by our parent. He soon learned to treat her shooing with indifference. Still, she hated him to put his nose in the food. And he loved to do it. And one day between them they overturned the cream-jug. Adolf deluged his little chest, bounced back in terror, was seized by his little ears by my mother and bounced down on the hearth-rug. There he shivered in momentary discomfort, and suddenly set off in a wild flight to the parlor.

This was his happy hunting ground. He had cultivated the bad habit of pensively nibbling certain bits of cloth in the hearth-rug. When chased from this pasture he would retreat under the sofa. There he would twinkle in Buddhist meditation[4] until suddenly, no one knew why, he would go off like an alarm clock. With a sudden bumping scuffle he would whirl out of the room, going through the doorway with his little ears flying. Then we would hear his thunderbolt hurtling in the parlor, but before we could follow, the wild streak of Adolf would flash past us, on an electric wind that swept him round the scullery and carried him back, a little mad thing, flying possessed like a ball round the parlor. After which ebullition he would sit in a corner composed and distant, twitching his whiskers in abstract meditation. And it was in vain we questioned him about his outburst. He just went off like a gun, and was as calm after it as a gun that smokes placidly.

Alas, he grew up rapidly. It was almost impossible to keep him from the outer door.

One day, as we were playing by the stile, I saw his brown shadow loiter across the road and pass into the field that faced the houses. Instantly a cry of "Adolf!"—a cry he knew full well. And instantly a wind swept him away down the sloping meadow, his tail twinkling and zigzagging through the grass. After him we pelted. It was a strange sight to see him, ears back, his little loins so powerful, flinging the world behind him. We ran ourselves out of breath, but could not catch him. Then somebody headed him off, and he sat with sudden unconcern, twitching his nose under a bunch of nettles.

His wanderings cost him a shock. One Sunday morning my father had just been quarrelling with a pedlar, and we were hearing the aftermath indoors, when there came a sudden unearthly scream from the yard. We flew out. There sat Adolf cowering under a bench, while a great black and white cat glowered intently at him, a few yards away. Sight not to be forgotten. Adolf rolling back his eyes and parting his strange muzzle in another scream, the cat stretching forward in a slow elongation.

Ha, how we hated that cat! How we pursued him over the chapel wall and across the neighbors' gardens.

Adolf was still only half grown.

"Cats!" said my mother. "Hideous detestable animals, why do people harbor them?"

But Adolf was becoming too much for her. He dropped too many pills. And suddenly to hear him clumping downstairs when she was alone in the house was startling. And to keep him from the door was impossible. Cats prowled outside. It was worse than having a child to look after.

Yet we would not have him shut up. He became more lusty, more callous than ever. He was a strong kicker, and many a scratch on face and arms did we owe to him. But he brought his own doom on himself. The lace curtains in the parlor—my mother was rather proud of them—fell on the floor very full. One of Adolf's joys was to scuffle wildly through them as though through some foamy undergrowth. He had already torn rents in them.

One day he entangled himself altogether. He kicked, he whirled round in a mad nebulous inferno. He screamed—and brought down the curtain-rod with a smash, right on the best beloved pelargonium, just as my

---

4. *Buddhist meditation,* a still, quiet pose of devotion by a member of the Buddhist religion.

mother rushed in. She extricated him, but she never forgave him. And he never forgave either. A heartless wildness had come over him.

Even we understood that he must go. It was decided, after a long deliberation, that my father should carry him back to the wild-woods. Once again he was stowed into the great pocket of the pit-jacket.

"Best pop him i' th' pot," said my father, who enjoyed raising the wind of indignation.

And so, next day, our father said that Adolf, set down on the edge of the coppice, had hopped away with utmost indifference, neither elated nor moved. We heard it and believed. But many, many were the heartsearchings. How would the other rabbits receive him? Would they smell his tame-ness, his humanized degradation, and rend him? My mother pooh-poohed the extrava-gant idea.

However, he was gone, and we were rather relieved. My father kept an eye open for him. He declared that several times passing the coppice in the early morning, he had seen Adolf peeping through the nettle-stalks. He had called him, in an odd-voiced, cajoling fashion. But Adolf had not responded. Wild-ness gains so soon upon its creatures. And they become so contemptuous then of our tame presence. So it seemed to me. I myself would go to the edge of the coppice, and call softly. I myself would imagine bright eyes between the nettle-stalks, flash of a white, scornful tail past the bracken. That insolent white tail, as Adolf turned his flank on us!

THINK AND DISCUSS

Understanding
1. Who brings Adolf home?
2. Why doesn't the narrator's mother want to keep Adolf?
3. What are some of Adolf's enjoyable and enchanting ways?
4. What actual harm or damage does Adolf cause?

Analyzing
5. What clues to **setting** are given in the story?
6. The narrator comments that they tried not to love Adolf. Why?
7. The father seems to have two sides to his **character**—a rough, dark side and a gentle, happy side. What details show these two sides?
8. Why do you think the narrator's mother tolerates Adolf as long as she does?

Extending
9. Do you think Adolf would survive in the wilderness? Why or why not?

REVIEWING:
Figurative language H⫶
See Handbook of Literary Terms, p. 638.

Figurative language is language expanded beyond its ordinary literal meaning. In figurative language, comparisons achieve new effects, provide fresh insights, or express a relationship between things essentially unlike.

For example, the author writes that Adolf "just went off like a gun." Rabbits and guns usually don't have anything in common, but in this case comparing Adolf's movement to the shooting of a gun provides a good picture of the rabbit's burst of energy. Decide whether or not each of the following comparisons is an example of figurative language.

1. The rabbit was like a tiny, obscure cloud.
2. The new wild creature was a tiny brown rabbit.
3. The parlor became a happy hunting ground.

VOCABULARY
Dictionary and Glossary

Look up in the Glossary the italicized words in the following sentences. Write each word on your paper. Next to it write the best definition for the way the word is used in the sentence.

1. "They dunna always pine," replied my father *testily*.
2. It sat still as if it was far away, retreated down some deep burrow, hidden, *oblivious*.
3. After him we *pelted*.
4. My father was *arrested* at the door.
5. Then I saw dabbles of milk all over the floor. . . . And there the *miscreant*, the tips of his ears showing behind a pair of boots.

COMPOSITION
Describing a Pet

Think about an animal that you or someone you know has had as a pet. Write one paragraph describing this pet. Before you begin, review "Adolf," noting descriptive words and phrases such as "twitching his nose," "fluttered his tiny fore-paws," and "his tail twinkling and zigzagging through the grass." Use good descriptive phrases in your own paragraph.

BIOGRAPHY

D. H. Lawrence
1885–1930

David Herbert Lawrence was born in a coal-mining town in the English county of Nottingham, where his father worked in the mines. The story "Adolf" recounts a happy incident from Lawrence's troubled early years. Lawrence was a delicate child; he struggled with tuberculosis throughout much of his life, and he died at the age of forty-four from the disease. He enjoyed the natural world and often wrote about it—from his early awareness of the pleasant land of Nottingham and his father working in darkness beneath it, to his later years traveling around the world. Lawrence became a leading writer of this century, producing novels, short stories, poems, essays, and travel books.

Reading FANTASY

All made-up stories are fantasy in that they are the creation of someone's imagination. Yet literature called **fantasy** has certain characteristics that set it apart from fiction that portrays realistic characters and settings.

The people, the places, and the events in fantasy are either impossible or improbable in the world as you know it. Fantasy stories contain fanciful settings, situations, and characters. The combination of these gives a sense of beauty, terror, or awe. Good fantasy stories may enchant you with all three.

Some writers of fantasy create whole new worlds. Recall that you read about Pern in "The Smallest Dragonboy" in Unit 1 of this book. Perhaps you have also read about Middle Earth or Narnia in books by J. R. R. Tolkien and C. S. Lewis.

Although the worlds created in fantasy are very different from the real world, the stories should nevertheless be convincing. The reader must believe that what is told— the unlikely or the impossible—could be true in a different time and place. In addition, fantasy often reveals insights about modern or ageless problems. An **author's purpose,** which may be to entertain, to inform, or to persuade, can be accomplished in fantasy as well as in realistic stories. Recall that Rikki-tikki-tavi, the mongoose, teaches about courage and persistence. In the story "The Hundredth Dove" in this unit, you will read about Hugh and from him learn about pride and blind devotion.

Some fantasy is about characters who perform impossible feats, such as Sam Angeli in "The Fallen Angel." Other fantasy is about animals that talk, as in "Rikki-tikki-tavi." Fairy tales, ghost stories, and fables are all fantasy.

In science fiction, there is an application of science and technology to a fantasy situation. The setting is generally the future. Rocket ships, visitors from outer space, trips to other galaxies, and machines that take on human traits are all found in science fiction. The story you will read next, "The Gift," is science fiction. It takes place in the year 2052 on a rocket headed for Mars. "Cutie Pie," in Unit 1, is another example of science fiction.

When you read fantasy, open your mind to receive the new world. Allow yourself to become involved in new places and with new ideas. You may discover that you are learning about the world in which you live right now. Fantasy does not mislead you about the real world if you recognize that it is fantasy. In fact, it should lead you to be more inventive in solving your own problems and wiser in viewing the world as you know it.

If you enjoy fantasy, you may want to check your library for the following well-known books: *The Book of Three* and *Westmark* by Lloyd Alexander, *The Martian Chronicles* by Ray Bradbury, *Alice in Wonderland* by Lewis Carroll, *The Dark Is Rising* by Susan Cooper, *Glory Road* by Robert Heinlein, and *The Crystal Cave* by Mary Stewart.

The Gift

Ray Bradbury

The rocket moved and left fire behind and left Earth behind on which the date was December 24, 2052, heading out into a place where there was no time at all, no month, no year, no hour.

---

omorrow would be Christmas, and even while the three of them rode to the rocket port the mother and father were worried. It was the boy's first flight into space, his very first time in a rocket, and they wanted everything to be perfect. So when, at the customs table, they were forced to leave behind his gift, which exceeded the weight limit by no more than a few ounces, and the little tree with the lovely white candles, they felt themselves deprived of the season and their love.

The boy was waiting for them in the Terminal room. Walking toward him, after their unsuccessful clash with the Interplanetary officials, the mother and father whispered to each other.

"What shall we do?"

"Nothing, nothing. What can we do?"

"Silly rules!"

"And he so wanted the tree!"

The siren gave a great howl and people pressed forward into the Mars Rocket. The mother and father walked at the very last, their small pale son between them, silent.

"I'll think of something," said the father.

"What . . . ?" asked the boy.

And the rocket took off and they were flung headlong into dark space.

The rocket moved and left fire behind and left Earth behind on which the date was December 24, 2052, heading out into a place where there was no time at all, no month, no year, no hour. They slept away the rest of the first "day." Near midnight, by their Earth-time New York watches, the boy awoke and said, "I want to go look out the porthole."

There was only one port, a "window" of immensely thick glass of some size, up on the next deck.

"Not quite yet," said the father. "I'll take you up later."

"I want to see where we are and where we're going."

"I want you to wait for a reason," said the father.

He had been lying awake, turning this way and that, thinking of the abandoned gift, the problem of the season, the lost tree and the white candles. And at last, sitting up, no more than five minutes ago, he believed he

Jim Dine, *Child's Blue Wall* (detail), 1962
Albright-Knox Art Gallery, Buffalo, New York

had found a plan. He need only carry it out and this journey would be fine and joyous indeed.

"Son," he said, "in exactly one half hour it will be Christmas."

"Oh," said the mother, dismayed that he had mentioned it. Somehow she had rather hoped that the boy would forget.

The boy's face grew feverish and his lips trembled. "I know, I know. Will I get a present, will I? Will I have a tree? You promised——"

"Yes, yes, all that, and more," said the father.

The mother started. "But——"

"I mean it," said the father. "I really mean

it. All and more, much more. Excuse me, now. I'll be back."

He left them for about twenty minutes. When he came back he was smiling. "Almost time."

"Can I hold your watch?" asked the boy, and the watch was handed over and he held it ticking in his fingers as the rest of the hour drifted by in fire and silence and unfelt motion.

"It's Christmas now! Christmas! Where's my present?"

"Here we go," said the father and took his boy by the shoulder and led him from the room, down the hall, up a rampway, his wife following.

"I don't understand," she kept saying.

"You will. Here we are," said the father.

They had stopped at the closed door of a large cabin. The father tapped three times and then twice in a code. The door opened and the light in the cabin went out and there was a whisper of voices.

"Go on in, son," said the father.

"It's dark."

"I'll hold your hand. Come on, Mama."

They stepped into the room and the door shut, and the room was very dark indeed. And before them loomed a great glass eye, the porthole, a window four feet high and six feet wide, from which they could look out into space.

The boy gasped.

Behind him, the father and the mother gasped with him, and then in the dark room some people began to sing.

"Merry Christmas, son," said the father.

And the voices in the room sang the old, the familiar carols, and the boy moved forward slowly until his face was pressed against the cool glass of the port. And he stood there for a long, long time, just looking and looking out into space and the deep night at the burning and the burning of ten billion billion white and lovely candles. . . .

THINK AND DISCUSS
Understanding
1. What is the **setting** of this story?
2. Why do the parents want the trip to be perfect?

Analyzing
3. Compare the gifts left behind and the substitute gift. Which do you think the boy prefers?
4. What elements of **fantasy** can you find in the story?

Extending
5. Compare what is known about rocket travel today with the way it is portrayed in this story. How does rocket travel differ from the way it is shown here?

READING LITERATURE SKILLFULLY
Author's Purpose
Recall that the **author's purpose** is the reason or reasons the author has for

writing. Three common purposes are to inform, to persuade, and to entertain.

1. In this short story, what do you think is the author's main purpose?
2. What do you think might be a secondary purpose the author had for writing this story?

COMPOSITION
Imagining a Trip into Space

Imagine yourself at the age you are now, but the year is 2052. The Interplanetary Committee is sponsoring a contest and the prize is a free trip to another planet. Write two or three paragraphs on "Why I would like to travel to ____." Choose your planet and explain why you would like to visit there. Like any good science-fiction writer, you will have to imagine what this particular planet will be like in 2052. You must also consider the reasons for going that would most impress the Interplanetary Committee.

Being a Story Character

Imagine you are the boy in the story. Write a two-paragraph account of your first rocket trip. The account is to be sent to your best friend back home. Before you begin, go back over the story and make a list of words to describe how the boy probably felt at the beginning of the trip and later, after he had been given the "gift." For example, when he reminds his parents that they promised a present and a tree, he seems to fear he won't get these things. Write your account from the first-person point of view, as if you really are the boy in the story.

BIOGRAPHY

Ray Bradbury
1920–

Although born in Illinois, Ray Bradbury attended high school in Los Angeles, where he founded *Futuria Fantasia*, a magazine of science fiction. His first story appeared in print when he was twenty years old. Since then he has published some five hundred short stories, novels, plays, and poems. He also has screenplays, two musicals, two space-age cantatas, and an animated film to his credit. One of the astronaut teams named a crater on the moon Dandelion Crater after Bradbury's novel *Dandelion Wine*.

See SYMBOL in the Handbook of Literary Terms, page 660.

The Hundredth Dove

Jane Yolen

He was offered riches, fame, love . . . But to accept, he would have to disobey the king's command.

---

here once lived in the forest of old England a fowler named Hugh who supplied all the gamebirds for the high king's table.

The larger birds he hunted with a bow, and it was said of him that he never shot but that a bird fell, and sometimes two. But for the smaller birds that flocked like gray clouds over the forest, he used only a silken net he wove himself. This net was soft and fine and did not injure the birds though it held them fast. Then Hugh the fowler could pick and choose the plumpest of the doves for the high king's table and set the others free.

One day in early summer, Hugh was summoned to court and brought into the throne room.

Hugh bowed low, for it was not often that he was called into the king's own presence. And indeed he felt uncomfortable in the palace, as though caught in a stone cage.

"Rise, fowler, and listen," said the king.

"In one week's time I am to be married." Then, turning with a smile to the woman who sat by him, the king held out her hand to the fowler.

The fowler stared up at her. She was neat as a bird, slim and fair, with black eyes. There was a quiet in her, but a restlessness too. He had never seen anyone so beautiful.

Hugh took the tiny hand offered him and put his lips to it, but he only dared to kiss the gold ring that glittered on her finger.

The king looked carefully at the fowler and saw how he trembled. It made the king smile. "See, my lady, how your beauty turns the head of even my fowler. And he is a man who lives as solitary as a monk in his wooded cell."

The lady smiled and said nothing, but she drew her hand away from Hugh.

"The Hundredth Dove" from *The Hundredth Dove and Other Tales* by Jane Yolen, original illustrations by David Palladini, as it first appeared in book form. First printed in *The Magazine of Fantasy and Science Fiction*, April 1977. (Thomas Y. Crowell) Copyright © 1976, 1977 by Jane Yolen. Reprinted by permission of Harper & Row, Publishers, Inc. and Curtis Brown, Ltd.

The king then turned again to the fowler. "In honor of my bride, the Lady Columba, whose name means dove and whose beauty is celebrated in all the world, I wish to serve one hundred of the birds at our wedding feast."

Lady Columba gasped and held up her hand. "Please do not serve them, sire."

But the king spoke to the fowler. "I have spoken. Do not fail me, fowler."

"As you command," said Hugh and he bowed again. He touched his hand to his tunic where his motto, *Servo*, "I serve," was sewn over the heart.

Then the fowler went back to the cottage deep in the forest where he lived.

There he took out the silken net and spread it upon the floor. Slowly he searched the net for snags and snarls and weakened threads. These he rewove with great care, sitting straight-backed at his wooden loom.

After a night and a day he was done. The net was as strong as his own stout heart. He laid the net down on the hearth and slept a dreamless sleep.

Before dawn Hugh set out into the forest clearing which only he knew. The trails he followed were less than deer runs, for the fowler needed no paths to show him the way. He knew every tree, every stone in the forest as a lover knows the form of his beloved. And he served the forest easily as well as he served the high king.

The clearing was full of life; yet so silent did the fowler move, neither bird nor insect remarked his coming. He crouched at the edge, his brown and green clothes a part of the wood. Then he waited.

A long patience was his strength, and he waited the whole of the day, neither moving nor sleeping. At dusk the doves came, settling over the clearing like a gray mist. And when they were down and greedily feeding, Hugh leapt up and swung the net over the nearest ones in a single swift motion.

He counted twenty-one doves in his net, all but one gray-blue and meaty. The last was a dove that was slim, elegant, and white as milk. Yet even as Hugh watched, the white dove slipped through the silken strands that bound it and flew away into the darkening air.

Since Hugh was not the kind of hunter to curse his bad luck but rather praise his good, he gathered up the twenty and went home. He placed the doves in a large wooden cage whose bars he had carved out of white oak.

Then he looked at his net. There was not a single break in it, no way for the white dove to have escaped. Hugh thought long and hard about this, but at last he lay down to the cooing of the captured birds and slept.

In the morning the fowler was up at dawn. Again he crept to the forest clearing and waited, quieter than any stone, for the doves. And again he threw his net at dusk and caught twenty fat gray doves and the single white one.

But, as before, the white dove slipped through his net as easily as air.

The fowler carried the gray doves home and caged them with the rest. But his mind was filled with the sight of the white bird, slim and fair. He was determined to capture it.

For five days and nights it was the same except for this one thing: on the fifth night there were only nineteen gray doves in his

John James Audubon, *Ground Dove*
The Newberry Library, Chicago

net. He was short of the hundred by one. Yet he had taken all of the birds in the flock but the white dove.

Hugh looked into the hearthfire but he felt no warmth. He placed his hand upon the motto above his heart. "I swear by the king whom I serve and by the lady who will be his queen that I will capture that bird," he said. "I will bring the hundred doves to them. I shall not fail."

So the sixth day, well before dawn, the fowler arose. He checked the net one final time and saw it was tight. Then he was away to the clearing.

All that day Hugh sat at the clearing's edge, still as a stone. The meadow was full of life. Songbirds sang that had never sung there before. Strange flowers grew and blossomed and died at his feet; yet he never looked at them. Animals that were once and were no longer came out of the forest shadows and passed him by: the hippocampus, the gryphon, and the silken swift unicorn.[1] But he never moved. It was for the white dove he waited, and at last she came.

In the quickening dark she floated down, feather light and luminous at the clearing's edge. Slowly she moved, eating and cooing and calling for her missing flock. She came in the end to where Hugh sat and began to feed at his feet.

He moved his hands once and the net was over her; then his hands were over her, too. The dove twisted and pecked, but he held her close, palms upon wings, fingers on neck.

When the white dove saw she could not move, she turned her bright black eyes on the fowler and spoke to him in a cooing woman's voice:

Master fowler, set me free,
Gold and silver I'll give thee.

"Neither gold nor silver tempt me," said Hugh. "*Servo* is my motto. I serve my master. And my master is the king."

Then the white dove spoke again:

Master fowler, set me free,
Fame and fortune follow thee.

But the fowler shook his head and held on tight. "After the king, I serve the forest," he said. "Fame and fortune are not masters here." He rose with the white dove in his hands and made ready to return to his house.

Then the bird shook itself all over and spoke for a third time. Its voice was low and beguiling:

Master fowler, free this dove,
The Queen will be your own true love.

For the first time, then, the fowler noticed the golden ring that glittered and shone on the dove's foot though night was almost on them. As if in a vision, he saw the Lady Columba again, slim and neat and fair. He heard her voice and felt her hand in his.

He began to tremble and his heart began to pulse madly. He felt a burning in his chest and limbs. Then he looked down at the dove and it seemed to be smiling at him, its black eyes glittering.

"*Servo*," he cried out, his voice shaking and dead. "*Servo*." He closed his eyes and

---

1. *hippocampus . . . unicorn*, mythical creatures. The *hippocampus* (hip′ə kam′pəs) has the front part of a horse and the tail of a fish; the *gryphon* (grif′ən) has the head and wings of an eagle and the body of a lion; and the *unicorn* (yū′nə kôrn) is like a horse but has a single long horn on its forehead.

twisted the dove's neck. Then he touched the motto on his tunic. He could feel the word *Servo* impress itself coldly on his fingertips. One quick rip and the motto was torn from his breast. He flung it to the meadow floor, put the limp dove in his pouch, and went through the forest to his home.

The next day the fowler brought the hundred doves—the ninety-nine live ones and the one dead—to the king's kitchen. But there was never a wedding. The Lady Columba came neither to the chapel nor the castle, and her name was never spoken of again in the kingdom.

The fowler gave up hunting and lived on berries and fruit the rest of his life. Every day he made his way to the clearing to throw out grain for the birds. Around his neck, from a chain, a gold ring glittered. And occasionally he would touch the spot on his tunic above his heart, which was shredded and torn.

But though songbirds and sparrows ate his grain, and swallows came at his calling, he never saw another dove.

THINK AND DISCUSS
Understanding
1. What is the motto that Hugh wears, and what does it mean?
2. Hugh says that he serves two things. What are these two things, and which comes first?
3. What does the king command Hugh to do?
4. What is Lady Columba's reaction to the serving of doves at the wedding feast?
5. What does the white dove offer Hugh as a reward for setting it free?

Analyzing
6. Why does Hugh deliver to the palace ninety-nine live doves and one dove that is dead?
7. Why does Hugh give up hunting?
8. Several elements in "The Hundredth Dove" set it apart from realistic fiction. Explain how each of the following is used in the story: (a) old-fashioned, unusual language; (b) fantastic plants and animals; (c) magic.

Extending
9. What are your feelings toward Hugh?
10. If Hugh were to decide to change his motto after the incidents in this story, what do you think he would choose to sew on his tunic?

APPLYING: Symbol HZ
See Handbook of Literary Terms, p. 660.

Although a **symbol** can be a person, an action, or a situation, many symbols are objects. These objects may have meanings in themselves, but they suggest other emotional meanings as well.
1. What is the symbol that Hugh wears over his heart in the beginning of the story, and what might it symbolize?
2. What is the symbol that Hugh wears around his neck at the end of the story, and what might it symbolize?

VOCABULARY

Context

Use context to figure out the meanings of the italicized words in the sentences. Then choose from the list the best definition for the italicized word.

1. The *fowler* supplied the cook with all the game birds for the king's table.
2. He touched his hand to his *tunic* where his motto was sewn over the heart.
3. He moved so silently that neither bird nor insect *remarked* his coming.
4. Although it was night, the *luminous* dove stood out against the dark forest.
5. The dove offered rewards in a voice so *beguiling* that the fowler trembled.
    (a) pleasing so as to deceive
    (b) paid attention to
    (c) person who hunts wild birds
    (d) man who enters a monastery
    (e) loose shirt, reaching to the knees
    (f) shining; full of light

COMPOSITION

Reading/Writing Log

The author of this story uses many words that appeal to the senses to portray the fantasy setting and characters. Note the examples listed below. If you are keeping a **reading/writing log,** copy them and add at least four more from the story.

> This net was soft and fine. . . .

> She was neat as a bird, slim and fair. . . .

> the cooing of the captured birds

Writing a Story Ending

Think of another ending for "The Hundredth Dove." For example, how might things have been different if Hugh had allowed the white dove to escape, or if he had captured it and brought it alive to the palace? Write several paragraphs that show a different conclusion for the story. Be sure to use words that appeal to the senses of sight, sound, touch, taste, and smell, as the author does. If you are keeping a **reading/writing log,** review the examples you copied earlier. You may wish to list additional examples before you begin to write.

BIOGRAPHY

Jane Yolen

1939–

Jane Yolen has been a full-time professional writer since 1965 and a teacher of writing since 1966. All of her books are for young people, and she says that fantasy gives her a chance to say what she wants to say poetically and allegorically—that is, with an underlying meaning different from the surface meaning. Among her recent books are *Heart's Blood* and *The Stone Silenus.*

Review SYMBOL in the Handbook of Literary Terms, page 660.

The Hummingbird That Lived Through Winter

William Saroyan

**It was a sad thing to behold. This wonderful little creature of summertime
in the big rough hand of the old peasant.**

ometimes even instinct is overpowered by individuality—in creatures other than men, I mean. In men instinct is supposed to be controlled, but whether or not it ever actually is I leave to others. At any rate, the fundamental instinct of most—or all—creatures is to live. Each form of life has an instinctive technique of defense against other forms of life, as well as against the elements. What happens to hummingbirds is something I have never found out—from actual observation or from reading. They die, that's true. And they're born somehow or other, although I have never seen a hummingbird's egg, or a young hummingbird.

The mature hummingbird itself is so small that the egg must be magnificent, probably one of the most smiling little things in the world. Now, if hummingbirds come into the world through some other means than eggs, I ask the reader to forgive me. The only thing I know about Agass Agasig Agassig Agazig (well, the great American naturalist) is that he once studied turtle eggs, and in order to get the information he was seeking, had to find fresh ones. This caused an exciting adventure in Boston to a young fellow who wrote about it six or seven years before I read it, when I was fourteen. I was fourteen in 1922, which goes to show you how unimportant the years are when you're dealing with eggs of any kind. I envy the people who study birds, and some day I hope to find out everything that's known about hummingbirds.

I've gathered from rumor that the hummingbird travels incredible distances on incredibly little energy—what carries him, then? Spirit? But the best things I know about hummingbirds are the things I've noticed about them myself: that they are on hand when the sun is out in earnest, when the blossoms are with us, and the smell of them everywhere. You can hardly go through the best kind of day without seeing a hummingbird suspended like a little miracle in a shaft of light or over a big flower or a cluster of little ones. Or turning like gay insanity and shooting straight as an arrow toward practically nothing, for no reason, or for the reason that it's alive. Now, how can creatures such as that—so delicately magnificent and mad—possibly find time for the routine business of begetting young? Or for the exercise of instinct in self-defense? Well, however it may be, let a good day come by the grace of God, and with it will come the hummingbirds.

As I started to say, however, it appears that sometimes even instinct fails to operate in a specie. Or species. Or whatever it is. Anyhow, when all of a kind of living thing turn and go somewhere, in order to stay alive, in order to escape cold or whatever it might be, sometimes, it appears, one of them does not go. Why he does not go I cannot say. He may be eccentric, or there may be exalted reasons—specific instead of abstract passion for another of its kind—perhaps dead—or for a place. Or it may be stupidity, or stubbornness. Who can ever know?

There was a hummingbird once which in the wintertime did not leave our neighborhood in Fresno, California.

I'll tell you about it.

Across the street lived old Dikran, who was almost blind. He was past eighty and his wife was only a few years younger. They had a little house that was as neat inside as it was ordinary outside—except for old Dikran's garden, which was the best thing of its kind in the world. Plants, bushes, trees—all strong, in sweet black moist earth whose guardian was old Dikran. All things from the sky loved this spot in our poor neighborhood, and old Dikran loved *them*.

One freezing Sunday, in the dead of winter, as I came home from Sunday School I saw old Dikran standing in the middle of the street trying to distinguish what was in his hand. Instead of going into our house to the fire, as I had wanted to do, I stood on the steps of the front porch and watched the old man. He would turn around and look upward at his trees and then back to the palm of his hand. He stood in the street at least two minutes and then at last he came to me. He held his hand out, and in Armenian he said, "What is this in my hand?"

I looked.

"It is a hummingbird," I said half in English and half in Armenian. Hummingbird I said in English because I didn't know its name in Armenian.

"What is that?" old Dikran asked.

"The little bird," I said. "You know. The one that comes in the summer and stands in the air and then shoots away. The one with the wings that beat so fast you can't see them. It's in your hand. It's dying."

"Come with me," the old man said. "I can't see, and the old lady's at church. I can feel its heart beating. Is it in a bad way? Look again, once."

I looked again. It was a sad thing to behold. This wonderful little creature of summertime in the big rough hand of the old

peasant. Here it was in the cold of winter, absolutely helpless and pathetic, not suspended in a shaft of summer light, not the most alive thing in the world, but the most helpless and heartbreaking.

"It's dying," I said.

The old man lifted his hand to his mouth and blew warm breath on the little thing in his hand which he could not even see. "Stay now," he said in Armenian. "It is not long till summer. Stay, swift and lovely."

We went into the kitchen of his little house, and while he blew warm breath on the bird he told me what to do.

"Put a tablespoonful of honey over the gas fire and pour it into my hand, but be sure it is not too hot."

This was done.

After a moment the hummingbird began to show signs of fresh life. The warmth of the room, the vapor of the warm honey—and, well, the will and love of the old man. Soon the old man could feel the change in his hand, and after a moment or two the hummingbird began to take little dabs of the honey.

"It will live," the old man announced. "Stay and watch."

The transformation was incredible. The old man kept his hand generously open, and I expected the helpless bird to shoot upward out of his hand, suspend itself in space, and scare the life out of me—which is exactly what happened. The new life of the little bird was magnificent. It spun about in the little kitchen, going to the window, coming back to the heat, suspending, circling as if it were summertime and it had never felt better in its whole life.

The old man sat on the plain chair, blind

but attentive. He listened carefully and tried to see, but of course he couldn't. He kept asking about the bird, how it seemed to be, whether it showed signs of weakening again, what its spirit was, and whether or not it appeared to be restless; and I kept describing the bird to him.

When the bird was restless and wanted to go, the old man said, "Open the window and let it go."

"Will it live?" I asked.

"It is alive now and wants to go," he said. "Open the window."

I opened the window, the hummingbird stirred about here and there, feeling the cold from the outside, suspended itself in the area of the open window, stirring this way and that, and then it was gone.

"Close the window," the old man said.

We talked a minute or two and then I went home.

The old man claimed the hummingbird lived through the winter, but I never knew for sure. I saw hummingbirds again when summer came, but I couldn't tell one from the other.

One day in the summer I asked the old man.

"Did it live?"

"The little bird?" he said.

"Yes," I said. "That we gave the honey to. You remember. The little bird that was dying in the winter. Did it live?"

"Look about you," the old man said. "Do you see the bird?"

"I see humming*birds*," I said.

"Each of them is our bird," the old man said. "Each of them, each of them," he said swiftly and gently.

THINK AND DISCUSS

Understanding

1. What does the narrator say is a fundamental instinct of most—or all—creatures?
2. Describe the **setting** of this story. Where does it take place and at what time of the year?
3. Why does Dikran ask the narrator so many questions about the hummingbird?
4. In what ways does the honey help bring the hummingbird back to life?

Analyzing

5. Explain the **figurative language** in ". . . a hummingbird suspended like a little miracle in a shaft of light. . . ."
6. Describe the **character** of Dikran. Tell about his physical appearance, his words, and his actions.
7. What is the major conflict in the **plot** of this story?
8. What does Dikran mean when he says, "Each of them is our bird"?

Extending

9. Would the hummingbird have lived if the narrator had held it? Explain.

REVIEWING: Symbol H*7*
See Handbook of Literary Terms, p. 660.

A **symbol** is a person, place, event, or object that has a meaning in itself but suggests other meanings as well. A particular symbol may mean different things to different people.

1. What does the hummingbird symbolize for the narrator?

2. What does the hummingbird symbolize for Dikran?
3. How might Dikran's garden be a symbol for the neighborhood?

VOCABULARY
Antonyms

An antonym is a word that means the opposite of another word. Match each word in the left column below with its antonym at the right. You will not use all of the choices.

1. eccentric   (**a**) experience
2. incredible   (**b**) believable
3. exalted   (**c**) sadness
4. abstract   (**d**) lowered
5. instinct   (**e**) usual
                 (**f**) concrete

COMPOSITION
Writing a Description

The narrator of this story includes information about hummingbirds. Write a one-paragraph description of the hummingbird. Before you begin, review the story and list details, such as the fact that they come out with the sun, to use in your description. See Lesson 3, "Writing a Clear Description," in the Writer's Handbook.

Writing About an Experience

Have you ever found a wounded bird or animal? Write a paragraph description of that experience. Tell where you found the animal, what you did to bring it back to health, and what happened to it afterward. Before you begin, list the events in the order in which they happened.

ENRICHMENT
Making a Booklet

Each state has a bird and a flower that represent that state. Your class will be divided into small groups, and each group will draw or be assigned states to research. Prepare a one-page report, with illustrations, for each state. You may include information about a motto, if the state has one. The pages can be put into a booklet about state flowers and birds.

BIOGRAPHY

William Saroyan
1908–1981

William Saroyan was born in California to Armenian parents. Many of his stories are based on his experiences as a boy growing up in Fresno, California. A highly productive writer, he once completed a play in six days, and the play won a Pulitzer Prize. Saroyan's writing reflects his delight in people, young and old, and his zest for experiencing life to the fullest. Probably his best-known novel is *The Human Comedy*, which was later made into a movie.

See STEREOTYPE in the Handbook of Literary Terms, page 659.

The Storyteller

H. H. Munro

**"She was horribly good," began the bachelor, and his little audience
sat up in surprise.**

t was a hot afternoon, and the railway carriage was correspondingly sultry, and the next stop was at Templecombe, nearly an hour ahead. The occupants of the carriage were a small girl, and a smaller girl, and a small boy. An aunt belonging to the children occupied one corner seat, and the further corner seat on the opposite side was occupied by a bachelor who was a stranger to their party, but the small girls and the small boy emphatically occupied the compartment. Both the aunt and the children were conversational in a limited, persistent way, reminding one of the attentions of a housefly that refused to be discouraged. Most of the aunt's remarks seemed to begin with "Don't," and nearly all of the children's remarks began with "Why?" The bachelor said nothing out loud.

"Don't, Cyril, don't," exclaimed the aunt, as the small boy began smacking the cushions of the seat, producing a cloud of dust at each blow.

"Come and look out of the window," she added.

The child moved reluctantly to the window. "Why are those sheep being driven out of that field?" he asked.

"I expect they are being driven to another field where there is more grass," said the aunt weakly.

"But there is lots of grass in that field," protested the boy. "There's nothing else but grass there. Aunt, there's lots of grass in that field."

"Perhaps the grass in the other field is better," suggested the aunt fatuously.

"Why is it better?" came the swift, inevitable question.

"Oh, look at those cows!" exclaimed the aunt. Nearly every field along the line had contained cows or bullocks, but she spoke as though she were drawing attention to a rarity.

"Why is the grass in the other field better?" persisted Cyril.

The frown on the bachelor's face was deepening to a scowl. He was a hard, unsympathetic man, the aunt decided in her mind. She was utterly unable to come to any satisfactory decision about the grass in the other field.

The smaller girl created a diversion by beginning to recite "On the Road to Mandalay." She only knew the first line, but she put her limited knowledge to the fullest possible use. She repeated the line over and over again in a dreamy but resolute and very audible voice; it seemed to the bachelor as though someone had had a bet with her that she could not repeat the line aloud two thousand times without stopping. Whoever it was who had made the wager was likely to lose his bet.

"Come over here and listen to a story," said the aunt, when the bachelor had looked twice at her and once at the communication cord.[1]

The children moved listlessly toward the aunt's end of the carriage. Evidently her reputation as a storyteller did not rank high in their estimation.

In a low, confidential voice, interrupted at frequent intervals by loud, petulant questions from her listeners, she began an unenterprising and deplorably uninteresting story about a little girl who was good, and made friends with everyone on account of her goodness, and was finally saved from a mad bull by a number of rescuers who admired her moral character.

"Wouldn't they have saved her if she hadn't been good?" demanded the bigger of the small girls. It was exactly the question that the bachelor had wanted to ask.

"Well, yes," admitted the aunt lamely, "but I don't think they would have run quite so fast to her help if they had not liked her so much."

"It's the stupidest story I've ever heard," said the bigger of the small girls, with immense conviction.

"I didn't listen after the first bit, it was so stupid," said Cyril.

The smaller girl made no actual comment on the story, but she had long ago recommenced a murmured repetition of her favorite line.

"You don't seem to be a success as a storyteller," said the bachelor suddenly from his corner.

The aunt bristled in instant defense at this unexpected attack.

"It's a very difficult thing to tell stories that children can both understand and appreciate," she said stiffly.

"I don't agree with you," said the bachelor.

"Perhaps *you* would like to tell them a story," was the aunt's retort.

"Tell us a story," demanded the bigger of the small girls.

"Once upon a time," began the bachelor, "there was a little girl called Bertha, who was extraordinarily good."

---

1. *communication cord,* cord pulled to signal the engineer to stop the train in case of an emergency.

George Handwright, *Going to and Coming from the Seashore*, Thomas Gilcrease Institute, Tulsa, Oklahoma

The children's momentarily aroused interest began at once to flicker; all stories seemed dreadfully alike, no matter who told them.

"She did all that she was told, she was always truthful, she kept her clothes clean, ate milk puddings as though they were jam tarts, learned her lessons perfectly, and was polite in her manners."

"Was she pretty?" asked the bigger of the small girls.

"Not as pretty as any of you," said the bachelor. "But she was horribly good."

There was a wave of reaction in favor of the story; the word *horrible* in connection with goodness was a novelty that commended itself. It seemed to introduce a ring of truth that was absent from the aunt's tales of infant life.

"She was so good," continued the bachelor, "that she won several medals for goodness, which she always wore pinned onto her dress. There was a medal for obedience, another medal for punctuality, and a third for good behavior. They were large metal med-als, and they clinked against one another as she walked. No other child in the town where she lived had as many as three medals, so everybody knew that she must be an extra good child."

"Horribly good," quoted Cyril.

"Everybody talked about her goodness, and the Prince of the country got to hear about it, and he said that as she was so very good she might be allowed once a week to walk in his park, which was just outside the town. It was a beautiful park, and no children were ever allowed in it, so it was a great honor for Bertha to be allowed to go there."

"Were there any sheep in the park?" demanded Cyril.

"No," said the bachelor, "there were no sheep."

"Why weren't there any sheep?" came the inevitable question arising out of that answer.

The aunt permitted herself a smile, which might almost have been described as a grin.

"There were no sheep in the park," said the bachelor, "because the Prince's mother had once had a dream that her son would either be killed by a sheep or else by a clock falling on him. For that reason the Prince never kept a sheep in his park or a clock in his palace."

The aunt suppressed a gasp of admiration.

"Was the Prince killed by a sheep or by a clock?" asked Cyril.

"He is still alive, so we can't tell whether the dream will come true," said the bachelor unconcernedly. "Anyway, there were no sheep in the park, but there were lots of little pigs running all over the place."

"What color were they?"

"Black with white faces, white with black spots, black all over, gray with white patches, and some were white all over."

The storyteller paused to let the full idea of the park's treasures sink into the children's imaginations; then he resumed:

"Bertha was rather sorry to find that there were no flowers in the park. She had promised her aunts, with tears in her eyes, that she would not pick any of the kind Prince's flowers, and she had meant to keep her promise, so of course it made her feel silly to find that there were no flowers to pick."

"Why weren't there any flowers?"

"Because the pigs had eaten them all," said the bachelor promptly. "The gardeners had told the Prince that you couldn't have pigs and flowers, so he decided to have pigs and no flowers."

There was a murmur of approval at the excellence of the Prince's decision; so many people would have decided the other way.

"There were lots of other delightful things in the park. There were ponds with gold and blue and green fish in them, and trees with beautiful parrots that said clever things at a moment's notice, and hummingbirds that hummed all the popular tunes of the day. Bertha walked up and down and enjoyed herself immensely, and thought to herself, 'If I were not so extraordinarily good, I should not have been allowed to come into this beautiful park and enjoy all there is to be seen in it,' and her three medals clinked against one another as she walked and helped to remind her how very good she really was. Just then an enormous wolf came prowling into the park to see if it could catch a fat little pig for its supper."

"What color was it?" asked the children, amid an immediate quickening of interest.

"Mud-color all over, with a black tongue and pale gray eyes that gleamed with unspeakable ferocity. The first thing that it saw in the park was Bertha; her pinafore was so spotlessly white and clean that it could be seen from a great distance. Bertha saw the wolf and saw that it was stealing toward her, and she began to wish that she had never been allowed to come into the park. She ran as hard as she could, and the wolf came after her with huge leaps and bounds. She managed to reach a shrubbery of myrtle bushes, and she hid herself in one of the thickest of the bushes. The wolf came sniffing among the branches, its black tongue lolling out of its mouth and its pale gray eyes glaring with rage. Bertha was terribly frightened, and thought to herself: 'If I had not been so extraordinarily good, I should have been safe in town at this moment.'

"However, the scent of the myrtle was so strong that the wolf could not sniff out where Bertha was hiding, and the bushes were so thick that he might have hunted about in them for a long time without catching sight of her; so he thought he might as well go off and catch a little pig instead. Bertha was trembling very much at having the wolf prowling and sniffing so near her, and as she trembled the medal for obedience clinked against the medals for good conduct and punctuality. The wolf was just moving away when he heard the sound of the medals clinking and stopped to listen; they clinked again in a bush quite near him. He dashed into the bush, his pale gray eyes gleaming with ferocity and triumph, and dragged Bertha out and devoured her to the last morsel. All that was left of her were her shoes, bits of clothing, and the three medals for goodness."

"Were any of the little pigs killed?"

"No, they all escaped."

"The story began badly," said the smaller of the two girls, "but it had a beautiful ending."

"It is the most beautiful story that I ever heard," said the bigger of the small girls, with immense decision.

"It is the *only* beautiful story I have ever heard," said Cyril.

A dissentient opinion came from the aunt.

"A most improper story to tell to young children! You have undermined the effect of years of careful teaching."

"At any rate," said the bachelor, collecting his belongings preparatory to leaving the carriage, "I kept them quiet for ten minutes, which was more than you were able to do."

"Unhappy woman!" he observed to himself as he walked down the platform of Templecombe station. "For the next six months or so those children will assail her in public with demands for an improper story!"

THINK AND DISCUSS
Understanding
1. Describe the **setting** that brings these people together.
2. What sort of story does the aunt tell to keep the children quiet?
3. What do the children think of the aunt's story? Why?
4. Why does the bachelor tell a story?
5. In the bachelor's story, how does the wolf know that Bertha is in the bushes?

Analyzing
6. Is this story told from the **point of view** of the bachelor, the aunt, one of the children, or a third-person omniscient observer? Explain.
7. Why do the children think the bachelor's story is "beautiful," while the aunt thinks it is "improper"?
8. Do you think the author of "The Storyteller" intends to poke fun at any ideas or attitudes? Explain.

Extending
9. Do you like Bertha, the main **character** in the bachelor's story? Why or why not?

APPLYING: Stereotype   H𝌡
See Handbook of Literary Terms, p. 659.
A **stereotype** is a person or a plot that rigidly follows a pattern and lacks individuality. A character that is a stereotype has only certain traits that are commonly expected. A plot that is a stereotype follows a predictable pattern.

The aunt, the children, and, to a certain extent, the bachelor are stereotypes.
1. What does the aunt do and say that

illustrate the stereotyped character of a guardian aunt?

2. What behaviors make the children stereotyped characters?
3. What traits of the bachelor suggest a stereotype?
4. What elements in the bachelor's story violate stereotypes?

THINKING SKILLS
Evaluating
To evaluate is to make a judgment based on some sort of standard. Work with a group of about four other classmates. Brainstorm ideas for stories that would be enjoyed by young children. Choose one and compose a story to be told aloud. Your class will evaluate its effectiveness for young listeners. You might consider retelling a famous tale, giving it a new ending and avoiding stereotypes.

COMPOSITION
Reading/Writing Log
The author of "The Storyteller" uses many words that appeal to the senses to help you experience the setting. Read the examples. Then copy them in your **reading/writing log** and add at least three more of your own from the story.

It was a hot afternoon, . . .

. . . the small boy began smacking the cushions of the seat, producing a cloud of dust at each blow.

Writing a Story
Consider the story told by the bachelor. Write your own short story of not more than two pages. Follow the bachelor's example and avoid a stereotyped plot. Choose characters, a setting, and a conflict in which you think young children would be interested. Be sure to use words that appeal to the senses. If you are keeping a **reading/writing log,** refer to it before you begin. See Lesson 9, "Writing Your Own Story," in the Writer's Handbook.

Writing a Journal Entry
Imagine you are the bachelor of this story. Write a journal entry for the events that occur on the day of the train trip. Use the first-person "I" point of view. Before you begin, review the story and imagine what the bachelor would have been thinking.

BIOGRAPHY

H. H. Munro
1870–1916

The bachelor in the train compartment who delights the children but confounds their aunt could almost be Hector Hugh Munro himself, one of the world's master storytellers. His tales, which often blend humor with an element of gruesomeness, and frequently contain characters who play tricks on each other, usually end in a surprising way. Munro's pen name is "Saki." Born in Burma, he was educated in England and traveled throughout Europe.

See INFERENCE in the Handbook of Literary Terms, page 642.

The Day the Sun Came Out

Dorothy M. Johnson

If it might be your last night on earth . . . , you would sit up by the smoky fire, wide-awake, remembering whatever you had to remember. . . .

---

 e left the home place behind, mile by slow mile. We were heading for the mountains, across the prairie where the wind blew forever.

At first there were four of us with the one-horse wagon and its skimpy load. Pa and I walked because I was a big boy of eleven. My two little sisters walked until they got tired. Then they had to be boosted up in the wagon bed.

That was no covered Conestoga, like Pa's folks came West in. It was just an old farm wagon, drawn by one tired horse. It creaked and rumbled westward to the mountains, toward the little woods town where Pa thought he had an old uncle who owned a little two-bit sawmill.

Two weeks we had been moving when we picked up Mary. She had run away from somewhere that she wouldn't tell. Pa didn't want her along. But she stood up to him with no fear in her voice.

"I'd rather go with a family and look after kids," she said, "but I ain't going back. If you won't take me, I'll travel with any wagon that will."

Pa scowled at her, and wide blue eyes stared back.

"How old are you?" he demanded.

"Twenty," she said. "There's teamsters[1] come this way sometimes. I'd rather go with you folks. But I won't go back."

"We're prid'near out of food," my father told her. "We're clean out of money. I got all I can handle without taking anybody else." He turned away as if he hated the sight of her. "You'll have to walk," he said.

So she went along with us. She looked after the little girls, but Pa wouldn't talk to her.

---

1. *teamsters,* persons who hauled things on wagons pulled by teams of horses.

On the prairie, the wind blew. But in the mountains, there was rain. When we stopped at little timber claims along the way, the homesteaders said it had rained all summer. Crops among the blackened stumps were rotted and spoiled. There was no cheer anywhere. The people we talked to were past worrying. They were scared and desperate.

So was Pa. He traveled twice as far each day as the wagon. He ranged through the woods with his rifle. But he never saw game. He had been depending on killing a deer. But we never got any deer meat except as a grudging gift from the homesteaders.

He brought in a porcupine once. And that was fat meat and good. Mary roasted it in chunks over the fire, half crying with the smoke. Pa and I rigged up the tarp sheet for a shelter to keep the rain from putting the fire clean out.

The porcupine was long gone, except for some of the tried-out fat[2] that Mary had saved, when we came to an old, empty cabin. Pa said we'd have to stop. The horse was wore out. It couldn't pull any more up those hills in the mountains.

At the cabin, at least there was a place to stay. We had a few potatoes left and some cornmeal. There was a creek that probably had fish in it, if a person could catch them. Pa tried it for half a day before he gave up. To this day I don't care for fishing. I remember my father's sunken eyes in his sad face.

He took Mary and me outside the cabin to talk. Rain dripped on us from branches overhead.

"I think I know where we are," he said. "I figure to get to old John's and back in about four days. There'll be food in the town.

They'll let me have some whether old John's still there or not."

He looked at me. "You do like she tells you," he warned. It was the first time he had admitted Mary was on earth since we picked her up two weeks before.

"You're my pardner," he said to me, "but it might be she's got more brains. You mind what she says."

He burst out with bitterness. "There ain't anything good left in the world. Or people to care if you live or die. But I'll get food in the town and come back with it."

He took a deep breath and added, "If you get too all-fired hungry, butcher the horse. It'll be better than starvin'."

He kissed the little girls good-bye. Then he plodded off through the woods with one blanket and the rifle.

The cabin was moldy and had no floor. We kept a fire going under a hole in the roof, so it was full of blinding smoke, but we had to keep the fire so as to dry out the wood.

The third night, we lost the horse. A bear scared him. We heard the racket. Mary and I ran out. But we couldn't see anything in the pitch-dark.

In gray daylight I went looking for him. I must have walked fifteen miles. It seemed like I had to have that horse at the cabin when Pa came or he'd whip me. I got plumb lost two or three times. I thought maybe I was going to die there alone and nobody would ever know it. But I found the way back to the clearing.

That was the fourth day. And Pa didn't

---

2. *tried-out fat,* lard or fat which has been purified by melting or boiling.

come. That was the day we ate up the last of the grub.

The fifth day, Mary went looking for the horse. My sisters cried. They huddled in a blanket by the fire, because they were scared and hungry.

I never did get dried out, always having to bring in more damp wood and going out to yell to see if Mary would hear me and not get lost. But I couldn't cry like the little girls did, because I was a big boy, eleven years old.

It was near dark when there was an answer to my yelling. Mary came into the clearing.

Mary didn't have the horse. We never saw hide nor hair of that old horse again. But she was carrying something big and white that looked like a pumpkin with no color to it.

She didn't say anything, just looked around and saw Pa wasn't there yet, at the end of the fifth day.

"What's that thing?" my sister Elizabeth demanded.

"Mushroom," Mary answered. "I bet it hefts ten pounds."

"What are you going to do with it now?" I said. "Play football here?"

"Eat it—maybe," she said, putting it in a corner. Her wet hair hung over her shoulders. She huddled by the fire.

My sister Sarah began to cry again. "I'm hungry!" she kept saying.

"Mushrooms ain't good eating," I said. "They can kill you."

"Maybe," Mary answered. "Maybe they can, I don't set up to know all about everything, like some people."

"What's that mark on your shoulder?" I asked her. "You tore your dress on the brush."

"What do you think it is?" she said. Her head was bowed in the smoke.

"Looks like scars," I guessed.

"'Tis scars. They whipped me, them I used to live with. Now mind your own business. I want to think."

Elizabeth cried, "Why don't Pa come back?"

"He's coming," Mary promised. "Can't come in the dark. Your pa'll take care of you soon's he can."

She got up and looked around in the grub box.

"Nothing there but empty dishes," I growled. "If there was anything, we'd know it."

Mary stood up. She was holding the can with the porcupine grease.

"I'm going to have something to eat," she said coolly. "You kids can't have any yet. And I don't want any crying, mind."

It was a cruel thing, what she did then. She sliced that big, solid mushroom and heated grease in a pan.

The smell of it brought the little girls out of their bed. But she told them to go back in so fierce a voice that they obeyed. They cried to break your heart.

I didn't cry, I watched, hating her.

I endured the smell of the mushroom frying as long as I could. Then I said, "Give me some."

"Tomorrow," Mary answered. "Tomorrow, maybe. But not tonight." She turned to me with a sharp command: "Don't bother me! Just leave me be."

She knelt there by the fire and finished frying the slice of mushroom.

If I'd had Pa's rifle, I'd have been willing

Robert Summers/American Masters Foundation, Houston, Texas

to kill her right then and there.

She didn't eat right away. She looked at the brown, fried slice for a while and said, "By tomorrow morning, I guess you can tell whether you want any."

The girls stared at her as she ate. Sarah was chewing on an old leather glove.

When Mary crawled into the quilts with them, they moved away as far as they could get.

I was so scared that my stomach heaved, empty as it was.

Mary didn't stay in the quilt long. She took a drink out of the water bucket and sat down by the fire and looked through the smoke at me.

She said in a low voice, "I don't know how it will be if it's poison. Just do the best you can with the girls. Because your pa will come back, you know. . . . You better go to bed. I'm going to sit up."

And so would you sit up. If it might be your last night on earth and the pain of death might seize you at any moment, you would sit up by the smoky fire, wide-awake, remembering whatever you had to remember, savoring life.

We sat in silence after the girls had gone to

sleep. Once I asked, "How long does it take?"

"I never heard," she answered. "Don't think about it."

I slept after a while, with my chin on my chest.

Mary's moving around brought me wide-awake. The black of night was fading.

"I guess it's all right," Mary said. "I'd be able to tell by now, wouldn't I?"

I answered gruffly, "I don't know."

Mary stood in the doorway for a while, looking out at the dripping world as if she found it beautiful. Then she fried slices of the mushroom while the little girls danced with anxiety.

We feasted, we three, my sisters and I, until Mary ruled, "That'll hold you," and would not cook any more. She didn't touch any of the mushroom herself.

That was a strange day in the moldy cabin. Mary laughed and was gay. She told stories. And we played "Who's Got the Thimble?" with a pine cone.

In the afternoon we heard a shout. My sisters screamed and I ran ahead of them across the clearing.

The rain had stopped. My father came plunging out of the woods leading a pack horse—and well I remember the treasures of food in that pack.

He glanced at us anxiously as he tore the ropes that bound the pack.

"Where's the other one?" he demanded.

Mary came out of the cabin then, walking sedately. As she came toward us, the sun began to shine.

My stepmother was a wonderful woman.

THINK AND DISCUSS

Understanding

1. How does Mary come to be traveling with the narrator and his family?
2. When is the first time Pa talks about Mary or gives her any credit?
3. When Mary begins cooking the wild mushroom, the narrator thinks she is doing a cruel thing. At the end of the story, does he feel the same way? Why or why not?

Analyzing

4. Describe the character who is the narrator of the story. Tell his age, how he shows responsibility through his actions, and how he seems to feel about the other people in his life.
5. What is the conflict between **characters** in this story?
6. What is the conflict within a single **character**?
7. What specific details might have been presented differently if this story had been told from Mary's **point of view**?

Extending

8. Have you ever thought that someone was acting selfishly and later found out you were wrong? Explain the circumstances and how you discovered the truth.

APPLYING: Inference H𝕏

See Handbook of Literary Terms, p. 642.

An **inference** is a reasonable conclusion drawn by the reader from hints or clues provided by the author. For example, from the narrator's description of the family's old farm wagon and its "skimpy load," you can infer that the family is poor.

1. After Mary eats the mushroom slice, what can you infer she means when she says, "By tomorrow morning, I guess you can tell whether you want any"?
2. What can you infer about the title of the story? Note that the same idea is expressed in the second to last paragraph of the story.
3. What reasonable conclusion can you draw from the last sentence of the story?

COMPOSITION
Writing a Diary Entry

Many pioneer women kept diaries. What do you think Mary would have included if she had kept one? Write three separate entries from Mary's point of view, based on experiences related in the story. Before you begin, review the story to choose three different days on which important things occur, such as the day Mary joins the family. Make notes and tell the way you, as Mary, felt about the situation.

Writing About Plot

Suppose your teacher asks you to write about the plot of "The Day the Sun Came Out." You will want to describe the pattern of events, the conflicts, the moment of greatest suspense, and the conclusion. Before you begin, make a list of the events in order. Think about the conflicts between individuals and within one of the characters and note these under a heading "Conflicts." Also write headings for "Suspense" and "Conclusion." For help in writing, see Lesson 6, "Writing About Plot," in the Writer's Handbook.

ENRICHMENT
Doing Research

Use encyclopedias and history books in your school or public library to research what it was like to travel west across North America during the nineteenth century. You might concentrate on the Homestead Act of 1862 and the part it played in the settlement of the American West.

BIOGRAPHY

Dorothy M. Johnson
1905–1984

Dorothy M. Johnson was born in Iowa and worked during the early years of her career as an editor in New York City, but her home was in the western United States, where many of her stories are set. Her books include *Warrior for a Lost Nation: A Biography of Sitting Bull; Famous Lawmen of the Old West;* and *Montana.* The films *The Man Who Shot Liberty Valance, A Man Called Horse,* and *The Hanging Tree* are based on her works. Among Johnson's honors was honorary membership in the Blackfeet tribe in Montana.

See **FLASHBACK** in the Handbook of Literary Terms, page 639.

Last Cover

Paul Annixter

I haven't the words to tell you what the fox meant to us. It was far more wonderful owning him than owning any dog. There was something rare and secret like the spirit of the woods about him. . . .

'm not sure I can tell you what you want to know about my brother; but everything about the pet fox is important, so I'll tell all that from the beginning.

It goes back to a winter afternoon after I'd hunted the woods all day for a sign of our lost pet. I remember the way my mother looked up as I came into the kitchen. Without my speaking, she knew what had happened. For six hours I had walked, reading signs, looking for a delicate print in the damp soil or even a hair that might have told of a red fox passing that way—but I had found nothing.

"Did you go up in the foothills?" Mom asked.

I nodded. My face was stiff from held-back tears. My brother, Colin, who was going on twelve, got it all from one look at me and went into a heartbroken, almost silent, crying.

Three weeks before, Bandit, the pet fox Colin and I had raised from a tiny kit, had disappeared, and not even a rumor had been heard of him since.

"He'd have had to go off soon anyway," Mom comforted. "A big, lolloping fellow like him, he's got to live his life same as us. But he may come back. That fox set a lot of store by you boys in spite of his wild ways."

"He set a lot of store by our food, anyway," Father said. He sat in a chair by the kitchen window mending a piece of harness. "We'll be seeing a lot more of that fellow, never fear. That fox learned to pine for table scraps and young chickens. He was getting to be an egg thief, too, and he's not likely to forget that."

"That was only pranking when he was little," Colin said desperately.

From the first, the tame fox had made tension in the family. It was Father who said we'd better name him Bandit, after he'd made away with his first young chicken.

"Maybe you know," Father said shortly. "But when an animal turns to egg sucking he's usually incurable. He'd better not come pranking around my chicken run again."

It was late February, and I remember the bleak, dead cold that had set in, cold that was a rare thing for our Carolina hills. Flocks of sparrows and snowbirds had appeared to peck hungrily at all that the pigs and chickens didn't eat.

"This one's a killer," Father would say of a morning, looking out at the whitened barn roof. "This one will make the shoats squeal."

A fire snapped all day in our cookstove and another in the stone fireplace in the living room, but still the farmhouse was never warm. The leafless woods were bleak and empty, and I spoke of that to Father when I came back from my search.

"It's always a sad time in the woods when the seven sleepers are under cover," he said.

"What sleepers are they?" I asked. Father was full of woods lore.

"Why, all the animals that have got sense enough to hole up and stay hid in weather like this. Let's see, how was it the old rhyme named them?

Surly bear and sooty bat,
Brown chuck and masked coon,
Chippy-munk and sly skunk,
And all the mouses
'Cept in men's houses.

"And man would have joined them and made it eight, Granther Yeary always said, if he'd had a little more sense."

"I was wondering if the red fox mightn't make it eight," Mom said.

Father shook his head. "Late winter's a high time for foxes. Time when they're out deviling, not sleeping."

My chest felt hollow. I wanted to cry like Colin over our lost fox, but at fourteen a boy doesn't cry. Colin had squatted down on the floor and got out his small hammer and nails to start another new frame for a new picture. Maybe then he'd make a drawing for the frame and be able to forget his misery. It had been that way with him since he was five.

I thought of the new dress Mom had brought home a few days before in a heavy cardboard box. That box cover would be fine for Colin to draw on. I spoke of it, and Mom's glance thanked me as she went to get it. She and I worried a lot about Colin. He was small for his age, delicate and blond, his hair much lighter and softer than mine, his eyes deep and wide and blue. He was often sick, and I knew the fear Mom had that he might be predestined. I'm just ordinary, like Father. I'm the sort of stuff that can take it— tough and strong—but Colin was always sort of special.

Mom lighted the lamp. Colin began cutting his white cardboard carefully, fitting it into his frame. Father's sharp glance turned on him now and again.

"There goes the boy making another frame before there's a picture for it," he said. "It's too much like cutting out a man's suit for a fellow that's say, twelve years old. Who knows whether he'll grow into it?"

Mom was into him then, quick. "Not a single frame of Colin's has ever gone to waste. The boy has real talent, Sumter, and it's time you realized it."

"Of course he has," Father said. "All kids have 'em. But they get over 'em."

"It isn't the pox we're talking of," Mom sniffed.

"In a way it is. Ever since you started talking up Colin's art, I've had an invalid for help around the place."

Father wasn't as hard as he made out, I knew, but he had to hold a balance against all Mom's frothing. For him the thing was the land and all that pertained to it. I was following in Father's footsteps, true to form, but Colin threatened to break the family tradition with his leaning toward art, with Mom "aiding and abetting him," as Father liked to put it. For the past two years she had had dreams of my brother becoming a real artist and going away to the city to study.

It wasn't that Father had no understanding of such things. I could remember, through the years, Colin lying on his stomach in the front room making pencil sketches, and how a good drawing would catch Father's eye halfway across the room, and how he would sometimes gather up two or three of them to study, frowning and muttering, one hand in his beard, while a great pride rose in Colin, and in me too. Most of Colin's drawings were of the woods and wild things, and there Father was a master critic. He made out to scorn what seemed to him a passive "white-livered" interpretation of nature through brush and pencil instead of rod and rifle.

At supper that night Colin could scarcely eat. Ever since he'd been able to walk, my brother had had a growing love of wild things, but Bandit had been like his very own, a gift of the woods. One afternoon a year and a half before, Father and Laban Small had been running a vixen through the hills with their dogs. With the last of her strength the she-fox had made for her den, not far from our house. The dogs had overtaken her and killed her just before she reached it. When Father and Laban came up, they'd found Colin crouched nearby holding her cub in his arms.

Father had been for killing the cub, which was still too young to shift for itself, but Colin's grief had brought Mom into it. We'd taken the young fox into the kitchen, all of us, except Father, gone a bit silly over the little thing. Colin had held it in his arms and fed it warm milk from a spoon.

"Watch out with all your soft ways," Father had warned, standing in the doorway. "You'll make too much of him. Remember, you can't make a dog out of a fox. Half of that little critter has to love, but the other half is a wild hunter. You boys will mean a whole lot to him while he's kit, but there'll come a day when you won't mean a thing to him and he'll leave you shorn."

For two weeks after that Colin had nursed the cub, weaning it from milk to bits of meat. For a year they were always together. The cub grew fast. It was soon following Colin and me about the barnyard. It turned out to be a patch fox, with a saddle of darker fur across its shoulders.

I haven't the words to tell you what the fox meant to us. It was far more wonderful owning him than owning any dog. There was something rare and secret like the spirit of the woods about him, and back of his calm, straw-gold eyes was the sense of a brain the equal of a man's. The fox became Colin's whole life.

Each day, going and coming from school, Colin and I took long side trips through the woods, looking for Bandit. Wild things' memories were short, we knew; we'd have to find him soon or the old bond would be broken.

Ever since I was ten I'd been allowed to hunt with Father, so I was good at reading signs. But, in a way, Colin knew more about the woods and wild things than Father or me. What came to me from long observation, Colin seemed to know by instinct.

It was Colin who felt out, like an Indian, the stretch of woods where Bandit had his den, who found the first slim, small fox-print in the damp earth. And then, on an afternoon in March, we saw him. I remember the day well, racing clouds, the wind rattling the tops of the pine trees and swaying the Spanish moss. Bandit had just come out of a clump of laurel; in the maze of leaves behind him we caught a glimpse of a slim red vixen, so we knew he had found a mate. She melted from sight like a shadow, but Bandit turned to watch us, his mouth open, his tongue lolling as he smiled his old foxy smile. On his thin chops, I saw a telltale chicken feather.

Colin moved silently forward, his movements so quiet and casual he seemed to be standing still. He called Bandit's name, and the fox held his ground, drawn to us with all his senses. For a few moments he let Colin actually put an arm about him. It was then I knew that he loved us still, for all of Father's warnings. He really loved us back, with a fierce, secret love no tame thing ever gave.

But the urge of his life just then was toward his new mate. Suddenly, he whirled about and disappeared in the laurels.

Colin looked at me with glowing eyes. "We haven't really lost him, Stan. When he gets through with his spring sparking he may come back. But we've got to show ourselves to him a lot, so he won't forget."

"It's a go," I said.

"Promise not to say a word to Father," Colin said, and I agreed. For I knew by the chicken feather that Bandit had been up to no good.

A week later the woods were budding and the thickets were rustling with all manner of wild things scurrying on the love scent. Colin managed to get a glimpse of Bandit every few days. He couldn't get close though, for the spring running was a lot more important to a fox than any human beings were.

Every now and then Colin got out his framed box cover and looked at it, but he never drew anything on it; he never even picked up his pencil. I remember wondering if what Father had said about framing a picture before you had one had spoiled something for him.

I was helping Father with the planting now, but Colin managed to be in the woods every day. By degrees he learned Bandit's range, where he drank and rested and where he was likely to be according to the time of day. One day he told me how he had petted Bandit again, and how they had walked together a long way in the woods. All this time we had kept his secret from Father.

As summer came on, Bandit began to live up to the prediction Father had made. Accustomed to human beings he moved without

Rien Poortvliet

fear about the scattered farms of the region, raiding barns and hen runs that other foxes wouldn't have dared go near. And he taught his wild mate to do the same. Almost every night they got into some poultry house, and by late June Bandit was not only killing chickens and ducks but feeding on eggs and young chicks whenever he got the chance.

Stories of his doings came to us from many sources, for he was still easily recognized by the dark patch on his shoulders. Many a farmer took a shot at him as he fled and some of them set out on his trail with dogs, but they always returned home without even sighting him. Bandit was familiar with all the dogs in the region, and he knew a hundred tricks to confound them. He got a reputation that year beyond that of any fox our hills had known. His confidence grew, and he gave up wild hunting altogether and lived entirely off the poultry farmers. By September the hill farmers banded together to hunt him down.

It was Father who brought home that news one night. All time-honored rules of the fox chase were to be broken in this hunt; if the dogs couldn't bring Bandit down, he was to be shot on sight. I was stricken and furious. I remember the misery of Colin's face in the lamplight. Father, who took pride in all the ritual of the hunt, had refused to be a party to such an affair, though in justice he could do nothing but sanction any sort of hunt, for Bandit, as old Sam Wetherwax put it, had been "purely getting in the Lord's hair."

The hunt began next morning, and it was the biggest turnout our hills had known. There were at least twenty mounted men in the party and as many dogs. Father and I were working in the lower field as they passed along the river road. Most of the hunters carried rifles, and they looked ugly.

Twice during the morning I went up to the house to find Colin, but he was nowhere around. As we worked, Father and I could follow the progress of the hunt by the distant hound music on the breeze. We could tell just where the hunters first caught sight of the fox and where Bandit was leading the dogs during the first hour. We knew as well as if we'd seen it how Bandit roused another fox along Turkey Branch and forced it to run for him, and how the dogs swept after it for twenty minutes before they sensed their mistake.

Noon came, and Colin had not come in to eat. After dinner Father didn't go back to the field. He moped about, listening to the hound talk. He didn't like what was on any more than I did, and now and again I caught his smile of satisfaction when we heard the broken, angry notes of the hunting horn, telling that the dogs had lost the trail or had run another fox.

I was restless and I went up into the hills in midafternoon. I ranged the woods for miles, thinking all the time of Colin. Time lost all meaning for me, and the short day was nearing an end, when I heard the horn talking again, telling that the fox had put over another trick. All day he had deviled the dogs and mocked the hunters. This new trick and the coming night would work to save him. I was wildly glad, as I moved down toward Turkey Branch and stood listening for a time by the deep, shaded pool where for years we boys had gone swimming, sailed boats, and dreamed summer dreams.

Suddenly, out of the corner of my eye, I saw the sharp ears and thin, pointed mask of a fox—in the water almost beneath me. It was Bandit, craftily submerged there, all but his head, resting in the cool water of the pool and the shadow of the two big beeches that spread above it. He must have run forty miles or more since morning. And he must have hidden in this place before. His knowing, crafty mask blended perfectly with the shadows and a mass of drift and branches that had collected by the bank of the pool. He was so still that a pair of thrushes flew up from the spot as I came up, not knowing he was there.

Bandit's bright, harried eyes were looking right at me. But I did not look at him direct. Some woods instinct, swifter than thought, kept me from it. So he and I met as in another world, indirectly, with feeling but without sign or greeting.

Suddenly I saw that Colin was standing

almost beside me. Silently as a water snake, he had come out of the bushes and stood there. Our eyes met, and a quick and secret smile passed between us. It was a rare moment in which I really "met" my brother, when something of his essence flowed into me and I knew all of him. I've never lost it since.

My eyes still turned from the fox, my heart pounding. I moved quietly away, and Colin moved with me. We whistled softly as we went, pretending to busy ourselves along the bank of the stream. There was magic in it, as if by will we wove a web of protection about the fox, a ring-pass-not that none might penetrate. It was so, too, we felt, in the brain of Bandit, and that doubled the charm. To us he was still our little pet that we had carried about in our arms on countless summer afternoons.

Two hundred yards upstream, we stopped beside slim, fresh tracks in the mud where Bandit had entered the branch. The tracks angled upstream. But in the water the wily creature had turned down.

We climbed the far bank to wait, and Colin told me how Bandit's secret had been his secret ever since an afternoon three months before, when he'd watched the fox swim downstream to hide in the deep pool. Today he'd waited on the bank, feeling that Bandit, hard pressed by the dogs, might again seek the pool for sanctuary.

We looked back once as we turned homeward. He still had not moved. We didn't know until later that he was killed that same night by a chance hunter, as he crept out from his hiding place.

That evening Colin worked a long time on his framed box cover that had lain about the house untouched all summer. He kept at it all the next day too. I had never seen him work so hard. I seemed to sense in the air the feeling he was putting into it, how he was *believing* his picture into being. It was evening before he finished it. Without a word he handed it to Father. Mom and I went and looked over his shoulder.

It was a delicate and intricate pencil drawing of the deep branch pool, and there was Bandit's head and watching, fear-filled eyes hiding there amid the leaves and shadows, woven craftily into the maze of twigs and branches, as if by nature's art itself. Hardly a fox there at all, but the place where he was— or should have been. I recognized it instantly, but Mom gave a sort of incredulous sniff.

"I'll declare," she said, "it's mazy as a puzzle. It just looks like a lot of sticks and leaves to me."

Long minutes of study passed before Father's eye picked out the picture's secret, as few men's could have done. I laid that to Father's being a born hunter. That was a picture that might have been done especially for him. In fact, I guess it was.

Finally he turned to Colin with his deep, slow smile. "So that's how Bandit fooled them all," he said. He sat holding the picture with a sort of tenderness for a long time, while we glowed in the warmth of the shared secret. That was Colin's moment. Colin's art stopped being a pox to Father right there. And later, when the time came for Colin to go to art school, it was Father who was his solid backer.

Comment

The Red Fox

The red fox, a member of the dog family, is considered one of the smartest and most cunning of native animals. Through the years it has been trapped for its fur and eagerly pursued by hunters, usually led by hounds following the fox's scent.

The fox has become very clever at escaping its pursuers. A fox will double back on its trail and then suddenly leap to one side. When the dogs reach the end of the trail, they are baffled, not realizing the fox is now behind them and getting farther away. A fox will also leave gaps in its trail by running along a fence top or plunging into water, as Bandit does. A tiring fox may jump into its den or the burrow of another animal and, after a rest, escape.

The red fox eats birds, frogs, insects, rabbits, and fruit, but mostly mice and other rodents. Because of a keen sense of hearing, a fox can hear a mouse squeak over a hundred feet away. By keeping the rodent population down, foxes are helpful to farmers. Few foxes dine on chickens these days because most chickens are raised indoors.

THINK AND DISCUSS

Understanding

1. How does the pet fox get his name?
2. Decribe the **setting** of this story. In what part of the country does it take place, and at what time of the year does most of the action occur?
3. How does each family member react to Colin?
4. What brings about the fierce hunt for Bandit, and how does it end?

Analyzing

5. Explain what the narrator means when he describes himself as being "just ordinary" but says that Colin "was always sort of special."

6. In what ways is the narrator's relationship to Colin similar to Colin's relationship to Bandit?
7. Why do you think the father changes his mind about Colin's art?

Extending

8. Do you think that Bandit could have stayed on the farm as a pet? Why or why not?

APPLYING: Flashback H**Z**
See Handbook of Literary Terms, p. 639.

A **flashback** is an interruption in the action of a story to show an episode that happened at an earlier time. It is used to provide background information necessary to understanding the characters or the plot.

1. The events below are listed in the order in which they are presented in the story. Put the events in the order in which they actually happen.
   (a) The narrator spends a winter afternoon hunting for Bandit.
   (b) Bandit runs away.
   (c) Colin brings home a fox cub.
   (d) The farmers organize a hunt for Bandit.
   (e) The narrator discovers Bandit's hiding place.
2. What words signal the beginning of the flashback?
3. What information does the flashback give?

VOCABULARY
Dictionary and Glossary

Most dictionaries give the etymology (et′ə mol′ə jē), of a word at the end of its definition, in a form like this:

invalid . . . [<French *invalide* < Latin *invalidus* < *in-* not + *validus* strong]

The bracketed information tells you that (1) *invalid* came from the French word *invalide;* (2) *invalide* came from the Latin word *invalidus;* and (3) *invalidus* was formed from the prefix *in-,* meaning "not," plus *validus,* meaning "strong."

Use the etymologies in your Glossary to answer the following questions.
1. Did the word *harry* come into English from French, Old English, or Latin?
2. What is the meaning of the Middle English word that *wily* is derived from?
3. Did *confound* come into English from Latin or Old French?
4. What did *pertain* mean in its Latin form *pertinere?*
5. What is the original word that *sanction* is derived from? What is the meaning of the original word?

COMPOSITION
Writing a Report

Do you agree with this statement the narrator makes about Bandit: "He really loved us back, with a fierce, secret love no tame thing ever gave"? Do wild animals love more fiercely than tame ones? Write a short report of three to four paragraphs. To gather information, you might consult a librarian for sources or write to a zoo keeper.

BIOGRAPHY

Paul Annixter
1894–

This short story is one of about five hundred that Howard Allison Sturtzel has published under the pseudonym Paul Annixter. Regarding the rural fox hunt, he says, "The most important rule and the one I referred to in the story is that only the dogs may do the killing. The fox hunters carry no weapons. . . . Having the fox killed at all is regrettable to most hunt clubs. The same fox is run time after time, season after season, and it is the chase, not the kill, that is important."

THINKING CRITICALLY
ABOUT LITERATURE

UNIT 5   SHORT STORY 2

■ CONCEPT REVIEW

The science-fiction story that follows contains many of the literary elements you have studied with the stories in this unit. It also includes notes and questions designed to help you think critically about your reading. Page numbers in the notes refer to an application. An extensive discussion of these terms is in the Handbook of Literary Terms.

Key Item

Isaac Asimov

Jack Weaver came out of the vitals of Multivac looking utterly worn and disgusted.

From the stool, where the other maintained his own stolid watch, Todd Nemerson said, "Nothing?"

"Nothing," said Weaver. "Nothing, nothing, nothing. No one can find anything wrong with it."

"Except that it won't work, you mean."

"You're no help sitting there!"

"I'm thinking."

"Thinking!"

Nemerson stirred impatiently on his stool. "Why not? There are six teams of computer technologists roaming around in the corridors of

■ As you read, think about what elements make this a fantasy.

■ **Inference** (page 390): You can infer that Multivac is a computer.

"Key Item" from *Buy Jupiter* by Isaac Asimov. Copyright © 1968 by Mercury Press. Reprinted by permission of Doubleday Publishing Group.

Multivac. They haven't come up with anything in three days. Can't you spare one person to think?"

"It's not a matter of thinking. We've got to look. Somewhere a relay is stuck."

"It's not that simple, Jack!"

"Who says it's simple? You know how many million relays we have there?"

"That doesn't matter. If it were just a relay, Multivac would have alternate circuits, devices for locating the flaw, and facilities to repair or replace the ailing part. The trouble is, Multivac won't only not answer the original question, it won't tell us what's wrong with it. —And meanwhile, there'll be panic in every city if we don't do something. The world's economy depends on Multivac, and everyone knows that."

"I know it, too. But what's there to do?"

"I told you, *think*. There must be something we're missing completely. Look, Jack, there isn't a computer bigwig in a hundred years who hasn't devoted himself to making Multivac more complicated. It can do so much now—it can even talk and listen. It's practically as complex as the human brain. We can't understand the human brain, so why should we understand Multivac?"

"Aw, come on. Next you'll be saying Multivac is human."

"Why not?" Nemerson grew absorbed and seemed to sink into himself. "Now that you mention it, why not? Could we tell if Multivac passed the thin dividing line where it stopped being a machine and started being human? *Is* there a dividing line, for that matter? If the brain is just more complex than Multivac, and we keep making Multivac more complex, isn't there a point where . . ." He mumbled down into silence.

Weaver said impatiently, "What are you driving at? Suppose Multivac were human. How would that help us find out why it isn't working?"

"For a human reason, maybe. Suppose *you* were asked the most probable price of wheat next summer and didn't answer. Why wouldn't you answer?"

"Because I wouldn't know. But Multivac would know! We've given it all the factors. It can analyze futures in weather, politics, and economics. We know it can. It's done it before."

- Note the external conflict between Multivac and the scientists.

- **Stereotype** (page 384): Note the elements of stereotype in the description of Multivac.

- Note that the plot is developed through dialogue.

- **Figurative language** (page 355): Multivac is compared to the human brain.

- Note that Nemerson compares Multivac to human beings.

- **futures:** commodities and stocks bought or sold to be delivered at a future date

"All right. Suppose I asked the question and you knew the answer but didn't tell me. Why not?"

Weaver snarled. "Because I had a brain tumor. Because I had been knocked out. In other words, because my machinery was out of order. That's just what we're trying to find out about Multivac. We're looking for the place where its machinery is out of order, for the key item."

"Only you haven't found it." Nemerson got off his stool. "Listen, ask me the question Multivac stalled on."

"How? Shall I run the tape through you?"

"Come on, Jack. Give me the talk that goes along with it. You do talk to Multivac, don't you?"

"I've got to. Therapy."

Nemerson nodded. "Yes, that's the story. Therapy. That's the official story. We talk to it in order to pretend it's a human being so that we don't get neurotic over having a machine know so much more than we do. We turn a frightening metal monster into a protective father image."

"If you want to put it that way."

"Well, it's wrong and you know it. A computer as complex as Multivac *must* talk and listen to be efficient. Just putting in and taking out coded dots isn't sufficient. At a certain level of complexity, Multivac must be made to seem human because—it *is* human. Come on, Jack, ask me the question. I want to see my reaction to it."

Jack Weaver flushed. "This is silly."

"Come on, will you?"

It was a measure of Weaver's depression and desperation that he acceded. Half sullenly, he pretended to be feeding the program into Multivac, speaking as he did so in his usual manner. He commented on the latest information concerning farm unrest, talked about the new equations describing jet-stream contortions, lectured on the solar constant.

He began stiffly enough, but warmed to this task out of long habit, and when the last of the program was slammed home, he almost closed contact with a physical snap at Todd.

He ended briskly, "All right, now. Work that out and give us the answer pronto."

For a moment, having done, Jack Weaver stood there, nostrils flar-

■ **Figurative language:** Note the metaphor, or implied comparison.

■ Note the repeat of the words in the title of the story.

■ **therapy:** informal for *psychotherapy*, the treatment of mental disorders or diseases

■ **Figurative language:** Note the comparison.

■ **solar constant:** the unchanging nature of the sun

■ **slammed; physical snap:** words that appeal to the sense of sound

■ **Stereotype:** Weaver is a cold, calculating scientist.

ing, as though he was feeling once more the excitement of throwing into action the most gigantic and glorious machine ever put together by the mind and hands of man.

Then he remembered and muttered, "All right. That's it."

Nemerson said, "At least I know now why *I* wouldn't answer, so let's try that on Multivac. Look, clear Multivac; make sure the investigators have their paws off it. Then run the program into it and let me do the talking. Just once."

Weaver shrugged and turned to Multivac's control wall, filled with its somber, unwinking dials and lights. Slowly he cleared it. One by one he ordered the teams away.

Then, with a deep breath, he began once more feeding the program into Multivac. It was the twelfth time all told, the dozenth time. Somewhere a distant news commentator would spread the word that they were trying again. All over the world a Multivac-dependent people would be holding its collective breath.

Nemerson talked as Weaver fed the data silently. He talked diffidently, trying to remember what it was that Weaver had said, but waiting for the moment when the key item might be added.

Weaver was done and now a note of tension was in Nemerson's voice. He said, "All right, now, Multivac. Work that out and give us the answer."

He paused and added the key item. He said *"Please!"* And all over Multivac, the valves and relays went joyously to work.

■ **Inference**: Note the inference Nemerson makes about Multivac.

■ **Figurative language:** Note the implied comparison.

■ **Irony** (page 336): Notice the irony in the conclusion of the story.

■ **Symbol** (page 373): Note the symbolism in the word *please*.

THINK AND DISCUSS
Understanding
1. What has happened to Multivac at the beginning of the story?
2. How important is Multivac to the world?
3. What do the teams of computer technologists think the problem is?
4. Why doesn't Nemerson agree with the teams' analysis of the problem?

Analyzing
5. What is the key item, the solution to Multivac's problem?

6. What elements of fantasy do you find in "Key Item"?
7. What do you think is the author's purpose—to entertain, to inform, or to persuade? Explain.

Extending
8. How does Multivac differ from computers as we know them today?

REVIEWING LITERARY TERMS
Irony
1. What is the irony in this story?

Figurative Language
2. To what does Weaver compare the

human condition of having a brain tumor?

3. Nemerson talks about the investigators' "paws." Why is this figurative language effective?

Symbol

4. What might be a symbol to Multivac? Consider the "key item," the solution to Multivac's problem.

Stereotype

5. In what way could Multivac be considered a stereotype?

Inference

6. What is the inference that Nemerson makes about Multivac?

■ CONTENT REVIEW

THINKING SKILLS

Classifying

1. Classify each story in this unit as "Fantasy" or "Realistic Fiction." Review "Reading Fantasy," page 364 if necessary.

Generalizing

2. Consider the stories "Adolf," "The Hummingbird That Lived Through Winter," and "Last Cover." What general statement or statements can you make that apply to all three stories?

Synthesizing

3. Hugh in "The Hundredth Dove" has the motto *Servo*. Choose at least four other characters in stories in this unit and create a motto for each. Explain why each motto is appropriate for the character.

Evaluating

4. Consider the stories in this unit. Which one would make the best play? Which one would make the best movie? Name movie, television, or stage performers that you would cast in the major roles.

■ COMPOSITION REVIEW

Supporting Your Choice

Insights are bits of wisdom or understanding. Which story in this unit do you think offers the best example of a character who gains an insight? Write a paragraph in which you identify your choice and explain why you feel the way you do.

Comparing and Contrasting Characters

Select two of the four fathers portrayed in "President Cleveland, Where Are You?," "Adolf," "The Day the Sun Came Out," and "Last Cover." Write two to four paragraphs contrasting and comparing the two fathers. Decide in what ways the two characters are alike and in what ways they are different. Review the two selections for details of characterization that illustrate these likenesses and differences. Use specific examples to support your statements.

Reviewing Writer's Craft: Use Words That Appeal to the Senses

In this unit you have seen how writers use words that appeal to the senses of sight, hearing, taste, smell, and touch. Now **try your hand** at creating images by using words that appeal to the senses. Write a paragraph describing the setting of any one of the following stories: "A Haircut," "Adolf," "The Gift," "The Storyteller," or "The Day the Sun Came Out." After you have chosen a story, review it, make notes about the time and place, and consult your **reading/writing log.**

OLK LITERATURE

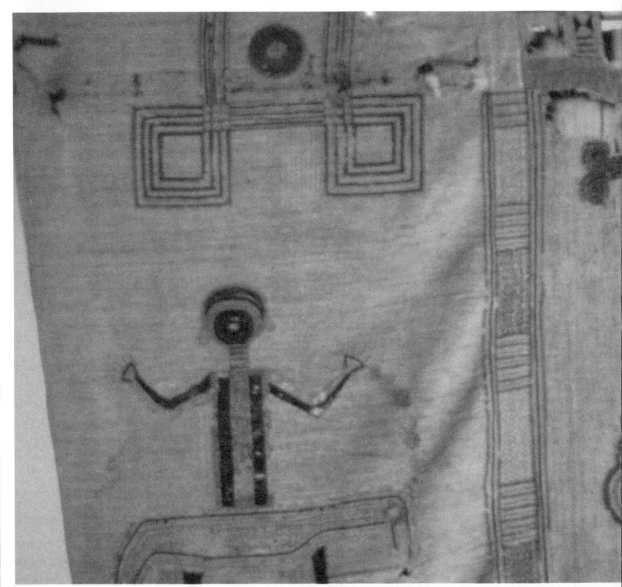

Man's Gown (detail), artist unknown, Collection of the Museum of the Philadelphia Civic Center, Philadelphia

PREVIEW

UNIT 6   FOLK LITERATURE

The Storytelling Stone / *from* North America
How the Lame Boy Brought Fire from Heaven / *from* Africa
How Raven Helped the Ancient People / *from* North America
Why the Sun and the Moon Live in the Sky / *from* Africa
How the Animals Got Their Color / *from* Africa
How the Animals Got Their Tails / *from* Africa
Why There Are Cracks in Tortoise's Shell / *from* Africa
The Fox and the Fish / *from* China
The Crow and the Pitcher / an Aesop fable
The North Wind and the Sun / an Aesop fable
A Tug-of-War / *from* Africa
The Two Strangers / *from* Africa
The Leftover Eye / *from* Africa
A Gift for a Gift / *from* Saxony
The Flying Ship / *from* Russia
Why the Stork Has No Tail / *from* Romania

Features
Reading Folk Literature
Comment: The Art of Ancient Cultures
The Writer's Craft: Write Good Endings

Review of Literary Terms
inference   stereotype

Reading Literature Skillfully
sequence   judgments
summarizing

Vocabulary Skills
context
dictionary and glossary

Thinking Skills
generalizing
classifying
evaluating

Composition Assignments Include
Describing the Beginnings of Writing
Comparing Myths
Writing an Animal Tale
Writing Dialogue
Creating Your Own Fable
Writing a Summary

Enrichment
Drawing a Mural
Participating in a Discussion
Retelling a Story

Thinking Critically About Literature
Concept Review
Content Review
Composition Review

The Storytelling Stone

from **North America**

"What does it mean to tell stories?" the orphan asked the stone. And
the stone answered, "It is telling what happened a long time ago."
What does the orphan learn from the stone?

In a Seneca[1] village lived a boy
whose father and mother died
when he was only a few weeks
old. The little boy was cared for
by a woman who had known his parents. She
gave him the name of *Poyeshao*.[2]

The boy grew to be a healthy, active little
fellow. When he was old enough, his foster
mother gave him a bow and arrows, and said,
"It is time for you to learn to hunt. Tomorrow morning, go to the woods and kill all the
birds you can find."

Taking cobs of dry corn, the woman
shelled off the kernels and parched them in
hot ashes; and the next morning she gave the
boy some of the corn for his breakfast and
rolled up some in a piece of buckskin and
told him to take it with him, for he would be
gone all day and would get hungry.

Poyeshao started off and was very successful. At noon he sat down and rested and ate
some of the parched corn; then he hunted till
the middle of the afternoon. When he began
to work toward home, he had a good string of
birds.

The next morning *Poyeshao*'s foster
mother gave him parched corn for breakfast
and, while he was eating, she told him that he
must do his best when hunting, for if he became a good hunter, he would always be
prosperous.

The boy took his bow and arrows and little
bundle of parched corn and went to the
woods; again he found plenty of birds. At
midday he ate his corn and thought over what
his foster mother had told him. In his mind
he said, "I'll do just as my mother tells me;
then sometime I'll be able to hunt big game."

Poyeshao hunted till toward evening, then
went home with a larger string of birds than
he had the previous day. His foster mother
thanked him, and said, "Now you have
begun to help me get food."

Early the next morning the boy's breakfast
was ready and as soon as he had eaten it, he
took his little bundle of parched corn and

---

1. *Seneca* (sen'ə kə), one of a tribe of Iroquoian Indians
of western New York.
2. *Poyeshao* (poi'ə shôn), orphan.

"The Storytelling Stone" from *Seneca Indian Myths* by Jeremiah
Curtin. Copyright 1923 by E. P. Dutton & Co., Inc.; renewal 1951
by Jeremiah Curtin Cardell. Reprinted by permission of Dr. Robert
A. Norton.

started off. He went farther into the woods and at night came home with a larger string of birds than he had the second day. His foster mother praised and thanked him.

Each day the boy brought home more birds than the previous day. On the ninth day he killed so many that he brought them home on his back. His foster mother tied the birds in little bundles of three or four and distributed them among her neighbors.

The tenth day the boy started off, as usual, and, as each day he had gone farther for game than on the preceding day, so now he went deeper into the woods than ever. About midday the sinew that held the feathers to his arrow loosened. Looking around for a place where he could sit down while he took the sinew off and wound it on again, he saw a small opening and near the center of the opening a high, smooth, flat-topped, round stone. He went to the stone, sprang up onto it, and sat down. He unwound the sinew and put it in his mouth to soften; then he arranged the arrow feathers and was about to fasten them to the arrow when a voice, right there near him, asked, "Shall I tell you stories?"

Poyeshao[n] looked up expecting to see a man. Not seeing anyone he looked behind the stone and around it; then he again began to tie the feathers to his arrow.

"Shall I tell you stories?" asked a voice right there by him.

The boy looked in every direction, but saw no one. Then he made up his mind to watch and find out who was trying to fool him. He stopped work and listened and when the voice again asked, "Shall I tell you stories?"

he found that it came from the stone; then he asked, "What is that? What does it mean to tell stories?"

"It is telling what happened a long time ago. If you will give me your birds, I'll tell you stories."

"You may have the birds."

As soon as the boy promised to give the birds, the stone began telling what happened long ago. When one story was told, another was begun. The boy sat, with his head down, and listened. Toward night the stone said, "We will rest now. Come again tomorrow. If anyone asks about your birds, say that you have killed so many that they are getting scarce and you have to go a long way to find one."

While going home the boy killed five or six birds. When his foster mother asked why he had so few birds, he said that they were scarce; that he had to go far for them.

The next morning *Poyeshao*[n] started off with his bow and arrows and little bundle of parched corn, but he forgot to hunt for birds; he was thinking of the stories the stone had told him. When a bird lighted near him he shot it, but he kept straight on toward the opening in the woods. When he got there he put his birds on the stone, and called out, "I've come! Here are birds. Now tell me stories."

The stone told story after story. Toward night it said, "Now we must rest till tomorrow." On the way home the boy looked for birds, but it was late and he found only a few.

That night the foster mother told her neighbors that when *Poyeshao*[n] first began to hunt he had brought home a great many

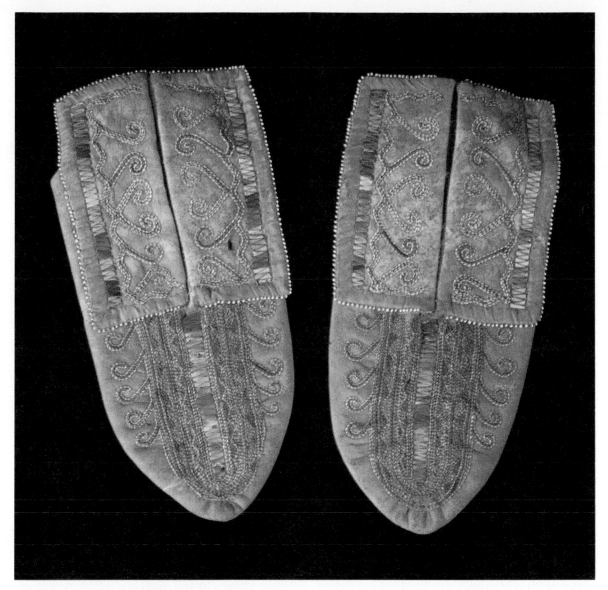

Sioux Moccasins, National Museum of Man, Ottawa

birds, but now he brought only four or five after being in the woods from morning till night. She said there was something strange about it; either he threw the birds away or gave them to some animal, or maybe he idled time away, didn't hunt. She hired a boy to follow *Poyeshao*[n] and find out what he was doing.

The next morning the boy took his bow and arrows and followed *Poyeshao*[n], keeping out of his sight and sometimes shooting a bird. *Poyeshao[n]* killed a good many birds; then, about the middle of the forenoon, he suddenly started off toward the east, running as fast as he could. The boy followed till he came to an opening in the woods and saw *Poyeshao[n]* climb up and sit down on a large round stone; he crept nearer and heard talking. When he couldn't see the person to whom *Poyeshao[n]* was talking, he went up to the boy and asked, "What are you doing here?"

"Hearing stories."

"What are stories?"

"Telling about things that happened long ago. Put your birds on this stone and say, 'I've come to hear stories.'"

The boy did as told and straightway the stone began. The boys listened till the sun went down; then the stone said, "We will rest now. Come again tomorrow."

On the way home *Poyeshao[n]* killed three or four birds.

When the woman asked the boy she had sent why *Poyeshao[n]* killed so few birds, he said, "I followed him for a while, then I spoke to him, and after that we hunted together till it was time to come home. We couldn't find many birds."

The next morning the elder boy said, "I'm going with *Poyeshao[n]* to hunt; it's sport." The two started off together. By the middle of the forenoon each boy had a long string of birds. They hurried to the opening, put the birds on the stone, and said, "We have come. Here are the birds! Tell us stories."

They sat on the stone and listened to stories till late in the afternoon; then the stone said, "We'll rest now till tomorrow."

On the way home the boys shot every bird they could find, but it was late and they didn't find many.

Several days went by in this way; then the foster mother said, "Those boys kill more birds than they bring home," and she hired two men to follow them.

The next morning, when *Poyeshao[n]* and his friend started for the woods, the two men followed. When the boys had a large number of birds, they stopped hunting and hurried to the opening. The men followed and, hiding behind trees, saw them put the birds on a large round stone, then jump up and sit there, with their heads down, listening to a man's voice; every little while they said, "Um!"

"Let's go there and find out who is talking to those boys," said one man to the other. They walked quickly to the stone and asked, "What are you doing, boys?"

The boys were startled, but *Poyeshao[n]* said, "You must promise not to tell anyone."

They promised; then *Poyeshao[n]* said, "Jump up and sit on the stone."

The men seated themselves on the stone; then the boy said, "Go on with the story; we are listening."

The four sat with their heads down and the stone began to tell stories. When it was almost night, the stone said, "Tomorrow all the people in your village must come and listen to my stories. Tell the chief to send every man, and have each man bring something to eat. You must clean the brush away so the people can sit on the ground near me."

That night *Poyeshao[n]* told the chief about

the storytelling stone, and gave him the stone's message. The chief sent a runner to give the message to each family in the village.

Early the next morning everyone in the village was ready to start. *Poyeshao*ⁿ went ahead and the crowd followed. When they came to the opening, each man put what he had brought, meat or bread, on the stone; the brush was cleared away, and everyone sat down. When all was quiet, the stone said, "Now I will tell you stories of what happened long ago. There was a world before this. The things that I am going to tell about happened in that world. Some of you will remember every word that I say, some will remember a part of the words, and some will forget them all—I think this will be the way, but each man must do the best he can. Hereafter you must tell these stories to one another—now listen."

Each man bent his head and listened to every word the stone said. Once in a while the boys said, "Um!" When the sun was almost down, the stone said, "We'll rest now. Come tomorrow and bring meat and bread."

The next morning, when the people gathered around the stone, they found that the meat and bread they had left there the day before was gone. They put the food they had brought on the stone, then sat in a circle, and waited. When all was quiet the stone began. Again it told stories till the sun was almost down; then it said, "Come tomorrow. Tomorrow I will finish the stories of what happened long ago."

Early in the morning the people of the village gathered around the stone, and, when all was quiet, the stone began to tell stories, and

it told till late in the afternoon; then it said, "I have finished! You must keep these stories as long as the world lasts; tell them to your children and grandchildren generation after generation. One person will remember them better than another. When you go to a man or a woman to ask for one of these stories, carry something to pay for it, bread or meat, or whatever you have. I know all that happened in the world before this; I have told it to you. When you visit one another, you must tell these things, and keep them up always. I have finished."

And so it has been. From the stone came all the knowledge the Senecas have of the world before this.

THINK AND DISCUSS
Understanding
1. What happens on the first nine days *Poyeshao*ⁿ goes into the woods to hunt?
2. What is different about the tenth day?
3. How does the stone define a story?
4. What does the stone ask the people of the village to give in return for the stories?

Analyzing
5. What is the purpose in having the whole village come to hear the stories?
6. What character traits does *Poyeshao*ⁿ reveal?
7. Why is the repetition that occurs in

"The Storytelling Stone" necessary in a story that is told orally?

Extending

8. If you had acted as *Poyeshao^n* does, would your parents and neighbors have approved of your actions? Why or why not?

9. Is there value in society today in knowing how to tell a good story? Explain.

READING LITERATURE SKILLFULLY
Sequence

The word *sequence* means "the coming of one thing after another." You use sequence when you follow the steps in a process to build a model or the directions in a recipe to make a casserole. You also follow the sequence of events when you read in order to understand and remember a story. Certain words, such as *first*, *next*, and *finally*, give clues to sequence. In "The Storytelling Stone" you read clues such as "the next morning" and "at midday."

Put the following events in the time sequence in which they occur in the story.

1. *Poyeshao^n* finds the storytelling stone.
2. The foster mother sends a boy to follow *Poyeshao^n*.
3. The foster mother sends *Poyeshao^n* into the woods to hunt.
4. The village comes to the storytelling stone.
5. The foster mother sends two men to follow *Poyeshao^n* and the boy.

THINKING SKILLS
Generalizing

To generalize is to draw a general conclusion from particular information.

The following items are mentioned in "The Storytelling Stone." What can you generalize about the Senecas from each of the things?

1. parched corn
2. bow and arrows
3. buckskin
4. sinew

COMPOSITION
Writing About Storytelling

Why might the Senecas have felt the storyteller should be honored? Write a paragraph in which you explain why the Senecas came to value storytelling. Before you begin, review what the stone tells the people of *Poyeshao^n*'s village, but when you write your paragraph, explain the importance of the stories in your own words. For help in writing, refer to Lesson 1, "Writing About Literature," in the Writer's Handbook.

Describing the Beginnings of Writing

Imagine that *Poyeshao^n*, as an old man, returns to the stone and that this time the stone reveals the art of writing. Write an account of not more than a page or two about what information the stone might give *Poyeshao^n*. Tell what might have been used as a writing implement and as writing material. What alphabet, or characters that represent the sounds of the language, might have been used? Before you begin, you may want to do research by looking up the development of writing under *Alphabet* in an encyclopedia, or you may be as creative as you want in developing your own account of the beginnings of writing.

Reading FOLK LITERATURE

For untold ages the art of storytelling flourished among people of all races. Throughout the ancient world a rich oral tradition existed prior to the adoption of writing. The stories were not the invention of any one person, but of the collective imagination of a tribe or a nation. They did not spring into being, but developed over hundreds of years, and they changed with time and circumstance and the whims of storytellers. The sum total of these stories that a particular group created for itself is called that people's **folk literature.**

Myths, or stories about gods, spirits, and the origin of things, form an important part of every people's folk literature. This world with its earth, sky, sun, moon, and stars, its variety of living things, its human institutions and customs, has been puzzling to people always and everywhere. Myths provide answers to such questions as: How did the world come into being? How did the sun and moon get into the sky?

Folk tales, or stories and legends originating in and handed down by the common people, are part of folk literature. Many folk tales are about animals. Like myths, animal tales often explain how various animals acquired certain habits and physical traits. A **fable,** in which the characters are generally animals, has a lesson, or moral.

Tales from various countries portray the early cultures of those countries. Some peoples considered their stories holy, and their preservation a sacred duty. Recall that in the story you just read the storytelling stone tells the people, "You must keep these stories as long as the world lasts." Other peoples recognized their stories as fiction.

In folk literature, characters are not fully developed. Instead they are defined by their station in life, how they behave, and what they accomplish. Setting is often merely mentioned: a road, a forest, or the king's palace. Events are usually related in the correct time **sequence** in these simple tellings. There is often not a plot as modern readers expect, but rather a dramatic happening that makes an important point. Since the stories were told aloud, repetition helped the memory of both the teller and the hearer.

The stories in this unit are only a sampling from the vast number of tales told in different parts of the world. Of unknown age and authorship, they have been handed down by word of mouth through the generations. To remember these stories, and perhaps retell them yourself, **summarize** after you read—ask yourself who did what, when, where, and why.

What can you learn from folk literature? As you read, make **judgments** about the value of these stories for people today by comparing the customs, beliefs, and behaviors depicted with your experiences.

From an article by Susan Taubes, *Projection in Literature*, Scott, Foresman and Company, Copyright © 1967.

Answers to some universal questions are given in the three myths that follow. Why did these questions plague people the world over?

How the Lame Boy Brought Fire from Heaven

from Africa

In the beginning of the world, Obassi Osaw[1] made everything but he did not give fire to the people who were on Earth.

Etim'Ne[2] said to the Lame Boy: "What is the use of Obassi Osaw sending us here without any fire? Go therefore and ask him to give us some." So the Lame Boy set out.

Obassi Osaw was very angry when he got the message, and sent the boy back quickly to Earth to reprove Etim for what he had asked. In those days the Lame Boy had not become lame, but could walk like other people.

When Etim'Ne heard that he had angered Obassi Osaw, he set out himself for the latter's town and said: "Please forgive me for what I did yesterday. It was by accident." Obassi would not pardon him, though he stayed for three days begging forgiveness. Then he went home.

When Etim reached his town, the boy laughed at him. "Are you a chief," said he, "yet could get no fire? I myself will go and bring it to you. If they will give me none, I will steal it."

That very day the lad set out. He reached the house of Obassi Osaw at evening time and found the people preparing food. He helped with the work, and when Obassi began to eat, knelt down till the meal was ended.

The master saw that the boy was useful

---

1. **Obassi Osaw** (o bäs'sē ō'sô), the creator.
2. **Etim'Ne** (e'tim'ne), a tribal chief.

"How the Lame Boy Brought Fire from Heaven" from *In the Shadow of the Bush* by P. A. Talbot. Copyright 1912.

and did not drive him out of the house. After he had served for several days, Obassi called to him and said: "Go to the house of my wives and ask them to send me a lamp."

The boy gladly did as he was bidden, for it was in the house of the wives that fire was kept. He touched nothing, but waited until the lamp was given him, then brought it back with all speed. Once, after he had stayed for many days among the servants, Obassi sent him again, and this time one of the wives said: "You can light the lamp at the fire." She went into her house and left him alone.

The boy took a brand and lighted the lamp; then he wrapped the brand in plantain leaves and tied it up in his cloth, carried the lamp to his master, and said: "I wish to go out for a certain purpose." Obassi answered: "You can go."

The boy went to the bush outside the town where some dry wood was lying. He laid the brand amongst the dry wood, and blew till it caught alight. Then he covered it with plantain stems and leaves to hide the smoke, and went back to the house. Obassi asked: "Why have you been so long?" And the lad answered: "I did not feel well."

That night when all the people were sleeping, the thief tied his clothes together and crept to the end of town where the fire was hidden. He found it burning and took a glowing brand and some firewood and set out homeward.

When Earth was reached once more, the lad went to Etim and said: "Here is the fire which I promised to bring you. Send for some wood, and I will show you what we must do."

So the first fire was made on Earth. Obassi

William Artis, *Head of a Boy*, 1940
Department of Art, Fisk University

Osaw looked down from his house in the sky and saw the smoke rising. He said to his eldest son Akpan Obassi: "Go, ask the boy if it is he who has stolen the fire."

Akpan came down to Earth and asked as his father had bidden him. The lad confessed: "I was the one who stole the fire. The reason why I hid it was because I feared."

Akpan replied: "I bring you a message. Up till now you have been able to walk. From today you will not be able to do so anymore."

That is the reason why the Lame Boy cannot walk. He it was who first brought fire to Earth from Obassi's home in the sky.

How Raven Helped the Ancient People

from **North America**

ong ago, near the beginning of the world, Gray Eagle was the guardian of the sun and moon and stars, of fresh water, and of fire. Gray Eagle hated people so much that he kept these things hidden. People lived in darkness, without fire and without fresh water.

Gray Eagle had a beautiful daughter, and Raven fell in love with her. At that time Raven was a handsome young man. He changed himself into a snow-white bird, and as a snow-white bird he pleased Gray Eagle's daughter. She invited him to her father's lodge.

When Raven saw the sun and the moon and the stars and fresh water hanging on the sides of Eagle's lodge, he knew what he should do. He watched for his chance to seize them when no one was looking. He stole all of them, and a brand of fire also, and flew out of the lodge through the smoke hole.

As soon as Raven got outside, he hung the sun up in the sky. It made so much light that he was able to fly far out to an island in the middle of the ocean. When the sun set, he fastened the moon up in the sky and hung the stars around in different places. By this new light he kept on flying, carrying with him the fresh water and the brand of fire he had stolen.

He flew back over the land. When he had reached the right place, he dropped all the water he had stolen. It fell to the ground and there became the source of all the fresh-water streams and lakes in the world. Then Raven flew on, holding the brand of fire in his bill. The smoke from the fire blew back over his white feathers and made them black. When his bill began to burn he had to drop the firebrand. It struck rocks and went into the rocks. That is why, if you strike two stones together, fire will drop out.

Raven's feathers never became white again after they were blackened by the smoke from the firebrand. That is why Raven is now a black bird.

Why the Sun and the Moon Live in the Sky

from **Africa**

Many years ago the sun and the water were great friends, and both lived on the earth together. The sun very often used to visit the water, but the water never returned his visits. At last the sun asked the water why it was that he never came to see him in his house. The water replied that the sun's house was not big enough, and that if he came with his people, he would drive the sun out.

The water then said, "If you wish me to visit you, you must build a very large compound; but I warn you that it will have to be a tremendous place, as my people are very numerous and take up a lot of room."

The sun promised to build a very big compound, and soon afterward he returned home to his wife, the moon, who greeted him with a broad smile when he opened the door. The sun told the moon what he had promised the water, and the next day he commenced building a huge compound in which to entertain his friend.

When it was completed, he asked the water to come and visit him.

When the water arrived, he called out to the sun and asked him whether it would be safe for him to enter, and the sun answered, "Yes, come in, my friend."

The water then began to flow in, accompanied by the fish and all the water animals.

Gordon Parks photograph

Very soon the water was knee-deep, so he asked the sun if it was still safe, and the sun again said, "Yes," so more water came in.

When the water was level with the top of a man's head, the water said to the sun, "Do you want more of my people to come?"

The sun and the moon both answered, "Yes," not knowing any better, so the water flowed in, until the sun and moon had to perch themselves on the top of the roof.

Again the water addressed the sun, but, receiving the same answer, and more of his people rushing in, the water very soon overflowed the top of the roof, and the sun and the moon were forced to go up into the sky, where they have remained ever since.

THINK AND DISCUSS

Understanding

1. Consider "How the Lame Boy Brought Fire from Heaven" and "How Raven Helped the Ancient People." What origin is explained differently in the two myths?
2. What is the punishment received by (a) the boy in the first myth and (b) the snow-white bird in the second myth?
3. What is the relationship between the sun and the moon in "Why the Sun and the Moon Live in the Sky"?
4. What origin does the myth about the sun and the moon explain?

Analyzing

5. Compare the motives of the Lame Boy and Raven for stealing fire.
6. What question does the water repeat four times in the myth about the sun and the moon? What is the purpose of the repetition?
7. Compare the **tone** in the first two myths with the tone in the third one. Which do you find serious? Which do you find humorous?

Extending

8. Do you think the people who heard these stories considered the Lame Boy and Raven thieves or heroes? Why? If they were heroes, why were they punished?
9. In the mythologies of many peoples, the essentials of life are stolen from a being who does not want to share them with people. Why do you think many ancient peoples imagined these essentials had to be stolen?

REVIEWING: Inference HT
See Handbook of Literary Terms, p. 642.

An **inference** is a reasonable conclusion drawn by the reader from hints, or implications, provided by the author. You can infer that Raven is willing to sacrifice his human form for the love of Gray Eagle's daughter when he becomes a snow-white bird.

1. What can you infer about the future relationship between Gray Eagle's daughter and Raven?
2. From the questions asked and answered in myths, what inferences can you make about the people who told them?

COMPOSITION
Comparing Myths

You have read two myths about the origin of fire, but there are many myths from different lands on the same subject. Probably the best known is the Greek myth about Prometheus.

According to one version, Prometheus stole fire from Mount Olympus, the home of the Greek gods, and brought it back to Earth in a hollow reed. As a punishment, Zeus, the chief god, had Prometheus chained to a rock on a mountain. Here an eagle preyed on Prometheus's liver all day. At night, the liver was miraculously renewed. Finally Prometheus was freed by Hercules, a son of Zeus known for his strength. Prometheus had to wear a ring containing a piece of the rock to which he had been chained, showing he had been a prisoner, and a willow wreath, a symbol that he had been freed.

Write two paragraphs. In the first compare the Lame Boy with Prometheus. In the second, compare Raven and Prometheus. In each comparison consider the situation, how the fire was stolen, and what the consequences were. For help in writing, refer to Lesson 4, "Writing to Compare and Contrast," in the Writer's Handbook.

ENRICHMENT
Drawing a Mural

With a group of classmates, draw or paint a mural to show the story of one of the myths you have read. Show one event or a series of them from the myth. Your group might want to read other myths, which are easily found in mythology collections in a library, and choose one of these to illustrate instead.

The Art of Ancient Cultures

Never in ancient cultures was art simply a source of pleasure. Art objects were necessary forms made for the religious, social, and economic needs of the community. Every figure, mask, and ceremonial object had its own particular function. Every design had a purpose. Even the materials the artist used were chosen for the blessings they were thought to contain.

The North American Indians believed that the spirit lived on after the body had perished. In most Indian traditions, the spirit went to the land of the dead—but only if the person had lived a moral life. The Indians buried objects with a body, among them pottery vessels, stone pipes, and small figures. These not only assured the dead person a place in the land of the dead, but they also showed the tribe's respect and were protection against the return of the spirit to harm the living.

All over the world, masks were used to draw the spirits of ancestors into communication with a tribe and to repel the threats of demons. There were masks for every purpose—to collect debts, end wars, settle quarrels, bring rain, and cure illness. Masks were respected and feared, and those with the most solemn functions were offered sacrifices.

Some art objects served practical purposes. Pottery, for example, was important as a cooking utensil.

Artists in widely separated countries used the same materials—wood, clay, stone, vegetable and mineral pigments. Geometric forms based on the circle and square are found in the art of all tribal peoples. The whirls made by the wind, the zig-zag course of lightning, the waves on water are basic to nature all over the world. These designs, adapted from natural surroundings, are common to the art of all ancient peoples.

The work of early artists is neither polished nor refined, but it is vigorous and strong and has about it a simplicity that has greatly influenced the art of the world.

Write Good Endings

A good ending for a story makes things clear to you. If there is a conflict, it should be resolved. If the characters have a goal, you should know if it is achieved or not. The ending can be happy, sad, or surprising, but it should tell you the outcome of whatever happens early in the story.

For example, in "The Storytelling Stone," *Poyeshao*[n] returns each day to hear more. As a result of his actions, by the end of the story, everyone in his village learns about the Senecas' heritage.

> Early in the morning the people of the village gathered around the stone, and, when all was quiet, the stone began to tell stories, and it told till late in the afternoon; then it said, "I have finished! You must keep these stories as long as the world lasts; tell them to your children and grandchildren generation after generation." (page 413, column 1)

The end of a myth is especially important because it generally tells how the world was changed. In the following passage from "How Raven Helped the Ancient People," notice the clever way in which the end of the story explains why the raven changed from a white bird into a black one. Notice how the simple language and conversational tone make this explanation easy to see and understand.

> Then Raven flew on, holding the brand of fire in his bill. The smoke from the fire blew back over his white feathers and made them black. . . . Raven's feathers never became white again after they were blackened by the smoke from the firebrand. That is why Raven is now a black bird. (page 418, column 2)

As you can see, the myth explains why ravens are black today.

Similarly, in "Why the Sun and the Moon Live in the Sky," the ending provides a humorous reason for the sun and moon being in the sky. The sun and moon have invited their friend, the water, to visit them. As the water continues to rise, however, the sun and moon are forced to move to a higher and higher location.

> Again the water addressed the sun, but, receiving the same answer, and more of his people rushing in, the water very soon overflowed the top of the roof, and the sun and the moon were forced to go up into the sky, where they have remained ever since. (page 419, column 2)

As you continue reading, pay special attention to the way each story ends. Consider how the outcome always brings everything to a clear conclusion. Try to write good endings for your own stories.

When you read, notice a good ending. When you write, choose a good ending.

How the Animals Got Their Color

from **Africa**

he color of all the animals is said to have been painted on by the meercat.[1] The meercat said to the animals, "If anyone will kill a buck and bring me the meat, I will paint color on him."

The hyena heard him, so he went and killed a buck; he ate all the meat himself and took the bones to the meercat.

The meercat said, "Lie down." The hyena knelt down and the meercat painted ugly marks on him, saying, "If anyone cheats me, I do the same to him."

The leopard went out hunting and killed a buck and brought it to the meercat unskinned. The meercat told him to kneel down and painted him a beautiful color, saying, "If anyone keeps his word with me, I will do the same to him."

The story is finished.

How the Animals Got Their Tails

from **Africa**

t is said that animals were created without tails by their maker. The maker one day called them to come and select what tails would suit them. The first group of animals appeared and selected the long and best tails. The second group came and received good tails. The last group were the hares, who are very lazy, and they told the other animals to pick out tails for them. The other animals, having taken the best tails for themselves, brought the short and ugly tails for the hares. If you want a thing well done, do it yourself.

The story is finished.

---

1. *meercat,* a burrowing, flesh-eating mammal.

"How the Animals Got Their Color" and "How the Animals Got Their Tails" from *The Bavenda* by H. A. Stayt. Reprinted by permission of International African Institute.

Why There Are Cracks in Tortoise's Shell

from **Africa**

Mr. Tortoise, who was married to Mrs. Tortoise, had in Vulture a friend who was constant in visiting him. But, having no wings, Tortoise was unable to return the visits, and this upset him. One day he bethought himself of his cunning and said to his wife, "Wife!"

Mrs. Tortoise answered, "Hello, husband! What is it?"

Said he, "Don't you see, wife, that we are becoming despicable in Vulture's eyes?"

"How despicable?"

"Despicable, because it is despicable for me not to visit Vulture. He is always coming here and I have never yet been to his house—and he is my friend."

Mrs. Tortoise replied, "I don't see how Vulture should think us despicable unless we could fly as he does and then did not pay him a visit."

But Mr. Tortoise persisted. "Nevertheless, wife, it is despicable."

Said his wife, "Very well, then, sprout some wings and fly and visit your friend Vulture."

Mr. Tortoise answered, "No, I shan't sprout any wings because I was not born that way."

"Well," said Mrs. Tortoise, "what will you do?"

"I shall find a way," he replied.

"Find it then," said Mrs. Tortoise, "and let us see what you will do."

Later Tortoise said to his wife, "Come and tie me up in a parcel with a lump of tobacco and, when Vulture arrives, give it to him and say it is tobacco to buy grain for us." So Mrs. Tortoise took some palm leaf and made him into a parcel and put him down in the corner.

At his usual time, Vulture came to pay his visit and said, "Where's your husband gone, Mrs. Tortoise?"

"My husband has gone some distance to visit some people, and he left hunger here. We have not a bit of grain in the house."

Vulture said, "You are in trouble indeed, not having any grain."

Mrs. Tortoise replied, "We are in such trouble as human beings never knew." And she went on: "Vulture, at your place is there no grain to be bought?"

"Yes," said he, "any amount, Mrs. Tortoise."

She brought the bundle and said, "My husband left this lump of tobacco thinking you would buy some grain with it for us and bring it here."

"Why There Are Cracks in Tortoise's Shell" from *The Ila-Speaking Peoples of Northern Rhodesia*, Vol. 2 by Edwin W. Smith and A. Murray Dale. Reprinted by permission of Macmillan Publishers Ltd.

Vulture willingly took it and returned to his home in the heights. As he was nearing his native town he was surprised to hear a voice saying, "Untie me, I am your friend Tortoise. I said I would pay a visit to you."

But Vulture, in his surprise, let go his hold of the bundle and down crashed Tortoise to the earth, *pididipididi*, his shell smashed to bits, and he died. And so the friendship between Tortoise and Vulture was broken; and you can still see the cracks in Tortoise's shell.

THINK AND DISCUSS
Understanding
1. What power does the meercat have in "How the Animals Got Their Color"?
2. What picture of the hares do you get from "How the Animals Got Their Tails"?
3. How does Mr. Tortoise plan to visit his friend Vulture?

Analyzing
4. These tales have underlying meanings. Match each with one of the following **themes.**
   (a) It is important to keep one's word.
   (b) Deceit, even for a good reason, works against the deceiver.
   (c) If you want a thing done well, do it yourself.
5. What social custom of Africa is shown in "Why There Are Cracks in Tortoise's Shell" and "Why the Sun and the Moon Live in the Sky"?

COMPOSITION
Reading/Writing Log
In the tales you have just read, the endings are important because they explain the underlying meanings of the tales. Consider this example from "How the Animals Got Their Color." If you are keeping a **reading/writing log,** add another example or two of your own.

> The meercat told him to kneel down and painted him a beautiful color, saying, "If anyone keeps his word with me, I will do the same to him."

Writing an Animal Tale
Think of some feature or marking that distinguishes a particular animal, such as the curly tail of a pig, the pink color of a flamingo, or the stripes of a zebra. Create a reason to explain how the animal got the feature or marking, and write a brief tale for others to read. Be sure to use a good ending, one that explains the meaning of the tale. Before you begin, refer to your **reading/writing log** of good endings.

Writing Dialogue
"How the Animals Got Their Color" and "Why There Are Cracks in Tortoise's Shell" include some words spoken by the animals, or dialogue. Rewrite "How the Animals Got Their Tails," changing into dialogue some of the actions. See Lesson 8, "Writing Dialogue," in the Writer's Handbook.

As you read, look for the lesson in each of the next three fables.

The Fox and the Fish

from China

fox saw a fish darting back and forth near the middle of a river. He asked, "Friend Fish, why don't you swim one way or the other?"

The fish replied, "If I go one way, I shall be swept over the waterfall and perish; if I swim the opposite way, a fisherman with a net hopes to catch me."

"Ah, my friend," said the cunning fox, "why not come ashore and avoid both dangers?"

"No, thank you," answered the fish. "My mother warned me that it is always safer to put up with known dangers than to face unknown ones."

Do not jump from the frying pan into the fire.

"The Fox and the Fish" from *Tales from Old China* by Isabelle Chang. Copyright © 1969 by Isabelle Chang. Reprinted by permission of Random House, Inc.

The Crow and the Pitcher

Aesop

thirsty Crow found a Pitcher with some water in it, but so little was there that, try as she might, she could not reach it with her beak, and it seemed as though she would die of thirst within sight of the remedy. At last she hit upon a clever plan. She began dropping pebbles into the Pitcher, and with each pebble the water rose a little higher until at last it reached the brim, and the knowing bird was enabled to quench her thirst.

Necessity is the mother of invention.

Aesop's Fables by Aesop.

The North Wind and the Sun

Aesop

A dispute arose between the North Wind and the Sun, each claiming that he was stronger than the other. At last they agreed to try their powers upon a traveler, to see which could soonest strip him of his cloak. The North Wind had the first try; and, gathering up all his force for the attack, he came whirling furiously down upon the man and caught up his cloak as though he would wrest it from him by one single effort. But the harder he blew, the more closely the man wrapped it round himself. Then came the turn of the Sun. At first he beamed gently upon the traveler, who soon unclasped his cloak and walked on with it hanging loosely about his shoulders. Then he shone forth in his full strength, and the man, before he had gone many steps, was glad to throw his cloak right off and complete his journey more lightly clad.

Persuasion is better than force.

Arthur Rackham

THINK AND DISCUSS
Understanding
1. In which fable are the main characters not animals?

2. What is the Crow's problem, and how does she solve it?

3. Which fable is about a contest, and what does the contest prove?

4. Why does the fox offer a friendly alternative to the fish's problem?

Analyzing

5. In the figure of speech called **personification,** human traits are given to nonhuman things. What human traits do the Sun and the North Wind have?

6. A fable is a brief story that teaches a lesson, or moral. The moral may be stated directly or it may be only implied. Match each of the following morals with one of the fables.

 (**a**) When you need something, you'll figure out how to get it.

 (**b**) It is safer to put up with known dangers than to face unknown ones.

 (**c**) Persuasion is better than force.

7. Find at least two examples of wit or cleverness in these fables.

Extending

8. Defend the following statement with examples from the fables: Aware of human faults, ancient people tried to correct them through stories.

THINKING SKILLS

Classifying

To classify things is to arrange them into categories or groups according to some system. Some of the characters in the tales in this unit use clever tactics to gain an advantage; other characters are outwitted. Decide which of the characters listed below show cleverness and which are outwitted.

1. the Crow
2. the North Wind
3. the Sun
4. the fish
5. the fox
6. the hyena
7. the leopard
8. the hares
9. Mr. Tortoise

COMPOSITION ◄━●

Creating Your Own Fable

Think of a lesson to teach through a story. Write a one-paragraph fable that illustrates that lesson. Before you begin, choose a character or characters from animals or objects, and decide on a situation for demonstrating the problem and its resolution. If you wish, write a one-line moral that states the underlying meaning of your fable. Be sure to include a good ending.

Three dilemma tales present problems for you to consider.

A Tug-of-War

from Africa

ortoise considered himself a great personage. He went about calling attention to his greatness. He said to people, "We three, Elephant, Hippopotamus, and I, are the greatest, and we are equal in power and authority."

Thus he boasted, and his boasts came to the ears of Elephant and Hippopotamus. They listened and then they laughed. "Pooh, that's nothing. He is a small person of no account, and his boasting can only be ignored."

The talebearer returned to Tortoise telling him what the two great ones had said. Tortoise grew very vexed indeed. "So, they despise me, do they? Well, I will just show them my power. I am equal to them, and they will know it before long! They will yet address me as Friend." And he set off.

He found Elephant in the forest, lying down; and his trunk was eight miles long, his ears as big as a house, and his four feet large beyond measure. Tortoise approached him and boldly called out, "Friend, I have come! Rise and greet me. Your Friend is here."

Elephant looked about astonished. Then spying Tortoise, he rose up and asked indignantly, "Tortoise, small person, whom do you address as Friend?"

"You. I call you Friend. And are you not, Elephant?"

"Most certainly I am not," replied the Elephant in anger. "Besides, you have been going about and saying certain things about your great power—that it is equal to mine. How do you come to talk in such a way?"

Tortoise then said, "Elephant, don't get angry. Listen to me. True, I addressed you as Friend and said we were equal. You think that because you are of such a great size, you can surpass me, just because I am small? Let us have a test. Tomorrow morning we will have a tug-of-war."

Said Elephant, "What is the use of that? I can mash you with one foot."

"Be patient. At least try the test." And when Elephant unwillingly consented, Tortoise added, "When we tug, if one pulls the other, he shall be considered greater, and if neither overpulls, then we are equal, and will call each other Friend."

Then Tortoise cut a very long vine and brought one end to Elephant. "This end is yours. I will go off with my end to a certain spot; and we will begin to tug, and neither of us will stop to eat or sleep until one pulls the other over or the vine breaks." And he went off with the other end of the vine and hid it on the outskirts of the town where Hippopotamus lived.

Hippopotamus was bathing in the river and Tortoise shouted to him, "Friend, I have come! You! Come ashore! I am visiting you!"

There was a great splashing as Hippopotamus came to shore, bellowing angrily, "You are going to get it now! Whom do you call Friend?"

"Why, you, of course. There is no one else here, is there?" answered Tortoise. "But do not be so quick to fight. I do not fear your size. I say we are equals, and if you doubt me, let us have a trial. Tomorrow morning we will have a tug-of-war. He who shall overcome the other, shall be the superior. But if neither is found superior, then we are equals and will call each other Friend." Hippopotamus thought the plan was absurd, but finally he consented.

Tortoise then brought his end of the vine to Hippopotamus and said, "This end is yours. And now I go. Tomorrow when you feel a pull on the vine, know that I am ready at the other end. Then you begin to tug, and we will not eat or sleep until the test is ended."

In the morning, Tortoise went to the middle of the vine and shook it. Elephant immediately grabbed his end, Hippopotamus caught up his end, and the tugging began. Each pulled at the vine mightily and it remained taut. At times it pulled in one direction, and then in the other, but neither was overpulling the other.

Tortoise watched the quivering vine, laughing in his heart. Then he went away to seek for food, leaving the two at their tug, and hungry. He ate his bellyful of mushrooms and then went comfortably to sleep.

Late in the afternoon he rose and said, "I will go and see whether those fools are still pulling." When he went there the vine was still stretched taut, with neither of them winning. At last, Tortoise nicked the vine with his knife. The vine parted, and at their ends Elephant and Hippopotamus, so suddenly released, fell with a great crash onto the ground.

Tortoise started off with one end of the broken vine. He came on Elephant looking doleful and rubbing a sore leg. Elephant said, "Tortoise, I did not know you were so strong. When the vine broke I fell over and hurt my leg. Yes, we are really equals. Strength is not because the body is large. We will call each other Friend."

Most pleased with this victory over Elephant, Tortoise then went off to visit Hippopotamus, who looked sick and was rubbing his head. Hippopotamus said, "So, Tortoise, we are equal. We pulled and pulled and despite my great size I could not surpass you. When the vine broke I fell and hurt my head. Indeed, strength has no greatness of body. We will call each other Friend."

After that, whenever they three and the others met in council, the three sat together on the highest seats. And always they addressed each other as Friend.

Do you think they were really equal?

The Two Strangers

from **Africa**

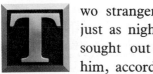wo strangers entered a village just as night was falling. They sought out the chief to greet him, according to custom, and to ask him for a place to spend the night. The chief replied, "Welcome, O strangers. We welcome you. There is a guesthouse in which you may sleep and there is food for you to eat. But know that in this village there is a custom of long standing. Strangers may sleep here, but on pain of death they may not snore. Remember this well, for if you snore you will be killed as you sleep." The chief then took the strangers to the guesthouse and they composed themselves for the night's rest.

The visitors had not been asleep for long when one of them began to snore: "Vo, vo, vo." His companion awoke. He heard also, "Ts, ts, ts." This was the sound the villagers made sharpening their knives. The stranger then knew that they were getting ready to kill the snorer. He thought quickly of a way that he might save his companion. As one stranger snored, "Vo, vo, vo," the other stranger composed a song:

> Vo, vo, lio, vo. Vo, vo, lio, vo.
> We walked on the road.
> We came to this town.
> We were welcomed.
> Vo, vo, lio, vo.
> Vo, vo, lio, vo.

He sang this song with a strong voice and the people could not hear the snoring above the song. They let their knives fall and began to dance. The drums were brought out and played. The people took up the song and sang. All the people—women, children, the chief, and all the men—came to join the dance.

All that night one stranger snored, one stranger sang, and the townspeople danced and played.

In the morning the strangers went to bid farewell to the chief before they took to the road again. The chief wished them a good journey and pressed a good-sized purse into their hands. "I give you this present of money for your fine song. Because of you, strangers, we spent the night in dance and play. We are grateful."

The strangers went out of the village. Once again on the road, they began to argue. How should the money be shared? The snorer said, "It is to me that the larger portion should fall. If I had not snored, you would not have been moved to compose the song, and we should have received no present at all."

The singer said, "True. If you had not snored, I would not have composed the song, but if I had not, you would have been killed. The people were already sharpening their knives. So I should certainly get the larger portion of the money." Thus they argued and could not decide. Can you?

The Leftover Eye

from **Africa**

 Pay heed to this tale. This is a tale of things that have never happened. But we will suppose these things did happen for certainly there are such things possible.

This is a tale of a man who was blind. His mother, too, was blind. His wife and his wife's mother were also blind. They dwelt together in a wretched condition; their farm was poor and their house was badly built. They consulted together and decided to go away. They would journey until they came to some place where their lot would be better.

They set out and traveled along the road. As they walked, the man stumbled over something. He picked it up and felt it, and then he knew he had come upon seven eyes. He immediately gave two eyes to his wife,

African art, Baule mask
Private Collection, France

and then took two for himself. Of the three eyes remaining to him, he gave one to his mother and another to his wife's mother. He was left with one eye in his hand. This was a startling thing. Here was his mother with her one eye looking at him hopefully. There was his wife's mother with her one eye looking at him hopefully. To whom should he give the leftover eye?

If he gives the eye to his mother, he will forever be ashamed before his wife and her mother. If he gives it to his wife's mother, he will fear the angry and disappointed heart of his own mother. A mother, know you, is not something to be played with.

This is difficult indeed. Here is the sweetness of his wife. She is good and loving. How can he hurt her? Yet his mother, too, is a good mother and loving. Can he thus injure her? Which would be easier, and which would be the right way to do this thing?

If this thing would come to you, which would you choose?

THINK AND DISCUSS
Understanding
1. Explain the problem raised in each of the three tales you have just read.
2. In which of the tales do you learn about the custom of travelers greeting the chief of a village to ask for a place to spend the night?
3. In which tale are the characters animals?

Analyzing
4. Find the exaggeration, or overstatement, in the description of the elephant in "A Tug-of-War."
5. What is improbable about the situations in "The Leftover Eye" and "The Two Strangers"?
6. From these tales, what seems to be the most important trait of a hero?

Extending
7. What do you think are the values of this type of story to a society that has no written laws to serve as guides for the people?

READING LITERATURE SKILLFULLY
Summarizing
A **summary** is a short statement of not more than a few sentences that gives the main ideas of an article or tells what happens in a story. To summarize, you may find it helpful to ask yourself who does what, when, and where. Why?

Prepare an outline that you could use to give an oral summary of one of the dilemma tales.

VOCABULARY
Context
From the context of each sentence decide the meaning of the italicized word.

Then choose the meaning for the word as it is used in the sentence.

1. The boy went to where the fire was burning, took a glowing *brand*, and set out for home.
   (**a**) iron stamp
   (**b**) piece of burning wood
   (**c**) mark of disgrace

2. The two strangers *bid* farewell to their hosts and left the village.
   (**a**) commanded
   (**b**) offered to pay (a certain price)
   (**c**) said or wished

3. The fox is a *cunning* animal who slyly outwits his enemies.
   (**a**) cute
   (**b**) clever in deceiving
   (**c**) skillful

4. During the tug-of-war between the elephant and the hippopotamus, the rope remained *taut* for hours.
   (**a**) tightly drawn
   (**b**) neat
   (**c**) tidy

5. The boy took *parched* corn to eat for a midday meal.
   (**a**) hot
   (**b**) thirsty
   (**c**) roasted

THINKING SKILLS
Evaluating

To evaluate is to make a judgment based on some sort of standard. Which dilemma tale raises the most meaningful question for people living today? Consider all three tales but choose only one. Explain why you judge this tale to be the most meaningful of the three.

COMPOSITION
Writing a Dilemma Tale

Think about a modern dilemma that you or someone you know has experienced. Write a short dilemma tale, posing the alternate choices at the end but not telling the solution. The dilemma should be one for which you don't have a ready answer. For example, suppose you really enjoy gymnastics and have skills in it as well. To achieve your goal and win a schoolwide competition, you must give up all other after-school activities for several months, including your newspaper route, but you really need the money you earn in order to buy a new bicycle. In writing your dilemma tale, remember to use repetition, exaggeration, and a question at the end.

Writing a Summary

If you did the assignment under Reading Literature Skillfully on page 433, you prepared an outline for an oral summary of one of the three dilemma tales. Now write a summary of not more than a few sentences. Remember to tell who does what, when, where, and why. For help in writing, refer to Lesson 5, "Writing to Summarize," in the Writer's Handbook.

ENRICHMENT
Participating in a Discussion

Work with a group of five or six classmates to decide on a solution *not* suggested by the questions in the tales. For example, does either one of the two strangers deserve a larger portion of the money? How else might the money be divided? Consider several ways to solve the problem before selecting one. Be sure you can defend your new solution.

H𝓛𝓣 Review STEREOTYPE in the Handbook of Literary Terms, page 659.

A Gift for a Gift

from **Saxony**

Two brothers, one poor and the other wealthy, receive very different gifts from the king in this folk tale from Saxony, a region in Germany. The tale dates back to the seventeenth century.

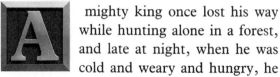 mighty king once lost his way while hunting alone in a forest, and late at night, when he was cold and weary and hungry, he at last reached the hut of a poor miner. The miner was away digging for coal, and his wife didn't realize that the gentleman who rapped on her door and begged for a night's lodging was the king himself.

"We are very poor," she explained, "but if you will be content, as we are, with a plate of potatoes for dinner and a blanket on the floor for a bed, you will be most welcome." The king's stomach was empty; his bones ached; and he knew that on this dark night he would never find his way back to his castle. And so he gratefully accepted the woman's hospitality. He sat down to dinner with her and greedily ate a generous portion of steaming potatoes baked in an open fire. "These are better than the best beef I've ever eaten," he

exclaimed. And still smacking his lips, he stretched out on the floor and quickly fell fast asleep.

Early the next morning the king washed in a nearby brook, and then returned to the hut to thank the miner's wife for her kindness. And for her trouble he gave her a gold piece. Then he was on his way to his palace.

When the miner returned home later that day, his wife told him about the courteous, kind, and distinguished guest who had stayed overnight in their home. Then she showed her husband the gold piece he had given her. The husband realized at once that the king himself must have been their overnight guest. And because he believed that the king had been far too generous in his payment for

---

their humble fare and lodging, he decided to go at once to present his majesty with a bushel of potatoes—fine, round potatoes, the very kind the king had enjoyed so much.

The palace guards refused at first to let the miner enter. But when he explained that he wanted nothing from the king—that in fact, he had come only to give the king a bushel of potatoes—they let him pass.

"Kind sire," he said when he finally stood before the king, "last night you paid my wife a gold piece for a hard bed and a plate of potatoes. Even if you are a great and wealthy ruler, you paid much too much for the little offered you. Therefore, I have brought you a bushel of potatoes, which you said you enjoyed as much as the finest beef. Please accept them. And should you ever pass by our house again, we will be happy to have the opportunity to serve you more."

These proud and honest words pleased the king, and to show his appreciation he ordered that the miner be given a fine house and a three-acre farm. Overjoyed by his good luck, the honest miner returned home to share the news with his wife.

Now it so happened that the miner had a brother—a wealthy brother who was shrewd, greedy, and jealous of anyone else's good fortune. When he learned of his brother's luck, he decided that he too would present the king with a gift. Not long before, the king had wanted to buy one of the brother's horses. But because he had been asked to pay an outrageously high price, the king had never bought the animal. Now, thought the avaricious brother, he would go to his sovereign and make him a gift of the horse. *After all*, he reasoned, *if the king gave a three-acre farm and a house to my brother in return for a mere bushel of potatoes, I will probably get a mansion and ten acres for my gift.*

He brushed the horse and polished its harness, and then rode to the palace. Past the sentries he walked, directly into the king's audience chamber.

"Gracious sir," he began, "not long ago you wanted to buy my horse, but I placed a very high price on it. You may have wondered why I did so, great king. Let me explain. I did not want to sell the horse to you. I wanted to *give* it to you, your majesty. And I ask you now to accept it as a gift. If you look out your window you will see the horse in your courtyard. He is, as you know, a magnificent animal, and I am sure that not even you have such a fine stallion in your royal stables."

The king realized at once that this was not an honest gift. He smiled and said, "Thank you, my friend. I accept your kind gift with gratitude. And you shall not go home empty-handed. Do you see that bushel of potatoes there in the corner? Well, those potatoes cost me a three-acre farm and a house. Take them as your reward. I am sure that not even you have a bushel of potatoes in your storeroom with so high a value on them."

What could the greedy brother do? He dared not argue with the king. He simply raised the heavy sack to his shoulders and carried it home, while the king ordered the horse put in his stables.

THINK AND DISCUSS
Understanding
1. When does the wife discover that the stranger who stops at her hut is the king?
2. What gift does the king give the miner?
3. What is the difference between the miner's gift to the king and his wealthy brother's gift?

Analyzing
4. What is the **irony** in the king's gift to the wealthy brother of the miner?
5. What is the underlying meaning, or **theme,** of this story?

Extending
6. The situation and events of this story are far removed from the world as it is today. What meaning can the story have for people living today?

REVIEWING: Stereotype H❢
See Handbook of Literary Terms, p. 659.

A **stereotype** is a character in fiction that fits a standardized mental picture of what members of a certain group are like, or a plot in which the action follows a predictable pattern. Characters portrayed as stereotypes lack the depth that people in real life have.

The hero in a tale often starts at the bottom of the social scale, and success may depend on the help of another. The hero may display the traits of kindness, modesty, trust, and obedience. After rising from a low station, the hero usually lives happily ever after.

1. Explain how the miner in "A Gift for a Gift" shows the characteristics of a stereotyped hero of a folk tale.
2. In what ways is the plot of "A Gift for a Gift" a stereotyped plot?

READING LITERATURE SKILLFULLY
Judgments
To make a **judgment** is to form an opinion about something or someone. For a judgment to have merit, it should be based on some standard, whether your own experience, your observation of others, or selections you have read.

1. What judgment does the king make about each of the two brothers?
2. In your opinion are most people today more like the miner or his wealthy brother?

COMPOSITION ✎
Writing a Good Ending
You have learned that a good ending is important because it draws everything in a story to a clear conclusion. Suppose that the greedy brother does not simply put the sack of potatoes on his shoulders and go home. Write a different ending for this story. Whatever direction you decide to take, be sure to conclude everything clearly.

The Flying Ship

from **Russia**

Dourak finds a flying ship and ventures into a fairy-tale world.

n a wild and lonely region of the great empire of Russia, there lived an old couple who had three sons. They loved the first and the second dearly, for these were quick-witted and prudent beyond their years; but they had no love to spare for the youngest, whom they nicknamed "Dourak," the fool, and whom they regarded as a dreamer and a good-for-nothing.

Now it chanced that the Tsar then ruling over Russia had an only daughter of great beauty, whom many princes came to woo. So he sent forth a proclamation to every corner of his dominions that whoever could make a Flying Ship should marry the Tsarevna—the daughter of the Tsar.

The eldest son of the old couple, and the second son, about this time decided to leave home and go and seek their fortunes. Their mother wept and kissed them, and gave each of them a flask of wine to cheer him on the way, and a bundle full of the best food she could afford. When they had gone Dourak had an even harder life than before, for his father and mother were always lamenting that their two wise and witty sons should be far away, while only this stupid fellow remained at home.

So at last Dourak decided that he, too, would go and seek his fortune.

"Whatever happens to me," he thought to himself, "I cannot be more unlucky than I am here. And perhaps I may find how Flying Ships are made. And then I should marry the Tsarevna. Tomorrow I will go forth."

When he told his mother that he, too, was bent upon seeking his fortune she laughed at him, and told him that the wolves that lived in the great dark forest would gobble him up. She wished Dourak to remain at home, not because she had any love for him, but because she could make him work for her, chopping wood and gathering sticks, and digging and weeding their little plot of garden.

Dourak, however, was determined to go. So the old woman gave him neither a kiss nor a blessing, but thrust a bundle with a piece of bread and a flask of water into his hands, and turned him roughly out of the house.

Poor Dourak trudged and trudged through the great dark forest, and at last he met a very old man, who asked him whither he was bound.

"The Flying Ship" from *A Treasury of Tales*, edited by Marjory Bruce. Copyright 1927 by Harper & Row, Publishers, Inc. Reprinted by permission of Harper & Row, Publishers, Inc. and Harrap Ltd.

"I am going to seek my fortune, father," returned the young man.

"But what if you should not find it?"

"Whatever happens to me, I cannot be more unlucky than I was at home."

The old man looked keenly at Dourak. "Last week," said he, "I met two young men in this forest, neither of whom would give me a bite or a sup from the bundle of food which each carried. You also have some food. Are you as hardhearted as they?"

"Truly, sir," said Dourak, "I would gladly give you all that I have—I fear there is not enough for two—but dry bread and plain water may not seem to you worth the having."

"Let us sit down under this tree," suggested the old man, "and do you untie your bundle."

Poor Dourak blushed as he untied the knot, for he was ashamed to offer such miserable fare to a stranger; but when the knot *was* untied, he was astonished to find that instead of bread and water his bundle contained white rolls, and sausages, and a flask of red wine.

He and his new friend shared the good things fairly between them. When they had finished, the old man asked, "Have you any plan by which you hope to make your fortune?"

"Well," said Dourak, simply, "the Tsar has promised his daughter to the man who can make a Flying Ship."

"Can *you* make such a ship?"

"Not I. But maybe I might find the place where they are made."

"Where is that place?"

"I can but look for it, father."

The old man smiled. "Listen, Dourak," said he, "go into the forest, follow the first path you see, stop at the first tree at the path's end, strike the tree once with your ax, then lie down with your face to the ground and wait. Only remember this. Fly where you will, but take on board whomever you meet by the way."

Dourak thanked his friend warmly, and hurried into the forest. At the end of the path he found a tall and beautiful fir tree. There he stopped, and carefully obeyed the advice which the old man had given him. As he lay with his face against the ground he fell fast asleep. After a time he woke up, and there, instead of the fir tree, he saw a beautiful ship, of polished and painted wood, with sails shaped like the wings of a bird.

Dourak jumped into the ship, and it immediately rose into the air and flew toward Moscow, where the Tsar held his court. Dourak peeped over the side and saw a man far below, lying with his ear pressed to the ground. He took the helm and steered the ship downward, and called out, "Good day, uncle! What are you doing?"

"Good day, my lad! I am listening to what is going on in the wide world."

"Will you come with me in my ship?"

"Gladly!"

So Dourak helped him to climb on board.

When they had flown a little farther they saw a man hopping on one foot, while the other was tied up against his ear.

"Good day, uncle," cried Dourak, "why do you tie one of your legs against your ear?"

"Because if I were to untie it, I should go halfway round the world in one stride."

"Come with us." And he came.

The ship flew, and flew, and presently they saw a man taking aim with a gun, though there was neither bird nor beast to be seen.

"God save you, uncle," quoth Dourak, "are you shooting at nothing?"

"Not I. I am aiming at a bird a hundred leagues away. That's what *I* call good sport."

"Come with us, uncle." And he came.

They flew, and flew, and presently they saw a man with a sackful of bread on his back.

"Whither bound, uncle?" asked Dourak.

"To get some bread for my dinner."

"Have you not got enough in that sack?"

"Indeed I have not. I could eat all *that* at one gulp."

"Come with us, Mr. Gobbler." And he came.

They flew, and flew, and they saw a man standing by a lake.

"Fair befall you, uncle," cried Dourak, "what do you seek?"

"Some water to drink."

"Why, there is a whole lake in front of you!"

"*That?* Oh, I should empty *that* at one draft."

"Come with us, Mr. Thirstyman." And he came.

They flew, and flew, and next they spied a man carrying a heap of straw.

"Whither bound with that straw, uncle?" inquired Dourak.

"To the village."

"Is there no straw in your village?"

"There is none like this. If you scatter it on the hottest midsummer day, the weather will become freezingly cold, and snow will begin to fall."

"Come with us, Mr. Strawmonger." And he came.

They flew, and flew, and soon they saw a man with a bundle of wood.

"Good morrow, uncle," said Dourak, "why are you taking wood into the forest where there is plenty already?"

"This is the most unusual wood, my young friend. Wherever it is scattered, an army will spring up."

"Come with us, Mr. Woodman." And he came.

They flew, and flew, and at last they reached the beautiful city of Moscow, with its clanging belfries and its many-colored domes. The Tsar was looking out of his palace window, and saw the Flying Ship, and as he looked, it circled thrice and came down in a field not far away. Greatly excited, he sent one of his most fleet-footed servants to find out who was the captain of the vessel, "For," thought His Imperial Majesty, "whoever he may be, he can claim the hand of my daughter, the Tsarevna."

The servant soon returned, and the news he brought alarmed the Tsar. He declared that the ship carried a crew of seven very odd-looking men, and that their leader was a simple peasant lad, in patched and threadbare clothes.

"This is exceedingly awkward," exclaimed the Tsar. "The only thing to be done is to give the fellow some impossible tasks to perform. Go," he exclaimed to his Lord High Chamberlain, "go and tell him that before I have finished my dinner he must bring me

Watercolor by Sylvie Selig

some water that lives and sings."

Now the first of Dourak's fellow travelers, he with the keen ear, heard what the Tsar was saying, and told the others.

"Alas," cried Dourak, "I see that I am to be as unlucky here as I was at home! Where could I find such water? And if I knew where, might it not take me a whole lifetime to fetch it?"

"Have no fear," said the hopping man, "I know where it is. And if I untie my leg I can bring it to you in a twinkling."

So when the Lord High Chamberlain arrived with the imperial message, Dourak replied, "His Majesty shall be obeyed."

And the hopping man untied his leg, and in one stride he reached the distant country where the living river flows and sings as it flows. When he had filled a jar with the singing water the hopping man felt tired. "I have plenty of time for a nap," he thought. So he lay down by the riverbank beside a mill wheel, and fell asleep.

Time passed, and his companions in the Flying Ship began to feel anxious. Then he with the keen ear laid himself flat on the ground and listened. "I hear a mill wheel turning, and I hear a man snoring," said he.

The marksman shaded his eyes with his hand. "I can see the mill," he said. So he raised his gun to his shoulder, took careful aim, and sent a bullet through the roof of the mill, which awoke the hopping man with its noise. Up jumped the hopping man, seized his jar, made one long stride, and was back in Moscow before the Tsar had finished his dinner.

Instead of being pleased at this prompt fulfillment of his commands, the Tsar was furious. He sent word to Dourak that before he could claim the hand of the Tsarevna he and his comrades must eat at one sitting twenty roast oxen and twenty loaves of bread.

"Alas," cried Dourak, "why, for my part, I could not eat *one!*"

"Be of good cheer," said his fellow traveler, Mr. Gobbler, "that will be a mere snack for *me*."

So they brought the twenty roast oxen and the twenty large loaves, and the Gobbler ate them all up in a trice. "All very well," he remarked, when he had finished, "but the Tsar might have sent me a little more while he was about it."

Then the Tsar commanded Dourak to drink forty barrels of red wine, each barrel holding forty buckets.

"Woe is me," cried Dourak, "I am as unlucky as ever!"

"Not so," said his fellow traveler, Mr. Thirstyman. "It will seem a mere thimbleful to me."

So when the Tsar's servants brought the forty barrels of wine, the thirstyman drained all the wine at a draft. "Very good," he remarked, wiping his lips, "but not enough of it!"

Then the Tsar became desperate, and cast about in his mind for some way of ridding himself of this tiresome Dourak. He sent word that before the Tsarevna's future husband could be presented to her he would no doubt wish to have a bath, and to array himself in new garments. And then he gave orders to his servants that they should heat the bath so hot that no man could come out of it alive.

He with the keen ear overheard these orders, and told the fellow traveler with the bundle of straw. So when Dourak, obeying the royal command, wended his way to the imperial bathroom, the Strawmonger said, "I am coming with you." And he went with him.

It was fearfully hot in the bathroom after the Tsar's servants had locked the door on the outside, and great clouds of steam rose from the bath.

Then Dourak's fellow traveler scattered some of his straw on the floor, and immediately the water in the bath froze, and Dourak was fain to clamber up onto the top of the stove lest he too should be frozen.

The next morning, when the Tsar's servants came and unlocked the door, they found Dourak perched on the stove, singing and whistling, not a whit the worse for his ordeal of fire and ice.

When tidings of these things reached the Tsar he was greatly alarmed and perplexed. How *could* he rid himself of this stubborn fellow? Then he had an idea. "Go," he said to his Lord High Chamberlain, "go and tell Dourak that he may now come and claim the hand of my daughter, but that *when* he comes he must come at the head of a great army."

This message reduced Dourak to despair. "When I was at home," he exclaimed, "I was unlucky, and I had no friends. Now, though I have seven friends I am still unlucky. What the Tsar asks is impossible."

"Nothing of the sort," cried his seventh fellow traveler with the bundle of wood. "You have forgotten *me!* Fear nothing. Tell the Lord High Chamberlain to inform the Tsar that you will come at the head of an army, as he desires, but that if he refuses you the hand of the Tsarevna, you will command your troops to lay siege to Moscow."

That night the seventh fellow traveler went out into the open plain, beyond the walls of the city, and scattered his fagots far and wide. And the next morning, when the Tsar looked out of his palace window he heard the braying of trumpets and the thunder of drums, and saw the glint of swords and breastplates and helmets, and the gay columns of banners and military attire.

"I can do no more," cried the Tsar. "He must marry the Tsarevna!"

So he sent his servants to Dourak, and they gave him a bath of perfumed water, and combed his locks with a comb of gold, and clothed him in the gorgeous robes of a Tsar's son. And nobody would have recognized poor Dourak, the despised and neglected Dourak, in the handsome youth who rode on horseback at the head of an army to claim the hand of the Tsarevna. All the seven fellow travelers were invited to the wedding feast, and for once in their lives the Gobbler had enough to eat, and the Thirstyman had so much to drink that even *he* wished for no more.

As for the Tsarevna, she was very happy as the wife of Dourak, and grew to love him as truly as he did her; and he, whose own father and mother had cared nothing for him, became a great favorite with his father-in-law and mother-in-law, the parents of the Tsarevna, his bride.

THINK AND DISCUSS
Understanding
1. Why does Dourak want a flying ship?
2. To whom does Dourak first show kindness, and how does this kindness determine what happens to him?
3. What examples of magic do you find in "The Flying Ship"?

Analyzing
4. Compare the king in "A Gift for a Gift" with the Tsar in "The Flying Ship."
5. Explain how Dourak demonstrates the following character traits: (**a**) kindness; (**b**) obedience; (**c**) modesty; (**d**) trust.
6. In what ways is the character of Dourak a **stereotype**?
7. What role does fate play in Dourak's success?

Extending

8. In what ways is the Tsarevna in "The Flying Ship" typical of princesses in fairy tales?

VOCABULARY
Dictionary and Glossary

The etymology, or origin, of a word is sometimes given at the end of its dictionary or glossary entry. The etymology, in brackets, tells what the earliest form of the word was, in what language it appeared, if the meaning has changed, and what the word originally meant.

Use the etymologies in the Glossary to answer the following questions.

1. There are two entries for the word *sup*. What is the meaning of the word that comes from Old English?
2. From what language does the other meaning for *sup* come?
3. In "A Gift for a Gift," the word *fare* means "food." What is the Old English meaning of the word?
4. From what language does the word *lament* come and what does it mean?
5. From what language does the word *array* originally come?

THINKING SKILLS
Classifying

To classify things is to arrange them into categories or groups according to some system. Make two columns on a sheet of paper, labeling them *Superhuman Ability* and *Magic Object*. Write under one of the two headings the name of each man Dourak meets on his journey. For example, the hopping man would be listed under "Superhuman Ability" because he can go halfway around the world in one stride.

COMPOSITION
Writing About a Character

What kind of hero is Dourak? Write two or three paragraphs in which you describe him and the significant obstacles that he faces in the story. Use examples to support your description of Dourak as a hero. Tell about his virtues, the odds against him in the beginning, his rise from obscurity to fortune, how he succeeds, and how the story ends.

Writing to Compare

How does Dourak compare to the kind of character who would be considered a hero today? Think about heroes you have seen pictured in movies or on television. Write three paragraphs in which you compare Dourak with your idea of a hero. In the first paragraph describe Dourak's character traits, in the second paragraph tell about the qualities you feel are considered heroic today, and in the final paragraph show likenesses and differences between the two kinds of heroes. Before you begin, make one list of Dourak's qualities and another list of qualities that define a hero today.

ENRICHMENT
Retelling a Story

Work with a small group of classmates. Choose one of the stories you have read in this unit and have each person take a turn retelling it for the group. Select someone who has retold the story well to relate it again to the rest of the class. Before the retelling, members of the group should advise the chosen storyteller about such things as the details to include, word choice, and tone of voice. The storyteller may also practice by using a tape recorder.

THINKING CRITICALLY
ABOUT LITERATURE

UNIT 6   FOLK LITERATURE

■ CONCEPT REVIEW

The ideas and skills you have studied in this unit are reviewed in the animal tale below. The notes in the margin are designed to help you think critically about your reading. Page numbers in the notes refer to a review of the literary term. A more extensive discussion of these terms is in the Handbook of Literary Terms.

Why the Stork Has No Tail

from **Romania**

A. M. Lysaght,
White Stork, c. 1800,
India Office Library,
London

Now Floria had once shown kindness to a stork, who afterward turned out to be the king of the storks. In return the stork gave Floria a feather, which, when taken up at any time of danger, would bring the stork to him and help him. Thus it came to pass that the hero, finding himself in danger, remembered the gift of the stork. He took out the feather from the place where he had hidden it and waved it. At once the stork appeared and asked Floria what he could do for him. He told him the king had ordered him to bring the water of life and the water of death.

■ **Floria:** a folk hero

■ Note the magic in the appearance of the stork.

■ **water of life . . . death:** The early Romanians believed that when the water of death was poured over a dead body, it would heal all wounds. The water of life restored breath to the healed body.

"Why the Stork Has No Tail" from *Roumanian Bird and Beast Stories* by Dr. Moses Gaster. Published by The Folklore Society. Reprinted by permission.

The stork replied that if it could possibly be got he would certainly do it for him. Returning to his palace, the stork, who was the king of the storks, called all the storks together, and asked them whether they had seen or heard or been near the mountains that knock against one another, at the bottom of which are the fountains of the water of life and death.

All the young and strong looked at one another, and not even the oldest one ventured to reply. He asked them again, and then they said they had never heard or seen anything of the waters of life and death. At last there came from the rear a stork, lame on one foot, blind in one eye, with a shriveled-up body, and with half of his feathers plucked out. And he said, "May it please Your Majesty, I have been there where the mountains knock one against the other, and the proofs of it are my blinded eye and my crooked leg." When the king saw him in the state in which he was, he did not even take any notice of him.

Turning to the other storks, he said: "Is there anyone among you who, for my sake, will run the risk and go to these mountains and bring the water?" Not one of the young and strong, and not even any of the older ones who were still strong replied. They all kept silence. But the lame stork said to the king, "For your sake, O Master King, I will again put my life in danger and go." The king again did not look at him, and turning to the others repeated his question; but when he saw that they all kept silence, he at last turned to the stork and said to him: "Dost thou really believe, crippled and broken as thou art, that thou wilt be able to carry out my command?"

"I will certainly try," he said.

"Wilt thou put me to shame?" the king again said.

"I hope not; but thou must bind on my wings some meat for my food, and tie the two bottles for the water to my legs."

The other storks, on hearing his words, laughed at what they thought his conceit, but he took no notice of it. The king was very pleased and did as the stork had asked. He tied on his wings a quantity of fresh meat, which would last him for his journey, and the two bottles were fastened to his legs. He said to him, "A pleasant journey."

The stork, thus prepared for his journey, rose up into the heavens, and away he went straight to the place where the mountains were

■ **Stereotype** (page 437): Consider the connection of strength with youth.

■ The old stork was injured where the mountains knock together.

■ **dost:** do
■ **thou:** you
■ **art:** are
■ **wilt:** will

■ **conceit:** too high an opinion of himself; vanity

knocking against one another and prevented anyone approaching the fountains of life and death. It was when the sun had risen as high as a lance that he espied in the distance those huge mountains which, when they knocked against one another, shook the earth and made a noise that struck fear and terror into the hearts of those who were a long distance away.

When the mountains had moved back a little before knocking against one another, the stork wanted to plunge into the depths and get the water. But there came suddenly to him a swallow from the heart of the mountains, and said to him, "Do not go a step further, for thou art surely lost."

"Who art thou who stops me in my way?" asked the stork angrily.

"I am the guardian spirit of these mountains, appointed to save every living creature that has the misfortune to come near them."

"What am I to do then to be safe?"

"Hast thou come to fetch the water of life and death?"

"Yes."

"If that be so, then thou must wait till noon, when the mountains rest for half an hour. As soon as thou seest that a short time has passed and they do not move, then rise up as high as possible into the air and drop down straight to the bottom of the mountains. There standing on the ledge of the stone between the two waters, dip thy bottles into the fountains and wait until they are filled. Then rise as thou hast got down, but beware lest thou touchest the walls of the mountains or even a pebble, or thou art lost."

The stork did as the swallow had told him; he waited till the noon-tide, and when he saw that the mountains had gone to sleep, he rose up into the air, and, plunging down into the depth, he settled on the ledge of the stone and filled his bottles. Feeling that they had been filled, he rose with them as he had got down, but when he had reached almost the top of the mountains, he touched a pebble. No sooner had he done so, when the two mountains closed furiously upon him; but they did not catch any part of him, except the tail, which remained locked up fast between the two peaks of the mountains.

With a strong movement he tore himself away, happy that he had saved his life and the two bottles with the waters of life and death, not caring for the loss of his tail.

■ **espied:** saw
■ **Inference** (page 420): Note the clue to the kind of natural phenomenon in the words "knocked against one another, shook the earth and made a noise."

■ Note that the hero, the old stork, receives help from the swallow.

■ **hast:** have

■ Note the use of personification in the mountains resting for half an hour at noon.

■ Note that the old stork obediently follows the swallow's advice.

■ The stork feels no sorrow over the loss of his tail.

And he returned the way he had come, and reached the palace of the king of the storks in time for the delivery of the bottles. When he reached the palace, all the storks were assembled before the king, waiting to see what would happen to the lame and blind one who had tried to put them to shame. When they saw him coming back, they noticed that he had lost his tail, and they began jeering at him and laughing, for he looked all the more ungainly, from having already been so ugly before.

But the king was overjoyed with the exploit of his faithful messenger; and he turned angrily on the storks and said, "Why are you jeering and mocking? Just look round and see where are your tails. And you have not lost them in so honorable a manner as this, my faithful messenger." On hearing this they turned round, and lo! one and all of them had lost their tails.

And this is the reason why they have remained without tails to this very day.

■ The other storks are more interested in the stork's lost tail than in the success of his mission.

■ **ungainly:** awkward; clumsy

■ **exploit:** bold act

■ Note what happens to all the storks, as if by magic.

■ Note the theme: one who is handicapped may prove to be the most courageous of all.

THINK AND DISCUSS
Understanding
1. Describe the old stork who offers to help the king stork. How did he receive his injuries?
2. Why does the king choose this stork over other younger and healthier storks?
3. How do the other storks treat the stork who volunteers to help?
4. Who helps the stork find the water?

Analyzing
5. Why doesn't the old stork regret losing his tail between the moving mountains?
6. What traits of a hero does the old stork have?
7. What kind of people are represented by the storks who refuse to perform the deed but jeer the old stork?
8. Summarize this story by telling who did what, when, where, and why.

Extending
9. Why do you think some people, like the storks, are cruel to those who are ugly?

REVIEWING LITERARY TERMS
Inference
1. What inference can you make about the natural phenomenon that occurs when the mountains knock together?

Stereotype
2. How are the young and strong storks stereotyped?
3. How is the king a stereotype?
4. In what way might the plot be considered a stereotype?

■ CONTENT REVIEW
THINKING SKILLS
Classifying
1. Label two columns "Animals" and "People." Write the titles of the stories in this unit under these categories. You

may not be able to include all of the selections.

Generalizing

2. Consider the myths, tales, and fables in this unit. What general conclusions can you make about the human traits thought to be desirable by early cultures? What can you conclude about human traits thought to be undesirable?

3. Think about the qualities shown in the behavior of the animals listed below. What qualities would a person given the name of each animal probably have?
   - (a) sheep
   - (d) monkey
   - (g) pig
   - (b) bull
   - (e) goose
   - (h) owl
   - (c) snake
   - (f) fox
   - (i) bear

Synthesizing

4. Make up a folk tale that does one of the following things:
   - (a) Explains why the cheetah is the fastest animal alive.
   - (b) Explains how the rainbow came into being.
   - (c) Illustrates the dilemma of being able to take only one brother, sister, or friend on a trip you have won.

Evaluating

5. If you were allowed to spend an hour with one of the characters from these folk tales, whom would you choose? Which one would be the most interesting? Which would probably teach you the most in the shortest time?

■ COMPOSITION REVIEW

Writing an Explanation

Suppose you know nothing about science or what causes the things that happen around you. Probably you would still wonder about them and make up explanations to answer your questions. Write a short explanation for one of the following natural occurrences. Keep your sentences simple, and use precise, active verbs.

1. Why is there thunder?
2. Why does the sun sink into the west at night?
3. Why does the moon change its shape?
4. What causes rain?

Writing from Another Point of View

The people who made up the animal tales placed the blame for what happened to certain animals on the animals themselves. Hares, for example, have short tails simply because they are lazy creatures. Write a tale from the point of view of one of the animals. How might the animal describe what happened? Would a spokesperson for the hares say that they have short tails because they are shy types who were pushed aside by the bigger animals? Put yourself in the place of one of the following animals and give your own description of the events: (a) hare; (b) hyena; (c) stork; (d) tortoise.

Reviewing Writer's Craft: Write Good Endings

In this unit you have seen how important a good ending is to the story. Now **try your hand** at creating your own good ending. Write no more than a paragraph to present the solution to one of the following dilemmas. Be sure to make clear the solution and why it is the best one.

1. If you could be either wealthy but hated or poor but admired, which would you choose?
2. If you could be either good-looking or wise, which would you choose to be?

OVEL KÄVIK, THE WOLF DOG

Al Stine, *The Waterway*, 1986, Collection of the artist

Frank E. Schoonover, *Sled Dog in Harness* (detail), 1919, Collection of Glenbow Museum, Calgary, Alberta

PREVIEW

UNIT 7 NOVEL

Kävik, the Wolf Dog / Walt Morey
from **Old Yeller** / Fred Gipson

Features
Reading a Novel
Comment: Sled Dogs
The Writer's Craft: Write Good Beginnings

Review of Literary Terms
characterization
setting
plot

Reading Literature Skillfully
cause/effect relationships
sequence

Vocabulary Skills
compound words
context
homophones and homonyms

Thinking Skills
evaluating
classifying
generalizing

Composition
Writing a News Story
Writing Your Own Story
Beginning a Chapter
Reporting an Interview
Writing a Chapter
Writing a Newspaper Article
Comparing Two Events
Supporting an Opinion

Enrichment
Making a Map
Giving a Speech
Finding Quotations
Doing Research

Thinking Critically About Literature
Concept Review
Content Review
Composition Review

Reading A NOVEL

A novel is a long fictional, or imaginary, story. It has characters, a pattern of events, and a time and place in which the events occur. The focus may be on the characters, or it may be on a series of events in which the action is the most important thing. Generally, the plot of a novel is more complex than the plot of a short story. In addition, a novel often has more characters, both major and minor. There are many kinds of novels, including historical, detective, romance, and adventure.

In the novel you will read in this unit, the wolf dog Kävik is the main character, the protagonist. A character who works against the main character is an antagonist. As you read this novel, look for a character who tries to stop Kävik from getting what he wants.

The other important characters in this novel are fifteen-year-old Andy Evans; his parents, Kurt and Laura Evans; Charlie One Eye, Kävik's first owner; George C. Hunter, a wealthy businessman who buys Kävik from Charlie One Eye; Tom McCarty, a handyman who works for Hunter; and Dr. Vic Walker, a friend who cares for Kävik when he is injured.

The characters act out the **plot** of the novel, a series of related events in a **cause-and-effect** pattern. The events also occur in a **sequence.** For example, in this novel Charlie One Eye trains Kävik because he wants to win an important dog-sled race; because Kävik participates in that race, he comes to the attention of George C. Hunter whose actions change the course of Kävik's life.

Just as life is filled with conflict, a plot is built on conflict. If the conflict is between characters or with nature or society, it is external. There is conflict between Charlie One Eye and Kävik at the beginning of this story. If the conflict is within a character, such as when Kurt Evans must make an important decision about his work, the conflict is internal. As you read, look for other conflicts between characters, between characters and nature, and within characters.

The process of facing and overcoming obstacles, whether external or internal, leads to suspense and, eventually, the climax, or point at which the action of the story changes. The resolution of the conflict is the conclusion of the story.

A novel has a **setting,** the time and place of the action. *Kävik, the Wolf Dog* takes place in Alaska and the state of Washington. The setting is important in this novel because it has an effect on Kävik and what happens to him.

In reading a good novel, you may be unaware of the work the author has done to create a story that will capture your imagination. The hallmark of a job well done is that the doer makes it seem easy. An author has written well when you are not conscious of the special techniques used to keep you involved in the action, from the opening chapter until the final resolution of the conflict.

Kävik, the Wolf Dog

Walt Morey

At full growth Kävik could travel all day on one small fish. He looked like a big arctic wolf with his grayish-white coat, his black-masked face, and huge head tapering down to powerful jaws and knife-sharp teeth.

CHAPTER ONE

harlie One Eye lifted the squirming pup by the scruff of the neck and looked at him. His careless grip pinched the pup's tender skin, and he wriggled and whimpered in protest. But the man studied him with no concern. The whimper turned to a growl. Suddenly the pup twisted his head and sank tiny needle-sharp teeth in Charlie's thumb.

Charlie One Eye dropped the pup. His big hand struck, and with a startled yelp of pain and surprise the pup was knocked rolling. He gathered himself and charged back to the attack, growling with puppy ferocity. Again the hand sent him spinning and howling. He was up and was bowled end over end a third time. Once more he wobbled uncertainly to his feet, prepared to do battle. The hand swept up—and the pup stopped. He had learned painfully what that hand could do. He sank to his belly in the grass, eyes on the upraised hand. The hand lifted him. He continued to growl and show his teeth. But he did not attempt to bite.

"You learn quick who's boss," Charlie One Eye said. "And you got fight. I like that."

Charlie studied the small growling bundle with his one good eye. "You've got wolf in you," he said. "You've got the shape, the feet and head and the eyes. You're gonna be big, strong, smart, and tough. Mean, too." Charlie One Eye was struck with a surprising thought.

He'd raised sled dogs to sell. Twice in the past he had tried to win the North American Sled Dog Derby at Fairbanks. A win would have made his dogs greatly sought after, and twice as valuable. But each time he'd lost because his lead dog collapsed. A good team begins with a good leader, and he'd never had one. In his mind's eye he saw this pup full grown and trained, the head of a team of strong, willing dogs. The old desire to try just once more flamed up in him anew.

"Why not?" he told himself. "I've got one good race left in me before I'm too old. It'll take two years for this pup to grow big and tough and be trained. I can wait that long. But this'll be my last try at the North American." He said to the pup: "You grow up smart and tough and mean. Not mean like the wolf. Mean like Kävik, the wolverine. He's the meanest in all the North. Grow up like him. Then we'll see what we can do."

The pup growled all through this inspection, and showed his teeth. His big yellow eyes never left the man's face. It was the man who finally looked away. He abruptly dropped the pup. "Go on, get big," he said, and watched the pup struggle away through the long grass.

In the months that followed, Kävik fulfilled all of Charlie One Eye's predictions. He grew big, strong, and smart. Charlie saw to it the wolf side of his nature was not neglected. "A lead dog's gotta be a fighter," he insisted. "Got to lick every dog in the team to keep 'em in line." He showed Kävik no sympathy or mercy. The dog never heard a kind or encouraging word or felt the touch of a gentle hand. Kävik took out his anger at Charlie on the rest of the team. This was as Charlie One Eye wanted.

It was not that Charlie was deliberately cruel. Dogs were machines to do his bidding, and he was training them for the grueling race he knew the North American to be. Properly trained, they could be the answer to a dream he'd had for many years. So he used the whip, and sometimes his feet or a club, unsparingly when they did something wrong. Day after day he ran them until they staggered and were ready to drop. He forced them to pull loads of logs and ice until they could not budge another pound. He made them lean and tough and mean. And Kävik was their leader.

To Kävik all humans were like Charlie One Eye. A truce existed between the man and the dog. Kävik recognized Charlie's authority, but he was not broken or cowed by the man's rough treatment.

At full growth Kävik could travel all day on one small fish. He looked like a big arctic wolf with his grayish-white coat, his black-masked face, and huge head tapering down to powerful jaws and knife-sharp teeth. His legs were long and heavy, his feet broad. His chest was wide, with massive muscles that gave him great pulling strength and amazing stamina. He moved with quick, gliding steps, big head down, yellow eyes slightly narrowed, as if he measured an opponent for a lightning attack. The little trick he had as a pup of looking Charlie straight in the eye he had never lost.

This was the manner of dog Kävik had become when Charlie One Eye took the team to Fairbanks for his last try to win the North American Sled Dog Derby.

Fairbanks was in the grip of electric excitement. Teams had come from all parts of North America to compete for the richest cash prize ever offered. Charlie had realized all odds were against him and his untried team, and the betting bore that out. But he knew what Kävik could do. He had banked everything on his big, tough leader, and Kävik did not let him down.

This was the dog George C. Hunter saw when he stepped out the door of the Hunter Enterprises Office on Fairbanks' main street just in time to witness the finish of the race. He saw the winning team stagger across the finish line, and collapse, the driver folding over the sled, exhausted. Then the hysterically happy, shouting crowd surged around them. Cameras snapped and whirred, horns blew, people shouted and laughed. A half-dozen public-address speakers blared the time and the winner's name into the bedlam.

This scene was not new to Hunter. It was the same every year.

He was about to turn away when the crowd parted and he again saw the team. Every dog but one was flat on the snow. The leader stood, head up, sharp ears pricked forward, utterly oblivious of the noise and the crowd milling about him. He had the dignity of a king, the bearing of a champion. In spite of the murderous miles he had just run, he looked alert and ready to lunge forward again at the command of his master.

For a surprised moment Hunter thought, Why, he's a wolf!

But no wolf could lead a dog team. This dog did have the heavy legs, the lean-muscled body of a wolf.

"What an animal!" Hunter marveled under his breath. He moved into the street for a better look.

People were fussing over the rest of the prostrate team, unhitching them, petting them, and trying to lift them up on wobbly legs. But no one went near the big leader. He stood alone in a small cleared space, his air of aloofness and calmness unchanged.

Hunter came to a stop an arm's length before the wolflike dog. The dog dropped his head in a typical wolf's gesture and looked back at Hunter with yellow eyes. So steady was the animal's gaze, the man had the odd sensation the dog was measuring him. The feeling annoyed him, and he tried to beat the

dog's gaze down with his own sharp black eyes. The absurdity of the situation came to him, and Hunter turned abruptly away. But as he quit the street, he had the uncomfortable feeling those yellow eyes were boring into his shoulder blades.

A thought came to him, and he stopped to let it work its surprising way through his mind. Once it had, he acted upon it immediately. He strode to where his mine manager stood watching the crowd, and asked, "John, was that the owner pushing the winning team?"

"Charlie One Eye, Mr. Hunter? Sure."

"Where can I find him—away from here?"

"He's staying temporarily in a cabin outside town about a mile. It's right on the road. You can't miss it. There'll be a lot of dogs staked out around the place."

"He doesn't live around here?"

"He's from up Kotzebue way. He'll be heading home in a day or two, I imagine."

George Hunter nodded. He turned, eyes searching for the wolflike dog again. He got only a glimpse; then the crowd surged in front of him. But the dog was standing as calm and impassive as ever.

Charlie One Eye was out in the yard checking over his staked dogs the next morning when George Hunter arrived in an old beat-up taxi. Hunter wasted no time.

"Saw you win the race yesterday. It was quite a show." His voice was sharp and businesslike. He pointed at Kävik staked to a chain some distance from the other dogs, watching him with that level yellow gaze. "I want him."

"You wanta look at 'im? There he is."

"I want to buy him."

"Buy him! That dog?" Charlie's one good eye opened wider.

"That's right."

"You gonna sponsor a team, Mr. Hunter?"

Hunter shook his head. "Got no taste for it; stupid sort of sport. I'll have him sent Outside to my home."

Charlie One Eye rubbed his long jaw while he absorbed this surprising information. "I really hadn't figured to sell Kävik," he said finally. "He's my lead dog."

"Start figuring now."

The thought of selling a dog to George C. Hunter pleased Charlie tremendously. It would be a real feather in his cap, almost as great as winning the North American. But he knew Hunter's reputation, and became wary. Beneath that small, dapper exterior lurked a very tough man. He'd heard how those black eyes could become glacier cold and his voice icy. By sheer drive, toughness, and shrewdness Hunter had become one of the North's wealthiest men. His mining, fishing, and lumbering interests were extensive. If he sold Hunter a dog he didn't like, the little man would make him no end of trouble. He said, "Kävik's no house dog, no pet, Mr. Hunter."

"That's obvious. What's his bloodlines?"

"Part malamute, part wolf."

"Part wolf?" Hunter seemed pleased. "He looks all wolf."

"He's a quarter, a throwback to a big arctic wolf father. He's got the arctic wolf's eyes, his cunning and strength—his meanness, too."

Hunter kept looking at the dog as if he hadn't heard. "What did you call him?"

"Kävik." Charlie pronounced it Kah-vik. "It's Eskimo for wolverine."

"Odd name for a dog."

"It fits him," Charlie said. "I never tried to make a pet of him. I've been mighty rough on him to make him the kind of lead dog I wanted. You saw it pay off yesterday. I'd rather sell you another dog, Mr. Hunter. I've got some good ones here."

"Can a man handle him? Could I handle him?"

"Sure. He's been trained to handle. But like I said, Kävik's no family pet. He's never been inside a house in his life or had anybody make a fuss over him. He's a sled-dog leader pure and simple. Now, I've got another dog here——"

"I want this one."

Charlie One Eye thought fast. Why did Hunter want Kävik? Then he thought he knew. Hunter collected objects of interest in the North and sent them home. Hunter wanted the animal to show off. Kävik was a dog bred of the wild, part wolf. The very traits he'd been pointing out in Kävik as undesirable were the things the little man wanted. Now that he had made up his mind about this, Charlie decided. The only thing left to do was bargain as shrewdly as possible.

"Give you five hundred," Hunter said sharply.

Charlie shook his head. "His first batch of pups will bring more than that."

"Seven fifty. That's a good price for a dog."

"Not for this dog. He just won the North American. Every racing club from Maine to Mexico will know about Kävik in a week."

"Then name your price."

Charlie One Eye hedged. "Like I said, I hadn't planned to sell him. I'll have to train a new lead dog. That takes time. And every dog won't make a big strong leader like Kävik. Fact is, I don't know where I'd find another like him. Then I'll lose his pups that I could sell. . . ."

"Never mind working up to it," Hunter said impatiently. "Name your price."

"Tell you what, Mr. Hunter. Make it two thousand and you've got a dog."

"That's a lot of money."

"He's a lot of dog. You want one that's part wolf, that looks like a wolf," Charlie said shrewdly. "You'll look a long time before you find another like him, if ever. Two thousand, Mr. Hunter."

George Hunter scowled. He started to argue, then thought better of it. "All right. You've sold him."

"When do you want to take him?"

"Smiley Johnson, the bush pilot, will pick him up this noon. He'll fly him out to my cannery at Copper City, where one of my tenders will take him aboard and deliver him to me in Seattle."

"You'd better make it before noon." Charlie pointed at the leaden sky. "We've got a blizzard comin'."

"Johnson knows. The weather station told him. But he's working on his plane this morning. It's his problem."

"You'll need some kind of strong box to put him in. He can chew right through ordinary wood with those jaws. And he'll try. He's never been cooped up."

"Got an iron cage. Johnson had it built to fly out a young polar bear for the zoo a year ago. It'll hold him."

"You had it all figured out before you came out here this morning," Charlie One Eye accused.

"I always figure things out ahead," Hunter answered.

In such casual manner was the course of Kävik's life changed forever.

CHAPTER TWO

Kävik did not understand the cage. Charlie One Eye led him up to the odd-looking thing, opened the door, and shoved him inside, slammed the door and padlocked it. Now he twisted about the small enclosure, growling and snarling. He clamped his big teeth on bar after bar, and bit and wrenched. It was no use. He was firmly imprisoned. Finally he lay down and glared out at Charlie One Eye and the blond young pilot, Smiley Johnson.

"He's pretty smart," Johnson said. "That polar bear fought th' cage all th' way down. It didn't take this fellow long to figure out he couldn't bite through those bars. Sure glad they're not wood. I'd hate to have that character loose in th' plane. Are you sure there's some dog in him?"

"Of course. He wouldn't do anything, if he did get loose."

"Maybe not. But I don't like the way he keeps lookin' at me with those yellow eyes. And I don't like the way he clamps down on those bars."

Charlie shook his head. "Scared of a malamute with a little wolf in him; but not scared to fly this tin box in a storm. If you was smart you'd lay over."

Smiley Johnson laughed. "Trouble with

you is, Charlie, you're still traveling by dog team. Why, I'll be eating lunch in Copper City in three hours. Come on, let's load this bundle of dynamite."

It took four men to lift the heavy metal crate with the snarling dog inside, and stow it in the back of the plane.

There in the inner dark Kävik crouched in the cage, yellow eyes shining like burning candles. He was worried and uneasy in these strange surroundings. He heard the roar of the starting motor, and the vibration came up through the bottom of the crate like a thing alive. He felt the plane begin to move and gather speed. The motor roar swelled and swelled until it filled all space. Kävik stood up uncertainly and whined softly. He scratched at the bars and once again tried them with his teeth. He turned around several times in his close confines. Finally he lay down with his big head on his forepaws, resigned to whatever terrible thing was about to happen.

The roaring went on, accompanied by a rushing sound like that of wind high up in the trees. The black compartment where he lay felt insecure, and there was a rolling, tossing motion that never quit and would not let him stand. He crouched on the floor of the cage while these strange sounds and sensations ate away at his courage. He had never been cooped up in the dark, in a cage, with no chance to move about, to fight to defend himself, or to run away. He felt helpless and trapped. Fear, as he had never known it, came to him, and he began to whimper.

In time the swaying motions of the ship became sharper, more violent. They were accompanied by the sickening feeling that he was falling. Then, momentarily they would be gone, only to begin again.

After a particularly violent lurch, Kävik scrambled to his feet and tried to stand. In a frenzy of fear he clawed at the iron bars, then chewed on them, until blood trickled from his straining jaws.

The motor roar quit suddenly on a series of jarring coughs. There was the sound of wind screaming along the sides of the plane, and again that sickening sensation of falling. The motor sputtered briefly to life, and the falling ceased. Then the motor died again. There was the feeling of sliding and never stopping, of spinning and falling, falling without end.

There came a sudden abrupt crash that hurled him against the bars with savage force, a thunderous explosion and a blinding light. The cage went hurtling and spinning through space. Kävik let out one long, unbroken wail of terror that was lost in the tortured rending of metal as the plane struck the frozen earth.

Smiley Johnson, Alaskan bush pilot, had come to the end of his luck.

The storm continued to howl over the mountains and down into the valley where the wreckage of the plane was strewn. It spread a white blanket over the tragic scene, and over an iron cage some feet off in which lay the battered, still form of a wolf-gray animal. The big body was pressed tight against the bars, as though with the last of his failing strength he had fought to get free.

When Kävik opened his eyes the blizzard was still raging, and night had drawn a black swirling mantle over the earth. He lay still, not trying to move. He remembered the dark inside the plane, the musty close smell, and the roaring sound that went on and on. He remembered the sensation of falling and the rolling and tossing that would not let him stand.

He raised his head painfully. The air was fresh and clean and laced with the wild, sweet tang of the out of doors. He heard the strident lashing of the wind in the trees, and felt the snow drive hard and fine against his face. The roaring motor sound and the falling sensations were gone. The solidness beneath him was the earth he knew so well. Through the blinding snow he saw the bulk of trees and brush. Once again the free world was all about him. But he was not free. He was still trapped inside the iron cage.

Kävik tried to stand, but could not. All that marvelous strength that had helped him win the North American was gone. His whole body ached, and every breath was a stabbing pain. He rested for a little, then tried again. On the third attempt he made it, but would have fallen had he not leaned against the bars of the cage. He trembled violently, and his hindquarters refused to hold his weight. He sank back to the floor of the cage.

He coiled into a tight ball, as northern dogs always do during a blizzard, and tucked his nose into the thick fur of his belly. In a little while he drifted off. The storm became a remote sound that grew farther and farther away. The aches and pains of his battered body seemed to follow the sounds of the storm, and finally disappeared as once again he sank into deep shock.

All that night the storm howled over the mountains and down into the valley, piling the snow deep. Normally such a storm would not have bothered Kävik. He had often slept out in forty-below weather when snow drifted completely over him to form a cocoon in which he was comfortably warm. But his many injuries and the terrifying crash had thrown him into shock. His normal body temperature was lowered. Now the cold of the blizzard got through the thick, wolf-gray coat. He shook uncontrollably, and his bruised, battered muscles stiffened.

The long, bitter night passed. Dawn came, gray and thin, and the storm still raged. It continued most of the day. Snow drifted through the bars of the cage and partially covered the dog. But not once did he move. Early in the afternoon the wind slacked off; the swirling curtain of snow began to thin. By the middle of the night the storm had blown itself out. A pale moon sailed into an ink-blue sky, and the stars shone with a frosty brilliance. The earth sank into utter stillness, held in the grip of biting cold.

The blizzard had laid a deep blanket over the wreckage of the plane and piled snow up the sides of the iron crate. To any eye the wreck was now only a mound of uneven snow. The cage was a stump or a rock with snow piled high on its flat top.

Kävik awoke late in the day. He did not try to stand or move about. He knew there was no strength left in his big body. He was ravenously hungry. He'd had nothing to eat the day of the race, and only one small fish and a drink of water afterward. His mouth and throat were on fire. He twisted his head and licked snow until his thirst was somewhat satisfied. He raised his head slightly and looked out at the free world so near.

The long night came with its intense cold

and deathlike hush. Dawn brought a pale sun that slid low across the sky but gave no warmth. All day Kävik lay curled in a tight bundle. A plane came over the mountains and dived low into the valley, trailing its thunderous sound directly over the wreck. Near the end of the day a second plane shot the full length of the valley and disappeared toward the sea.

Dark closed over the earth, and the moon and stars came out. They threw long shadows across the snow. A wolf pack howled far back in the hills as it raced down some unfortunate animal's trail. The sound of their voices rose and fell and rose again, riding the frigid silence. Sometime later a pair of coyotes woke the night with a series of shrill yappings.

This valley was rich in game, and the blizzard had driven every living thing to cover. Now they were all out, hungry and searching for food. Woe to any animal without wings or swift feet or powerful jaws or claws to defend itself. The very cage that held Kävik prisoner now saved him from being eaten.

With the dawn two coyotes came out of the brush and stopped to look at the cage. After a time they moved cautiously forward to investigate. They sniffed carefully about the cage. Kävik represented food, and their keen minds told them he was helpless. But the cage kept them suspicious and nervous. Finally, the boldest stretched a paw through, and clawed at the body. So feeble was the life that flickered in the big dog that this failed to rouse him. The coyote next tried to pull him close so he could reach between the bars with his teeth. But he could not move the heavier dog. In time they trotted away in search of easier game.

A snow-white weasel humped across the clearing within a few feet of the cage without stopping. His mind was on other things. A red fox came to the edge of the brush and hung there like a shadow, sharp ears pricked forward while he studied the odd structure with the still form of an animal inside. After a moment he turned and silently disappeared.

The cold sun was dropping toward the rim of the distant mountains when the lynx came. He was a big fellow, and in his prime. A full-grown lynx will fight a wolf and kill it, for he has not only teeth to fight with but four feet studded with razor-sharp claws with which he can rip an enemy to shreds. The lynx was a stranger here, a long way from his natural habitat. He had wandered into the valley some time before. Because he had found that it abounded in snowshoe rabbits, his favorite food, he stayed. Along with the other wildlife, he had been driven to cover by the blizzard, and had not eaten for several days. Since the storm he had caught one rabbit. This was not enough to sate the appetite of a full-grown lynx. He was hungry.

The lynx moved through the valley on big fur-padded feet—seeming almost to drift over the deep snow. His tufted ears were pricked forward, and his round yellow eyes glistened as he slipped silently from thicket to thicket in his search for food. In time he came to the small clearing where the wrecked plane and the iron cage lay. He stopped at the edge of the clearing and studied the cage with interest. He saw where the coyotes had beaten a path around the cage, and he saw the still form of a big animal inside. Finally he moved forward, his stub tail twitching.

The lynx stopped a few feet from the cage,

Glen Loates, *Canada Lynx*, 1971
Private Collection

and examined it carefully. Then he walked completely around it several times. At last he sat down close to the bars and looked at the still form inside. He couldn't understand why this big animal didn't wake up and run or turn and fight. He reached a tentative paw through the bars, dug razor-sharp claws into the dog's flank, and yanked. He immediately jerked the paw out again, and waited expectantly.

The searing pain roused Kävik momentarily. His big head came up; his eyes flickered open and his lips lifted briefly in a snarl. Then his head dropped again and he lay still.

The lynx reached between the bars again. He was bolder now. He was about to hook his claws into the yielding body and jerk it against the bars where his teeth could reach it when he heard the sound. For an instant he froze, the paw upheld, claws extended. The sound swelled to a thunderous roar that filled the valley. A great white "bird" burst over the treetops and rushed down upon him. He streaked for the nearby thicket in utter terror.

The "bird" passed overhead and disappeared, trailing the sound after it, even before the cat reached the patch of brush. The lynx dived into cover and crouched trembling beneath a cluster of limbs. The "bird" did not return. Deathly silence settled over the valley again.

CHAPTER THREE

Andy Evans was up before daylight. He tiptoed about the kitchen, getting his own breakfast and putting up a lunch. This was Saturday, and he had to run his trapline. He hadn't run it since before the blizzard, and it was going to be a rough all-day job after that storm. He needed an early start. This was his second year running the line. Last year he'd made almost five hundred dollars. He hoped to do as well this season.

Breakfast over, he closed the damper on the stove. He stacked the dishes in the sink, got his bottle of matches and shells from the cupboard, and slipped on his parka. He took his rifle and belt ax from behind the door, and was ready to go. Before he left, Andy tiptoed to the bedroom door, and listened. Normally, his father and mother slept late Saturday and Sunday mornings. His father was watchman at the Hunter's Point Cannery, and in winter there was little to do. This morning he heard his father stirring about. Ever since Smiley Johnson's plane had been lost, his father had been rising early and spending all day at the cannery's shortwave radio, keeping in check with the six bush pilots who were combing the country, searching for the downed plane.

Andy quietly let himself out the kitchen door, took down his packsack, stuffed his lunch inside, and slipped the straps over his shoulders. He stepped into his snowshoes and headed off through the deep snow toward the distant valley and his trapline. Fifty yards from the house he stopped and loaded his rifle.

Andy Evans was fifteen. He was rather thin and bony, with brown hair and a scattering of pale freckles across his face. His heavy-boned frame held the promise of a big man. After he had loaded the rifle, he stood a moment, looking at the night scene spread out below him. The moon was just dropping to its bed in the sea. It and the stars threw a soft light over the earth. Against the whiteness of the snow, the scene lay in black relief.

Their home, furnished by the Hunter Cannery, perched on a rise of ground some hundred yards above the sea. He could see the pale ribbon of trail leading down to the dark bulk of the cannery buildings, the long pattern of the dock, and the outreaching sea. A single boat lay at the dock. It was the cannery tender waiting for the dog Smiley Johnson was flying out. A second trail from the house plunged into a black mass of timber on the right. The trail threaded its way through those trees for a mile, and emerged at the end of the one short street of Copper City.

It wasn't really a city, just a collection of houses and a few stores. A half century ago there'd been a big copper mine here, and the town had held a thousand people. The copper ran out some years ago, and the mine was abandoned. So were most of the homes. A hundred or so people still lived here.

"It should be called Fish Town now," Andy's father said. "Everyone who lives here either works in the cannery or seines[1] during the summer."

Andy's father worked in the cannery.

The moon dropped into the sea, and Andy knew daylight was only an hour or so away.

---

1. *seines* (sāns), catches fish with a net that hangs straight down in the water, with floats at the upper edge and sinkers at the lower.

He turned abruptly and slogged off across the tundra.

The valley that held Andy's trapline had been punched into the center of a massive nest of snow-covered peaks. The valley was wide and deep; the floor was sprinkled with brush and timber, ideal for fur-bearing animals. The sides were steep, and rimmed with jagged, bare ridges.

By the time the cold sun broke over the mountains and down into the valley, Andy had taken two muskrats and a weasel. He kept going until the sun told him it was near noon, but he took no more fur. He sat on a stump and ate his sandwiches, then went on again. He guessed he was about halfway over the line. It would be long past dark when he returned home this day.

Sometime later he ran onto the lynx tracks. He kept a sharp lookout. A lynx would bring good money, a lot more than all the muskrat and weasels he could take today. He caught another weasel, and began to feel good. It should be a pretty fair payday. The next two traps had been sprung. He reset them. The next three had not been touched.

The sun was dropping toward the jagged rim of the valley and the night's cold was beginning to set in when he heard the plane. He stopped and watched it race down the valley and pass over him. It was Swede Ecklund's white job. Swede was one of the bush pilots searching for Smiley Johnson.

Andy went on, keeping a sharp lookout for the lynx. He took another weasel. There were two traps to go. The next was empty. One more, then he could head back for home.

He came to the edge of a small clearing, and there was the lynx moving stealthily into the open from the opposite side. His body was crouched, ready to spring. His eyes were fixed on something straight ahead. Andy raised the rifle, and fired. The cat caught the motion, and whirled. Andy saw his bullet kick up the snow beyond. He'd shot an inch over the cat's head. In two lightning bounds the lynx disappeared into the brush.

Andy stepped into the clearing, disappointed that he'd missed. Then he saw what the odd-shaped mound of snow covered. There was twisted yellow metal under that snow. He saw half a blade of bent propeller, and a broken ski dangled at a grotesque angle. He saw a side of metal and bold black letters, SMI, that ended in a great jagged hole. An odd-looking crate with iron bars lay some distance off.

He had found Smiley Johnson!

For a little he just stood there, shocked by the realization. A single thought kept running through his mind: Smiley almost made it. Two more minutes, and laughing, happy-go-lucky Smiley Johnson would have been safe. Two minutes, less than five miles! Finally he looked all about the clearing. There was no sign of life. No human tracks led away from the wreck. The stillness of death was in the frigid air.

Andy forced himself to go to the plane. There he stepped out of his snowshoes and worked his way through the wreckage until he could look through the door's broken window. Smiley was bent double over the wheel as though asleep. He was still strapped to the seat. Without thinking, Andy said in a small, frightened voice, "Smiley, oh, Smiley!" Then he turned quickly away. He was trembling, and felt half sick.

He saw the crate, the tramped-down snow around it, and moved that way. He dropped on his knees and looked in at the still form of the wolflike dog. At first he thought the dog was dead. His eyes were closed, and there was no movement of breathing along his thin sides. Then Andy noticed the flank where the lynx had torn the skin. Fresh blood was oozing from the wound.

Andy removed his mitten, put his bare hand through the bars, and laid it on the dog's head. He was not sure he felt warmth. He ran his hand down the muzzle to the nose. There was warmth there. The dog was alive. But Andy had seen enough in a year and a half of trapping animals to recognize the gray look of death. He sat back on his heels and studied the dog critically. So this was the lead dog of the team that had won the North American Sled Dog Derby at Fairbanks. He didn't look like much now.

Andy knew he'd have to start back immediately and tell his father what he'd found. But he couldn't leave the dog here like this. Night was coming on. By the time he reached home, and his father could get a party together to come up here, it would be tomorrow morning. The dog would never live that long. He'd die. Or some wild animal like the lynx, or that pack of wolves that was running the ridges every night, would somehow get at him and kill him. It would be better to put the dog out of his misery before he left.

Andy thought of the dog lying helpless and injured, trapped for three days in the cage. At least he should die outside, free once more.

Andy smashed the padlock with his belt ax and opened the cage door. He reached inside, carefully turned the dog, and slid him out head first. Then he lifted the rifle, placed the muzzle against the dog's forehead, and drew back the bolt. He was about to pull the trigger when the dog's eyes opened and he looked at the boy. The blue eyes of the boy and the yellow ones of the dog studied each other. His eyes held the boy's with as direct a gaze as Andy had ever known. Scarcely realizing what he was doing, Andy tilted the rifle muzzle away and eased back the bolt. As though that was what he had waited for, the dog's eyes closed. Andy watched for them to open again. Then he realized they weren't going to.

He knelt there, trying to decide what to do. Until a moment ago the solution had been simple. Then he had looked into those yellow eyes and was no longer sure. Maybe the dog had a chance to live. If he did, he deserved it after all he'd been through. Andy decided he'd have to take the dog home with him. That would be a real job with some five miles of deep, soft snow to plow through. He'd need some sort of sled to put the dog on. Andy studied the cold sky, gauging the daylight he had left: about another hour. It would be very late when he got home. He'd better face the prospect that he might become too tired and have to spend the night out. In subzero weather that was a thing no one deliberately did. He'd never done it, but he was sure he could. He had plenty of matches and his rifle.

Maybe the dog will die on the way home anyway, he thought. If he does, I'll just leave him.

His mind made up, Andy's thoughts turned to something he could haul the dog on. He didn't want to, but he returned to the plane and began searching through the wreckage. He found a four-foot wing tip that had been torn away. It was light and would make a good sled. Now he needed straps or rope to make a harness for himself and to tie the dog on. There might be some inside the plane. Andy wrenched the door open and crawled inside. He made his way to the back carefully, keeping his eyes from the still figure in the seat. There he found a coil of rope.

Andy cut holes through the thin aluminum wing and threaded the rope through. He made a loop big enough to slip over his shoulders and across his chest. He pulled this makeshift sled to the iron cage.

The dog opened his eyes briefly as Andy carefully worked the animal's body onto the sled and tied it with ropes across the shoulders and hips.

With the dog secured, Andy took up his rifle. He worked the rope across his shoulders and chest, leaned into the loop, and began the long slow miles home.

At the end of the first quarter mile, Andy knew he had tackled a bigger job than he'd thought. The snow was deep, and though the wing section slid easily enough, the dog was heavy.

The pale sun fell behind the ridges, and night spread swiftly across the land. The moon came up and the stars were bright, casting an eerie, soft light over the snow, in which the boy could see a surprising distance.

Andy continued his slow pace back down the valley, stopping to rest only when he could go no farther. At each stop he went back, knelt beside the dog, and stroked his head and spoke to him. Several times the dog opened his yellow eyes briefly.

Andy's stops became longer and oftener. After several hours, he realized he hadn't the strength to get home. He'd better look for a place to spend the night before he was too tired to get a fire going and drag up enough wood for the long hours ahead.

He found a spot some minutes later against a down tree. At the big end of the tree he kicked the snow away to make a hollow to start a fire. He gathered dead limbs in the nearby brush and dragged them up. With his belt ax he chopped an armload of sliver from the side of the tree. Luckily, he had cut into a pocket of pitch.

The pitch flamed up with the first match, and he carefully added chips. He broke up the limbs and fed them into the flames until the fire was big and roaring. Then he pulled the broken wing with the dog close to the log. The heat hit the log and bounced back. It made a small pocket of warmth in the freezing cold of the night.

Andy loosed the ropes and felt the dog's nose. It was hot and dry. He guessed that the dog had a fever, and hadn't had a drink for several days.

Andy packed his handkerchief with snow and held it close to the heat and let the melting snow soak the handkerchief. He lifted the dog's head, pried his jaws apart, and squeezed the precious drops into his mouth. The dog could not swallow, and Andy stroked his throat. At last he felt the muscles work once, convulsively. He repeated the procedure several times, and each time he had to stroke the animal's throat.

Andy gathered more wood, and built the

fire high. He sat with his back against the down tree and let the heat soak in. He watched the dog closely, hoping the heat would rouse him. But there was no change. Andy wondered if his folks were worrying, and guessed they were. He wasn't too worried or disturbed. He had his rifle; the fire was big and warm; and there was plenty of wood. The presence of the dog, even in his present condition, wiped out all feeling of loneliness.

Sometime later he heard the wolf pack running the barren ridges high above. Their voices came down into the valley in a series of high, savage notes that echoed and reechoed up and down the valley.

Their sound seemed to get to the dog, or Andy imagined that he moved slightly. The boy tossed more wood on the fire, and the flames leaped up, spreading their light across the snow. He laid the rifle across his knees and leaned over to stroke the dog's head. He said gently, "It's all right. It's all right." But he couldn't tell if the dog heard him or not.

THINK AND DISCUSS
Understanding
1. What methods does Charlie One Eye use to train Kävik?
2. How does Kävik react to Charlie One Eye's training?
3. What does Charlie One Eye believe is George Hunter's reason for wanting Kävik?
4. After surviving the plane crash, what dangers does Kävik face?
5. What is the important decision Andy makes after he finds Kävik?

Analyzing
6. From what **point of view** is this story told? How do you know?
7. How would you describe Andy?
8. How would you **characterize** Charlie One Eye?

9. Is **setting** important to this story? Why or why not?

Extending
10. Do you remember a coach or teacher who pushed you beyond what you thought you could do? Did you perform your best, or not? How did you feel about this person while you were in training? How do you feel now?

READING LITERATURE SKILLFULLY
Cause/Effect Relationships
In most stories and novels, there is a **cause-and-effect** pattern in the events. Each incident is caused by and logically follows the one that happened before it. For example, Charlie One Eye has always

wanted to win the North American Dog Sled Derby. The effect, or result, is that when he finds a pup with the qualities that will make a good lead dog, he decides to enter the race one more time.

For each of the following causes, give the effect.

1. Charlie One Eye trains Kävik to be a fighter.
2. George C. Hunter leaves his office just in time to see the finish of the race.
3. Smiley Johnson works on his plane in the morning and doesn't leave for Copper City until noon.
4. A great white "bird" flies overhead just as the lynx is about to attack Kävik through the bars of the cage.
5. Kävik opens his eyes and stares at Andy.

VOCABULARY
Compound Words

What are the two separate words in the word *snowshoes*? The words when put together mean "shoes for walking in the snow." *Snowshoes* is a compound word, a word made up of two or more words that do not change in form or meaning when they are put together. Note that *snowshoe rabbit* is also a compound.

Decide whether each word below is or is not a compound. Write the word. Then write either the meaning of the compound or "not a compound."

1. massive	6. bush pilot
2. bedlam	7. cannery
3. bloodlines	8. trapline
4. throwback	9. shortwave
5. wolverine	10. tundra

THINKING SKILLS
Evaluating

To evaluate is to make a judgment based on some sort of standard. How do you evaluate Charlie One Eye's methods of training Kävik? Are they fair? Are they effective? Does Kävik benefit or suffer?

You may want to compare the methods and effectiveness of teachers or trainers who have appeared in other selections in this book. Recall, for example, Brownie in "Nobody's Better Off Dead," Anne Sullivan in the excerpt from Helen Keller's autobiography, and Harriet Tubman.

COMPOSITION
Writing a News Story

Charlie One Eye tells George Hunter that every racing club from Maine to Mexico will know Kävik's name within a week. Write a short news story about the race. Focus on Kävik as the winner. Describe his physical appearance and the qualities that make him a winner. Also tell about the scene at the finish line. If you prefer, you may write a news story about the missing plane. For either story, remember to tell what happened, when, where, why, and who was involved.

Writing Your Own Story

Imagine that you are the age you are now and live near Charlie One Eye in Alaska. Write a short story of no more than three or four paragraphs about watching Charlie train his dog team. Suppose you have observed Charlie on several different days. Include a description of Charlie's training methods as they are explained in the novel, but also invent new incidents or techniques that are not told in the book. Be sure the things you make up fit with Charlie's methods. You might begin with the sentence, "When I watched Charlie One Eye with his dog team, I could not take my eyes off Kävik, the leader." For help, refer to Lesson 9, "Writing Your Own Story," in the Writer's Handbook.

ENRICHMENT
Making a Map

On a large piece of paper on a bulletin board, start making a map to show Kävik's travels. At each place in which something happens to Kävik, use a symbol that stands for his experience there. As you continue reading the novel, add to the map.

Comment

Sled Dogs

There are several thousand professional and amateur sled-dog racers, or mushers as they are called, worldwide, but most live in the United States and Canada. They come from all walks of life. It is the musher, the sled driver, who generally trains a team of dogs and who decides which dog works best in what position.

Sled dogs fall into four general categories. The *lead dog*, the brains of the team, is the most important dog. It keeps the other dogs moving, the lines tight, and the sled on the trail. It must be the fastest dog and accepted as lead by the other dogs. The lead dog follows the trail by feeling the firmness of the snowpack and by scenting teams that have gone before.

The *swing dogs* come right behind the lead dog and are needed in the "swings," or the turns, the sled makes. These dogs make sure the others stay on the trail rather than fall into deep snow.

The main job of the *team dogs* is to pull, and they must have power and stamina.

Although a dog usually pulls its own weight, it is capable of pulling more.

Wheel dogs, the brawn of the team, are usually the largest and strongest. They run right in front of the sled, steering it and withstanding the pressure as it bounces behind them.

The dogs are connected to each other and the sled by a gangline, or towline, of nylon or aircraft cable. Each dog wears a padded harness of webbing around the shoulders and under the chest. Booties are used to keep snow from balling up between the pads on a dog's feet and also to keep the pads from freezing or being cut.

The lead dog is the one that responds to all the driver's commands. Many of the terms come from the old mule-skinners' vocabulary. *Gee* and *haw* mean "veer right" and "veer left." *Come gee* and *come haw* mean "turn the team and sled completely around to the right or left." *Whoa* means "stop." *Hike*, *go*, or *come on* means "start," and the word *mush* is never used.

Writer's Craft

Write Good Beginnings

A good beginning is one that captures your attention and gets you involved right from the start. Since there is not just one way to begin, an author must decide which aspect of the story to emphasize first. Some authors like to begin by describing the time and place, or setting. Other authors may choose to focus your attention on an important character. All good beginnings, however, make you want to keep on reading in order to find out what happens next.

Walt Morey begins his novel, *Kävik, the Wolf Dog*, with an incident that happened when Kävik was only a puppy. Notice how in the first sentences, the author establishes the relationship between the trainer and his dog.

> Charlie One Eye lifted the squirming pup by the scruff of the neck and looked at him. His careless grip pinched the pup's tender skin, and he wriggled and whimpered in protest. But the man studied him with no concern. (page 454, column 1)

Morey also uses this early episode to demonstrate one of the dog's most important qualities—his unusual spirit.

> Again the hand sent him spinning and howling. . . . Once more he wobbled uncertainly to his feet, prepared to do battle. The hand swept up—and the pup stopped. He had learned painfully what that hand could do. . . . He continued to growl and show his teeth. But he did not attempt to bite. (page 454, column 1)

It is this quality that causes Charlie to consider entering the North American Sled Dog Derby for the third time. Thus, you meet these two characters and also are given Charlie's goal. Will he win the race? The beginning of this novel makes you want to know.

In a novel, the author usually begins each chapter as carefully as the first to maintain your level of interest. Chapter Two begins with a detailed picture of the dog's frustration at being in a cage.

> Now he twisted about the small enclosure, growling and snarling. He clamped his big teeth on bar after bar, and bit and wrenched. It was no use. He was firmly imprisoned. (page 458, column 2)

As you continue reading, pay special attention to the beginning of each chapter. Look for the seed of a conflict or problem. See the way the story unfolds as a result of what happens during the opening paragraphs. Notice how the author makes you wonder what will happen next and keeps you moving through the novel.

When you read, notice a good beginning. When you write, choose a good beginning.

CHAPTER FOUR

Andy wakened with his father's big hand shaking him, his voice saying gently, "Andy. Wake up, Andy. Wake up."

Andy started up, clutching the rifle. The fire had sunk to a bed of glowing coals; the dog lay on the broken wing tip as he had been, motionless. Andy rubbed his eyes. In spite of the freezing cold and the wolves running the ridgetops, he had slept several hours.

His father was saying: "When it was way after dark and you still didn't come home, we got worried. It's awfully easy to fall and break a leg or something."

"I'm glad you came," Andy said. "I was played out. I had to stop."

His father looked down at the still form of the dog, and asked, "Where did you find Smiley Johnson?"

"About two miles back. He came down in a little clearing on the valley floor. He—He's still in the plane. He didn't even have a chance to get out of the seat. I found the dog in an iron crate about fifty feet away. It had been thrown right through the side of the plane."

Kurt Evans knelt and looked at the motionless dog. "So this is Kävik, the wild dog that won the North American." He ran a big hand lightly down the dog's body and over the wolflike head. "I'd like to have seen him

before this happened. Too bad you dragged him this far. He's almost dead. You should have put him out of his misery."

"I tried to. But at the last minute he opened his eyes and looked at me." Andy searched for words to explain what that look had done to him, but could find none. "If he'd been running or had jumped me, or if he just hadn't looked at me, I could have done it."

"Maybe it's just as well," his father said. "We'll take him in—if he lives to make it that far. Then Mr. Hunter will know we made every effort to save his dog. Well, let's tie him on the sled and get moving."

It took but a minute to fasten Kävik; then his father slipped the rope over his shoulders, leaned his big chest into the loop, and moved off effortlessly. Andy followed, carrying his rifle and packsack. They made the full distance home without a stop.

At home, Andy and his father carried Kävik, still on the wing tip, into the kitchen. They laid him carefully on the floor. Andy's mother said, "What on earth! Where did you get a dog?" She kissed Andy. "You had me worried, staying out this way. Now, get out of that parka. I've kept your supper hot." Her eyes went to Kävik again, then up at Andy's father. She caught her breath and stood perfectly still, her gray eyes wide with shock, as Kurt told her what had happened.

At the end she murmured: "Poor Smiley. He never would believe he couldn't fly through any storm. 'Put wings on the coffeepot,' he used to say, 'and I'll fly it.' " She looked at the dog again. "What are you going to do with him?"

"I'll have to leave him here for a while," Kurt explained. "I've got to go to the airport and tell Swede Ecklund to call off the search, and arrange for a party to go out and bring Smiley in. And I'd better call Mr. Hunter long distance and ask him what he wants to do about his dog."

"Dad," Andy asked anxiously, "what will you tell him?"

Kurt Evans dug big fingers through his short brown hair, and studied Kävik. "I'll have to tell him how he seems to me," he said finally.

"How's that, Dad?"

"Almost dead."

After his father had left, Andy knelt beside Kävik, loosed the ropes about him, stroked his head, and looked anxiously for some change for the better. There was none.

Laura stole glances at her son as she bustled about, getting his dinner on the table. She sat across from him and watched him pick absently at his food, frowning and silent. Finally she asked, "Andy, when did you find Kävik?"

"About three o'clock," he said, not looking up.

"And you're wrapped up in him already."

"I guess so." Andy looked up, his eyes very blue. "I never felt this way about a dog or anything else before." He shook his head, at a loss to explain the sick shock that had rushed over him at the sight of the wreck with Kävik lying in the cage, trapped and helpless. He'd visualized the dog lying there through the blizzard, and the following two days of bitter cold, with no one to care for him and nothing to eat and drink. Wild animals had tried to get at him and rip him to pieces. A great sympathy had welled up in Andy. He ran fingers through his hair with the same gesture his father used. "Maybe I should have put him out of his misery," he said. "But after all he'd been through, I couldn't do it. He was trying so hard to live. He needed all the help he could get."

"Of course." Laura smiled. "I'm glad you brought him home."

Andy finished his dinner, helped his mother with the dishes, and was bending over Kävik again when his father returned.

"What did Mr. Hunter say?" Andy asked immediately.

Kurt Evans looked at his son soberly. "He said, 'Take the dog out and shoot him.' "

"But he's not dead."

"He's practically dead. You were going to shoot him."

"But I didn't. Dad, what did you tell Mr. Hunter?"

"I told him how the dog seemed to me. That he's got broken bones and probably internal injuries. That he's unconscious most of the time. I told him that there's not a veterinary within two hundred miles and that I didn't think the dog would live to be taken that far, if I could find one."

"Did you have to make it sound so bad?"

"I learned long ago that Mr. Hunter wants all the facts, not hopeful guesses and surmises. I gave him the facts as I see them. I'm not exactly an amateur with dogs, you know."

"But Kävik might live," Andy argued. "I

didn't think he'd live till we got him home. But he has. And he doesn't look any worse now than when I found him."

"He couldn't, and still breathe!" Kurt said flatly. "It's no use, Andy. Mr. Hunter said what to do, and he expects me to do it. I think he's right." He reached for Andy's rifle behind the door. "I wish I could have given him a promising report. But I honestly couldn't."

Andy knew his father for a gentle, compassionate man who thought things out carefully and slowly. There seemed to be no argument.

Then he thought of one last thing.

"Why can't we have Dr. Walker look at him first?"

"Vic Walker's a medical doctor, not a vet."

"He *is* a doctor," Andy argued. "He can tell us things."

Kurt shook his big head. "Why can't you give up, Andy?"

Dr. Walker was a bachelor. He lived in a neat white house at the end of Copper City's one street. The front part of the house was his office. He lived in the rear.

There was light in his living quarters when Andy pounded on the door.

Dr. Walker, wearing carpet slippers and an old robe, answered the door. He was tall and lean, about Andy's father's age. He had snapping eyes and straight black hair beginning to thin on top.

"Andy! What brings you out this time of night?" His voice sounded grumpy and annoyed.

"Can you come to the house right away?" Andy asked.

Dr. Walker looked at him, then grunted and began slipping out of the robe. "Accident?" he asked.

"Sort of. Can you hurry?" Andy mumbled.

"Happens every time," Walker grumbled to himself. "Can't get sick or hurt in the daytime so they can come to the office. Got to wait till the middle of the night. What's wrong?" he asked, buckling his overshoes. "Your dad hurt?"

"Dad's all right. He—He's with Mother."

"Your mother, eh? What's wrong with Laura?"

Andy just stood there. All his fine courage had leaked away in the face of Dr. Walker's forbidding manner. He feared if he told the doctor that he was taking him out to see a dog, he'd never go.

Dr. Walker didn't seem to notice Andy's hesitation. He took up his bag. "Let's go."

Outside, there was no chance to talk, and Andy was glad. He was hard put to match the doctor's long swinging legs.

They passed through the dense woods to the house in a matter of minutes. Andy held his breath as they entered the kitchen. Dr. Walker growled at his father, "Kurt, fine time to get a man out. What's wrong, Laura?" He saw Kävik, and turned to Andy, eyes snapping. "You brought me out here to treat a dog?"

"Didn't he tell you?" Kurt Evans asked.

Walker's eyes dug into Andy accusingly, "He let me believe Laura was sick."

Andy looked at his father, "I just said you were with Mother."

"You let me jump to a conclusion," Walker said angrily.

"I didn't know what to say. I was afraid he wouldn't come if I told him it was for Kävik."

Watercolor by Daniel Schwartz

Laura said: "Andy should have told you, Vic. He was supposed to. But you can understand why he wouldn't. Now, as long as you are here, would you mind looking at the dog?"

"Yes, I mind!" Walker said shortly. "I'm a doctor. I don't treat mutts, especially mutts that look like wolves."

"This is no average mutt," Kurt said. "This is the lead dog of the team that just won the North American at Fairbanks."

"Well—bully for him!" Walker said acidly.

"This is the dog Smiley Johnson was flying out when he was lost."

Walker stopped. "Smiley's been found? Good!"

"Andy found him. Smiley's dead."

"That's too bad. Where'd he crash?"

"On Andy's trapline up in the valley."

"Kävik's laid out there ever since the crash, trapped in an iron cage," Laura added.

"Quite an ordeal," Walker observed dryly.

"Vic!" Laura said, "this dog has been through an awful lot and he's still alive. Won't you at least look at him?" Walker hesitated, and she added, "What possible harm can that do?"

"Well," Walker finally agreed, "all right." He knelt beside Kävik, opened his bag, and took out the stethoscope. Andy watched anxiously as Dr. Walker listened to Kävik's heart, took his temperature, looked at his eyes, pried open his mouth and examined his gums. He ran his long hands down the dog's flanks, probing gently. At last he sat back on his heels and looked up.

"Well?" Laura asked.

"He's got broken ribs and a broken leg. He's in shock. He can't swallow. His pelvis may be broken and he may have internal injuries that only X ray would show. And he's running a temperature."

"Isn't there anything good?" Laura asked.

"His pulse isn't bad, considering. About the best I can say is that his heart's beating and he's breathing."

"Could a good vet bring him through?" Andy's father asked.

"It'd be nip and tuck. Where'd you find one?"

"I don't know."

"Even if a vet saved him," Dr. Walker observed, "his chances of full recovery are slim. My advice is to put him to sleep. I'll do that if you like."

"No!" Andy cried instantly. "Can't you doctor him like you do people?"

"A vet doesn't doctor people," Dr. Walker said, "and I don't doctor animals."

"I suppose there is a great difference," Andy's mother observed. "A doctor couldn't possibly treat a dog. He wouldn't know how."

"Oh, he could," Walker admitted grudgingly. "A broken bone's a broken bone. As for medicines, some are interchangeable. There's a lot I could do."

"Then do it for Kävik," Laura said quietly.

Dr. Walker looked at her a long moment, his sharp eyes boring into her calm face. He shook a long finger at her, and growled positively: "You don't trap me like that! There's more to this than just treating a dog. Suppose this town should learn I'd used the same medicines, the same instruments to operate on this dog that I use on their wives and husbands and kids? The fact that everything is sterilized would make no difference. If I used medicines and instruments meant for humans on a dog, pretty soon they'd be asking which certificate I had—one to practice on dogs and cats or one for people. They'd crucify me, run me out of town."

"I hadn't thought about that," Andy's father agreed. "Folks up here wouldn't stand for it."

"Then take care of Kävik here," Laura suggested.

Dr. Walker shook his head. "He needs intravenous feeding, X ray for internal injuries. He should be checked every couple of hours. Somebody'd start asking why I was coming out here so often. Just forget the whole thing, Laura. It won't work."

Andy knew his mother wasn't listening.

She was biting a fingernail thoughtfully. "Victor," she mused, "your house sits at the end of the street, almost up against the trees, doesn't it?"

"You know it does."

"That trail we take to town comes out practically at your back door. Kurt and Andy could take Kävik through the woods and into your house without being seen. You could fix up a place for him in the back room and you'd have him there where you could do all the things necessary and look in on him whenever you liked. No one need ever know. When Kävik is well enough, Kurt and Andy can bring him home the same way."

Dr. Walker was shaking his head emphatically all through Laura's plan. The moment she finished, he said, "That's a crazy idea. No!"

"You mean it wouldn't work? Or you can't do anything for Kävik?"

"Oh, it might work."

Andy's mother smiled. "Then you'll do it?"

He continued to glare at her. Finally he threw up his hands. "All right! Anything to get you off my back." He turned to Andy's father: "You fellows carry the dog on that wing slab, and don't shake him around or jolt him. And don't let the whole town see you. I'll go home and have the back door open."

"Victor," Laura said.

"Now what?"

"Thank you."

Dr. Walker grunted. He gave her his sourest look, jammed on his hat, and went out without a word.

CHAPTER FIVE

While Copper City slept, Andy and his father carried Kävik through the dark woods and into the back door of Dr. Walker's house. Dr. Walker had fixed a pallet with an old blanket in a corner of the room off his kitchen. They put the dog down carefully and untied the ropes from around his body.

Andy's father asked, "Do you want us to stay and help?"

"I'll take it from here. I want both of you out of here—now!"

"Vic, we appreciate this. We really do."

"Sure! Sure! Now get, will you?"

Andy stroked the unconscious Kävik's big head, and asked Dr. Walker, "Can I see him tomorrow night?"

"Make it late," Dr. Walker said. "The later, the better. If there's a light in the office, don't come in because I'll have a patient. Wait until the light's in the back here. Be careful. If somebody sees you coming and going out my back door every night, they'll start to wonder."

"I'll be very careful," Andy promised.

"Don't expect too much," Walker warned. "I'll do all I can, but I'm only human."

"Yes, sir," Andy said. "I know."

Andy and his father peeked out the kitchen door, saw all was clear, and went hurriedly across the yard into the black protection of the trees.

When Andy slipped through the doctor's back door late the following night, he was sure, for a sick minute, that Kävik was dead. The dog lay as if he had never moved, his eyes closed. There was a cast on one front leg, as well as a white patch on his flank where the lynx had torn him. A bottle was fastened to the back of a chair, with a tube running down to the dog's leg. The liquid in the bottle was half gone. It seemed to Andy's anxious eyes that Kävik looked thinner, weaker than ever.

"He's still alive," Dr. Walker said. "He's got three broken ribs, but luckily none of them punctured a lung. His front leg is broken; his pelvis is broken. There's a hole on his other side as big as a fifty-cent piece where a piece of metal stabbed almost completely through him. He's lost a lot of blood."

"Is he going to live?" Andy asked fearfully.

"I'm not sure yet."

Andy knelt beside Kävik and began stroking his head gently. Dr. Walker picked up a book, sat in an old rocker under the light, and began reading. From time to time he glanced at the boy. Finally he closed the book and said gruffly: "I've done all I can for him. The rest is up to him and nature. But he's got one big thing in his favor."

"What's that?"

"He's part wolf. That gives him a toughness an all-dog doesn't have. Anyway," Dr. Walker grumbled, "he'd have to be tougher than whalebone to live through your horsing him up on that chunk of plane wing and then dragging him through the snow."

"I was very careful," Andy said. "I eased him out of the cage and slid him on the wing. I didn't lift or pull him. I didn't tie him tight on the wing either, just tight enough so he wouldn't slide off. And I didn't jerk when I pulled the wing through the snow. I did give him a drink. Maybe I shouldn't have."

"How'd you do that?"

Andy explained how he'd packed his handkerchief with snow, let it melt, then dribbled the few drops from the soaked handkerchief into Kävik's mouth.

"Giving him a drink was good. You're sure he swallowed?"

"I stroked his throat, like this. I felt him swallow."

Dr. Walker's dark eyes studied the boy. "Did you have first aid in school?"

"We've never had such a thing."

"Hm-m-m." Walker opened his book and began to read again. After a minute he glanced at Andy, and muttered again, "Hm-m-m."

"I'd better go." Andy rose. He stood looking down at the wasted figure of the dog. The breath of life barely stirred his sunken flanks, and not once tonight had he looked at Andy. Andy's eyes followed a drop of liquid from the bottle, down the tube where it disappeared into the dog's vein. By so little was his life held. A wave of despair rushed over Andy, and he said in a thick voice: "He's going to die. I know he is." He turned and went quickly out the door.

But Kävik did not die. There was nothing soft or flabby in his makeup. He clung to the slender thread of life with a tenacity only a half-wild creature, raised and toughened to the trail by a man such as Charlie One Eye, could know.

Each night Andy was relieved to find Kävik still alive. He watched as the bottle slowly fed the precious life drops into the dog's bloodstream. But Kävik didn't move or open his eyes. It was on the third night, when Andy knocked softly on Dr. Walker's door and was admitted, that he found Kävik's eyes open and the bottle and tube no longer attached to him.

"He's going to live, isn't he?" Andy asked happily.

Dr. Walker permitted himself a faint smile. "He'll live. But he's not out of the woods yet."

Andy knelt beside Kävik, and reached out to stroke his head. As the dog's eyes watched the hand, he seemed to try to draw away, but was too weak.

"He's not used to being petted or handled," Dr. Walker said. "All he knows about a hand is getting belted by it."

Andy let his fingers touch the sharp, pointed ears, stray down, and scratch gently at their roots. "What do you mean, he's not out of the woods?"

"I don't know if he's going to make a full recovery."

"How can we tell when he has?"

"If he doesn't limp on that front leg, if the pelvis heals properly, and if his back legs get strong again. I've done all I can. He's getting no medicine now, no intravenous feeding. He just needs a lot of rest and all he can eat. He can get that at your place just as well as here. Get that wing section out of the corner."

They eased Kävik onto the wing tip and tied him securely. Then Dr. Walker and Andy carried him back through the dark trees to the Evans home.

Laura brought blankets and made him a bed in a corner of the kitchen. "He's not used to a house and being around people, so this will be good for him," she said.

"You may be right," Dr. Walker agreed. They eased Kävik off the wing tip and onto the blankets. Dr. Walker said: "All he needs is the usual care, water and food. Let him sleep. He should do a lot of sleeping."

"What if he tries to get up?" Laura asked.

"He won't, until he knows he can. He's smarter than some patients I've had. When he does get up, have Andy come for me. I'll take the cast off his leg, and we'll see how he looks. And, Andy, come at night."

"Then you think he'll make a full recovery?" Andy's father asked.

"I don't know. But we'll get a pretty good idea once he starts moving around."

So Kävik was settled in a corner of Laura's warm kitchen. Every night when Andy came in from school his first questions were: "Has Kävik got up yet? Has he walked?"

"Not yet," his mother would answer. "Remember, Dr. Walker said it would take time."

Andy would kneel beside the dog, stroke his fur, scratch at the roots of his sharp ears, and say anxiously: "He's looking better, don't you think, Mother? I'm sure he's gaining a little weight. His ribs don't stick out so much. He ought to get up soon, hadn't he?"

But Kävik didn't get up. He didn't even try. He continued to sleep long hours. He heard the cold winter wind bite at the corners of the house while he lay warm on his blanket. His delicate black nostrils were filled with the delicious odors of cooking food. And he ate this food every night from a white bowl. Not once did he taste the half-thawed fish that had been his chief diet for the two years of his life.

Kävik was three-quarters dog, but Charlie One Eye had cultivated the wolf in him. The dog part wanted the companionship, the love, and attention of people. Now these dormant emotions came alive in him.

At first he tried to object to the hands stroking and petting him, but he was too weak. Then he became accustomed to their touch, and soon he was waiting expectantly for it. He knew the different hands without opening his yellow eyes. The man's hands were heavy; his strokes and pats were solid, but gentle. The boy's touch was lighter, but it was sure and smooth, and he spent much more time stroking him. The woman's hands were soft and light. Not once did he receive a stinging cuff followed by shouted commands and curses. These hands stroked and petted, and the voices were quiet and friendly.

Kävik was a young dog, and the time he'd spent under the rough treatment of Charlie One Eye had not yet made his nature permanently harsh and unyielding. He responded to these people, but it was to the boy he gave his love. As Andy's mother said: "It's logical. There's not much difference between a boy and a dog. And considering that a dog's years are seven-to-one in ratio to a human, they're about the same age. It's youth answering to youth."

Each day Kävik waited for the boy's return from school. He would lie head up, ears pricked forward. He could catch the quick crunch of the boy's feet in the snow long before human ears could.

Andy always went straight to Kävik, and knelt beside him to stroke his head and scratch at the base of his ears while he searched for improvement. He would say anxiously: "Seems like he ought to walk pretty soon. He ought to try, anyway. He can't get strong just lying here."

And his mother always answered: "Stop trying to rush it. Dr. Walker said Kävik will know when he can get up."

Kävik would lift his head toward the boy, and his black nostrils sucked in the clean, fresh scent of the outdoors that clung to the boy's clothing. The boy would talk to him, his voice low and intimate, while his fingers went on exploring at the roots of his ears or under his chin. Kävik learned to roll his big head so this marvelous sensation was transferred from one side to the other.

Each night Andy would hold forth some tempting morsel of food and coax him to take it. But for a reason that went back to the first time Charlie One Eye had sent the pup sprawling with that stinging slap of his big hand, he could not bring himself to stretch forth his head and take it. Andy always ended by putting the morsel of food in his bowl, whence it was immediately taken.

Kävik enjoyed most the time after dinner. The kitchen was warm, and the faint aroma of cooking still lingered. The three people sat about the table, taking advantage of the overhead light. The boy would be studying, his brown head bent over books. The man read a paper or magazine, and the woman was usually mending some article of clothing or knitting on a sweater she was making for the man. Kävik would stretch full length, close his eyes, and listen to their low voices and bask in the wonderful feeling of belonging.

After a time the boy would put away his books, get out a comb and brush, and sit on the floor beside him. "All right," he'd say, "time to get beautiful." Then for half an hour he'd brush and comb the dog's wolf-gray coat. Finally the boy would put the comb and brush away, set a pan of fresh water before him, smooth the wrinkles from his blanket, give his big head some final pats, and disappear up the stairs. The older people would stay a while longer. Then the man put out the light, and they followed the boy. Kävik would be alone in the kitchen.

There came a night when the family was eating dinner, and Andy's father was talking about the coming canning season. Andy felt a touch at his arm and looked down to find Kävik at his elbow, balancing shakily on three legs.

Andy yelled: "Dad! Mom! Look, look! He's got up. Kävik's got up!" He put his arms around the dog's neck and looked at his father, his eyes smiling, "He can walk, Dad. He's going to make it! He's going to be all right, isn't he?"

Kurt leaned across the table and studied the dog. "Looks promising," he agreed. "We'll see what Vic Walker says."

Andy started up. "I'll go get him so he can take the cast off his front leg. He said to come for him when Kävik got up."

"It's too early," his mother said. "Victor told you to come when it was dark. You eat your supper."

Andy sank back in his chair. Kävik kept looking at him, his tail waving.

Andy took a bite of meat and held it under the dog's nose as he'd been doing every night for days. Kävik licked his lips and looked at the meat, then up at Andy. "Come on," Andy coaxed. "I'm going to keep right on until you take it. You might as well start now." The yellow eyes of the dog and the blue ones of the boy looked into each other. Then Kävik rolled back his lips from the big tearing teeth and reached forward cautiously.

He lifted the meat from Andy's palm so deftly the boy scarcely felt it. Andy patted his head and crooned, "That's a good boy. That's good!" He proffered another piece. Kävik took it. Andy reached for a third.

"No you don't," his mother said. "You eat that. Kävik's had his dinner, and he's stuffed."

Kävik stood expectantly at Andy's elbow for another minute, then hobbled back to his blanket and lay down. That had taken all his strength.

Andy was so excited he scarcely touched his food. His father and mother held him back two endless hours before they finally let him go for Dr. Walker.

After Dr. Walker had examined the dog critically, he said: "He's looking surprisingly good. He's put on weight. He's a mighty tough animal."

They gathered around and watched silently as he carefully cut the cast away.

Kävik lay there for several minutes, as if he weren't sure what he should do. Then he scrambled up. He wobbled uncertainly on three legs, then carefully, slowly put the fourth on the floor. The act seemed to give him confidence. His sharp ears shot forward; his back straightened. He seemed to grow taller and to stand with purpose. He dropped his head in a typical wolf gesture and looked obliquely up at them with yellow eyes.

"Good heavens!" Andy's mother said. "He does look like a wolf!"

"A big arctic wolf," Andy's father said. "A throwback sure."

"Lead him around a little," Dr. Walker said to Andy. "Let's see how he walks."

Andy coaxed Kävik through the kitchen,

into the dining room, the living room, and back into the kitchen. The moment he began to walk, all that fine confidence deserted him. His head dropped and his ears flattened. He limped terribly, and when he reached the kitchen again, he collapsed panting on his blanket in the corner.

Andy looked at Dr. Walker fearfully, trying to read his long, sober face as he studied Kävik. Andy's father looked at his feet and said nothing. His mother bit her lips.

Andy knelt and stroked Kävik's head, and waited, scarcely daring to breathe. He could hear Kävik's labored panting and feel his whole body tremble with the effort. He wanted Dr. Walker to say Kävik was going to be all right more than he'd ever wanted anything. But he feared the doctor wasn't going to. The wreck, the injuries, and lying out there in that iron cage in the storm had been more than even his wolf-tough constitution could overcome. He was not making a full recovery. Maybe they should have put Kävik to sleep that first night when Dr. Walker wanted to.

"Sure he's weak and he's got a bad limp," Dr. Walker said. "He's been through a mighty tough ordeal. I wouldn't have given a plugged nickel for his chances that first night." He leaned forward and scratched Kävik's ears. "You're about as tough as they come." He looked at Andy then, and said, "I told you that wolf strain was tough, boy."

Andy's heart almost stopped, then began to race madly. "You mean he's going to be all right? He's going to get well. He'll make a—a——"

"A full recovery?" Dr. Walker asked. "I'd bet on it. Naturally, he's stiff and weak. But with exercise he'll grow strong again. That stiffness will limber up and disappear."

Andy put his head down to Kävik, and murmured: "You hear that? You're going to be all right again."

Kävik sniffed at the boy. Then, for the first time in his life, he ran out his pink tongue and licked a human face.

Dr. Walker snapped his bag closed, and rose.

Andy's father asked, "How much do we owe you, Vic?"

"I said I'd pay it, Dad," Andy said quickly.

"Never mind, Andy. . . ."

"It was Andy's idea to get Dr. Walker," Andy's mother said. "He should pay his own bill."

Dr. Walker looked at Andy. "Where you going to get this money?"

"Out of my trapping money."

"I see." Dr. Walker rubbed his long jaw thoughtfully. "Bring me about five dollars sometime."

"Now, Vic . . . !" Kurt began.

"That will hardly pay for the cast," Andy's mother said.

"You said that was Andy's bill. Then let Andy and me settle it. Of course that five dollars won't pay the whole bill, not by a long shot," he said to Andy. "But if I know your folks, you're going to college. You just might decide to study medicine. If you do, and some kid brings you a sick dog, see that you take care of him. Understand?"

"Yes, sir," Andy said. "And I'll bring the money to your office tomorrow morning."

"Good enough." Dr. Walker picked up his hat.

After Dr. Walker had gone, Andy coaxed Kävik into two more tours of the kitchen, dining and living rooms, and each time he collapsed panting on his blanket. But it seemed to Andy he was a little steadier the last time. He patted Kävik's head, and said, "You did fine. Just fine." Kävik thumped his tail on the floor and lifted his lips in a grin.

Andy's father said: "You're not forgetting that Kävik belongs to Mr. Hunter. You'll have to give him up, you know."

"I know," Andy said. He straightened the blanket a little; then he said "Good night" to his parents, patted Kävik's head again, and climbed the stairs. The dog watched him out of sight.

A little later Laura and Kurt turned out the light, and Kävik was left in the darkness of the kitchen. He lay for some time looking at the stairway up which the boy had disappeared. Finally he rose laboriously, limped to the foot of the stairs, and looked up.

The boy was up there somewhere. He put a paw on the first step, and began to climb. Lifting his weight up each step was much harder than walking. Soon his legs began to tremble; halfway up, he sat down on the steps, and rested. Then he went on. At the top he faced a short hall with two doors. His delicate nose led him unerringly to the boy's door. The door was ajar, and he pushed it open. He walked across to the bed and put his cold nose against the boy's cheek.

Andy sat up with a start. "Kävik! You climbed the stairs. You climbed the stairs!" He put his hands on either side of the big head and pressed his face against the furry forehead. "You're sure getting strong fast. I knew you would. I knew it!" Kävik waved his tail gravely and licked Andy's face.

"So you want to sleep with me," Andy said. "That's dandy!"

Andy pulled a throw rug on the floor to a place at the head of the bed. He patted it and said, "Come on, lie down. Right here."

Kävik curled up on the rug with a tired sigh. He felt the nearness of the boy in the bed beside him, his hand trailing over the side touching him. The smell of the boy filled his nostrils. This was where he wanted to be.

CHAPTER SIX

Now that Kävik was able to move about, he improved rapidly. In the first couple of days he inspected every inch of this strange house where he'd come to live with people. Laura let him out every afternoon, and he remained out until Andy returned home from school.

Once again Kävik enjoyed the crisp winter air and deep snow. It provided just the sort of violent exercise he needed to build back his strength. He spent his time traveling between the cannery and the house at Kurt's heels, or exploring the slopes behind the house almost to the valley where Andy's trapline began. He was never out of sight of the house for long. He would come limping back through the snow to make sure everything was just as he'd left it.

But Kävik never missed meeting Andy when he returned from school through the dark belt of trees. That time sense, which all animals have and which tells them when important things are to happen to them, told him within a minute or two just when Andy was due. He'd stand in the yard waiting, head up, ears pricked forward expectantly, yellow eyes watching the trail where it emerged from the timber.

The moment Andy appeared, Kävik would let out a glad yelp and go struggling through the snow to him.

He still ate in a corner of the kitchen and begged morsels while standing at Andy's elbow each night. After dinner he would curl at Andy's feet, close enough so the boy could reach down and scratch his ears while he did his homework. But he no longer slept on a blanket in a corner of the kitchen. When Andy climbed the stairs to go to bed, Kävik now climbed beside him. He slept on the rug on the floor at the head of Andy's bed.

In this manner was the memory of Charlie One Eye and the two brutal years of his life wiped out of his mind. These three people and the house were his whole life. It was as if he had never had any other.

Kävik's thin flanks filled out; the sheen returned to his thick, wolf-gray coat; and last of all the limp completely disappeared. Once again he looked like the magnificent animal George Hunter had seen win the North American at Fairbanks.

On the third weekend, Andy took Kävik with him when he ran the trapline. It was still dark. The earth was bathed in the soft light of a half-moon when they crept down the stairs, let themselves quietly out of the house, and went up the slope. All morning Kävik tore through the snow, leading the way. He'd make short side excursions to investigate,

then rush back to check on the plodding Andy. He was particularly interested in the traps, and stood close at each set to watch as the boy removed the game and reset the trap.

At noon they ate lunch sitting side by side in the snow in the protection of a log. Andy carefully tore each sandwich in two and fed half of it to Kävik. "I'll bet this is the first trapline you've ever run," Andy said. "Like it?"

Kävik waved his tail, and grinned.

"Me too," Andy said, and ruffled the fur between the yellow eyes. "It gets real lonesome running a line alone."

They came in time to the wreck of the plane and the iron cage. Kävik advanced cautiously. He sat down a few feet from the cage, and studied it. He looked back at Andy, as if asking for an explanation.

The boy said, "You sort of remember, is that it?" As if the boy's voice gave him confidence, Kävik got up and moved closer, then sat down again.

"Go ahead," Andy said; "look at it good."

Kävik moved forward again, thrust out his nose, and sniffed the iron bars.

"See," Andy said, "it can't hurt you." Kävik walked all around the cage, then returned to Andy.

Andy bent and put his arms around the dog's neck. Kävik whined softly and licked Andy's face. "Do you remember that cage?" Andy asked. "Do you know that Smiley was killed here? They say dogs sense things like that. Is that what's bothering you?" Kävik continued to whine, and stayed close to Andy until the boy rose and started up the valley again.

"It's lucky for you I came when I did that

day," Andy said. "I guess it was lucky for both of us."

After that first time, they passed the broken plane and iron cage many times, but Kävik never went near them again.

The end of the trapping season came, and with its passing Andy knew that spring and the annual salmon run would soon be here. George C. Hunter would return and find Kävik. Again the rock was in Andy's stomach, and each new indication of spring made it heavier. The daylight hours grew swiftly longer. The first warm breath blew softly across the land, shaking the snow burden from the trees.

A dozen men flew in from Seattle to overhaul the cannery's machinery and make ready for the season. A pair of early seine boats came in from the south and tied to the dock to await the coming salmon run. The first salmon stragglers fought their way up the tiny stream. The rock in Andy's stomach grew heavier and heavier.

School let out for the summer. The next day Andy went to town to look for a job. During fishing season every man in town, who could get away, went seining. This left vacancies in the local stores. Andy figured that this year he was old enough and big enough to fill one of these temporary openings.

For the first time he took Kävik with him. They walked the full length of the town's one street to Tom Murphy's hardware store. This would be a good place to start. Murphy's son, Bob, who worked in the store with his father, had gone seining last summer.

Mr. Murphy scratched his head, and said:

"Bob's out right now, trying to contact the skipper of the *Lady Claire*. That's the boat he was on last year. If he gets it, he'll go. Come see me again tomorrow, Andy." He leaned over the counter, adjusted his glasses, and looked down at Kävik. "That's quite a dog you've got there. Or is he a dog?"

"He's part wolf," Andy said proudly. "His name's Kävik. It means wolverine."

"Hm-m-m," Mr. Murphy said. "Seems like I heard that name somewhere."

"He won the North American at Fairbanks," Andy said. "He—He's Mr. Hunter's dog."

"Sure. I remember. Well, you come see me tomorrow, Andy."

On the street again, Pinky Davis hailed Andy. Andy had always liked Pinky. He was short and fat and jolly. Now he called, "Hey, Andy, where'd you get the wolf?"

Andy stopped in the middle of the dirt street and said: "He's only part wolf. He's the lead dog that won the North American."

"That's the dog Smiley Johnson was flyin' out for Hunter?"

"Yes," Andy said. "His name's Kävik. It means wolverine."

"That so," Pinky said, and he and the seiners looked on Kävik with approval.

A half-dozen dogs swung into the far end of the street and trotted forward in a tight pack. They were all local mongrels that seemed to belong to no one, and they scrounged their living where they could. As a pack they terrorized every cat and every other dog in town. They were led by a big, ungainly houndlike mongrel named Blackie.

Blackie spotted Kävik, and stopped. Here was an outsider, a stranger, and to add incentive, an animal that looked like a wolf. Blackie plunged forward, bawling at the top of his voice. The whole scrubby pack howled at his heels.

Kävik waited until they were almost upon him; then he whirled suddenly, and, tail between his legs, dashed into the opening between the Alaska Bar and Murphy's Hardware. The pack charged into the opening after him. They cornered him against a high fence, and Blackie rushed in, struck the cringing Kävik, and bowled him over. He leaped upon Kävik, big jaws sprung wide. Kävik dodged Blackie, charged through the rest of the milling pack and out into the street again. A small long-haired dog, too slow to keep up with the pack, was just arriving to join in the fight. He charged into Kävik on short legs, got hold of a flying hind leg, and bit down. Kävik shook the small dog off with a frightened yelp of pain, raced the full length of the street with the pack in howling pursuit, and vanished among the trees, heading for home.

"Well, holy mackerel!" Pinky Davis looked at the men around him. "Did you see that? Why, the little old Rags even took a bite outa him and he wouldn't fight back." He looked at Andy. "What'd you say his name meant? Wolverine? You sure it ain't rabbit, Andy?"

"Couldn't be a rabbit," one of the seiners said seriously, "a good healthy rabbit'ud kill 'im."

Andy turned without a word and went blindly up the street, the laughter following him. He felt sick and bewildered and fighting mad. He'd like to take a club to that fat little Pinky Davis and his friends, and to that whole pack of dogs—especially Blackie. Oh, especially Blackie!

Andy found Kävik crouched far back under the front porch in the dark. He coaxed him out and patted his head and scratched at the roots of his ears. "What's wrong with you?" he asked gently. "You could have licked that big Blackie easy. Then the rest would have left you alone. And that little mutt of a Rags. You could eat him in one bite. Why'd you run away like you were scared to death? You did act like a rabbit. Why? Why?" Kävik's ears were laid flat to his big head, and he whined pleadingly while his tail thumped the ground hopefully. "I don't understand," Andy said miserably. "I just don't understand."

He took Kävik into the house with him. The dog went to his corner of the kitchen and lay down and looked disgraced. The dishes and food were on the table. Andy's father had just finished his lunch and was slipping on his coat in preparation to go back to the cannery. He looked down at Kävik, and asked, "What's wrong with him?"

"That bunch of dogs in town," Andy said angrily. "That Blackie . . ." He told them what had happened. His father just stood there looking down at Kävik. "So he didn't make a complete recovery after all," Kurt Evans said.

"But he's well and strong," Andy insisted. "You said yourself he couldn't look better."

"Physically he made a fine recovery," his father agreed. "But here"—he tapped his chest—"he didn't make it. He's lost his confidence and courage."

"How, Dad?"

"Probably the plane wreck. He sustained

injuries that would have killed any other dog. Then he lay out there in the storm all that time, more dead than alive. It knocked all the fight out of him."

"You said, if he didn't make a complete recovery . . ." Andy began fearfully.

"I was thinking physically. He's made it physically."

"Will Mr. Hunter want him like this?" Andy asked.

"No," Andy's mother said positively.

"Then maybe Mr. Hunter will sell him to me," Andy said hopefully.

"You wouldn't mind that every dog in town can run him ragged?"

"I'd mind. I just won't take him to town. Do you think he might sell Kävik to us, Dad?"

"He might. A coward would be distasteful to Mr. Hunter. And no one else up here will want him. Selling him to you for anything he can get would be a way to recoup a little of his loss."

Laura nodded. "That's how he'll look at it." She smiled at Andy. "I think you're going to have a dog."

"It all depends on Mr. Hunter," Kurt said.

"When he comes, you'll tell him how Kävik is?"

"I'll tell him," his father said grimly. "Mr. Hunter wouldn't take kindly to learning the sort of dog he's become after he'd taken him home."

Andy looked at Kävik, and said with helpless anger: "He even ran away from that little old Rags. It doesn't make sense."

"It makes sense."

"When he's five times bigger, a part-wolf lead dog?" Andy pointed out. "What's he got to fear from that little mutt?"

"It's not really fear. It goes much deeper."

"All I know is, he ran away like he was scared to death," Andy said.

His father studied him a long moment; then he said quietly, "Sit down, Andy. I'll try to explain."

Andy slipped into a chair. His father sat across from him and said: "Andy, I've wanted to tell you something for some time, but I didn't know how to make it clear to you. Now maybe I can."

"What's that, Dad?"

His father looked at his clenched hands, and said, "Haven't you wondered why I'm working as a handyman around the cannery and as watchman in winter, when I was once one of the top seiners in the North?"

Laura said in a sharp voice, "Kurt!"

"It's time he understood," Evans said deliberately. "If he hasn't asked himself already, he soon will. And now that he's older, he'll be getting around these fishermen more. He'll hear talk, and he should have it straight. Andy's not a child anymore."

Kurt Evans looked at Andy, and Andy said, "Boats cost a lot of money."

His father shook his head. "That's only part of the reason. Several people have offered to finance me. Mr. Hunter tried to get me to take the *Hustler,* that big seiner he has lying at the dock. I've said no every time." His father rubbed his hands together with a faint nervousness. "That's where Kävik and I are so much alike."

"How do you mean, Dad?"

"Remember when we lost our own boat, the *Freedom,* five years ago?"

"I remember," Andy said.

She had struck a rock in the fog, and sunk. Two crewmen and his father's brother, his Uncle Eddie, had been lost. Before it was over, their home and all his father's and mother's savings were gone.

"That night," his father said quietly, "I lost my confidence. I'm not physically afraid. But a man can take such a beating he loses the desire to try again. The heart is knocked out of you. You're empty. That something you should have—that makes you want to fight—is gone."

Andy felt sick and shocked at hearing his father talk so. He suddenly wanted to protect him, to make excuses. He said, "But, Dad, it likely wouldn't happen again."

His father nodded. "I know that. But there is always the possibility. It's one of the hazards of seining, especially in these waters. In the past five years your mother and I have managed to save a little. We want our own home. You've got college ahead of you. It would all be wiped out if it happened to me a second time. I tell myself I can't take that chance. But there's more to it than that. I simply don't have the desire to make a fight of it."

"And it's something like that with Kävik?" Andy asked. "The plane crash, almost being killed, then lying in the cage for days knocked all the fight out of him?"

"That's about it. He finds it easier to run away than to put up a rousing fight. Nothing is driving him to make the effort. It's easier for me to go along as I am, saving a little, getting our home, putting you through school, being secure—than to take any chance, however slim it might be."

"I see," Andy said. And he really did.

"But you still want Kävik, if Mr. Hunter will sell him?"

"Yes."

"All right. I'll see what I can do." His father rose.

"Dad," Andy asked, "will it always be this way with Kävik and . . ." He bogged down, embarrassed.

"With Kävik and me?" his father finished. "With Kävik I'd say yes. For myself . . . I don't know. I just don't know." Then he went out and down the trail to the cannery.

Andy got the job at Murphy's Hardware. Every morning when he went to work Kävik accompanied him through the trees to the edge of town, and there he stopped. Never again did he venture into the street. He stopped well back in the trees where he could not be seen. Andy would pat his head and scratch his sharp ears and say: "I've got to go to work now. You'd better go back home." Kävik would watch him enter the street, then turn and trot back down the trail.

At night Kävik always waited in the fringe of trees for him. The dog's time sense was amazingly accurate. He never missed. He'd be standing in the middle of the trail, his bushy tail waving as he did a little dance step with his front feet to show how happy he was to see Andy.

Andy would kneel in front of him so Kävik could put his big head against the boy's chest while Andy scratched his ears and talked to him. "Did you have a good day?" he'd ask. "Did you go to the cannery with Dad?" Then he'd tell Kävik about his day. "I didn't do much. I don't know why Mr. Murphy keeps me around. Everybody's out fishing." Then he and Kävik would race home through the trees together.

Andy had never had a pet to love before, and Kävik had never been loved or given his love. Now each was discovering how wonderful their companionship could be. Andy had stopped worrying about Mr. Hunter's eventual arrival. He was convinced that Mr. Hunter would never want Kävik once he knew what a coward he was. And to ease his mind further his father and mother were equally convinced. His one remaining problem was, How much would he have to pay for Kävik? And again his reasoning, and that of his father, told him, not much. "Who else would want him?" his father asked. "A dog that's a coward is no good up here."

The short seining season was half over when Andy, heading home one night, found no Kävik waiting for him in the fringe of trees. He looked about for several minutes, whistling and calling. Blackie and his pack heard the whistling, and padded down the street to investigate. Andy picked up a club and hurled it at them. Blackie stopped, and the pack stopped behind him. Andy picked up another club and started forward. "You want a fight," he said to the big black dog, "I'll give you one." Blackie swung about with a disdainful toss of his head and started down the street. The pack fell in at his heels. Rags, the little feist, trotted in the rear, his short legs pumping to keep up.

Andy dropped the club and turned toward home. Maybe Kävik had gone to the cannery with his father and had forgotten the time. But he never had before. Or maybe Blackie and his pack had discovered him waiting here in the trees and had chased him home. He bet that was it. One of these days he'd get even with that Blackie. He'd get him good!

Dinner was on the table when he walked in, and his father and mother were waiting for him. Kävik was not lying in his corner in the kitchen. "Where's Kävik?" he asked. "He wasn't waiting for me."

Andy's father looked at him and said nothing.

"Mr. Hunter was here right after lunch," his mother said gently.

"Oh." Andy looked at his father. "You talked to him about Kävik? You told him how he was? How much does he want for him?"

Andy's father shook his head. "He took him, Andy."

"Took him! You mean Kävik's gone?" Andy's voice was high and a little sharp. "You said he wouldn't want him. You said we could buy him."

"I said I didn't think he'd want him," his father said patiently. "Well, I was wrong."

"Did you tell him how he was? That he won't go to town because he's afraid of the other dogs? Did you tell him, Dad?"

"I told him, Andy. I even offered to take him downtown with Kävik and let the dogs chase him to prove it. He just stood there and smiled and didn't believe me. He thought I was just making up a story so he wouldn't want his dog and we could keep him. I can't blame him for thinking that. Kävik looks wonderful, as you know. Big, healthy, and strong. He looks like the Kävik Mr. Hunter saw win the North American in Fairbanks. That other part of Kävik, that we know about, doesn't show on the surface. Mr.

Hunter was just glad to get his dog back."

"But did you offer to buy him?" Andy persisted.

"I didn't get a chance. That dog wasn't for sale at any price."

"Where is he now?"

"Gone south aboard the *Copper Queen*. They've been gone about four hours."

"Mr. Hunter was very nice about it," Andy's mother said. "He wanted to pay the doctor bill, and offered us two hundred dollars for his keep. But we wouldn't accept it because we'd all enjoyed Kävik."

"He should have been nice," Andy said bitterly. "You could have come and got me so I could have said good-bye to him."

"I thought it was better for both of you this way," his mother said. "It would have been awfully hard on Kävik to be taken away with you standing there. Anyway, you knew this could happen. You've always known it."

"I thought maybe we could keep him when Mr. Hunter understood how he was. I—I counted on it."

"I counted on it too," his father said thoughtfully. "But how do you show a man when he refuses to be shown? When he won't look?"

"It's disappointing, but it's not a tragedy," Andy's mother said practically. "We had Kävik for a while and we all loved and enjoyed him. Mr. Hunter likes him and will give him a fine home and the best of care. That's the way we have to look at it. Now, come and eat your dinner before it gets cold."

Andy shook his head. "I'm not hungry," he mumbled.

"There's no sense being a child about this," his father said sharply. "Come and eat."

"Let him go," Laura said quietly. "Let him go."

Andy went upstairs and sat on the bed and looked down at the rug where Kävik had slept every night. That rock was back in the pit of his stomach again. This time he felt it would never leave.

THINK AND DISCUSS
Understanding
1. Who helps Andy return to Copper City with Kävik?
2. Why does the town doctor object to treating Kävik?
3. When does Andy know that Kävik will live?

4. To what animal do Pinky Davis and the seiners compare Kävik and why?

Analyzing
5. Compare Kävik's response to Andy and his family with his response to Charlie One Eye.
6. How are Kävik and Andy's father alike?

7. Why doesn't Mr. Hunter believe that Kävik is now a coward?

Extending

8. Do you think Kävik would have recovered from his injuries if he had been returned to Charlie One Eye? Explain.

REVIEWING: Characterization

See Handbook of Literary Terms, p. 635.

Characterization is the method an author uses to create a fictional person. An author may develop a character through describing the individual's physical appearance, speech, actions, and inner thoughts or by revealing the attitudes and reactions of other characters.

1. Give examples from Chapters One to Six that show Andy Evans to be each of the following: (**a**) enterprising; (**b**) sympathetic; (**c**) resourceful; (**d**) optimistic.
2. Characterize each of the following: (**a**) Kurt Evans; (**b**) Dr. Walker; (**c**) Laura Evans.

VOCABULARY

Context

You can sometimes understand the meaning of an unfamiliar word because the context provides a synonym. Other times you can figure out an unfamiliar word because it appears in context with a group of words that you know.

Use the context for each italicized word to determine its meaning. Choose from the meanings below the sentences.

1. Unlike Charlie One Eye, some trainers use words of encouragement, rewards that motivate, and other *incentives*.
2. A *compassionate* man, Kurt Evans is

sympathetic toward Kävik, but he feels he has to follow Mr. Hunter's orders.

3. Although they are used in different situations, cots, *pallets*, and sleeping bags have the same purpose.
4. Without his wolf-tough makeup and strong *constitution*, Kävik probably would not recover as he does.
5. Blackie gives a *disdainful* toss of his head to show his scornful response to Andy's threats.

Meanings
nature
rejected
small beds
showing contempt
desiring to help another's suffering
things that urge one on

COMPOSITION

Reading/Writing Log

The author of *Kävik, the Wolf Dog* begins each new chapter in such a way as to immediately draw you into the action and capture your interest. For example, read the paragraph below from the beginning of Chapter Four. Copy the sentences in your **reading/writing log** and add another example of your own from the beginning of Chapter Five or Chapter Six.

Andy wakened with his father's big hand shaking him, his voice saying gently, "Andy. Wake up, Andy. Wake up."

Beginning a Chapter

Chapter Six ends when Andy discovers that Mr. Hunter has taken Kävik away. Suppose that the scene between Hunter and Kurt and Laura Evans were included in the book and that it began a new chapter. Write a paragraph that will make the reader want to continue reading to find out what happens next. Include dialogue, if you wish. If you are keeping a **reading/ writing log,** compare your beginning with the ones you copied.

Reporting an Interview

Imagine you are a newspaper reporter who has interviewed Laura Evans about Kävik's recovery. Write a brief account, telling what happened, how Laura felt about Kävik, what effect Kävik had on her son, how she felt when Mr. Hunter took Kävik away, and what she thinks will happen now. To capture your readers' interest, you might begin with a quotation.

ENRICHMENT
Giving a Speech

Imagine that Dr. Walker asks Andy to defend his physician's treatment of Kävik. Since the townspeople have heard that Walker used the same instruments to treat them and to treat Kävik, the wolf dog, Andy is to present his defense at a special town meeting of the Copper City Council.

In small groups, plan a short speech that Andy might give and choose one person to present that speech to the class. The class may wish to decide by vote which speech provides the most convincing defense of Dr. Walker.

 Review SETTING in the Handbook of Literary Terms, page 656.

CHAPTER SEVEN

George C. Hunter had built a palatial home high in the hills above the city. Far below lay the pattern of the streets that led toward the concrete canyons of the city's core. The canyons pointed toward the bay where the commerce of the world came in by sea. Here hundreds of industries and warehouses lined the half-moon shore, and miles of docks reached into the bay. Some docks were lined with great ships from foreign ports. Others, called fishermen's wharves, were packed solid with fishing crafts of all kinds and sizes, idled here for the coming winter. Beyond the bay lay the distant blue line of the open sea. It was to this home George C. Hunter brought Kävik.

The first day he proudly led the dog through the big hall into the immense living room. "Look, Edna," he called. "Here he is. This is Kävik. He didn't die after all. Isn't he marvelous? Isn't he some animal?"

The woman looked at Kävik. She was tall and slender. Her blue eyes were chill, and her voice was sharp and unfriendly. "So this is the great dog? George, are you out of your mind? Bringing home an animal like that. I never heard of such a thing. Get him out of this house."

"You don't understand," Hunter explained. "This is the dog that won the North American Sled Dog Derby at Fairbanks. He's part wolf, Edna. There isn't another dog like him in the country today. They don't breed these fellows anymore."

"I don't care what he is," the woman said angrily. "And I don't care what he's won. He looks like a wild animal to me. I won't have him running through this house, breaking up furniture, imported glassware, and antiques, and muddying up floors."

"He's not breaking anything or muddying up anything," Hunter said stiffly.

"He will, if you take that chain off him. This is a home, George, not a museum for all the junk you drag back here from the great North. If you want to keep this brute, you put him in that run you had built and keep him there."

George C. Hunter said quietly, "All right, Edna. All right."

He took Kävik back outside and put him in the wire and concrete-floored run he'd had built in the backyard.

Kävik lay in a corner of the six-by-ten enclosure day after day, big head on forepaws, yellow eyes staring out over the city and over the bay to the distant line of the sea—staring toward the North.

This was a strange and frightening world into which Kävik had been brought. The threshing umbrella of sound that hung over the city drifted up to him. From the bay came the occasional deep-throated bellow of a great ship entering or leaving the harbor. Some of the sounds were repeated all day and half the night on the road in front of the house. At regular intervals planes roared low over him, the thunder of their passing shaking the earth.

The deep silences he had known all his life were gone. There was only, at rare intervals, a little less sound. His freedom of movement was now confined to a six-by-ten foot concrete and wire enclosure. There was no boy to meet each night, to race wildly home through the trees with him, no kitchen with its delicious odors, no family sitting about a table talking in low voices, no bedroom where he slept the night on a rug at the head of a boy's bed. The very air he breathed here was different. He missed the clean sweet smell of the tundra, the fresh, biting tang of the open sea. This air was heavy with acrid fumes from a thousand different sources. They irritated his delicate nostrils. The voice and the smell of this strange world reacted on two of his strongest senses, his hearing and his sense of smell. The same fear he had known when he'd been placed in the iron cage and shoved into the mysterious darkness of Smiley Johnson's plane came alive within him again, and never left.

Even the people who came to see him were different. They'd stand outside his run, hold their hands behind their backs as though they expected at any moment to have one bitten off, and stare at him. "He sure is different," they'd say. "He doesn't look like he's got any dog in him. A real wolf, that's what he looks like. I'll bet he's all wolf. I'd sure hate to have those big teeth after me." Sometimes George Hunter would enter the pen and pet him just to show his friends that Kävik was tame. They'd go away talking among themselves and telling George Hunter he was foolish to keep such a vicious-looking animal around.

But no one ever spoke to Kävik. Not one of the many who came to stare ever put forth a friendly hand to pet him.

Then Tom McCarty returned from the funeral of a relative, and Kävik found one friend. McCarty was a lean, tough old man with a permanent limp. His leg had been crushed in a cave-in at George Hunter's mine ten years ago. McCarty had been with Hunter ever since the little man first went north to seek his fortune working in the mine, so Hunter took him south to work around his home as a gardener and handyman.

The first time Tom McCarty saw Kävik lying in a corner of the wired-in run, big head on forepaws, yellow eyes staring out over the city and the bay, his heart went out to him. In the past he had worked countless times behind such animals, in weather so cold a man could freeze to death in minutes if he stood still. He unlatched the gate, went inside, and squatted on his heels before Kävik. Unhesitatingly he reached out, scratched at the roots of the dog's ears, and said gently, "Hello, Big Fella. You and me, we're two of a kind."

Kävik's yellow eyes came back from that great distance and looked into the bright gray eyes of the old man.

"You don't belong in this cage or in this country anymore'n I do. A blind man could see that. We're outsiders, you an' me. We belong up where th' wind howls across th' tundra and th' snow flies. Where your ancestors run th' ridges and where I could walk for a month and never see a livin' soul—before I had this gimp leg, that is. Me, I got no choice but to live down here—with my gimp leg.

But they took your choice away from you. So here we are." Tom McCarty reached forth a big rough hand, lifted Kävik's paw, and gravely shook it.

Kävik's tail thumped the concrete, and Tom McCarty smiled. "That's more like it. Let's have no more of this mopin', eh?"

But as the days passed, Kävik continued to mope. He was still a big healthy-looking animal, but his wolf-gray coat no longer had quite the same bright sheen; his sharp ears were down flat to his head; and his eyes were not clear and interested in all that went on.

George Hunter noticed. He stood before the enclosure, and scowled at Kävik lying in a corner. "Mac," he called to McCarty, his voice sharp and annoyed, "what's wrong with Kävik? All he does is lie there in that corner and stare out. You know about these northern dogs. What's eating him?"

McCarty had been waiting for this. He knew just how far he dared go in crossing Hunter, and he went right up to it now. "He's homesick and he's lonesome, Mr. Hunter."

"He's been here more than a month. It's time he got over that. Anything else?"

"There's another thing that would sure help."

"What's that?"

"Get him outa that pen once in a while. He's a working dog, remember? Dogs like him are used to lots of exercise and plenty of room to run. Cooped up in a pen like that is no good for him. Exercise would do him a world of good. His appetite would improve and his coat would come back some."

"Exercise, eh." George Hunter was not one to prolong acting on a decision. "We've got two acres of ground here, and it's all fenced so he can't get away. Let him out, Mac."

"Here? Now?"

"Certainly."

McCarty opened the gate and stood aside. Kävik looked at the open gate, then up at McCarty, and walked out. He stood uncertainly, looking about, not understanding this sudden freedom. McCarty waved his arm, taking in the house and two acres of yard. "Go on, Big Fella," he said.

Kävik trotted off a few feet and smelled a rhododendron bush. The soft grass beneath his feet felt good after the weeks of concrete runway. He trotted on. It was wonderful to stretch his legs again, to feel the spring in his muscles, and the softness of the earth beneath his feet. Suddenly he burst into full stride, raced through a rhododendron hedge, and came to the five-foot fence. He turned along the fence at top speed, raced around a towering fir tree, burst through a stand of shrubbery, reached the next fence corner, and turned again, following it. He was a gray-white shadow streaking through shrubbery and across flower beds, running low to the ground, bushy tail stretched out, running as his wolf ancestors had run for centuries, and with their tremendous speed. His sharp ears were forward, his mouth open, sucking in great gulps of air. He was enjoying every lunging stride. He made a complete circuit of the yard, seeming to flow over the ground. Flower stems snapped; plants ripped at his passing.

Then he heard the shrill voice of the woman, high and angry. "George! Mac! Stop him! Stop him! Get that wolf out of there! He's ruining the yard. Get him out. Get him out right now!"

McCarty hobbled to cut off the racing Kävik. "Whoa!" he shouted. "Whoa! Whoa! Big Fella." George Hunter ran from the opposite direction, trying to corner him. At McCarty's voice Kävik came to a panting stop, ears cocked forward, studying the old man. "Come here, Big Fella." McCarty snapped his fingers. "Come on. The party's over." He held out his hand, walked up to Kävik, and twisted his fingers in the thick ruff of his neck. "We're gonna get in serious trouble and lose our happy home if you bust down any more shrubbery," he said in a low soothing voice. Patting the dog, he led him back to the wire enclosure and locked him in.

"Of all the stupid things to do," the woman railed. "Turning that brute loose in this yard. Just look what he's done. Look at it!"

"I know, Edna," Hunter soothed. "Mac'll fix it up tomorrow. I didn't realize the dog would take off this way. I won't let him out again."

"Well, I certainly hope not." The woman turned on her heel and went back into the house muttering angrily under her breath.

"I guess you'd better clean up these beds and get rid of the broken limbs tomorrow," Hunter said to McCarty. "And we can't let Kävik out again. But you're right. He needs exercise. Man, wasn't he a sight! I'll get a chain with a snap ring, and you can take him walking every day. I don't want a leather collar on him. It'd wear the hair off his neck and spoil his ruff." He looked at the dog thoughtfully. "He seems to like you, Mac. Maybe if you spent some extra time with him, besides the walking, it'd help him get over being lonesome and homesick and he'd look a little sharper. Take him up to the apartment with you or anything else you like. Just don't let him loose again," he said wryly.

Thereafter Tom McCarty took Kävik for a walk every day it didn't rain. They'd go up the hill because the street ended within two blocks, and that was about as far as McCarty could walk without resting. McCarty would sit on a log, stretch his bad leg before him, and look out at the bay below and the distant sea. Kävik would sit beside him, yellow eyes searching far beyond the bay and the sea— looking always toward the north. Tom Mc-Carty would pat the big head, and say: "You might as well forget it, Big Fella. It's a long long way by boat or plane, farther than you could ever go. So quit breakin' your heart over somethin' that can never be." Kävik listened to the old man's gentle voice, cocking his head first one way, then the other. At the end he placed a paw on McCarty's knee, where the man patted it. McCarty lifted the paw and shook it gravely. "It does no good to tell you this," he said. "But believe me, I know."

Winter came, but not as Kävik had known winter. It was drizzling rain that lasted for days, with the sun peeking through for a few hours at odd intervals.

During one of these sunny days George Hunter decided that he would take Kävik for his walk. "I want him to get more used to me," he explained to Tom McCarty. "I'm going to make a speech on Alaska soon, and show my slides. I bought some of Kävik winning the North American. I want to tell 'em about him. Then I want him there so people

can see him in the flesh. That ought to give them a thrill, eh, Mac?"

"It sure ought to, Mr. Hunter," McCarty agreed.

A few minutes later Hunter strode out of the yard with Kävik on the chain, trotting dutifully at his heels.

McCarty spent the time Hunter and Kävik were gone cleaning up around the pen and the yard. He was still at this when Hunter returned, walking fast. The little man's face was stormy, and his thin lips were pressed tightly together. Kävik trotted obediently at his heels, head down, plumed tail drooping. Hunter went straight to the enclosure, shoved Kävik inside, unsnapped the chain from his neck, and slammed the door. He whirled on McCarty, black eyes snapping, his voice cutting. "Did you know about him?"

"Know what?"

"That he's the biggest coward on earth. That a good-sized chipmunk can run him to death?"

McCarty glanced at Kävik. "I don't believe it."

"Listen, Mac," Hunter was savagely angry. "You know that long white house at the end of the block? Well, they've got a dog there. As we went past, he came tearing out, barking his head off."

"What kind of a dog?" McCarty asked.

"How should I know. Just a dog, a little more than half as big as Kävik, I'd guess. Well, I thought Kävik would eat him alive. He could have, Mac. But did he? Oh, no," he said bitterly. "He almost tore the chain out of my hands trying to get away. When he couldn't he tried to hide behind me. He actually lay down on the sidewalk, Mac. Can you feature that? A man finally came out and called the dog off." Hunter shook his head. "That great big tough-looking wolf lying there on the sidewalk, whimpering. It was humiliating, Mac. Humiliating. You never ran into that with him?"

"We always went the other way. Up to the end of the street. There's no dogs there." McCarty glanced at Kävik lying in a corner of the cage and looking as if he knew he'd disgraced himself and Hunter. "I just can't believe it."

"I can," Hunter said. "I saw it. And Kurt Evans at the cannery tried to tell me how he was, but I wouldn't believe him. Kurt said the beating he took in the plane wreck knocked all the courage out of him. Well, something did." Hunter scowled at Kävik. "I paid two thousand dollars for that dog, and he's not worth a plugged nickel. Two weeks from now he's the star attraction when I show those slides and make that speech at the club. How can I show a thing like that? Why, I'd be a laughingstock."

"No, you won't," McCarty said. "Nobody needs to know. There won't be any other dogs there to scare him. You wouldn't have known today, if you hadn't run into another dog that showed fight. Let him sit up there with you and take his bows. They'll never guess."

Hunter considered that possibility. "It could work, at that. You could hold him outside until I'm ready for him; then I'll take him in. He won't have to be in the room more than ten or fifteen minutes while I make my little speech about him and everybody gets a good look at him. Yeah, it'll work." Hunter's voice turned tough, "Then I'm getting rid of him—quick."

Tom McCarty prepared Kävik for the night of what he called "Hunter's One-Man Show." The day of the show he took Kävik to his quarters above the garage to groom him. After finishing, he stood back and studied the dog. "You look fine, Big Fella," he said. "Big and strong, with plenty of good beef on your frame. Hard muscles, big chest, fine posture. You look like th' lead dog that won th' North American, all right. Nobody'd ever guess." He took the dog's big head in his hands, and said: "I've got an idea what happened to you, and I understand. He don't. I'd like to keep you around, Big Fella, but Mr. Hunter won't have it. He's a mighty proud man and he's got himself out on a limb with all his big talk about you."

Kävik twisted his head, listening to the sound of McCarty's gentle voice. He put his paw on the old man's knee, and McCarty smiled and shook it again. "You're gettin' pretty good at that," he said. "Well, let's go. You'll knock these city lads dead tonight."

Mr. Hunter's club was small and exclusive. It was situated in a grove of big trees well back in the hills above the city. Tom McCarty held Kävik in an outer room while the banquet was in progress and George Hunter showed his slides. Then Hunter came out and said, "All right, Mac, we're ready for the vicious brute." He took the chain from McCarty's hand. "You might as well wait in the car. I won't keep him long."

He led Kävik into the roomful of people and up on a small platform. There he removed the chain and ordered the dog to sit. Kävik sat on his tail, yellow eyes narrowed, and looked out over the sea of faces. George Hunter began to talk, telling about Kävik and his life in the North, his bloodlines, part wolf and malamute. He told about the North American Sled Dog Derby and what it took to be a good lead dog and how important he was to winning a race.

The room was warm. The air was heavy and oppressive with tobacco smoke. Kävik began to pant. He turned his head. There was a window near the platform. His sharp ears shot forward; his yellow eyes opened wide and his big jaws snapped shut. He rose to his feet, his whole body tense. Throughout the room people began nudging each other and smiling and whispering: "Look, he's posing! Putting on a real show, just as if he knew George is talking about him. What a ham actor!"

Kävik was not putting on a show. It was a bright moonlight night, and through the window he could see the massive bulk of mountains rising against the pale sky. Flowing down those mountain slopes like a loose cape thrown over them was a forest. It looked wild and primitive. It looked like the mountains of his far northern home.

Tonight there was no chain to hold him back. He didn't hear George Hunter's sharp, "Down, Kävik! Sit, sit, I say!" He took two quick steps, muscles bunched, and launched his hundred pounds through the air. He struck the window and burst through with a tremendous crash of breaking glass and startled shouts.

Kävik landed on the soft earth amid a shower of glass, gathered himself, and streaked into the protection of the bushes beside the building. He heard doors slam as people rushed outside; voices called. He heard George Hunter's angry voice, and belly-crawled to the opposite side of the brush, and sneaked away. He came to a high stone wall and turned, following it, hunting a way out. Men searching came close, beating through the shrubbery, calling, "Here, Kävik. Here, boy. Come, Kävik. Come on."

He made a running leap at the wall and fell back feet short of the top. Another party of searchers came near, and he began to run in fear. It was bright moonlight, and he dared not show himself. He took advantage of every shrub, rosebush, and tree to keep hidden. He was slinking now in typical wolf fashion, trying to avoid detection. He was a gray shadow crouching behind a tree until a man beat past. He was a faint whisper of sound as he slipped through a rhododendron hedge on another man's heels. He was part of the rock itself as he crouched in the deep shadow of a boulder as a party went by, calling and beating the shrubbery. Finally he crept through a laurel hedge and edged his way along in its shadows. He was heading for the big front gate.

The gate was closed. A group of men led by George Hunter came threshing toward him. The rock wall on either side closed in to form a narrow opening to the gate. He was trapped.

Tom McCarty got out of the car parked nearby, hobbled forward, and looked down at Kävik crouched in the shadows of the laurel hedge. He looked up at the approaching men, and called: "Mr. Hunter, you'd better check that wall out back. There's a lot of brush for him to hide out in there, and the wall's pretty low. He might be able to jump it."

"All right, Mac," Hunter answered. "We'll check the shrubbery and the wall right away. You keep an eye out here." The search party turned away.

McCarty watched them leave, then said softly to Kävik: "All right, Big Fella, they're gone. You can come out now." He bent and snapped his fingers, and coaxed, "Come on. This's old Mac. You know me."

Kävik rose stealthily and crept to him. McCarty squatted on his heels before the dog and scratched his ears and patted his big head. "So, ya didn't like 'em in there and decided to leave in a hurry. Fact is, you don't like it down here no more'n I do. But you're doin' somethin' about it, and I can't. I know where ya wanta go. But it's farther than you'll ever get. It's more than two thousand miles of water and mountains and snow and ice and rivers. No dog on earth could cover that distance. I'd talk you out of it, if I could. But I know you'll try. You'll wind up someplace, maybe even dead. That would be better for the likes of you than staying here."

Kävik cocked his head and studied the old man's face and listened to the gentle words he could not understand. But he did understand the voice and its notes of sadness and longing. He put a paw on McCarty's knee, and the man lifted the paw and gravely shook it. "You know a lot. An awful lot. We had some mighty fine talks, didn't we? You let an old man dream about his past, and you were gentleman enough to listen and not interrupt. I

thank you for that. But it's over now." He glanced up, listening. "They'll be comin' back soon. You'd better be on your way." He rose and swung the gate open. He waved his hand outside. "There it is, what you've been waitin' for and wantin' since th' day you got here. It's all yours now. Go get it, Big Fella."

Kävik walked through the gate. Outside, he stopped and looked back. "Good-bye," the old man called softly, "and good luck."

Tom McCarty closed the gate carefully and stood looking at the spot of thick brush beside the road where the wolf-gray form had vanished. Then he sighed, and hobbled back to the car.

CHAPTER EIGHT

Kävik did not keep to the road. He traveled swiftly through the brush and timber, for here he was more at home and he was well hidden. He did not head back for George Hunter's palatial home, nor did he cut up the mountain into the heavy growth of timber. He was headed north. That sixth sense of direction told him the way to go.

He traveled near the road for some distance; then it began turning and twisting. He left it and cut through thick brush straight down the hill. He came in time to a network of paved streets and sidewalks with row on row of homes. Still heading north, he crossed some streets, traveled a block or two on others, then left them to cut across vacant lots and lawns. He came to a spot where he was looking down a steep street directly into one of the deep canyons of the city. The street was brilliantly lighted, and great lighted buildings punched deep into the night sky.

This was the origin of the sounds he'd been hearing for weeks. Now the noise boiled up the long hill and washed over him in a continuous wave.

He slunk warily down the street. The noise kept coming up to him in increasing volume. He stopped uncertainly many times. Once he turned back. Then the desire that had never left him since the day he'd been put aboard the boat in Copper City drove him forward again.

So Kävik came into the heart of the big city. As he trotted fearfully along he kept swinging his head, watching for something to rush down upon him, to pounce upon him, or fall and crush him. People turned and stared, startled to find such an unleashed animal trotting among them so intently. Several spoke to him uncertainly. Some were startled by his wolflike appearance and size; but before they could react he had disappeared in the crowd.

Surprisingly, Kävik was halfway through the worst of the traffic, following the course he knew he must keep, before he finally came to grief. He knew nothing of traffic lights. When he reached a corner where the crowd was thickest and seemed to be waiting, he threaded his way among the legs to the curb. He had learned something about traffic in the past hour. He waited until he saw an opening between the speeding cars, then dashed across the street. He had almost made the opposite side when a horn blasted almost on top of him, brakes screamed, and an automobile bore down upon him. A blow smashed into his side and hurled him through the air to land in a heap on the sidewalk among a forest of legs. He staggered dizzily to his feet.

People had moved back quickly, and he found himself in a small cleared space. A man in a blue uniform stood in front of him.

The man said, "What're you doing down here without a leash?" and lunged for Kävik. Had he reached slowly or said, "Come here, boy," he'd have caught the dog. But at the sudden movement Kävik leaped away instinctively, and dodged through the circle of people with the man plunging after him.

He turned in the direction he'd originally been following, and raced away. So swift was his flight, and so startling his appearance, that pedestrians hardly had time to gasp, "Look! Look there! What sort of animal was that? A dog? It couldn't be!"

Kävik raced down the brightly lighted street until it curved in the wrong direction. He darted across, was narrowly missed by several cars, and entered another. Soon he was leaving the lighted streets, the big crowds of people, and the open stores. The streets became dimly lit, empty of traffic and people. All the buildings were dark and closed. The city racket became muffled by distance and intervening buildings. Panic left him, and he dropped back to a steady trot that ate up the blocks.

Much later he rounded the corner of a darkened building, and there before him lay a flat body of water. A narrow dock stretched out into the water for an amazing distance. Hundreds of boats of all sizes and descriptions lined both sides of the dock. For the first time in months the wild and wonderful salt tang of the sea was in his nostrils. He heard the sleepy complaint of a nearby gull, the faint creakings of boat fenders rubbing against the dock. The dock lay in darkness except for a light at the shore end. Here the boiling sounds of the busy city were a faint echo. He did not know this was the dock on which he'd landed when he'd been brought from the North. He knew only that it was familiar and that something inside him had led him to this spot.

Kävik came to the end of the dock, and halted. The bay stretched outward in the darkness before him farther than his eyes could see. He searched for some nearby land that he might swim to, something that would take him in the direction he was traveling. There was none. But somewhere across that water was a house overlooking the sea, with the tundra rising gently behind it. In that house were warmth and love and the companionship of people. There was a boy, at the head of whose bed he'd slept and for whom he'd waited in the dark fringe of trees each day so they could race home together. It was the boy's gentle hands and understanding voice he missed most. It was to the boy he'd given the only love he'd ever known. It was to the boy and that house he was returning. He had come as far as he could. So here he would wait, for what or for how long he didn't know.

Kävik lay down, his big head on forepaws, and looked out over the water. He lay there the rest of the night.

With the coming of dawn, Kävik rose stiffly and searched the outreaching water again. He had his long look, then turned and trotted down the dock to the boat. The tide was out now. It was too far down to jump to the deck. But he could see there was no one about.

Kävik went on down the dock to the shore side. He didn't know where to go from here or what to do. He was standing looking about when several men approached, laughing and talking. He turned and trotted around a near corner. He found a dark passageway between two buildings, and went in, looking for a place to hide. An old covered stairway ran diagonally up the side of one building. Far back under the stairway he found a holelike depression, and crouched in it. The men passed the opening without looking in.

Kävik remained in this hiding place all day. He heard the distant sounds as the city awoke and the activity around the dock increased. But in comparison to the city itself, it was quiet here. Now and then people went by. There was an occasional coming or going of a boat. Nearby a seiner was being repaired. There was the constant sound of hammering and sawing. From time to time a car would arrive or depart. Trucks made irregular appearances.

Kävik lay in the hole under the stairs, and napped and waited out the day. Late that afternoon it began to rain, but beneath the covered stairway he was dry.

With darkness, Kävik again ventured forth. He was thirsty and ravenously hungry. He found rainwater collected in an old pail on the dock, and slaked his thirst. But he did not know where to turn for food. He was standing there uncertainly when his nostrils picked up a faint, familiar scent. It was the same scent he'd known in that kitchen in the North so far away. It was food cooking. He turned and followed the scent unerringly. It led him a block away from the dock to a small restaurant. He looked through lighted windows and saw people sitting on stools, eating.

He watched for several minutes, nose twitching hungrily, licking his lips in anticipation. But he knew of no way to get the food.

He was about to trot on when a pair of dogs slipped along the side of the building toward the back. A few seconds later there was a crash, then another.

A man's voice shouted angrily, "Get out of here. Get!" The two dogs raced around a corner of the building and down the street. A man in a white apron ran out and hurled a stick after them. He went grumbling toward the back again.

A woman's voice called, "What did they do this time?"

"Knocked over the garbage cans and scattered the stuff all over," the man said angrily. "I'll pick it up when I've got more time." He disappeared inside.

Kävik looked after the fleeing dogs, then in the direction the man had disappeared. The aroma of food coming from there was very strong. Those dogs had been hungry, too, and had been searching for something to eat. He crept toward the back. The scent of food became stronger and stronger. He found two tipped-over garbage cans, their contents strewn about. He could see the man through the window, working at a stove. Kävik studied the man and the garbage cans. The cans lay in deep shadows. By detouring around the pool of light thrown by the window, he could reach them. He lay flat on his belly and, keeping in the shadows, edged across the concrete. Among a clutter of paper plates, napkins, and other restaurant discards he found cold potatoes, halves of doughnuts, wedges of pie, and other pastries and chunks of sandwiches. Under the very nose of the restaurant cook he ate his fill, then crept silently away.

Kävik had learned how to survive on the docks. In succeeding nights he added to his store of knowledge. There were other restaurants scattered for more than a mile along the waterfront, and late at night he would visit them.

All day Kävik would spend sleeping in the hole under the stairway where he went undetected. At night he crept forth. He came to know the docks and every building on them. He knew every other dog in the area, and there were many strays. They ran in two's and three's, or small packs of half a dozen, and they made life miserable for the restaurant people. Kävik kept to himself. The restaurant people never saw him. Even the other dogs caught only an occasional glimpse as he disappeared around a corner or slunk briefly through a shadow. He seldom trotted in the open, even at night. He was clever and furtive and swift of foot.

But every night, rain or fog or wind, he trotted the full length of the first dock he'd visited, and stood at the end, looking out over the dark stretch of water—looking to the north—still waiting. Only at that time would Kävik seem to be unaware of his surroundings and forget to peer furtively about. He'd stand straight and tall, head up, sharp ears pricked forward, eyes searching farther than eyes could see, ears straining for sounds that never came.

It was here one night that he first saw the woman. A fishing boat had been moored within a few feet of the end of the dock for days. He was looking out over the bay when the woman's voice came to him, kind and soft, "Hello, there! You're late tonight."

Kävik turned his head and looked at her. The woman sat motionless on the low, stepped-down section of the deckhouse. She wore a slicker and sou'wester hat pulled low over white hair. "Are you lost?" she asked. "Or are you waiting for somebody special? I've seen you every night. You're not like the other mutts. They're here because they've got no other place to go. You're here for a reason. I can tell."

Kävik's sharp ears came forward, and he listened to the gentle voice. "You have the class and dignity of a gentleman. You look well fed, too, not half starved like some of these others. But you're just as dirty. I'd like to give you a bath and cut that tar off you. You're not a local dog. I've seen your kind before—in the North. Did you come down on a boat and get lost somehow? Are you waiting for your boat to come back?"

Kävik continued to watch her as long as she talked to him. When she stopped, he turned and trotted back down the dock.

The woman sat on the low deckhouse every night, waiting for him. She talked to him, and he'd prick his ears forward, and listen. He liked her voice. Soon he came to look for her. One night she had something for him to eat. She came ashore, put the plate on the edge of the dock, and returned to the boat. "There you are," she said. "It's what we had left over from dinner."

Quite often a big, sturdy-looking man in a short oilskin coat, sou'wester hat, and knee-high boots sat beside the woman. He'd listen impassively while the woman chattered.

"He's such a nice dog. Don't you think he's a nice dog, John?" the woman would ask.

John would say, deliberating, "Seems to be."

"He comes out to the end of the dock every night," the woman said. "I'll bet he's looking or waiting for someone."

"Maybe he just likes to look at the bay," John said. "I've seen animals go to certain spots and stand and look for no apparent reason."

"He has a reason. Haven't you noticed how sad he looks, John?"

John laughed. "Every stray looks sad, Martha. Don't let your sympathies run away with you."

"John, does he look like any breed you know about?"

John Kent shook his head. "No one breed. But I have seen dogs in the North that resemble him. I'd bet he's got some wolf in him. It's in the shape of his head and in his eyes. Especially in the eyes. I've seen wolves trot just like he does. Not slinking, not really trotting. But sort of gliding over the ground. I've got a hunch about this fellow."

"What's that?" Martha asked.

"Years ago, when the dog sled was the chief mode of travel in the North, the Indians and Eskimos often bred their dogs to wolves so they'd get a tougher, smarter, and stronger animal. But since the airplane has come into being and is so much faster, dogs are now bred principally for the sport of sled-dog racing, very little for work. To find one this size and with his looks is unusual. My guess is that he's a 'throwback' to a wolf ancestor, and not far removed. The dog in him could be malamute, Siberian husky or McKenzie River husky. In all likelihood he was born in the North and brought down here. If he's not acquainted with a dog sled in some manner, he should be."

"He has to have a collar," Martha said. "A big studded collar."

"I'll get it first time I go to town."

Kävik got his collar, a glistening leather circlet studded with iron heads. He'd never worn a collar, but he soon became used to it. Martha combed and brushed him daily until his coat shone with the same wonderful gloss it had in the North. She took him for daily walks on the leash. In the love these two people showed him, Kävik might have been expected to forget and become happy with his new home. But he did not forget.

The weeks passed. They loaded the galley shelves with grub, filled the gas tanks, and one morning eased away from the dock. Martha and Kävik were in the wheelhouse with John when he swung the bow north and headed out across the bay toward the distant sea.

Kävik suddenly reared front paws against the wheelhouse window and looked out. His yellow eyes were sprung wide, and his lips lifted in a grin. Miraculously, he was at last crossing the impossible water.

Day after day they plowed north at a steady nine knots. The cities and towns bordering the coast became smaller, until they were no more than villages. There were great stretches of open beach and sometimes stands of timber came down to the water's edge. The silence Kävik had known all his life was there once again.

This was not the country he remembered, but he was traveling steadily in the direction he knew he must go, and the restlessness in-

creased within him. He paced about the deck, the galley, and the wheelhouse all day. His black nose sampled the sea breezes, and reached for scents that were not there. His sharp ears were pricked forward, listening. When they came near the coastline or stopped somewhere to gas up, his eyes were constantly searching.

The evening of the tenth day they came in from out at sea and entered a tiny, sheltered cove. The cove had been punched into the side of a mountain that crowded to the edge of the beach. There were a small dock far back in the cove, an oil-storage tank, and a caretaker's house. They tied to the dock, and John went ashore to hunt up the attendant. He returned in a few minutes and said, "Nobody here. A sign on the door says he'll be back in the morning. We'll lay the night here and gas up tomorrow."

Martha prepared supper, and after they'd eaten, Kävik began pacing again, from the door to the window and back to the door again. Martha stood it for a few minutes, then reached for her coat and the lead rope. "All right, we'll go for a walk on the dock. I guess it does get pretty tiresome for a dog cooped up aboard all the time." She put the rope on Kävik, and the three of them went out and climbed to the dock.

The day was ending, and the shadow of the mountain lay across the dock and the small cove. Biting cold flowed down off the mountain slope. Martha pulled her coat tight, and they walked about the dock looking at the cove and the mountain. Finally Martha sat on a piling end, holding the rope loosely in her hand. John Kent stood beside her, hands buried in his pockets as he looked about, smiling. This was the big land he loved. Kävik stood in front of them. His ears were erect, his nose tilted slightly as he reached hard for some scent. Martha said, "If I just knew what you were looking for I'd get it, so you could relax and be happy with us."

Kävik paid no attention to her voice. He was reaching, feeling, smelling, hearing with that animal sensitivity no human possesses. He had no way of knowing that once again he stood in Alaska. He knew only that the very breeze funneling down off the high mountain beckoned to him, heavy with the remembered tang of spruce and hemlock forests. The chill bite of snowfields was laced with the faintly musty scent of deep, sunless canyons. The great forest hung a black mantle over the mountain and swept down to within a hundred feet of the dock. Up there, among the trees, he could see the edge of the white cover of snow. Silence hung over the mountain, and in it he heard the soft whisper of wind through the trees. All these sights, smells, and sounds were old friends with whom he'd spent his whole life. They reached for him now, holding forth a promise that nothing else could.

Kävik looked to the north, as he had for months. For the first time there was no impassable water. He was looking across land. Up there, through those trees and across the mountain, was the way to go. Somewhere beyond waited the boy and the only life he knew and wanted. Somewhere out there was home.

He trotted forward so quickly that before Martha could tighten her fingers around the rope it had slipped through her hand.

He turned his big head and looked at the two people. The look he gave them was as impersonal as if he'd never seen them before. Then he trotted on purposefully toward the beckoning trees and the snowline.

CHAPTER NINE

Kävik entered the dark fringe of trees and climbed steadily until he came to the snowline. Here he stopped and stood, nose lifted, as if he quested the breeze, seeking direction. Then he struck out without hesitation, going straight north, going home to the boy.

Kävik traveled all night under brilliant stars and a full moon that made weird patterns of the birch and hemlock trees. He crossed the face of the mountain, followed the backbone of a barren rocky ridge, and finally dropped down the opposite side. Near dawn he came out on a high, sharp point. Below him lay a great expanse of snow-covered tundra that stretched away to the black mass of a range of mountains. The tundra was thinly dotted with small clumps of willows and groves of scrub trees. A keener wind cut across this flat land. He was starting down to the flat tundra plain when he heard a sound. It began on a low note. As it rose higher and higher, other voices joined in, until it was a whole chorus filling the night. Wild and beautiful it beat against the mountain slopes behind him and flowed down to spread across the tundra plain below. Then it died slowly away, only to begin again and rise and swell as other voices joined in. A whole pack, or family, of wolves was congregated somewhere on a hill and was singing its high, wild song to the beauty of the night.

Kävik listened, his whole body tense and waiting, searching for one special call. His own voice swelled, ready to answer. But the call did not come. Finally he dropped his head, trotted down the slope out onto the tundra plain, and headed toward the distant bulk of the mountains. The song of the wolves followed him for a long time.

Here on the flat, open land the going was harder. Wind had drifted the snow into great ridges, and he had to detour around, floundering chest deep. Dawn found him ravenously hungry, and beginning to tire. Hunger now became uppermost in his mind. He began watching for small animals. There were a few fresh tracks here in the open. For the most part, animals kept to the timber where there was food. Finally he came to a fresh rabbit track with small doglike prints running beside it. The tracks eventually dived into a tangle of willows that had been laid almost flat by the weight of snow, and there Kävik left them. He circled the willows and picked up the tracks again. Not a hundred yards beyond the willows he came onto a red fox crouched in the snow over the fresh-killed body of a snowshoe rabbit.

Kävik stopped. Fox and dog studied each other. The fox lifted his lips in a warning snarl, but Kävik paid no attention. His eyes were on the rabbit, and the thick, warm smell of blood was in his nostrils. He licked his lips and started forward. The fox snarled again. Suddenly he snatched up the rabbit and bolted away at top speed. Kävik leaped after him.

The fox was not so fast as the dog, and he was further hampered by the weight of the rabbit. They charged through a thicket, across a cleared space, and into a dense growth of scrub trees. The fox dodged about among the trees, trying to shake Kävik. But Kävik gained steadily. They burst out of the trees, and the fox started straight across a wide open space to the next brush patch. Halfway across, he dropped the rabbit and raced on at top speed.

Kävik stopped at the rabbit, dropped into the snow, and began to eat.

The rabbit was small, and it had been many hours since Kävik had last eaten. The rabbit did not satisfy his hunger, but the sharp edge was gone. Now as he trotted on he began searching for a place to rest.

He found a small hole in the snow against a steep bank. A few seconds of digging uncovered the opening to a cave. He started in, then stopped as a rank odor filled his nostrils. This was the winter den of a sleeping bear. He backed out hurriedly.

A brittle sun burst from behind the distant mountains and flooded the earth with cold sunlight. Finally Kävik entered a stand of timber and found an upended tree. There was a hollowed-out depression at the base of the roots. He crept in, turned around several times, lay down with a tired sigh, and curled into a tight ball.

It was still light when Kävik awoke. After a good stretch and a test of the chill breeze with his delicate nose, he began plowing through the snow again—heading north. He was ravenously hungry, and on the lookout for food. The distant mountains gradually drew nearer. The brush patches increased in number, and the tree groves became larger. The flat land gave way to rolling hills and brush-choked ravines. Signs of game became more numerous, and it was not long before he jumped a snowshoe rabbit and tore through the snow after it. Like a white wraith the rabbit, with its big furred feet, skipped lightly over the snow ahead of him. But Kävik broke through at every lunging stride. Soon he began to tire, and the rabbit pulled easily away from him and vanished into a thick patch of brush. He raised several others before dark, but each time he gave up after a short chase when the rabbit began to leave him.

The moon and stars came out, and once again it was almost as light as day. The night's cold clamped down with biting intensity, and the earth became utterly still.

Kävik stopped on a hillside to rest, and keened the dead silence for what it might bring. He heard the call begin, and his head came up. His whole body became tense with expectation. The sound swelled and swelled until it filled the night and there was no telling from which direction it came. The wolves were singing again.

Kävik listened intently as he had before, searching each voice, waiting for one special note. It did not come. When it was over, he started to move on. Then a new call brought him up short. It began so softly it seemed a part of the night, and he was not sure just when his keen ears first heard it. In the stillness it rose slowly, soaring to a high, clear call of sadness and longing. It faded away into the massive blackness of the mountains. A deathlike hush—then it began again, rising to the same high soulful cry and dying away. This was the note he'd been listening for. He'd heard it many times as a pup. As he grew older, it had taken on meaning.

Somewhere out there a wolf was singing, pouring her loneliness and longing into the night, calling for love, calling for a mate. It was the most natural thing in the world for Kävik to sit on his haunches, tilt his big nose toward the stars, and send forth his own far-reaching cry.

As his voice died away, the answer came, rising high and clear, riding over valleys and mountains to hang trembling on the still night air.

Kävik went plunging headlong down the slope. He stopped once and called again, and again the answer came back, much closer now. He charged on through the snow at top speed, and came, finally, to a tiny clearing nestling at the foot of towering mountains. There, waiting in the black fringe of trees, he found her.

He paused at the edge of the clearing. He could see her sitting in the snow in the deep shadows across from him. He advanced cautiously into the open, and stopped uncertainly. The wolf moved as carefully from the darkness of the timber, and sat down. The two regarded each other.

She was younger than Kävik. She was slim and strong and alert. Her color was dark gray, and in the moonlight he could see that her fur was soft and sleek. Kävik crossed the little clearing and sniffed noses with her. The next moment she was leaping about him with all the friskiness of a puppy. She raced around the little clearing, dashed at him and nipped him, then spun away. Kävik leaped after her, his manner every bit as puppyish as hers. Finally she streaked into the dark trees, coyly leading him a mad chase. Kävik stayed at her flying heels as they circled about

Frederic Remington, *Moonlight, Wolf,* Addison Gallery of American Art, Phillips Academy, Andover, Massachusetts

through the trees and returned again to the clearing. They were sniffing noses, tails waving happily, when the female suddenly lifted her head, and her ears shot forward.

Kävik looked. There across the glade, standing at the edge of the tree shadows, watching them, was another wolf. He too had answered the female's call for a mate. Now he advanced slowly into the clearing, head down, watching Kävik. He went straight to the female, and they sniffed noses. Then the female turned, trotted off a few feet, and sat down, leaving Kävik and the male wolf facing each other.

This new wolf was almost as big as Kävik, and several years older. His coat was thick and coarse and almost black. He stood stiff-legged, head lowered. His manner said plainly he meant to fight for the favor of the sleek female.

As he watched the wolf approach, ears laid back, lips beginning to lift, Kävik knew what was coming. He and the black wolf must fight to the death for the favor of the young female. And she, remaining completely aloof, would go with the victor. The wolf in Kävik accepted this, but the domestic dog in him, bent to man's will for thousands of years, hesitated. It was almost his undoing.

The attack came so suddenly it bowled Kävik completely off his feet, and the wolf's teeth were at his throat. The battle might have ended there, but as the wolf struck for the throat, his teeth clamped down on Kävik's studded collar instead. The next instant, Kävik reared up with a snarl of rage and threw the wolf off. Then he was fighting with a savagery he had never known before.

The wolf was an experienced fighter. He knew all the tricks: the speed of attack and wiles of retreat; how to defend, and how to feint and strike and get away. And his incentive to win was as great as Kävik's.

Kävik was bigger and stronger. But he was not so quick, and he had never fought a wolf before. The dogs he had met were slow and plodding, in comparison to this wolf. Again and again he tried to close with the wolf and sink his teeth in the soft flesh of his throat. But whenever Kävik struck, he was always met by the wolf's clashing fangs. Soon both their mouths and lips were cut and bleeding. No matter how he tried, Kävik could not penetrate the wolf's lightning-quick guard. He enveloped the wolf in a whirlwind of rushes as he tried to hurl his greater weight against the animal to bowl him over and so expose his throat. But the wolf always avoided him, danced away, then back to slash the dog's shoulders and neck and the side of his face with razor-sharp teeth.

The wolf remained almost untouched, while Kävik's blood streamed from numerous cuts. He was beginning to tire badly.

The wolf took to rushing. He kept the dog turning and twisting wildly to protect his feet and throat from those slashing fangs. Once those teeth closed on a leg or reached his throat, Kävik knew he would be finished.

In his desperation he no longer fought with wolfish instinct. He was fighting with his head. He rushed, jaws low to the snow, and at the last instant swept in to snap at the wolf's front legs. Twice he did this, and each time the wolf danced aside. The third time he rushed, feinted low, and as the wolf leaped aside, Kävik whirled on his hind legs and lunged after him so quickly he caught the wolf just as he struck the ground with all four feet bunched. For the first time Kävik's driving shoulder smashed into the lighter animal and threw him back on his haunches. Then Kävik was on him, and his big jaws found the throat. The wolf fought madly to free himself, but it was useless. Kävik was merciless. He bore the wolf to the ground. His teeth drove deep for the jugular, and found it.

He held on for several minutes, even after the wolf had ceased to struggle. Finally he let go and looked across his fallen foe to the female. She still sat in the snow, watching. His head came up; his sharp ears shot forward, and he looked at her with steady yellow eyes. He had the dignity of a king and the bearing of a champion. Once again he was a throwback to an arctic wolf father. He was Kävik, the wolf dog.

Kävik stalked across to the female, and they sniffed noses. She licked the wounds on his face and neck. Then she trotted into the darkness of the timber, where she stopped and looked back, waiting for him.

Kävik hesitated. This was not the direction he wanted to go. The female returned to him. She licked his face again, and whined pleadingly. Once more she trotted into the timber, and stopped to wait. Kävik followed to the edge of the trees, and halted. He turned his head to the north and stood utterly still, as if listening for some far-off sound. The female whined again, and he looked back at her.

Kävik went to her, and she touched his face gently with her muzzle. They trotted into the gloom together, traveling not north now—but due east. He was answering the age-old call of his kind. With the female at his side, Kävik ran through the vastness of the land and the magic of the night.

THINK AND DISCUSS

Understanding

1. Where is Kävik kept after Edna Hunter refuses to allow him in her home?
2. Why does Hunter become worried about Kävik?
3. What happens to change the way Hunter feels about Kävik?
4. How does Kävik escape from Hunter?
5. Kävik learns to survive while on the docks in Seattle. How does he get (a) water; (b) food; (c) shelter?
6. How do John and Martha Kent help Kävik?

Analyzing

7. In what ways are Kävik and Tom McCarty alike?
8. What **inference** can you make about Kävik from his actions during the time he spends in Seattle?
9. Recall that authors develop characters through physical appearance, words, actions, thoughts, and what others say about them. **Characterize** (a) Edna Hunter and (b) Tom McCarty.

10. Consider that the events in a novel occur in a cause-and-effect pattern. What is the effect of Kävik's fight with the wolf?
11. Kävik is the leading character, or protagonist, in this novel. Who has become his opponent, or antagonist? Explain.

Extending

12. Do you know of other animals in real life or fiction that have traveled long distances to return to someone they love? How do their stories compare to *Kävik, the Wolf Dog?*

REVIEWING: Setting HT
See Handbook of Literary Terms, p. 656.

Setting is the time, place, and general environment in which the events of a narrative occur. The details of setting may be directly stated or only suggested.

1. What are the sounds and smells that frighten and irritate Kävik when he is kept in the dog run?
2. How does the environment of the big city affect Kävik after his escape from Hunter?

3. After Kävik leaves the Kents, he travels over land. Describe that land.
4. Are the details of setting stated or only suggested in this novel? Explain.

THINKING SKILLS
Classifying

To classify things is to arrange them in categories or groups according to some system.

How does the author of this novel appeal to the five senses of sight, sound, smell, taste, and touch? Consider the part of the novel in which Kävik escapes from Hunter and makes his way north. Label five columns, one for each of the senses, and write details in the appropriate columns. For example, you could put "wonderful salt tang of the sea was in his nostrils" under *Smell*.

COMPOSITION
Reading/Writing Log

The author of *Kävik, the Wolf Dog* created a fast-paced, action-filled novel by using a good beginning for each chapter. For example, the first paragraph of Chapter Eight begins with the following two sentences:

> Kävik did not keep to the road. He traveled swiftly through the brush and timber, for here he was more at home and he was well hidden.

If you are keeping a **reading/writing log**, copy the above example and add examples of sentences from the beginnings of Chapters Seven or Nine.

Writing a Chapter

In Chapter Eight, John Kent gets a collar for Kävik and Martha Kent combs and brushes him daily. At this point the author writes that "the weeks passed" and then the Kents head out to sea. Write a chapter about what happens during the weeks that pass. Describe the relationship that develops between Kävik and the Kents. Create a new event, some minor conflict that is resolved in the chapter. Be sure to use a good beginning to keep the fast pace of the novel. Before you begin, review your **reading/writing log** and the events that take place in Chapter Eight.

Writing a Newspaper Article

Imagine you are a journalist attending Hunter's speech at his club. Kävik and his spectacular escape interest you. Write an article about the leap through the window and the subsequent search for Kävik. Before you begin to write, review that part of the novel and list details to include in your article. You may also want to write a follow-up article based on what you, as journalist, learn from interviewing dock workers, restaurant owners, and boat owners.

ENRICHMENT
Finding Quotations

Look up the word *courage* in a book of quotations. Choose an example that you think applies to Kävik and the courage he shows. Explain to the class why the quotation you have chosen fits him. Use details and examples from the novel to support your choice.

CHAPTER TEN

Kävik and the female ran through the deep blackness of the timber and the intermittent moonlight. The speed of their travel was geared to his slow pace. The battle with the black wolf had not only sapped his strength; his injuries were painful, and he'd lost a great deal of blood. Sometime during the fight the remaining foot of rope had been chewed away. Only the studded collar remained. The female ran close at his side, giving him the comfort of her presence. But finally he could go no farther. He crawled into the protection of a patch of brush, and lay down. He was panting and trembling with fatigue, and every injury he'd sustained was on fire.

The female lay beside him, and began to lick his wounds. Kävik relaxed with a tired sigh and let her minister to him. In time he fell asleep, and his last sensation was of her soft tongue cleansing his feverish head wound.

When he awoke it was daylight, and the female still lay beside him, head up, watching. She turned and touched the wound on his head gently, and whined. They stayed there most of the day while Kävik rested and the female continued to cleanse his wounds.

The sun dropped behind the massive peaks, and night spread its shadows over the land. The night wind came up with a biting edge, and the temperature fell many degrees. A rising moon painted bright silver patches on the snow and deepened the dark under the trees. Kävik rose stiffly, stretched, and scented the crisp air with his nose for whatever messages it carried. He was ready to travel.

For the first few hours their pace was little more than a good trot. The female ran close at his shoulder, her warm muzzle touching his neck often in encouragement. Gradually stiff, bruised muscles loosened, and at last Kävik was again running with most of his swift, gliding stride. They fled through the night like silent gray ghosts, noses close to the snow, hunting their first meal together.

Late that night they raised their first rabbit, and the female taught Kävik the wolf's trick of chasing a rabbit in relays until they caught it. He had never shared his food with any animal. As a sled dog he'd bolted his food quickly before some other dog could rob him. Now he and the female devoured the rabbit together, growling amicably. They caught two more before the night was over. While they were eating the third, Kävik again heard a single wolf singing. He listened, but had no desire to answer. With the coming of dawn they found a hole under a rock ledge, and lay down side by side to sleep the daylight hours away.

So the days passed, and they ran together through moon and starlit nights, traveling ever deeper into the primitive mountain range. Under the female's constant ministrations Kävik's many wounds healed. He thought of the boy and the home farther north, and tried to turn the female. But she always led him away east, and he followed. She was his mate, and in the law of the wolf they would remain together as long as they lived.

The fact that wolves mate for life makes a wolf pair particularly solicitous of each other. Kävik was now living, thinking, and acting like a wolf. He had never before experienced this close companionship with any of his kind; nor had the female. She had lived her life with the pack. They became a good team. As they ran shoulder to shoulder hunting, they learned to act together. They were sure of each other and were happy and content in each other's company.

The female knew their existence was precarious, and wariness was a part of her life. This wariness she communicated to Kävik. When they rested, one or the other of them would occasionally rise up to look about and listen to make sure all was well.

As they traveled steadily inland, the snow became deeper, and most animal life disappeared. Moose and deer traveled to other parts of the country where they could feed better and where they could not be helplessly trapped by predatory animals in belly-deep snow. Most of the small animals retired to subterranean passages under the snow, leaving the upper world to the grouse, ptarmigan and snowshoe rabbits. In this deep snow it was easy for the rabbits to avoid the heavier Kävik and his mate, and it was next to impossible to stalk grouse and ptarmigans. So the two found lean feeding.

Now the female became tired struggling through the snow, and Kävik took the lead, bulldozing a foot-deep trail with his powerful chest. The female began to grow restless, and she displayed an increased interest in holes under stumps and rocks or the caves in the edge of banks. She spent much time nosing about among them, digging the snow away and inspecting them. Kävik did not understand. At such times he good-naturedly lay down in the snow and waited for her to finish.

They were traveling in this manner one day when they came upon a small cabin in a grove of trees. They stopped and inspected the cabin from a safe distance. Though there was a rick of snow-covered stovewood near the door, there was no sign of life about. No smoke curled up from the chimney. No fresh tracks were about the cabin. Kävik was about to go on, when a wayward breeze brought a faint scent to his delicate nostrils. His head came up and he stepped forward toward the cabin, big head swinging about, his yellow eyes searching. He found what he was looking for hanging from a rope fastened to a tree limb, a haunch of caribou.

Kävik sat down under the meat. He looked up and drooled and licked his lips. Days of good eating hung there.

The female came forward cautiously. She sat down beside him, looked up at the haunch, licked her lips, and whined. She was very hungry. An occasional rabbit and a few mice and shrews dug from the deep snow had been slim fare, especially for her. Now, looking up at the meat, she forgot her natural caution. She crouched, eyes on the haunch so invitingly near. Her body gathered, and suddenly she shot upward. Her straining jaws snapped a foot beneath the prize, and she fell back in the snow. She tried again, driving upward with all her strength, but she came no nearer. Six weeks ago she'd have made the leap, but now she was getting heavy and a little clumsy. She crouched panting, staring hungrily upward. She knew she could never make the leap.

Kävik had been watching her, and now he made his own leap upward. His big jaws snapped shut just inches short of the haunch. He crouched again, yellow eyes fixed on the meat. He gathered his legs well under him, big muscles bunched like coiled springs. He launched himself upward with a mighty leap. When his jaws clamped shut, his teeth were firmly sunk in the haunch. He hung, swinging gently back and forth, refusing to let go. His added weight was more than the thin rope could hold. It snapped, and dog and caribou haunch crashed into the snow.

Both animals were instantly after it. Crouched side by side, they tore ravenously at the frozen flesh. It had been many days since they'd enjoyed such a feast. They were not aware of anything but food until the shot tore into the silence. The female let out a startled yelp, and jumped, then fell. She was up instantly, and they both raced for the protection of the trees. The gun crashed again, and bark flew from a stump inches from Kävik's head. Then they were dodging swiftly through the trees.

They ran until the female collapsed exhausted in the snow. Kävik returned to her. She lay panting heavily, and there was a great spreading red stain on her sleek side. Kävik licked her face, and whined. He pushed at her with his nose, trying to get her to rise.

But she did not move. He licked the spreading stain, found the wound, and cleansed it with his tongue. He kept watching anxiously down the trail, expecting any minute to see the man appear. After a long rest the female finally got to her feet.

Kävik once again took the lead, breaking trail for her, and they continued on. Their pace was terribly slow now. She did not go far before she stopped to rest. Kävik returned to her. The wound was bleeding again, and he licked it clean, but it continued to ooze. He rubbed against her, and whined, urging her on. In this way they moved forward for several hours, and finally began to climb a long, gentle slope toward a barren, rocky ridge. Several hundred yards short of the ridge she staggered under a ledge of overhanging rock, and lay down. No matter how he tried, Kävik could not get her up again.

Kävik lay down close beside her for a time. He licked her face gently, and cleansed the wound again. It had almost stopped bleeding. He laid his big head lightly over her neck in a protective gesture. Then he turned and crept outside and climbed to the top of the ridge where he could watch their back trail.

The man was not in sight. He waited for some time, but the man did not appear. Kävik turned and started back to the female. He jumped a snowshoe rabbit on the way. The ridge had been blown almost barren of snow by the wind, and his footing was good. He caught the rabbit within a hundred feet. He carried it back with him, crept under the ledge, and laid it in front of her. She had not moved since he'd left. She lay stretched on her side, eyes closed. Her flanks scarcely moved as she breathed. She opened her eyes briefly when she smelled the rabbit, then sighed, and closed them again.

Kävik whined and nudged the rabbit closer. He touched her neck, her face, and her closed eyes gently with his nose, whining anxiously all the while. But she did not rouse. He tore the skin from the rabbit, exposing the warm red meat. Other than a faint twitching of her nostrils, she gave no sign. He cleansed the wound again, though it had stopped bleeding. Finally he lay down close beside her and stretched his big head out flat, touching her in understanding and sympathy. He lay there and watched the daylight hours slip away. The sun disappeared. The stars came out one by one, and the northern night closed down, bringing its cold. A cutting wind swept over the barren ridge and into the valley below. It passed with a low moaning over the ledge under which Kävik and his mate lay. But it did not touch them.

For hours Kävik lay beside his mate. The untouched rabbit froze solid. Though he had not satisfied his hunger at the cabin where the man had shot at them, he did not touch the rabbit.

Once during the night he felt her shiver violently. He licked her face and whined softly, but she did not rouse. Again he laid his head across her neck lightly, as though he would reassure and warm her. He stayed in that position for a long time. Finally he crept out and climbed to the ridge again to make sure all was well. Under the stars and a thin moon he could see their back trail clearly. He sat down to watch, and at last he saw movement against the darkness of the trees. Soon the figure of a man plodding steadily up the slope on snowshoes came into view.

Kävik slipped far down the ridge toward the man; then he deliberately stood in plain sight, etched against the sky. The man stopped, raised his gun, and fired. The echoes slapped back and forth against the hills. Kävik ducked behind a rock as the bullet snarled angrily above him into the night. He showed himself again briefly. Then he ducked over the opposite side of the ridge in an effort to lead the man away from his mate.

Kävik peeked back over the ridge a minute later, but the man was not following. He was a trapper who understood the ways of the wild. The bloodstained trail stretched ahead, leading him straight to the ledge where Kävik's mate lay. The man was following that trail.

Kävik tried once again to lead the trapper astray. But this time the man merely glanced up at him, and then went on.

Kävik rushed back along the ridge to warn his mate. She lay utterly still, as before. He whined and nudged her with his nose. He put a paw on her shoulder and scratched to rouse her. His whine turned to an urgent bark. She did not move. Her eyes did not open. He sat down on his haunches and looked at her, ears cocked forward anxiously. She would never move again, no more than would the half-skinned rabbit that lay frozen solid before her nose.

He crept to her and sniffed over her for several minutes. He cleaned the wound on her side, though it no longer bled. He touched her nose gently with his.

Finally the knowledge that the man approached claimed all his thought. He licked her face, and whined a last time. Then he crept out from under the ledge and went up

Zoltan Szabo, *Cuddlers* (detail),
Courtesy of the artist

the slope to the top of the ridge.

Kävik stopped there and looked back. Though he could see the ledge and the opening where she lay, her still form was hidden from view. Far down, the black shape of the man climbed steadily. Kävik felt the wind cut into him, and heard its mournful sighing through the trees. The man kept coming.

He turned, at last, and went slowly down the far side of the ridge. Once again he was going due north—alone.

CHAPTER ELEVEN

Kävik traveled steadily all that night and the next day. He was in very low spirits. Never in his life had he felt so alone. Hunger ate at him, but he had no desire for food. He made no effort to catch the few rabbits he jumped or the grouse that exploded out of the snow under his nose. He stopped often at first and looked back, remembering his unprotected mate lying under the ledge and the approaching man. But he went on. Once he sat on a barren hill, tipped up his head, and poured his heartbreak into the frigid silence. His cry echoed through the mountains, and died away. There was no answering call from anywhere.

But grief, like winter, cannot last forever. Soon hunger drove Kävik to hunting again as he traveled ever north. As his grief dulled, the memory of the boy and the home increased, until once again the driving urge within him was all-possessive.

The first warm breath of Chinook blew up from the south and sliced deep into the snow pack. Almost overnight lavender crocuses, the first unmistakable harbingers of spring, pushed slender stems through the hard crust of snow and spread their blooms to a warming sun. Long before he saw it, Kävik heard running water beneath the melting snow-pack.

Then, by sea and by air, the great tide of wildlife began its annual surge into the North. And Kävik was part of it. But his travels were harder. Geese, ducks, and swans flew high over the jagged mountain ranges, over glaciers and streams, mile-deep canyons and valleys. Kävik had to travel them on foot, covering many extra miles that were beset with dangers the flyers knew nothing of.

In winter the glaciers and streams were easy to travel, for they were covered with snow; but now the warm winds and longer hours of sunlight were fast melting the snow-pack. In summer they present an obstacle that most men, even when especially equipped, do not care to tackle. They are huge lakes and rivers of ice hundreds of feet deep, sometimes miles wide. They snake great distances through canyons and valleys. When the snow has melted off their surfaces, they present a barrier more formidable than the land itself. Sun and running water turn the surfaces slick and sharp, and gouge out impassable crevasses and unscalable cliffs. Footing is precarious. There is the constant danger of slipping into a crevasse from which escape is impossible. The lands jammed between the glaciers are the rugged tops of mountains and mile-high ridges where traveling is equally hard and dangerous. There is little food in this area for a dog to eat.

Kävik knew none of this. The glaciers lay across his line of travel, so he must cross them. Now his forward progress was slow. At times he detoured so far to go around a barrier that it seemed he might have lost his way or forgotten the reason for his endless journey. But this was not true. Once the way was clear, he always came back on course again. He became leaner than ever from lack of food. The pads of his feet were worn down by the sharp ice ridges. The trails he left across some of these glaciers were spotted red.

Only once did he hesitate at the sight of a glacier. He came down off a high ridge and stopped on a point of rock above the immense ice pack. The timbered slopes of the far side were almost lost in misty distance. The surface of the glacier was cut and gouged with pressure ridges and a whole network of deep crevasses. Here, near the edge, was a deep crevasse he could not cross. He would go around.

He started on the long trip to circle the ice field. He had no way of knowing he would have to travel almost a hundred miles to get around it. Hour after hour he worked his way along the edge of the glacier, traveling east. Sometimes the land jutted into the glacier mass, and he thought he'd found a way around. He would go out to the very tip of the land. There he met the ice again, going on and on. He was always traveling east when his way led north.

Finally the glacier narrowed down, and he came out at the tip of a headland and looked at the far shore. Here it was no wider than many others he had crossed. Unhesitatingly he stepped out upon it.

He came to a series of small crevasses. Some were so narrow he jumped them easily; several he detoured around. An ice slide, where huge blocks of ice lay scattered like a child's building blocks, held him up for a few minutes until he found a trail through it. He was almost across when he came to a sheer ice wall across his path. It was six to eight feet above his head, too high to try to jump. He began following along its base, looking for some sort of trail to the top.

He found a spot where a section of the wall had broken off and piled a mound of ice at the base. From the top of the mound to the top of the ice wall was no more than four feet. He climbed gingerly to the top of the mound, balanced and crouched, then leaped for the top of the wall. He got his front legs over the top, but there was no grip for his claws. He scratched frantically with his hind legs, trying to find footing, but there was none. He slipped back over the edge, and fell. One hind leg caught in a crevice. His body swung back against the face of the wall, wrenching his imprisoned leg. Then he fell onto the pile of ice and rolled to the bottom. He lay there, momentarily stunned.

When he scrambled to his feet, one hind leg hung useless. He tried to put it down, but the sudden stab of pain made him whimper. He stood for a minute balanced on three legs. Then he began hobbling along the face of the wall. A half mile farther on, the ice wall ran out to nothing, and Kävik found himself standing on top.

It was not far to hobble to the edge of the glacier and to the timberline. There he found a runoff of a small stream from the glacier, and followed it a short way until he came to a holelike depression against the bank. He crept in and lay down. The coolness of the earth felt good. He looked himself over, but there were no open wounds to lick. There was a large lump high up on the injured hip, but it was nothing to cleanse with his tongue. He put his head on his forepaws and looked out at the day and watched the light slowly fade as night came on. A breeze blew across the glacier, cooled by the ice, and this coolness felt good.

He tried to sleep, but the pain in his leg would not let him. He lay through the night and watched the dawn sun spray light across the face of the glacier and chase the dark from under the trees. Finally he pulled himself stiffly to his feet and hobbled out. The leg had stiffened during the night, and the pain was a steady throb. He could not bear the slightest weight upon it.

Kävik hobbled to the creek, and drank long. Afterward he stood for a moment and looked to the north. Then he started painfully off on three legs. He was very hungry.

He could not travel far without resting, and his pace was a three-legged hop. It took him all day, hobbling painfully on three legs, to travel the distance he'd have made before in two hours.

He spent the night curled against the side of a log. The next morning he could still put no weight on the leg. But at dawn he was again on his way.

Though game became plentiful, he could not catch it. And the animals seemed to know. The rabbits made no great effort to dash off at his slow, painful approach. A squirrel sat up within a few feet of him and boldly scolded him, then flicked its tail disdainfully and ran up a tree. He did not know that at last he had passed the glacier area. He knew only that his one chance for food lay in finding it already dead or in stumbling on some sort of cache he could raid. He went hungry another day, and spent the night curled up beside a bush near a small stream.

With the dawn he was again traveling, moving at the same slow pace, but going north. His leg was worse. A clump of grass touching it as he passed brought a whimper of pain. The distance he could travel in a day was becoming less and less. Lack of food was sapping what little strength the injured leg had not already taken. He hobbled along, head down now, eyes sick and unseeing. Sometimes he staggered.

At last, the good back leg gave way, and his hindquarters sank to the ground. He sat there for some time, head down. When he tried to rise by leaning forward and pulling with his front legs, the good back leg refused to hold his weight, and he fell over on his side. He lay full length, eyes closed, gathering the last of his strength for one more try. He heard the voices of a flock of crows going over. And he caught the far-off cries of gulls,

riding a fresh, sharp breeze. But he was too tired for these sounds to take on meaning. He did not know that at last he had crossed the high mountains and the greatest glacier area in the world. There, before him, less than half a mile away, lay the sea.

CHAPTER TWELVE

There were two days of school left, but Andy Evans was not thinking of that as he tramped through the woods on the way home. He was thinking of Kävik, as he did almost every day when he made this mile walk home. He remembered how the big dog used to wait for him here and how they went racing back down the trail together. He should stop thinking of that, he told himself. Kävik was two thousand miles away. He'd never see him again.

And so, coming home through the trees on the next to last day of school, Andy Evans could not believe his eyes when he saw a dog standing in the trail before him. But such a dog! This dog wavered on three legs, and his ragged coat was matted and dirty. His flanks were sunken, and he was so thin Andy could count his ribs through the mat of hair. He stood with his head down, looking obliquely up at the boy. Only the general shape of the big head and the steady look from the yellow eyes were the same. The ragged, bushy tail waved slightly in recognition.

For a moment Andy hesitated, blinking his eyes. Part of his mind said he was really seeing Kävik, and another part rejected the idea as impossible. This was not Kävik. This was a specter.

Then Andy dropped his books, and fell on his knees in the trail. He wrapped his arms around the thin neck. Kävik lifted his head and licked the boy's face, and then Andy knew he was not dreaming. This was really his dog, and in some marvelous, unbelievable way he was back again.

"Kävik," Andy murmured, putting his head down against the dog's, "it's really you! It's really you! How did you get here? What happened to you, Kävik? What happened?"

Kävik could only lick his face, and continue to whine.

Andy wanted to carry the dog home, but then he saw the terrible swelling on his hip. When he tried to turn Kävik so he could lift him, the dog cried out with pain. There was no way Andy could carry him without hurting him more. For the short distance left, he would have to continue his painful way.

"Come, boy," Andy said gently. "We're going home. You can make it. Come on."

They went slowly along the trail over which they'd run pell-mell so often in the past. Andy walked close beside the dog, his hands steadying the weak animal. Kävik hobbled beside him, every step a painful, deliberate effort that took all his strength and racked his wasted body. So they made their way through the trees with many stops to rest.

Andy's mother saw them approaching from the kitchen window, and ran out. She looked at Kävik, then at Andy. "Kävik!" she said. "Kävik!"

Andy's father was coming up the trail from the cannery, and she called to him, "Kurt, it's Kävik!" Then she dropped on her knees before him and ran her hands gently down his sides and over his big head. "Oh, Kävik," she crooned, "where did you come from? What happened to you?"

"He was waiting for me back there in the trees just like he used to," Andy said. "I couldn't believe it. I'd have carried him home, but that hind leg . . . Maybe it's broken or something. I didn't dare try to lift him."

Kurt knelt beside the dog, too, and touched him with big, gentle hands. "You've had a rough time, boy! You've had a mighty rough time!"

Kävik could only stand there, balancing weakly on three legs, and wave his pitiful brush of a tail.

Laura jumped up purposefully, "Bring him on to the house right away. I'll get a blanket. He needs food. He's almost starved." She ran back into the house.

Kävik went ahead again in the same painful, jerky hop, a step and a rest, a step and a rest. Kurt was on one side of him, Andy on the other. Their hands steadied the dog, and their voices encouraged him. "You can do it," Andy's father kept saying. "Just a little more. Just a few steps."

And Kävik was doing it. His mouth was open, panting with effort, and his yellow eyes were fixed unwaveringly on the open kitchen door. He tried to hurry, but he could not. When he hobbled through the door, Laura had a blanket spread on the floor in the corner of the kitchen where it had always been.

Kävik reached the blanket, turned around painfully once, and collapsed with an exhausted sigh. He lay full length, scarcely breathing, his eyes closed. In spite of his injury and his terribly emaciated condition, he was utterly at peace and contented at last. The terrible, driving instinct that had drawn him from two thousand miles away and had taken him across a great winter-locked mountain range, almost impassable glaciers, and river breakups was gone. He had kept faith with the greatest demand of his life. He was lying in the one spot where he wanted to be, soaking in remembered warmth and family closeness, hearing the voices he wanted to hear, and being soothed by these loving hands.

Things began to happen in rapid succession. Andy's mother was busy heating a bowl of milk. His father knelt beside the dog, and stroked him gently. He looked at the swollen hind leg, and murmured wonderingly: "I can't believe it. I can't believe it. All that way. How'd he ever do it? How'd you do it, boy?" He turned to Andy and said, "Go get Vic Walker."

"Now?" Andy asked. "He always said to come when it was dark."

"Tell him I said to get over here now!" Andy had never heard his father's voice so commanding and sharp. "Tell him it's Kävik and he's got a broken leg or something."

"But what if he won't . . . " Andy began.

"Then we'll figure some way to carry Kävik right into his office in broad daylight so the whole town can see, " Kurt said angrily. "You tell him I said that."

"Yes, sir!" Andy said, and ran.

Old Mrs. Nichols was just leaving the doctor's office when Andy burst in. Dr. Walker glanced up, frowning, then asked, "Well, Andy?"

"Can you come to the house right away?" Andy panted.

"Kind of early to leave the office. Can't it wait?"

"No, sir. Dad said right away."

Dr. Walker stood up and reached for his coat and black bag. "What's the emergency?"

"Kävik's home."

Dr. Walker stopped and looked at Andy. "The dog? That wolf I doctored last winter? I thought Hunter took him south with him."

"Yes, sir. He did."

"Let's get this straight. Hunter's come back and brought the dog with him and something's happened to him? Is that what you're saying?"

"No, sir," Andy rushed on. "Mr. Hunter's still down in Washington, as far as we know. But Kävik's here. We don't know where he came from or how he got here. But he's in terrible shape. He looks half starved and he's got a broken hind leg or something. Dad says you should come right away."

Walker's black eyes began to snap. "I told you that where that dog's concerned you should come at night. Remember?"

"Yes, sir," Andy said. Then he sucked in a deep breath and threw his father's threat at Dr. Walker: "Dad says if you don't come right now, he'll carry Kävik over here to your office so the whole town can see."

Dr. Walker looked hard at Andy. "He's just bullheaded enough to do it, too." He reached for his coat and bag. "All right," he said. "Let's go."

Walker questioned Andy as they hurried along. "Where'd you find the dog?"

"Right about here," Andy said. "He was standing in the trail waiting for me when I came home from school."

"Hunter's not here, and he didn't send him north with somebody else?"

"No, sir. Not that we know of. He's traveled an awful long way, Dad says."

"Hm-m-m," Walker mused. "Sounds interesting."

Kävik had just finished a big bowl of warm milk when they walked in. Dr. Walker bent over him, and the three people stood by anxiously. He went over the dog carefully, talking, asking questions as he worked. Finally he sat back on his heels and looked at Kävik. "Well," he said, "he's taken quite a beating in more ways than one. I'd guess he hasn't had anything to eat in about a week. He's traveled a long way. His pads are all cut and scarred, and he's got a lot of fresh scars on his body. This dog's been in a terrific fight or a couple of fights."

"Him in a fight?" Kurt said. "Not Kävik."

"Some animal has done a pretty good job of chewing him," Walker said. He unfastened the collar from around Kävik's neck and handed it to Laura. "He didn't have this on before, as I remember. It's got some mighty big teeth marks on it."

"Maybe Mr. Hunter put it on him," Andy said.

Kurt shook his head. "Mr. Hunter didn't want a collar on him. Said it'd spoil the wolf look."

"Somebody wanted one on him." Walker moved his inspection to the injured leg again. "It's not broken," he announced after a moment. "It's been wrenched out of the socket. I'd guess it's been out quite a few days." He shook his head. "I'm surprised he traveled at all. No wonder he's nearly half

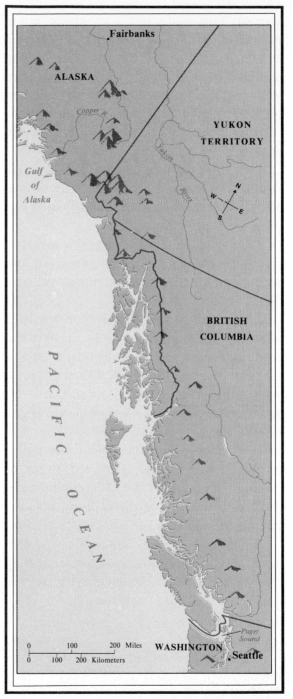

This map shows the area from Fairbanks, Alaska, to Seattle, Washington. Find the Copper River. Where do you think Copper City would be located?

starved. That wolf strain is amazingly tough. Amazing!" He opened his bag and began selecting instruments. "I'll put him to sleep and snap his hip back into the socket. Then we'll put it in a cast for four or five days, and he'll be as good as new."

"He's going to be all right?" Andy asked anxiously.

"Of course he is. He's still alive—he drank that milk. He's going to need plenty of food and rest. As for the leg, the cast will hold it in place until his muscles take over again. It'll be sore, and he'll favor the leg for a few days. But with exercise it'll strengthen. In two weeks you'll never know anything had happened to him."

In less than an hour Kävik's hip was back in place, the cast was on, and Dr. Walker was ready to leave. "Give him about five days in that cast," he said to Kurt. "Then cut it off with your jackknife. Well, that's it." He stood looking down at Kävik, who was beginning to wake up. "He's a mighty tough animal. He should have died that other time."

"Vic," Kurt asked, "do you think he walked all the way from Hunter's home? I can't believe that's possible. Why, it's over two thousand miles."

"It certainly seems impossible," Walker agreed. "But here he is. We can't argue that. And by the looks of him he hiked a lot of it. Seems he's learned something a lot of us never do."

"What's that?"

"You can do anything you have to. It'd be interesting if he could talk. I'll bet he'd have a humdinger of a story to tell." He snapped his bag shut, prepared to leave.

"I'll bring you some money tomorrow on my way to school," Andy said.

Dr. Walker nodded. "Make it a dollar, Andy. That'll pay for the cast and the shot."

Laura shook her head, smiling. "Victor, you'll never get rich."

"If I'd wanted to, I'd have gone to Anchorage or some other city," Walker grunted. "Anyway"—he nodded at Kävik—"this was for him. He earned it fifty times over." He bent and scratched Kävik's ears. "You're quite a dog," he said. "Quite a dog."

At dinner that night Kävik managed to hobble to his feet and stand at Andy's elbow to beg tidbits as he had before. Andy and his mother both fed him.

Kurt watched them, and scowled. "You're both working yourselves up a lot of hurt," he said. "Kävik still belongs to Mr. Hunter. He'll want him back when he comes this summer."

"If we have to give him back, we have to," Laura said. "But that's no reason we can't love him while he's here. It's not Kävik's fault he doesn't want to stay with Mr. Hunter. I wouldn't either."

"I just don't see any sense letting yourselves in for more hurt," Andy's father pointed out stiffly.

Till now Andy hadn't thought of George C. Hunter or what his return this spring would mean to Kävik. That rock settled in his stomach again, bigger than ever.

Kävik slept on his old blanket in the kitchen that first night. Andy heard him moving about in the middle of the night, and rose to investigate. His mother joined him at the head of the stairs, and they descended together. The light was on in the kitchen. They opened the door to find Kurt bending over Kävik, pouring him a fresh bowl of milk.

Laura folded her arms and smiled archly. "Who's letting who in for more hurt?" she asked.

"He was thirsty," Kurt said sheepishly. "And he was hungry. Look at him lapping up that milk."

"You could tell that from upstairs in bed?"

"Well, he was," Andy's father defended. "You can see."

"I'm going back to bed," Laura said. "Come on, Andy."

School let out the next day. After that, Andy had two weeks' free time. Then the salmon run would begin, and most of the men in Copper City would go fishing. Andy hoped to return to work at Tom Murphy's Hardware Store for the summer.

During this free time Andy gave Kävik all his attention, and never was a dog better cared for. Kävik spent all day lying on his blanket in the kitchen, sleeping. He woke up only to eat. Each night Andy got the comb and brush out and worked on his ragged coat. Gradually it regained its wolf-gray color and sheen. Kävik was so thin that after the first few nights Andy easily carried him upstairs and put him on the rug beside the bed. In the morning he carried him down again. But Kävik gained rapidly, and his weight and strength returned. On the fifth day Andy's father cut the cast away. Kävik put his foot gingerly on the floor, and began to limp about the room. And that night he laboriously climbed the stairs himself.

Andy's father sat back on his heels, studying the dog; then he said: "Don't take him downtown, Andy. Remember what happened the other time when he ran into that pack of mongrels? The beating he took in the plane wreck caused that timidity. He's taken another beating trying to get home. Now he's probably more timid than ever. Keep him here at home."

"I will," Andy said. "But if he should get there somehow, and that Blackie or any of those others bother him, I'll take a club to 'em."

Seiners began arriving. Soon the bay at the cannery was choked with boats. When Andy went to town, the city dock was lined with boats. Booted fishermen tramped the town's one street, awaiting the opening of the season. Andy could almost feel the electric tension that gripped everyone.

Kävik had recovered marvelously, and by the time opening day arrived no one would have guessed at the ordeal he'd been through. He was again strong and vital, a big healthy animal who trotted with a spring in his step, head up, yellow eyes taking in everything. Andy could have been completely happy but for one thing. Mr. Hunter would arrive any day and see his dog. The knowledge was a black cloud over the Evans household.

Andy tried to talk to his father about it. "Maybe this time we can buy Kävik, Dad. Maybe since he ran away and all, Mr. Hunter will be willing to sell him."

"Maybe," his father said.

"Will you ask him, Dad? Will you try?"

"All right," his father agreed. "I'll try. But don't expect anything. Mr. Hunter's a tough, stubborn man. He makes up his own mind. The fact that Kävik ran away, if he did, might make him more determined to keep him."

"Maybe he knows what a coward Kävik is now——" Andy began.

"I told him before and got nowhere," his father interrupted. "I'll try to buy Kävik, if Mr. Hunter gives me the ghost of a chance. That's the best I can promise you, Andy. Now stop plaguing me."

Andy said no more. He tried to take his mother's advice and enjoy Kävik as much as possible. But it was hard when each day some new thing happened that made him realize that Mr. Hunter would soon return.

Opening day arrived. Copper City emptied of men; the fishing fleet put to sea; and the cannery doors swung open to await the first boatload of salmon. Andy returned to work at the hardware store.

Andy's mother locked Kävik in the kitchen with her when he left for work. A half hour later she'd let him out. In the evening, before Andy was to come home, she'd call Kävik and close him in the kitchen with her until Andy arrived. In that way Kävik was kept away from Copper City and Blackie and his pack of mongrels. But every night when it was time for Andy, Kävik scratched and whined at the door.

Andy waited fearfully for Mr. Hunter.

After the first week of fishing season his father said: "Hunter probably stopped off on the way here to look at some of his other interests. He'll be along one of these days."

On Wednesday of the second week, Andy started home for the night. Kävik entered the far end of the street and trotted happily toward Andy. Andy started to run to the dog to lead him out of sight before anyone would see him. But it was too late. Kävik broke into a run.

As if it had all been arranged by some evil genius, Blackie and his pack trotted into the street from between two of the stores. The whole group of dogs stopped, surprised. They looked at Kävik. Kävik stopped and looked at them. He was suddenly tense.

Andy glanced about for a club. There was nothing. With fists clenched he started toward Blackie. He opened his mouth to yell when Blackie lunged toward Kävik with a bellow. The whole scrubby pack boiled noisily at his heels. Little long-haired Rags trotted from between the stores into the street. He saw the others bearing down on the lone Kävik; letting out a yelp of delight, he took out after them.

Andy watched. He could do nothing now. At any second Kävik would turn tail and run, with the whole clamoring pack pursuing him ingloriously the full length of the street. But Kävik just stood there. His wolflike head had dropped and his yellow eyes were staring straight at the advancing Blackie. Andy wanted to yell, "Run, Kävik, run for home!" But he couldn't.

Then Kävik charged with a blood-chilling snarl. Not away from Blackie, not racing ignobly up the street, tail tucked between his legs, but straight into the face of the pack. His great jaws were sprung wide, his teeth gleamed.

Andy had heard how wolves fought, what tremendous strength their jaws possessed, how their teeth could slash and rip with the speed of knives. Now he saw it.

Blackie was several lengths ahead of the pack. Kävik's lunge caught him squarely in the chest and hurled him rolling in the dust. Kävik was on him in a flash, driving for the unprotected throat. Blackie let out one startled bleat of surprise and fear; then Kävik's jaws snapped and ripped. Blackie never regained his feet. The pack was on Kävik then, and buried him beneath the sheer weight of their numbers.

Kävik disappeared beneath their straining bodies. The next instant he heaved into sight, rearing to his full height on hind legs in the very center of the pack, twisting, turning, teeth slashing right and left. He was leaping and dodging through the snarling dogs so fast it seemed to Andy he must be two dogs fighting at once. The scrubby pack had never met anything like this. They were used to easy victories over the softer town dogs. Their fighting howls turned to yelps and cries of pain and fright.

A rangy mongrel hobbled frantically off on three legs. A white, short-haired dog ran blindly up the street, the side of his face laid open. Then the whole pack disintegrated as dogs scattered, terrified, in all directions to escape the demon in their midst.

Kävik's very air challenged every dog in Copper City. Here was Kävik, the wolf dog. The leader of the team that had won the North American Sled Dog Derby in Fairbanks.

Andy found his voice and called Kävik to him. He put an arm around the dog's neck.

A voice called behind Andy, "Come over here."

Andy turned, and there was Mr. Hunter standing across the street in front of the post office. He had a handful of letters.

Andy said, "Come on, Kävik." He turned and ran all the way home and burst into the kitchen. His mother was getting dinner, and his father was sitting at the table reading the paper.

"Dad! Mother!" he cried. "He's here. He's here! He's seen Kävik! He's coming to get him!"

Both parents looked startled. His mother said, "Who's here?"

"Mr. Hunter. He's seen Kävik. He's coming after him right now. I know he is."

Andy's father laid down the paper and asked calmly: "Mr. Hunter's here? He hasn't been to the cannery. Where'd you see him? Calm down, Andy, and begin at the beginning."

Andy drew a deep breath, and said, "When I got off work, Kävik came right into town to meet me."

"So that's where he disappeared to," his mother said. "I couldn't find him to put him in the kitchen. He must have figured out the reason."

"Did that bunch of curs get to him?" his father asked.

Andy nodded, and told them what had happened. The fight lost nothing in his telling. "Mr. Hunter was standing in front of the post office with a bunch of letters. I just know he saw it all. He yelled at me to wait. But I didn't. I know he's coming, Dad! I know it."

"He stopped to pick up the mail before going on to the cannery," Andy's father said. He looked down at Kävik then, and seemed to forget about George C. Hunter.

"So you found your courage again, after all

you must have gone through," he said wonderingly. "But how?"

Andy's mother leaned down and patted Kävik's big head. "Maybe he found something to fight for. Something that was very important to him. Did you, Kävik?"

"What?" Andy's father wondered.

"Who knows?" she said, still talking to the dog. "Somebody thought enough of you to put that big collar on you. Did you love him, maybe fight for him? Or maybe you had a mate. Did you have a mate, Kävik?"

Kävik waved his tail and lifted his lips in a grin.

"If somebody loved him so much, why didn't he stay with them?" Andy's father asked. "If he had a mate, where is she?"

"We'll never know," Andy's mother said softly. "But one thing I do know. He came back to us because he loves us so much."

Andy's father continued looking at Kävik as if he were seeing him for the first time. He rubbed his big chin and shook his head.

Andy, who'd been watching out the window, cried: "Here he comes! I knew he'd follow me home. Dad, do something. Please!" Andy begged. "Try to buy him, Dad. Please, try."

As Kurt Evans walked out the door, he did not answer. Andy and his mother followed, with Kävik between them. The four of them waited in the yard for Mr. Hunter.

George Hunter stopped before Andy's father, but his eyes were on Kävik. "So he came back here. I couldn't believe it when I saw him in town just now. How'd he do it, Kurt?"

"I was hoping you could tell us," Andy's father said. "He showed up here over three weeks ago, one hind leg out of the socket, almost starved to death. He had a lot of new scars from fighting. Somebody put a collar on him. Did you?"

George Hunter shook his head. "He ran away one night at my club. I advertised for a week, but nothing came of it. I figured he'd taken off into the hills back of the club." He frowned, black eyes staring hard at Kävik. "How'd he get here? It's more than two thousand miles. And who put a collar on him? And where'd he learn to fight? Down home he was the biggest coward I've ever seen. But not now. I just saw him scatter the whole mangy pack. What a sight! Standing there in the middle of the street, he looked just like he did when he won the North American. King of the world! I'm glad I found him again."

Kurt Evans said nothing. He rubbed the back of his neck thoughtfully, then his big jaw. He scowled down at Kävik, then at Mr. Hunter.

"Something wrong, Kurt?" Hunter asked.

Andy's father kept rubbing his jaw. Finally he drew a deep breath, like a swimmer about to plunge into icy water, and said, with measured deliberation, "Mr. Hunter, I can't let you take Kävik."

George Hunter's black eyes bored into Kurt Evans for a long, surprised moment. Then he said: "I bought that dog. I've got a bill of sale for him. Maybe you'd better explain, Kurt."

"I'll try. When Andy found him after the plane wreck, you told me to shoot him. Well, I didn't, as you know, and he recovered. Then you took him south. He ran away after you'd had him there for months. Somehow he got back here to us, so his running away wasn't just a spur-of-the-moment thing. He didn't want to stay with you. He wanted us because this is his home. We're his family. You had your chance with him, Mr. Hunter, and he said no. We did the right thing the first time, and gave him back to you. After all he went through to get here, what he wants this time should be considered."

George Hunter's black eyes were cold, his voice deadly, "This is the craziest thing I've ever heard. Are you just taking him, Kurt?"

"I'll buy him from you."

"I paid two thousand dollars for him."

Kurt Evans swallowed. "That's a lot of money."

"He was a lot of dog when I bought him. He is again."

"I've got eight hundred dollars," Andy said stoutly. "You can have that, Dad."

Laura, who had never taken her eyes from Kurt's face, said, "Be still, Andy."

Andy held his breath and watched his father.

Hunter said: "If you're thinking of fighting me in court, forget it, Kurt. I can beat you to death with the change in my pocket."

Kurt nodded heavily. "I know that." He was looking down at Kävik, and the yellow eyes of the dog gazed steadily back into his. "It seems to me that sometimes too much store is put in legal ownership," he said thoughtfully. "What about moral ownership, or—or a feeling of belonging somewhere special? It's not ownership with us. Kävik's part of the family. He belongs. He proved it when he came back more than two thousand miles. Now we ought to look at his side of it. This is where he wants to be. If I let you take him, without putting up some sort of fight, then

I'm a traitor to him. It's like saying loyalty and devotion don't stand for much. And I don't believe that, Mr. Hunter. I know Kävik's just a dog to you, to buy and sell, or to do with as you like. It's not that way with me. I have to fight for him. I just have to fight for what I believe."

"How do you figure to do that, Kurt?" George Hunter asked caustically. "A judge or jury would laugh such a defense right out of the courtroom."

Evans continued, following his thought: "I'd guess you had some serious problems with Kävik down south. I'll bet you discovered it's a real chore to keep such a big, active dog on a city lot. So you had him confined. That's one of the reasons he ran away. And he will again if he gets the chance. You're going to have no end of trouble with this dog in the city. He belongs up here, and I think you know it. As the winner of the North American last year, he could have been worth two thousand dollars. But there'll be a new winner this year. Half that sum would be big money for him now. I'll give you a thousand, Mr. Hunter."

"And I lose a thousand?"

Kurt Evans met George Hunter's sharp black eyes. "You won't lose a cent!" he said in a calm, sure voice.

"How so?"

"That big seiner of yours that you wanted me to take is still lying down there at the dock, doing nothing. You've tried three skippers on her in three years, and none of them has worked out. So the *Hustler* spends half the season tied to the dock, waiting for a good skipper when she should be out seining for your cannery, bringing in thousands of salmon a season. Well, I can work that boat, Mr. Hunter, as we both know. I'll take her off your hands. The same terms you offered me before. Interested?"

George Hunter's black eyes looked into Kurt Evans's calm gray ones. Evans was right about keeping such an animal on a city lot. Tearing through his wife's flower gardens once had been enough. Finding Kävik again presented too much of a problem at home. But, more important, here was a way to get Evans seining for him again. He thrust out a hand. "You've got a deal."

They shook hands, and Kurt said: "I'll go aboard the first thing in the morning and get the *Hustler* ready. You round up a crew. There's still two and a half weeks of fishing left. At the rate the salmon are running, we should have the first load in the cannery within a few hours."

"Good enough." George Hunter looked down at Kävik, then at Andy. "You've got quite a dog there, boy!" he said, and strode down the hill toward the cannery.

The Evans family returned to the house and their neglected dinner. Once again Kävik waited for tidbits at Andy's elbow.

Kurt looked at his wife, and smiled suddenly. "Seems I'm going to be a seiner again. You know, I'm glad. I should have gone back long ago."

"I know." Andy's mother smiled. "I'm happy it's over——"

Andy had pushed back his chair and was holding Kävik's head in his hands. He spoke to him in a low, intimate voice. "I wish I knew all the things that happened to you—where you've been and the people you met. How you got those scars, who put the collar on you. I'd like to know how you got your courage back again. And I'd like to know how you came back all those miles to us. But it doesn't really matter. You're home again—home for good. But I wish I knew. I just wish I knew."

Kävik cocked his head and listened to the boy's voice. Then he licked Andy's face and lifted his lips in a grin as if he understood what the words were all about.

THINK AND DISCUSS
Understanding
1. Why does Kävik change direction and head east?
2. What causes him to change direction and once again head north?
3. What happens as the result of a natural barrier, or external conflict, that Kävik faces?
4. How does Kävik show that he has regained his courage?
5. What deal allows Andy to keep Kävik?

Analyzing
6. Would you describe the **mood** when Kävik meets his mate as (**a**) suspicious and aloof; (**b**) playful and quick-paced; (**c**) hostile and angry?
7. Why do you think the author included the chapter about Kävik and his mate?
8. How does Kurt Evans's attitude change toward (**a**) Kävik; (**b**) Dr. Walker; (**c**) Mr. Hunter; (**d**) himself?

9. Although the Evans family does not know all that happened to Kävik, what conclusions do they draw about his experiences? What evidence supports their conclusions?

Extending

10. Do you think it is fair that Kurt Evans agrees to pay one thousand dollars for Kävik? Why or why not?

REVIEWING: Plot H𝓩
See Handbook of Literary Terms, p. 649.

To develop a **plot,** an author chooses a pattern of events to present and resolve a conflict. The events are usually arranged in a cause-and-effect relationship, with each event becoming a necessary link to the climax and conclusion of the work.

1. What is the major conflict in this novel?
2. Describe several of the less important conflicts that are part of the plot.
3. What is the turning point, or climax, in the novel?
4. How is the major conflict resolved in the conclusion?

READING LITERATURE SKILLFULLY
Sequence

There is a **sequence,** or order, for the events that make up the plot in a novel or story. Whether or not the events are actually told in the order in which they occur in time, you can figure out the sequence by considering how one event grows out of and follows another.

Put the following events in the correct time sequence.

1. Kävik is injured in a plane crash.
2. Kävik fights a wolf and wins a mate.
3. Hunter buys Kävik from Charlie One Eye.
4. Kävik escapes from Hunter.
5. Kävik returns to Alaska with the Kents.
6. Andy Evans discovers Kävik in an iron cage.
7. Kurt Evans makes a deal with Hunter.
8. Kävik is injured crossing a glacier.
9. Kävik becomes accustomed to the care he is given by the Evans family.
10. Kävik wins the North American Race.

VOCABULARY
Homophones and Homonyms

A homophone is a word that is pronounced the same as another word but has a different origin and meaning. You will recognize homophones because their pronunciations as shown in a dictionary are identical. For example, *ate* (āt) and *eight* (āt) are homophones.

A homonym is a word that is pronounced and often spelled the same as another word, but it has a different origin and meaning. In a dictionary, there will be separate entries for homonyms. For example, there is one entry for *flounder* meaning "to struggle awkwardly" and a second entry for *flounder* meaning "a kind of flatfish."

1. Identify three pairs of homophones in the list below. Write six sentences, one for each word. Use the Glossary, if necessary.
2. What are the two words below that have homonyms in the Glossary? Write four sentences, one to show a meaning for each separate entry in the Glossary.

faint   cash   idyll   gimp
cache   idle   keen   feint

THINKING SKILLS
Generalizing

To generalize is to draw a general conclusion from particular information. In *Kävik, the Wolf Dog*, Dr. Walker states, "You can do anything you have to." This could mean acting bravely or putting up with something unpleasant and difficult. Give examples from the novel to support the generalization made by Dr. Walker.

COMPOSITION
Comparing Two Events

Dr. Walker treats Kävik on two occasions. What is alike and what is different about these two visits? Write two paragraphs, one in which you describe the similarities and one in which you describe the differences. For example, in each situation Dr. Walker takes a medical interest in Kävik, but he treats Kävik secretly at his own home the first time and goes to the Evanses' home the second time. Before you begin, reread the passages about the two visits and list details to use.

Supporting an Opinion

Can a wild animal ever become a pet? Recall, for example, Adolf, the rabbit, and Bandit, the fox, who both must be set free in the end. Write a paragraph in which you support either the idea that a wild animal can never be tamed or the idea that a wild animal can become a pet. You may want to use examples of Kävik's behavior. See Lesson 2, "Supporting Your Ideas," in the Writer's Handbook.

ENRICHMENT
Finishing Your Map

If you have started a map of Kävik's journey, complete it. Be sure to add appropriate place names and symbols for the events that occurred at these places.

Doing Research

Locate information about how wolves live, eat, and learn to survive in the wild. What are the myths about wolves? What are the facts? Are wolf pairs in reality anything like they are in this account? Report your findings to the class.

BIOGRAPHY

Walt Morey
1907–

Walt Morey was born in Hoquiam, Washington, and throughout his life has held a number of jobs that helped acquaint him with the outdoors. At various times, Morey was a millworker, shipbuilder, deep-sea diver, and fish-trap inspector. He and his wife currently operate a nut grove in Oregon.

Morey's outdoor experiences led him to write many adventure stories with wilderness settings. *Kävik, the Wolf Dog; Gentle Ben;* and *Canyon Winter* are three adventure novels that are set in the Alaskan wilderness.

THINKING CRITICALLY
ABOUT LITERATURE

UNIT 7   NOVEL   Kävik, the Wolf Dog

CONCEPT REVIEW

The following excerpt is from a novel about a frontier boy, Travis, and his dog, Old Yeller. Before Travis's father leaves on a six-hundred-mile cattle drive, he asks Travis to take care of Mama and Little Arliss. The notes in the margin will help you think critically about the selection. Page numbers in the notes refer to a review of the term mentioned. Consult the Handbook of Literary Terms for a more complete discussion.

from Old Yeller

Fred Gipson

That Little Arliss! If he wasn't a mess! From the time he'd grown up big enough to get out of the cabin, he'd made a practice of trying to catch and keep every living thing that ran, flew, jumped, or crawled.

Every night before Mama let him go to bed, she'd make Arliss empty his pockets of whatever he'd captured during the day. Generally, it would be a tangled-up mess of grasshoppers and worms and praying bugs and little rusty tree lizards. One time he brought in a horned toad that got so mad he swelled out round and flat as a Mexican tortilla and bled at the eyes. Sometimes it was stuff like a young bird that had fallen out of its nest before it could fly, or a green-speckled spring frog or a striped water snake. And once he turned out of his pocket a wadded-up baby copperhead that nearly threw Mama into spasms. We never did figure out why the snake hadn't bitten him, but

■ **Setting** (page 509): As you read, look for clues, such as *cabin*, that place the story in frontier days.

■ Note the humor in the listing of things Arliss keeps in his pockets.

■ **Characterization** (page 490): Little Arliss is curious.

■ **Setting:** Copperheads and horned toads suggest a southern location.

Mama took no more chances on snakes. She switched Arliss hard for catching that snake. Then she made me spend better than a week, taking him out and teaching him to throw rocks and kill snakes.

That was all right with Little Arliss. If Mama wanted him to kill his snakes first, he'd kill them. But that still didn't keep him from sticking them in his pockets along with everything else he'd captured that day. The snakes might be stinking by the time Mama called on him to empty his pockets, but they'd be dead.

■ Again, note the humor.

Then, after the yeller dog came, Little Arliss started catching even bigger game. Like cottontail rabbits and chaparral birds and a baby possum that sulked and lay like dead for the first several hours until he finally decided that Arliss wasn't going to hurt him.

Of course, it was Old Yeller that was doing the catching. He'd run the game down and turn it over to Little Arliss. Then Little Arliss could come in and tell Mama a big fib about how he caught it himself.

■ The protagonists are Old Yeller and Little Arliss.

■ The novel is told from the first-person point of view.

I watched them one day when they caught a blue catfish out of Birdsong Creek. The fish had fed out into water so shallow that his top fin was sticking out. About the time I saw it, Old Yeller and Little Arliss did, too. They made a run at it. The fish went scooting away toward deeper water, only Yeller was too fast for him. He pounced on the fish and shut his big mouth down over it and went romping to the bank, where he dropped it down on the grass and let it flop. And here came Little Arliss to fall on it like I guess he'd been doing everything else. The minute he got his hands on it, the fish finned him and he went to crying.

But he wouldn't turn the fish loose. He just grabbed it up and went running and squawling toward the house, where he gave the fish to Mama. His hands were all bloody by then, where the fish had finned him. They swelled up and got mighty sore; not even a mesquite thorn hurts as bad as a sharp fish fin when it's run deep into your hand.

■ Note the flashback that provides further insight into Arliss's character.

But as soon as Mama had wrapped his hands in a poultice of mashed-up prickly-pear root to draw out the poison, Little Arliss forgot all about his hurt. And that night when we ate the fish for supper, he told the biggest windy I ever heard about how he'd dived 'way down into a deep hole under the rocks and dragged that fish out and nearly got drowned before he could swim to the bank with it.

■ **poultice:** a soft, moist mass applied as a medicine

But when I tried to tell Mama what really happened, she wouldn't let me. "Now, this is Arliss's story," she said. "You let him tell it the way he wants to."

I told Mama then, I said: "Mama, that old yeller dog is going to make the biggest liar in Texas out of Little Arliss."

But Mama just laughed at me, like she always laughed at Little Arliss's big windies after she'd gotten off where he couldn't hear her. She said for me to let Little Arliss alone. She said that if he ever told a bigger whopper than the ones I used to tell, she had yet to hear it.

Well, I hushed then. If Mama wanted Little Arliss to grow up to be the biggest liar in Texas, I guessed it wasn't any of my business.

All of which, I figure, is what led up to Little Arliss's catching the bear. I think Mama had let him tell so many big yarns about his catching live game that he'd begun to believe them himself.

When it happened, I was down the creek a ways, splitting rails to fix up the yard fence where the bulls had torn it down. I'd been down there since dinner, working in a stand of tall slim post oaks. I'd chop down a tree, trim off the branches as far up as I wanted, then cut away the rest of the top. After that I'd start splitting the log.

I'd split the log by driving steel wedges into the wood. I'd start at the big end and hammer in a wedge with the back side of my ax. This would start a little split running lengthways of the log. Then I'd take a second wedge and drive it into this split. This would split the log further along and, at the same time, loosen the first wedge. I'd then knock the first wedge loose and move it up in front of the second one.

Driving one wedge ahead of the other like that, I could finally split a log in two halves. Then I'd go to work on the halves, splitting them apart. That way, from each log, I'd come out with four rails.

Swinging that chopping ax was sure hard work. The sweat poured off me. My back muscles ached. The ax got so heavy I could hardly swing it. My breath got harder and harder to breathe.

An hour before sundown, I was worn down to a nub. It seemed like I couldn't hit another lick. Papa could have lasted till past sundown, but I didn't see how I could. I shouldered my ax and started toward the cabin, trying to think up some excuse to tell Mama to keep her from knowing I was played clear out.

That's when I heard Little Arliss scream.

Well, Little Arliss was a screamer by nature. He'd scream when he was happy and scream when he was mad and a lot of times he'd scream just to hear himself make a noise. Generally, we paid no more mind to his screaming than we did to the gobble of a wild turkey.

■ **Setting:** Note the state in which the story takes place.

■ **to a nub:** to a state of exhaustion

■ **lick:** blow; brief stroke

But this time was different. The second I heard his screaming, I felt my heart flop clear over. This time I knew Little Arliss was in real trouble.

I tore out up the trail leading toward the cabin. A minute before, I'd been so tired out with my rail splitting that I couldn't have struck a trot. But now I raced through the tall trees in that creek bottom, covering ground like a scared wolf.

■ Note the simile in the narrator's comparison of himself to a scared wolf.

Little Arliss's second scream, when it came, was louder and shriller and more frantic-sounding than the first. Mixed with it was a whimpering crying sound that I knew didn't come from him. It was a sound I'd heard before and seemed like I ought to know what it was, but right then I couldn't place it.

Then, from way off to one side came a sound that I would have recognized anywhere. It was the coughing roar of a charging bear. I'd just heard it once in my life. That was the time Mama had shot and wounded a hog-killing bear and Papa had had to finish it off with a knife to keep it from getting her.

My heart went to pushing up into my throat, nearly choking off my wind. I strained for every lick of speed I could get out of my running legs. I didn't know what sort of fix Little Arliss had got himself into, but I knew that it had to do with a mad bear, which was enough.

The way the late sun slanted through the trees had the trail all cross-banded with streaks of bright light and dark shade. I ran through these bright and dark patches so fast that the changing light nearly blinded me. Then suddenly, I raced out into the open where I could see ahead. And what I saw sent a chill clear through to the marrow of my bones.

There was Little Arliss, down in that spring hole again. He was lying half in and half out of the water, holding onto the hind leg of a little black bear cub no bigger than a small coon. The bear cub was out on the bank, whimpering and crying and clawing the rocks with all three of his other feet, trying to pull away. But Little Arliss was holding on for all he was worth, scared now and screaming his head off. Too scared to let go.

How the bear cub ever came to prowl close enough for Little Arliss to grab him, I don't know. And why he didn't turn on him and bite loose, I couldn't figure out, either. Unless he was like Little Arliss, too scared to think.

But all of that didn't matter now. What mattered was the bear cub's mama. She'd heard the cries of her baby and was coming to save him. She was coming so fast that she had the brush popping and breaking as she crashed through and over it. I could see her black heavy figure piling off down the slant on the far side of Birdsong Creek. She was roaring mad and ready to kill.

And worst of all, I could see that I'd never get there in time!

Mama couldn't either. She'd heard Arliss, too, and here she came from the cabin, running down the slant toward the spring, screaming at Arliss, telling him to turn the bear cub loose. But Little Arliss wouldn't do it. All he'd do was hang with that hind leg and let out one shrill shriek after another as fast as he could suck in a breath.

Now the she bear was charging across the shallows in the creek. She was knocking sheets of water high in the bright sun, charging with her fur up and her long teeth bared, filling the canyon with that awful coughing roar. And no matter how fast Mama ran or how fast I ran, the she bear was going to get there first!

I think I nearly went blind then, picturing what was going to happen to Little Arliss. I know that I opened my mouth to scream and not any sound came out.

Then, just as the bear went lunging up the creek bank toward Little Arliss and her cub, a flash of yellow came streaking out of the brush.

It was that big yeller dog. He was roaring like a mad bull. He wasn't one-third as big and heavy as the she bear, but when he piled into her from one side, he rolled her clear off her feet. They went down in a wild, roaring tangle of twisting bodies and scrambling feet and slashing fangs.

As I raced past them, I saw the bear lunge up to stand on her hind feet like a man while she clawed at the body of the yeller dog hanging to her throat. I didn't wait to see more. Without ever checking my stride, I ran in and jerked Little Arliss loose from the cub. I grabbed him by the wrist and yanked him up out of that water and slung him toward Mama like he was a half-empty sack of corn. I screamed at Mama. "Grab him, Mama! Grab him and run!" Then I swung my chopping ax high and wheeled, aiming to cave in the she bear's head with the first lick.

But I never did strike. I didn't need to. Old Yeller hadn't let the bear get close enough. He couldn't handle her; she was too big and strong for that. She'd stand there on her hind feet, hunched over, and take a roaring swing at him with one of those big front claws. She'd

■ **Plot** (page 529): Note the developing conflict between Little Arliss and the bear cub's mother.

■ The antagonist is the bear cub's mother.

■ Note the strong descriptive words: *roaring tangle, twisting bodies, scrambling feet, slashing fangs.*

■ **Plot:** Note the climax, or turning point, here.

slap him head over heels. She'd knock him so far that it didn't look like he could possibly get back there before she charged again, but he always did. He'd hit the ground rolling, yelling his head off with the pain of the blow; but somehow he'd always roll to his feet. And here he'd come again, ready to tie into her for another round.

I stood there with my ax raised, watching them for a long moment. Then from up toward the house, I heard Mama calling: "Come away from there, Travis. Hurry, son! Run!"

That spooked me. Up till then, I'd been ready to tie into that bear myself. Now, suddenly, I was scared out of my wits again. I ran toward the cabin.

■ **tie into:** attack vigorously

But like it was, Old Yeller nearly beat me there. I didn't see it, of course; but Mama said that the minute Old Yeller saw we were all in the clear and out of danger, he threw the fight to that she bear and lit out for the house. The bear chased him for a little piece, but at the rate Old Yeller was leaving her behind, Mama said it looked like the bear was backing up.

But if the big yeller dog was scared or hurt in any way when he came dashing into the house, he didn't show it. He sure didn't show it like we all did. Little Arliss had hushed his screaming, but he was trembling all over and clinging to Mama like he'd never let her go. And Mama was sitting in the middle of the floor, holding him up close and crying like she'd never stop. And me, I was close to crying, myself.

Old Yeller, though, all he did was come bounding in to jump on us and lick us in the face and bark so loud that there, inside the cabin, the noise nearly made us deaf.

■ Notice how the author breaks the tension of the fight with humor.

The way he acted, you might have thought that bear fight hadn't been anything more than a rowdy romp that we'd all taken part in for the fun of it.

THINK AND DISCUSS
Understanding
1. How does Little Arliss get in trouble with the blue catfish?
2. In what real trouble does Little Arliss find himself?
3. Who saves him and how?

Analyzing
4. What quality do Little Arliss and Old Yeller share?
5. Compare Old Yeller's actions during his fight with the bear to his actions afterwards.
6. How do you think Travis feels about his brother? Explain.

Extending

7. Why do you think people in scary situations are sometimes unable to move or act as they normally would?

REVIEWING LITERARY TERMS
Plot

1. What is the effect produced by each of these causes: (**a**) Arliss tries to catch a bear cub; (**b**) Old Yeller attacks the mother bear?
2. What is the external conflict in this excerpt?
3. What is the internal conflict?
4. What is the climax, or turning point, in the action?

Characterization

5. How does the author reveal the character of Travis?
6. What is Little Arliss like, and how is his character revealed?

Setting

7. What are the clues to where this story takes place?
8. What details suggest when this story occurs?

■ CONTENT REVIEW
THINKING SKILLS
Classifying

1. Classify the main events in the novel about Kävik according to where they take place. Use these categories: Fairbanks, Copper City, Seattle, and the Alaskan wilderness.

Generalizing

2. Which character do you think has the greatest impact on Kävik's ability to survive? Explain your choice.
3. Kävik is said to have a sixth sense, an extra sense often possessed by animals but not human beings. From details in the novel and examples in your own experience, draw some general conclusions about that sixth sense.

Synthesizing

4. What do you think would have happened if Hunter had taken Kävik back to his home a second time? Outline the events that might have occurred. Make up a different ending, or conclusion, for the novel.

Evaluating

5. Is Kävik a hero? Give reasons for your answer.
6. Which event or events in the novel are most effective in arousing your sympathy for Kävik? Explain.

■ COMPOSITION REVIEW
Writing as a Story Character

Choose a character in the novel and an event in which that character plays an important role. Write three or four paragraphs about the event from that character's point of view. For example, you might describe the fight between Kävik and the male wolf from the female wolf's point of view.

Reviewing Writer's Craft: Write Good Beginnings

In this unit you have seen how Walt Morey used good beginnings for the chapters in his novel. You may have read, copied, and found examples of good beginnings. Now **try your hand** at creating your own good beginning. Suppose Kävik's mate does not die. Write the beginning for a chapter in which Kävik and Andy get back together but through a series of events that are different from those described in this novel.

EPIC

THE ADVENTURES OF ULYSSES

Mt. Olympus, Photo by Erich Lessing

UNIT 8

PREVIEW

UNIT 8 EPIC

The Adventures of Ulysses
/ Bernard Evslin
Ships and Men
The Ciconians
The Lotus-Eaters
The Cyclops's Cave
Keeper of the Winds
Circe
The Land of the Dead
The Sirens

Scylla and Charybdis
The Cattle of the Sun
Calypso
Ino's Veil
Nausicaa
The Return
Penelope / Dorothy Parker
An Ancient Gesture
/ Edna St. Vincent Millay

Features
Reading the Adventures of a Hero
The Writer's Craft:
    Use Precise, Active Verbs
Comment: English Borrowings from Greek
Comment: Uncovering the Real Troy

Review of Literary Terms
figurative language
flashback
imagery

Reading Literature Skillfully
graphic aids
cause/effect relationships

Vocabulary Skills
inflected forms
synonyms and antonyms
dictionary

Thinking Skills
classifying
generalizing

Composition
Narrating an Adventure
Summarizing an Event
Being a Story Character
Persuading a Friend
Imagining the Future
Retitling an Author's Work
Writing Dialogue
Comparing or Contrasting

Enrichment
Researching the Greek and Roman Gods
Illustrating Ulysses' Adventures
Interviewing Ulysses

Thinking Critically About Literature
Concept Review
Content Review
Composition Review

Reading THE ADVENTURES OF A HERO

The selection you are about to read is based on the *Odyssey* (od'ə sē), an epic poem that was written in Greece about 800 B.C. Epic poetry, which narrates heroic adventures, historical and mythical, is the earliest surviving form of Greek literature. Although the authorship of the epics the *Iliad* (il'ē əd) and the *Odyssey* is usually attributed to a blind poet named Homer, scholars disagree about who Homer was or whether he existed at all. Some say the famous works were written by at least two poets. Others argue that the same man wrote both poems, the *Iliad* when he was young and the *Odyssey* when he was old.

Regardless of their authorship, the stories of the Trojan War recounted in the *Iliad* and of the wanderings of Ulysses found in the *Odyssey* have appealed to people for over 2,500 years. Both epics have been repeatedly translated for different audiences in different ages and nations. And at times, as in the case of *The Adventures of Ulysses*, major episodes from one of the epics have been retold in modern prose.

As you will soon discover, *The Adventures of Ulysses* is both like and unlike selections you have already read. Like a short story, the selection has **setting, plot,** and **characterization.** But unlike a short story, it has a multitude of settings, many of them exotic; it features numerous external conflicts; and it contains scores of characters, some of whom are glimpsed only briefly.

The selection differs in another important way from the usual short story. It features a hero, not a typical human being, as its main character. As a hero, Ulysses possesses characteristics shared by few men. He displays unusual feats of strength, remarkable wit and cunning, and exceptional loyalty to his men.

Though a hero, Ulysses is far from perfect. He is capable of making errors of judgment, and he can be a braggart. A man distantly related to the gods and known by them, Ulysses is not himself a god. He is an aging mortal, who faces and overcomes extraordinary obstacles.

Everyday language seems hardly adequate to describe Ulysses' character, the persons, gods, and monsters he meets, and the feats he performs. Notice, as you read, how the author makes frequent use of **figurative language,** particularly simile and metaphor, and **imagery** to enrich descriptions of individuals and events. Note, too, the **point of view** the author employs and ask yourself, "Why has he selected this point of view rather than another?"

The map on pages 544–545 is a **graphic aid** that will help you follow Ulysses' many exploits. In addition, on pages 546–547 you will find a glossary that briefly identifies each proper name and indicates how to pronounce it. Frequent use of these two aids will lead you to greater understanding and enjoyment of *The Adventures of Ulysses*.

INTRODUCTION

The gods and goddesses of ancient Greece seem to us a peculiar lot. They established themselves after a long and terrible war that the brothers Zeus, Poseidon, and Hades waged against the race of older gods called the Titans. Once the Titans were finally overthrown, Zeus, Poseidon, and Hades drew lots to divide the earth among them. Zeus won the sky; Poseidon, the sea; and Hades, the underworld. From that time on, Zeus ruled the earth, along with his brothers, sisters, various spouses, and a few additional gods and goddesses, all of them making their home on Mount Olympus.

These Olympians were a quarrelsome family. They ruled the universe, but not peacefully. Though immortal, they nevertheless displayed the same range of emotions one finds among mortals—and often the same bad manners. Petty jealousies would often spring up between one god or goddess and another, and fights would follow. They played favorites among humans: to one they might give special powers, while they made life difficult for another. Since Olympians could influence events and determine mortals' fates, life on earth was largely unpredictable.

It was against this background that the Trojan War started—touched off by jealousy among the gods. Eris, the goddess of discord, was not invited to a feast. Angry at being snubbed, she threw into the banquet hall a golden apple on which were the words *For the Most Beautiful*. Three goddesses each immediately claimed the apple for her own: Hera, wife of almighty Zeus; Athene, his daughter, goddess of both wisdom and battle; and Aphrodite, his daughter-in-law, goddess of love. The three appealed to Zeus to choose, but he knew better than to get involved in that argument. Instead, he advised them to go to young Prince Paris, son of King Priam of Troy. Paris was known for his fairness as a judge.

But the goddesses did not ask Paris to select the most beautiful among them; instead, they offered him bribes. From Hera came the offer to be ruler of Europe and Asia; from Athene, the chance to lead the Trojans to victory against the Greeks; from Aphrodite, the love of the most beautiful woman in the world. Paris gave Aphrodite the golden apple.

The woman who was most famous for her beauty was Helen, wife of King Menelaus of Sparta. Most of the kings and princes of Greece had wanted to marry her, in fact, and had come to Sparta bearing rich presents for King Tyndareus, Helen's father. Tyndareus was fearful of being accused of favoritism if he accepted the presents of any one suitor. If the rejected suitors took offense, they might wage war. Sensing the problem, King Ulysses of Ithaca offered Tyndareus a solution. Ulysses was well known for his cleverness, and so the king quickly accepted his advice. Tyndareus asked all the suitors solemnly to swear to defend and protect Helen and her chosen husband. Since each suitor hoped to be the one chosen, all of them swore to the oath. Then Tyndareus chose Menelaus to be Helen's groom, and appointed him king of Sparta as well. As reward for his advice, Ulysses asked to marry Penelope, Tyndareus's niece.

Guided by Aphrodite, Paris later arrived in Sparta. Menelaus treated him hospitably, as was the custom, but Menelaus was soon called away because of his father's death. Menelaus left Helen to rule in his absence.

Under Aphrodite's spell, Helen fell deeply in love with her visitor. She eloped with Paris, taking with her most of the palace treasures. Paris took her home with him to Troy, where his father, King Priam, found Helen so lovely he vowed to protect her and Paris and never to return her to Sparta.

Menelaus returned to find Helen gone. Hurt and angry, he called upon the kings and princes of all Greece to keep their vows and to help him. They responded, and eventually a thousand ships carrying troops sailed to Troy.

Troy, however, was a walled city, built for defense, and it was not easy to conquer. The war raged for ten years, with first one side, then the other, favored by the gods. Aphrodite, of course, sided with Paris and Troy; Hera—goddess of marriage—just as strongly opposed them. The rest of the gods and goddesses played their favorites as well, although Zeus remained neutral most of the time to avoid Hera's wrath.

After ten years the Greeks finally took Troy—through a trick. The clever Ulysses had built a huge wooden horse, the famous Trojan Horse, inside which warriors could hide. They left this horse outside the gates of Troy and sailed away—only to hide behind a nearby island. The Trojans assumed their foes had given up; nevertheless, they were puzzled by the enormous horse outside their gates. A Greek soldier, who had volunteered to remain behind and be captured, was brought before King Priam. He played his part well. He declared that both he and the horse were intended to be offerings to Athene, but that he had escaped. The horse had been built so large, the soldier claimed, to discourage the Trojans from carting it into their city. The Trojans were supposed to destroy the wooden offering and thereby bring the wrath of Athene upon themselves.

The scheme worked. The Trojans dragged the horse through the gates and into their city, thinking to win Athene's favor away from the Greeks. Then that night, the Greeks who had hidden in the horse, Ulysses included, climbed out through a trap door and threw wide the city gates. The remaining Greek soldiers, returned from hiding, stormed through the gates of Troy, set fire to buildings, and killed those who rushed out into the streets in confusion. By morning the city was in ruins. Helen was taken to Menelaus, who gladly received her back, and together they sailed home to Sparta.

When Ulysses had joined the Greek forces ten years earlier, he had been forced to leave behind in Ithaca his attractive and devoted wife, Penelope, and his young son, Telemachus. Throughout the war he had fought with courage, coolness, and—whenever necessary—cunning. His plan to take Troy had worked and had brought an end to the war. But Ulysses was weary of battle. He had begun to long increasingly for home. Ten years away from his wife, his son, and his native land seemed like an eternity.

In the story that follows, Ulysses begins his homeward journey, unaware of what the gods might yet have in store for him.

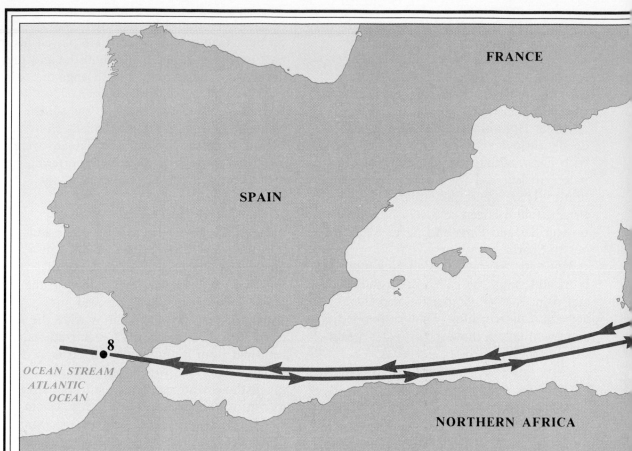

FRANCE

SPAIN

8

OCEAN STREAM
ATLANTIC
OCEAN

NORTHERN AFRICA

The Voyages of Ulysses

1 **Troy.** The site of the Trojan War is the beginning of Ulysses' journey home.
2 **The Ciconians.** Ulysses' men attempt to loot a rich city.
3 **Lotusland.** The god Morpheus gives sleep and dreams.
4 **Island of the Cyclopes.** Ulysses' men are trapped by the one-eyed giant, Polyphemus.
5 **Aeolus.** The god of the winds offers Ulysses help.
6 **The Bag of Winds.** Ulysses' men release a terrible gale.
7 **Island of the Dawn.** Circe, the sorceress, turns men into beasts.
8 **Tartarus.** Ulysses seeks advice in the Land of the Dead.
9 **The Sirens.** Monsters sing to lure sailors to destruction.
10 **Scylla and Charybdis.** Ulysses tries to steer between a monster who eats sailors and a monster who creates a great whirlpool.
11 **Thrinacia.** The Sun Titan Hyperion demands revenge for the loss of his golden cattle.
12 **Storm at sea.** Ulysses is shipwrecked.
13 **Ogygia.** The sorceress Calypso offers Ulysses immortality.
14 **Ino.** The sea nymph lends Ulysses her magic veil.
15 **Phaeacia.** Nausicaa sings of heroes at a banquet in Ulysses' honor.
16 **Ithaca.** Ulysses arrives home—in disguise.

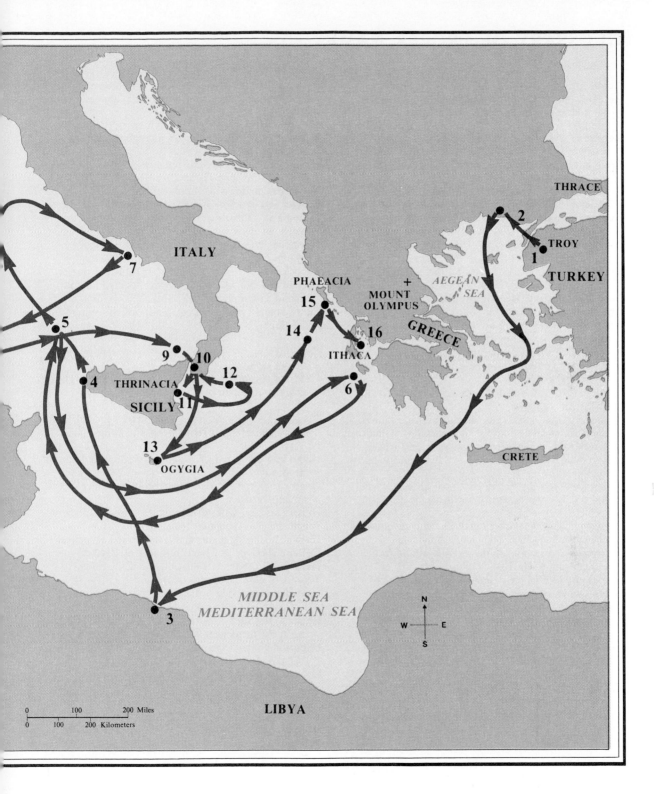

GLOSSARY OF PROPER NAMES

Achilles (ə kil′ēz), Greek hero at the Trojan War.

Actaeon (ak tē′ən), hunter changed into a stag by the goddess Artemis and killed by his own hounds.

Aegean (i jē′ən) **Sea,** arm of the Mediterranean Sea between Greece and Turkey. See map.

Aeolian (ē ō′lē ən) **Island,** home of **Aeolus** (ē′ə ləs), god of the winds. See map.

Agamemnon (ag′ə mem′non), Menelaus's brother, leader of the Greeks in the Trojan War.

Agelaus (aj ə lā′əs), suitor for Penelope.

Ajax (ā′jaks), Greek hero at the Trojan War.

Alcinous (al sin′ō əs), king of Phaeacia, father of Nausicaa.

Amphitrite (am′ fə trī′tē), sea goddess, wife of Poseidon.

Anticleia (an ti klē′ə), mother of Ulysses.

Antinous (an tin′ō əs), suitor for Penelope.

Aphrodite (af′ rə dī′tē), goddess of love and beauty.

Apollo (ə pol′ō), god of the sun, poetry, and music.

Arcadia (är kā′dē ə), mountain district in the south of ancient Greece.

Ares (er′ēz), god of war.

Arete (ə rē′tē), queen of Phaeacia, mother of Nausicaa.

Argo (är′gō), Ulysses' old, faithful hunting hound.

Artemis (är′tə mis), goddess of the chase, or hunt.

Athene (ə thē′nē), goddess of wisdom and battle.

Atlas (at′ləs), Titan who supports the heavens on his shoulders.

Attica (at′ə kə), district in southeast Greece.

Aulis (ô′lis), town on east coast of Greece.

Calypso (kə lip′sō), Titan sorceress who rules island of Ogygia.

Charybdis (kə rib′dis), monster who swallows the sea, causing a whirlpool.

Ciconian (si kō′nē ən), person from village near Troy where Ulysses first stops.

Cimmerian (sə mir′ē ən), one of people said to live in perpetual mists and darkness and to eat shipwrecked sailors.

Circe (sèr′sē), sorceress who turns men into animals.

Cretan (krēt′n), person from **Crete** (krēt), Greek island southeast of mainland. See map.

Cyclops (sī′klops), *pl.* **Cyclopes** (sī klō′pēz), one of a race of one-eyed giants.

Cythera (si thir′ə), island in southern Greece.

Demeter (di mē′tər), goddess of agriculture.

Diomedes (dī′ə mē′ dēz), Greek hero at the Trojan War.

Elpenor (el pē′nôr), sailor accidentally killed on voyage to Tartarus.

Elysian (i lizh′ən) **Fields,** place of bliss where heroes and good persons reside after death.

Eos (ē′os), goddess of the dawn.

Eris (er′is), goddess of strife and discord.

Ethiopian (ē′thē ō′pē ən), person from region in northeast Africa, south of Egypt.

Eumaeus (yü mē′əs), aged swineherd on Ithaca.

Euryalus (yü rī′ə ləs), young man of Phaeacia.

Eurycleia (yü ri klī′ə), Ulysses' faithful old nurse.

Eurylochus (yü ril′ō kəs), Ulysses' companion and second in command.

Eurymachus (yü rim′ə kəs), leader of the suitors for Penelope.

Fate (fāt), one of three goddesses who determine human destiny.

Fields of Asphodel (as′fə del), meadow where ghosts of heroes wander.

Gorgon (gôr′gən), monster with snakes for hair and a horrible face that turns people to stone.

Hades (hā′dēz), god of the lower world, the home of the dead.

Hector (hek′tər), Paris's elder brother, leader of the Trojan warriors.

Helen (hel′ən), wife of Menelaus, whose elopement with Paris caused the Trojan War.

Helios (hē′lē os), a sun god. Also called Hyperion.

Hellene (hel′ēn), a Greek; any one of Ulysses' men.

Hera (her′ə), wife of Zeus, queen of the gods, goddess of women and marriage.

Heracles (her′ə klēz′), hero renowned for strength and courage. Also called Hercules (hèr′kyə lēz′).

Hermes (hèr′mēz), god of travel, science, invention, and luck; messenger for the other gods.

Hyperion (hī pir′ē ən), Sun Titan, sometimes called Helios, whose chariot is the sun.

Hypnos (hip′nos), god of sleep.

Immortal (i môr′tl), any god or goddess; anyone who lives forever.

Ino (ī′nō), lesser sea goddess who rescues Ulysses.

Iros (ī′rəs), beggar in Ulysses' court.

Island of the Dawn, home of Circe. See map.

Ithaca (ith′ə kə), island west of Greece, home of Ulysses. See map.

Jasion (jā′zē ən), Titan lover of Demeter, crippled by Zeus.

Libya (lib′ē ə), part of northern Africa west of Egypt.

Menelaus (men′ə lā′əs), king of Sparta, husband of Helen.

Middle Sea, now called Mediterranean. See map.

Minos (mī′nəs), king and lawgiver of Crete who became a judge in the lower world.

Morpheus (môr′fē əs), god of dreams.

Naiad (nā′ad), lesser goddess guarding water.

Nausicaa (nô sik′ā ə), princess of Phaeacia who finds Ulysses and helps him.

Neoptolemus (nē′ op tol′ə məs), Greek hero, son of Achilles.

Nereid (nir′ē id), lesser sea goddess.

Nymph (nimf), lesser goddess of nature in seas, rivers, fountains, hills, trees, etc.

Ocean Stream, great stream supposed to surround all land. See map.

Oceanus (ō sē′ə nəs), god of the Ocean Stream.

Ogygia (ō jij′ē ə), island of Calypso. See map.

Olympus (ō lim′pəs), **Mount,** mountain in northeast Greece, home of the gods. See map.

Orion (ô rī′ən), famous hunter, killed by Artemis.

Paris (par′is), prince of Troy, whose elopement with Helen caused the Trojan War.

Penelope (pə nel′ə pē), wife of Ulysses, mother of Telemachus.

Perimedes (per i mē′dēz), one of Ulysses' crew.

Perse (pėr′sə), daughter of Oceanus, grandmother of Circe.

Persephone (pər sef′ə nē), goddess of the lower world, wife of Hades.

Phaeacia (fē ā′shə), island west of Greece, home of Nausicaa. See map.

Polyphemus (pol′ə fē′məs), Cyclops (one-eyed giant) whom Ulysses blinds.

Poseidon (pə sīd′n), god of the sea.

Priam (prī′əm), king of Troy.

Samos (sā′mos), Greek island in the Aegean Sea.

Scylla (sil′ə), monster who snatches sailors off ships and eats them.

Sicily (sis′ə lē), island near Italy. See map.

Siren (sī′rən), monster whose singing lures sailors to destruction on the rocks.

Sisyphus (sis′ə fəs), grandfather of Ulysses, condemned forever in the lower world to roll a heavy stone up a steep hill.

Sparta (spär′tə), city in Greece, home of Helen and Menelaus.

Styx (stiks), river in the lower world that souls of the dead must cross to reach Tartarus.

Tantalus (tan′tl əs), king punished in lower world by standing in water up to his chin under branches of fruit, yet unable to reach either.

Tartarus (tär′tər əs), the lower world; Hades.

Teiresias (tī rē′sē əs), famous blind prophet.

Telemachus (tə lem′ə kəs), prince of Ithaca, son of Ulysses and Penelope.

Thrinacia (thri nā′shə), island now called Sicily, home of Hyperion's golden cattle. See map.

Titan (tīt′n), one of family of giants who ruled the world before the gods of Olympus.

Trojan (trō′jən), person from **Troy** (troi), city in northwest Turkey, site of Trojan War. See map.

Tyndareus (tin der′ē əs), former king of Sparta, father of Helen.

Ulysses (yü lis′ēz), king of Ithaca, hero of the Trojan War.

Zeus (züs), god of the sky, ruler of gods and mortals.

The Adventures of Ulysses

Bernard Evslin   *based on the* Odyssey *by Homer*

SHIPS AND MEN

After Troy was burned, Ulysses sailed for home with three ships holding fifty men each.

Three thousand years ago ships were very different; through the years they have changed much more than the men who sail them.

These beaked warships used by the pirate kingdoms of the Middle Sea were like no vessels you have ever seen. Imagine a very long narrow rowboat with twenty oars on each side. The timbers of the bow curve sharply to a prow, and this prow grows longer and sharper, becomes in fact a long polished shaft tipped by a knife-edged brass spearhead. This was called the ram, the chief weapon of ancient warships.

In battle, the opposing ships spun about each other, swooping forward, twirling on their beams,[1] darting backward, their narrow hulls allowing them to backwater very swiftly. The object was to ram the enemy before he rammed you. And to ram first was the only defense, for the brass beak of the ramming ship sheared easily through the timbers of its victim, knocking a huge hole in the hull and sinking it before its men could jump overboard.

These warships were also equipped with sail and mast—used only for voyaging, never in battle—a square sail, and a short mast, held fast by oxhide stays. The sail was raised only for a fair wind, or could be tilted slightly for a quartering wind, but was useless against headwinds.

This meant that these ships were almost always at the mercy of the weather, and were often blown off course. Another thing that made them unfit for long voyages was the lack of cargo space. Only a few days' supply of food and water could be carried, leaving space for no other cargo. That is why these fighting ships tried to hug the coast and avoid the open sea.

Ulysses' problem was made worse by victory. When Troy was sacked, he and his men captured a huge booty—gold and jewels, silks, furs—and, after ten years of war, the

---

1. *twirling on their beams,* turning very quickly, as if the beam—the widest part of the ship—were a pivot.

Abridged by permission of Scholastic Magazines, Inc. from *Greeks Bearing Gifts* by Bernard Evslin. Text copyright © 1969 by Scholastic Magazines, Inc., text copyright © 1971 by Bernard Evslin.

men refused to leave any loot behind. This meant that each of his ships could carry food and water for a very few days.

This greed for treasure caused many of his troubles at first. But then troubles came so thick and fast that no one could tell what caused them; hardships were simply called bad luck, or the anger of the gods.

But bad luck makes good stories.

THE CICONIANS

The voyage began peacefully. A fair northeast wind blew, filling the sails of the little fleet and pushing it steadily homeward. The wind freshened at night, and the three ships scudded along joyfully under a fat moon.

On the morning of the second day Ulysses saw a blue haze of smoke and a glint of white stone. He put in toward shore and saw a beautiful little town. The men stared in amazement at this city without walls, rich with green parks and grazing cattle, its people strolling about in white tunics. Ten years of war had made Ulysses' men as savage as wolves. Everyone not a shipmate was an enemy. To meet was to fight; property belonged to the winner.

Ulysses stood in the bow, shading his eyes with his hand, gazing at the city. A tough, crafty old warrior named Eurylochus stood beside him.

"We attack, do we not?" he asked. "The city lies there defenseless. We can take it without losing a man."

"Yes, it looks tempting," said Ulysses. "But the wind blows fair, and good fortune attends us. Perhaps it will spoil our luck to stop."

"But this fat little city has been thrown into our laps by the gods, too," said Eurylochus, "and they grow angry when men refuse their gifts. It would be bad luck *not* to attack."

Ulysses heard the fierce murmur of his men behind him, and felt their greed burning in his veins. He hailed the other ships and gave orders, and the three black-hulled vessels swerved toward shore and nosed into the harbor, swooping down upon the white city like wolves upon a sheepfold.

They landed on the beach. The townsfolk fled before them into the hills. Ulysses did not allow his men to pursue them, for there was no room on the ship for slaves. From house to house the armed men went, helping themselves to whatever they wanted. Afterward they piled the booty in great heaps upon the beach.

Then Ulysses had them round up a herd of the plump, swaying, crook-horned cattle, and offer ten bulls in sacrifice to the gods. Later they built huge bonfires on the beach, roasted the cattle, and had a great feast.

But while the looting and feasting was going on, the men of the city had withdrawn into the hills and called together their kinsmen of the villages, the Ciconians, and began preparing for battle. They were skillful fighters, these men of the hills. They drove brass war chariots that had long blades attached to the wheels, and these blades whirled swiftly as the wheels turned, scything down the foe.

They gathered by the thousands, an overwhelming force, and stormed down out of the hills onto the beach. Ulysses' men were full of food and wine, unready to fight, but he had posted sentries, who raised a shout when they saw the Ciconians coming down from the hills in the moonlight. Ulysses raged among his men, slapping them with the flat of his sword, driving the fumes of wine out of their heads. His great racketing battle cry roused those he could not whip with his sword.

The men closed ranks and met the Ciconians at spearpoint. The Hellenes retreated slowly, leaving their treasure where it was heaped upon the beach and, keeping their line unbroken, made for their ships.

Ulysses chose two of his strongest men and bade them lift a thick timber upon their shoulders. He sat astride this timber, high enough to shoot his arrows over the heads of his men. He was the most skillful archer since Heracles. He aimed only at the chariot horses, and aimed not to kill, but to cripple, so that the horses fell in their traces, and their furious flailing and kicking broke the enemy's advance.

Thus the Hellenes were able to reach their ships and roll them into the water, leap into the rowers' benches, and row away. But eighteen men were left dead on the beach— six from each ship—and there was scarcely a man unwounded.

Eurylochus threw himself on his knees before Ulysses and said, "I advised you badly, O Chief. We have angered the gods. Perhaps, if you kill me, they will be appeased."

"Eighteen dead are enough for one night," said Ulysses. "Our luck has changed, but what has changed can change again. Rise, and go about your duties."

The ships had been handled roughly in the swift retreat from the Ciconian beach. Their hulls had been battered by axes and flung spears, and they had sprung small leaks. The wind had faded to a whisper, and the men were forced to row with water sloshing around their ankles. Ulysses saw that his ships were foundering, and that he would have to empty the holds. Food could not be spared, nor water; the only thing that could go was the treasure taken from Troy. The men groaned and tore at their beards as they saw the gold and jewels and bales of fur and silk being dropped overboard. But Ulysses cast over his own share of the treasure first— and his was the largest share—so the men had to bite back their rage and keep on rowing.

As the necklaces, bracelets, rings and brooches sank slowly, winking their jewels like drowned fires, a strange thing happened. A shoal of naiads—beautiful water nymphs— were drawn by the flash of the jewels. They dived after the bright baubles and swam alongside the ships, calling to the men, singing, tweaking the oars out of their hands, for they were sleek mischievous creatures who loved jewels and strangers. Some of them came riding dolphins, and in the splashing silver veils of spray the men thought they saw beautiful girls with fishtails. This is probably how the first report of mermaids arose.

Poseidon, God of the Sea, was wakened from sleep by the sound of this laughter. When he saw what was happening, his green beard bristled with rage, and he said to himself, "Can it be? Are these the warriors whom I helped in their siege of Troy? Is this their gratitude, trying to steal my naiads from me? I'll teach them manners."

He whistled across the horizon to his son, Aeolus, keeper of the winds, who twirled his staff and sent a northeast gale skipping across

Ulysses. Marble statue from Rome, found in 1885. A Roman work of about A.D. 50.
Boston, Mrs. Stewart Gardner Museum. Photo by Erich Lessing

the sea. It pounced upon the little fleet and scattered the ships like twigs. Ulysses clung to the helm, trying to hold the kicking tiller, trying to shout over the wind. There was nothing to do but ship the mast[2] and let the wind take them.

And the wind, in one huge gust of fury, drove them around Cythera, the southernmost of their home islands, into the open waters of the southwest quarter of the Middle Sea, toward the hump of Africa called Libya.

THE LOTUS-EATERS

Now, at this time, the shore of Libya was known as "the land where Morpheus plays."

Who was Morpheus? He was a young god, son of Hypnos, God of Sleep, and nephew of Hades. It was his task to fly around the world, from nightfall to dawn, scattering sleep. His father, Hypnos, mixed the colors of sleep for him, making them dark and thick and sad.

"For," he said, "it is a little death you lay upon man each night, my son, to prepare him for the kingdom of death."

But his aunt, Persephone, sewed him a secret pocket, full of bright things, and said: "It is not death you scatter, but repose. Hang the walls of sleep with bright pictures, so that man may not know death before he dies."

These bright pictures were called dreams. And Morpheus became fascinated by the way a little corner of man's mind remained awake in sleep, and played with the colors he had hung, mixing them, pulling them apart, making new pictures. It seemed to him that these fantastic colored shadows the sleepers painted were the most beautiful, most puzzling things he had ever seen. And he wanted to know more about how they came to be.

He went to Persephone, and said, "I need a flower that makes sleep. It must be purple and black. But there should be one petal streaked with fire-red, the petal to make dreams."

Persephone smiled and moved her long white hand in the air. Between her fingers a flower blossomed. She gave it to him.

"Here it is, Morpheus. Black and purple like sleep, with one petal of fire-red for dreams. We will call it lotus."

Morpheus took the flower and planted it in Libya, where it is always summer. The flower grew in clusters, smelling deliciously of honey. The people ate nothing else. They slept all the time, except when they were gathering flowers. Morpheus watched over them, reading their dreams.

It was toward Lotusland that Ulysses and his men were blown by the gale. The wind fell while they were still offshore. The sky cleared, the sea calmed, a hot sun beat down. To Ulysses, dizzy with fatigue, weak with hunger, the sky and the water and the air between seemed to flow together in one hot blueness.

He shook his head, trying to shake away the hot blue haze, and growled to his men to unship the oars, and row toward land. The exhausted men bent to the oars, and the ships crawled over the fire-blue water. With their last strength they pulled the ships up on the beach, past the high-tide mark, and then lay down and went to sleep.

As they slept, the Lotus-eaters came out of

---

2. **ship the mast.** The mast was short and could be *shipped*, or *unstepped*—that is, taken down—and sometimes was even carried off the ship for security.

The palm trees of the Lotus-eaters. The island of Djerba off the coast of Tunis was already regarded in ancient times as the dwelling place of the Lotus-eaters of the legend.
Photo by Erich Lessing

the forest. Their arms were heaped with flowers, which they piled about the sleeping men in great blue and purple bouquets, so that they might have flowers to eat when they awoke, for these people were very gentle and hospitable.

The men awoke and smelled the warm honey smell of the flowers, and ate them in great handfuls—like honeycomb—and fell asleep again. Morpheus hovered over the sleeping men and read their dreams.

"These men have done terrible things," the god whispered to himself. "Their dreams are full of gold and blood and fire. Such sleep will not rest them."

And he mixed them some cool green and silver dreams of home. The nightmares faded. Wounded Trojans stopped screaming, Troy stopped burning; they saw their wives smile, heard their children laugh, saw the green wheat growing in their own fields. They dreamed of home, awoke and were hungry, ate the honeyed lotus flowers and fell into a deeper sleep.

Then Morpheus came to Ulysses who was stretched on the sand, a little apart from the rest. He studied his face—the wide grooved brow, the sunken eyes, the red hair, the jutting chin. And he said to himself, "This man is a hero. Terrible are his needs, sudden his deeds, and his dreams must be his own. I cannot help him."

So Morpheus mixed no colors for Ulysses' sleep, but let him dream his own dreams, and

The Lotus-Eaters 553

read them as they came. He hovered above the sleeping king and could not leave.

"What monsters he makes," he said to himself. "Look at that giant with the single eye in the middle of his forehead. And that terrible spider-woman with all those legs. . . . Ah, the things he dreams, this angry sleeper. What bloody mouths, what masts falling, sails ripping, what rocks and reefs, what shipwrecks . . . how many deaths?"

Ulysses awoke, choking, out of a terrible nightmare. It seemed to him that in his sleep he had seen the whole voyage laid out before him, had seen his ships sinking, his men drowning. Monsters had crowded about him, clutching, writhing. He sat up and looked about. His men lay asleep among heaped flowers. As he watched, one opened his eyes, raised himself on an elbow, took a handful of flowers, stuffed them into his mouth, and immediately fell asleep again.

Ulysses smelled the honey sweetness, and felt an overpowering hunger. He took some of the flowers and raised them to his mouth. As their fragrance grew stronger, he felt his eyelids drooping, and his arms grew heavy, and he thought, "It is these flowers that are making us sleep. Their scent alone brings sleep. I must not eat them."

But he could not put them down; his hand would not obey him. Exerting all the bleak force of his will, he grasped his right hand with his left—as if it belonged to someone else—and one by one forced open his fingers and let the flowers fall.

Then he dragged himself to his feet and walked slowly into the sea. He went under and arose snorting. His head had cleared. But when he went up on the beach, the sweet fragrance rose like an ether and made him dizzy again.

"I must work swiftly," he said.

One by one he carried the sleeping men to the ships, and propped them on their benches. His strength was going. The honey smell was invading him, making him droop with sleep. He took his knife and, cutting sharp splinters of wood to prop open his eyelids, staggered back among the men. He worked furiously now, lifting them on his shoulders, carrying them two at a time, throwing them into the ships.

Finally, the beach was cleared. The men lolled sleeping upon the benches. Then, all by himself, using his last strength, he pushed the ships into the water. When the ships were afloat in the shallow water, he lashed one to another with rawhide line, his own ship in front. Then he raised his sail and took the helm.

The wind was blowing from the southwest. It filled his sail. The line grew taut; the file of ships moved away from Lotusland.

The men began to awake from their dreams of home, and found themselves upon the empty sea again. But the long sleep had rested them, and they took up their tasks with new strength.

Ulysses kept the helm, grim and unsmiling. For he knew that what he had seen painted on the walls of his sleep was meant to come true, and that he was sailing straight into a nightmare.

THE CYCLOPS'S CAVE

After he had rescued his crew from Lotusland, Ulysses found that he was running from one trouble into another. They were still at sea, and there was no food for the fleet. The men were hungry and getting dangerous. Ulysses heard them grumbling: "He should have left us there in Lotusland. At least when you're asleep you don't know you're hungry. Why did he have to come and wake us up?" He knew that unless he found food for them very soon he would be facing a mutiny.

That part of the Aegean Sea was dotted with islands. On every one of them was a different kind of enemy. The last thing Ulysses wanted to do was to go ashore, but there was no other way of getting food. He made a landfall on a small mountainous island. He was very careful; he had the ships of the fleet moor offshore and selected twelve of his bravest men as a landing party.

They beached their skiff and struck inland. It was a wild hilly place, full of boulders, with very few trees. It seemed deserted. Then Ulysses glimpsed something moving across the valley, on the slope of a hill. He was too far off to see what they were, but he thought they must be goats since the hill was so steep. And if they were goats they had to be caught. So the men headed downhill, meaning to cross the valley and climb the slope.

Ulysses had no way of knowing it, but this was the very worst island in the entire sea on which the small party could have landed. For here lived the Cyclopes, huge savage creatures, tall as trees, each with one eye in the middle of his forehead. Once, long ago, they had lived in the bowels of Olympus, forging thunderbolts for Zeus. But he had punished them for some fault, exiling them to this island where they had forgotten all their smithcraft and did nothing but fight with each other for the herds of wild goats, trying to find enough food to fill their huge bellies. Best of all, they liked storms; storms meant shipwrecks. Shipwrecks meant sailors struggling in the sea, who could be plucked out and eaten raw; and the thing they loved best in the world was human flesh. The largest and the fiercest and the hungriest of all the Cyclopes on the island was one named Polyphemus. He kept constant vigil on his mountain, fair weather or foul. If he spotted a ship, and there was no storm to help, he would dive into the sea and swim underwater, coming up underneath the ship and overturning it. Then he would swim off with his pockets full of sailors.

On this day he could not believe his luck when he saw a boat actually landing on the beach, and thirteen meaty-looking sailors disembark, and begin to march toward his cave. But here they were, climbing out of the valley now, up the slope of the hill, right toward the cave. He realized they must be hunting his goats.

The door of the cave was an enormous slab of stone. He shoved this aside so that the cave stood invitingly open, casting a faint glow of firelight upon the dusk. Over the fire, on a great spit, eight goats were turning and roasting. The delicious savors of the cooking drifted from the cave. Polyphemus lay down behind a huge boulder and waited.

The men were halfway up the slope of the hill when they smelled the meat roasting. They broke into a run. Ulysses tried to restrain them, but they paid no heed—they were too hungry. They raced to the mouth of the cave and dashed in. Ulysses drew his sword and hurried after them. When he saw the huge fireplace and the eight goats spitted like sparrows, his heart sank because he knew that they had come into reach of something much larger than themselves. However, the men were giving no thought to anything but food; they flung themselves on the spit, and tore into the goat meat, smearing their hands and faces with sizzling fat, too hungry to feel pain as they crammed the hot meat into their mouths.

There was a loud rumbling sound; the cave darkened. Ulysses whirled around. He saw that the door had been closed. The far end of the cavern was too dark to see anything, but then—amazed, aghast—he saw what looked like a huge red lantern far above, coming closer. Then he saw the great shadow of a nose under it, and the gleam of teeth. He realized that the lantern was a great flaming eye. Then he saw the whole giant, tall as a tree, with huge fingers reaching out of the shadows, fingers bigger than baling hooks. They closed around two sailors and hauled them screaming into the air.

As Ulysses and his horrified men watched, the great hand bore the struggling little men to the giant's mouth. He ate them, still wriggling, the way a cat eats a grasshopper; he ate them clothes and all, growling over their raw bones.

The men had fallen to their knees and were whimpering like terrified children, but Ulysses stood there, sword in hand, his agile brain working more swiftly than it ever had.

"Greetings," he called. "May I know to whom we are indebted for such hospitality?"

The giant belched and spat buttons. "I am Polyphemus," he growled. "This is my cave, my mountain, and everything that comes here is mine. I do hope you can all stay to dinner. There are just enough of you to make a meal. Ho, ho. . . . " And he laughed a great, choking phlegmy laugh, swiftly lunged, and caught another sailor, whom he lifted into the air and held before his face.

"Wait!" cried Ulysses.

"What for?"

"You won't enjoy him that way. He is from Attica, where the olives grow. He was raised on olives and has a very delicate oily flavor. But to appreciate it, you must taste the wine of the country."

"Wine? What is wine?"

"It is a drink. Made from pressed grapes. Have you never drunk it?"

"We drink nothing but ox blood and buttermilk here."

"Ah, you do not know what you have missed, gentle Polyphemus. Meat-eaters, in particular, love wine. Here, try it for yourself."

Ulysses unslung from his belt a full flask of unwatered wine.[3] He gave it to the giant, who put it to his lips and gulped. He coughed violently, and stuck the sailor in a little niche high up in the cave wall, then leaned his great slab of a face toward Ulysses and said:

"What did you say this drink was?"

"Wine. A gift of the gods to man, to make women look better and food taste better. And now it is my gift to you."

"It's good, very good." He put the bottle to his lips and swallowed again. "You are

---

3. *unwatered wine.* Greek wine was made especially strong; it was the custom to dilute it with water before drinking.

The blinding of Polyphemus. Early Attic amphora from Eleusis, found in 1954. Second quarter of the seventh century B.C. Eleusis Museum. Photo by Erich Lessing

An amphora is a jar used by the ancient Greeks and Romans for storing grain, oil, etc. Attica is a district in southeastern Greece. Its chief city is Athens. It was famous in ancient times for its literature and art.

very polite. What's your name?"

"My name? Why I am—nobody."

"Nobody. . . . Well, Nobody, I like you. You're a good fellow. And do you know what I'm going to do? I'm going to save you till last. Yes, I'll eat all your friends first, and give you extra time, that's what I'm going to do."

Ulysses looked up into the great eye and saw that it was redder than ever. It was all a swimming redness. He had given the mon-ster, who had never drunk spirits before, undiluted wine. Surely it must make him sleepy. But was a gallon enough for that great gullet? Enough to put him to sleep—or would he want to eat again first?

"Eat 'em all up. Nobody—save you till later. Sleep a little first. Shall I? Won't try to run away, will you? No—you can't, can't open the door—too heavy, ha, ha. . . . You take a nap too, Nobody. I'll wake you for breakfast. Breakfast. . . . "

The great body crashed full-length on the cave floor, making the very walls of the mountain shake. Polyphemus lay on his back, snoring like a powersaw. The sailors were still on the floor, almost dead from fear.

"Up!" cried Ulysses. "Stand up like men! Do what must be done! Or you will be devoured like chickens."

He got them to their feet and drew them about him as he explained his plan.

"Listen now, and listen well, for we have no time. I made him drunk, but we cannot tell how long it will last."

Ulysses thrust his sword into the fire; they saw it glow white-hot.

"There are ten of us," he said. "Two of us have been eaten, and one of our friends is still unconscious up there on his shelf of rock. You four get on one side of his head, and the rest on the other side. When I give the word, lay hold of the ear on your side, each of you. And hang on, no matter how he thrashes, for I am going to put out his eye. And if I am to be sure of my stroke you must hold his head still. One stroke is all I will be allowed."

Then Ulysses rolled a boulder next to the giant's head and climbed on it, so that he was looking down into the eye. It was lidless and misted with sleep—big as a furnace door and glowing softly like a banked fire. Ulysses looked at his men. They had done what he said, broken into two parties, one group at each ear. He lifted his white-hot sword.

"Now!" he cried.

Driving down with both hands, and all the strength of his back and shoulders, and all his rage and all his fear, Ulysses stabbed the glowing spike into the giant's eye.

His sword jerked out of his hand as the head flailed upward, men pelted to the ground as they lost their hold. A huge screeching curdling bellow split the air.

"This way!" shouted Ulysses.

He motioned to his men, and they crawled on their bellies toward the far end of the cave where the herd of goats was tethered. They slipped into the herd and lay among the goats as the giant stomped about the cave, slapping the walls with great blows of his hands, picking up boulders and cracking them together in agony, splitting them to flinders, clutching his eye, a scorched hole now from which the brown blood jelled. He moaned and gibbered and bellowed in frightful pain; his groping hand found the sailor in the wall, and he tore him to pieces between his fingers. Ulysses could not even hear the man scream because the giant was bellowing so.

Now Ulysses saw that the Cyclops's wild stampeding was giving place to a plan. For now he was stamping on the floor in a regular pattern, trying to find and crush them beneath his feet. He stopped moaning and listened. The sudden silence dazed the men with fear. They held their breath and tried to muffle the sound of their beating hearts; all the giant heard was the breathing of the goats. Then Ulysses saw him go to the mouth of the cave, and swing the great slab aside, and stand there. He realized just in time that the goats would rush outside, which is what the giant wanted, for then he could search the whole cave.

Ulysses whispered, "Quickly, swing under the bellies of the rams. Hurry, hurry!"

Luckily, they were giant goats and thus

able to carry the men who had swung themselves under their bellies and were clinging to the wiry wool. Ulysses himself chose the largest ram. They moved toward the mouth of the cave, and crowded through. The Cyclops's hands came down and brushed across the goats' backs feeling for the men, but the animals were huddled too closely together for him to reach between and search under their bellies. So he let them pass through.

Now, the Cyclops rushed to the corner where the goats had been tethered, and stamped, searched, and roared through the whole cave again, bellowing with fury when he did not find them. The herd grazed on the slope of the hill beneath the cave. There was a full moon; it was almost as bright as day.

"Stay where you are," Ulysses whispered.

He heard a crashing, peered out, and saw great shadowy figures converging on the cave. He knew that the other Cyclopes of the island must have heard the noise and come to see. He heard the giant bellow.

The others called to him: "Who has done it? Who has blinded you?"

"Nobody. Nobody did it. Nobody blinded me."

"Ah, you have done it yourself. What a tragic accident."

And they went back to their own caves.

"Now!" said Ulysses. "Follow me!"

He swung himself out from under the belly of the ram, and raced down the hill. The others raced after him. They were halfway across the valley when they heard great footsteps rushing after them, and Polyphemus bellowing nearer and nearer.

"He's coming!" cried Ulysses. "Run for your lives!"

They ran as they had never run before, but the giant could cover fifty yards at a stride. It was only because he could not see and kept bumping into trees and rocks that they were able to reach the skiff and push out on the silver water before Polyphemus burst out of the grove of trees and rushed onto the beach. They bent to the oars, and the boat scudded toward the fleet.

Polyphemus heard the dip of the oars and the groaning of the oarlocks, and, aiming at the sound, hurled huge boulders after them. They fell around the ship, but did not hit. The skiff reached Ulysses' ship, and the sailors climbed aboard.

"Haul anchor, and away!" cried Ulysses. And then called to the Cyclops, "Poor fool! Poor blinded drunken gluttonous fool—if anyone else asks you, it is not Nobody, but Ulysses who has done this to you."

But he was to regret this final taunt. The gods honor courage, but punish pride.

Polyphemus, wild with rage, waded out chest-deep and hurled a last boulder, which hit mid-deck, almost sunk the ship, and killed most of the crew—among them seven of the nine men who had just escaped.

And Polyphemus prayed to Poseidon, "God of the Sea, I beg you, punish Ulysses for this. Visit him with storm and shipwreck and sorceries. Let him wander many years before he reaches home, and when he gets there let him find himself forgotten, unwanted, a stranger."

Poseidon heard this prayer, and made it all happen just that way.

KEEPER OF THE WINDS

Now the black ships beat their way northward from the land of the Cyclopes. And Ulysses, ignorant of the mighty curse that the blind giant had fastened upon him, was beginning to hope that they might have fair sailing the rest of the way home. So impatient was he that he took the helm himself and kept it night and day although his sailors pleaded with him to take some rest. But he was wild with eagerness to get home to his wife, Penelope, to his young son Telemachus, and to the dear land of Ithaca that he had not seen for more than ten years now.

At the end of the third night, just as the first light was staining the sky, he saw something very strange—a wall of bronze, tall and wide, floating on the sea and blocking their way. At first he thought it was a trick of light, and he rubbed his eyes and looked again. But there it was, a towering bright wall of beaten bronze.

"Well," he thought to himself, "it cannot stretch across the sea. There must be a way to get around it."

He began to sail along the wall as though it were the shore of an island, trying to find his way around. Finally, he came to a huge gate, and even as he gazed upon it in amazement, the gate swung open and the wind changed abruptly. The shrouds snapped, the sails bulged, the masts groaned, and all three ships of the fleet were blown through the gate, which immediately clanged shut behind them. Once within the wall, the wind fell off and Ulysses found his ship drifting toward a beautiful hilly island. Suddenly there was a great howling of wind. The sun was blown out like a candle. Darkness fell upon the waters. Ulysses felt the deck leap beneath him as the ship was lifted halfway out of the water by the ferocious gust and hurled through the blackness. He tried to shout, but the breath was torn from his mouth and he lost consciousness.

Ulysses had no way of knowing this, but the mischievous Poseidon had guided his ships to the island fortress of Aeolus, Keeper of the Winds. Ages before, when the world was very new, the gods had become fearful of the terrible strength of the winds, and had decided to tame them. So Zeus and Poseidon, working together, had floated an island upon the sea, and girdled it about with a mighty bronze wall. Then they set a mountain upon the island and hollowed out that mountain until it was a huge stone dungeon. Into this hollow mountain they stuffed the struggling winds, and appointed Aeolus as their jailer. And there the winds were held captive. Whenever the gods wanted to stir up a storm and needed a particular wind, they sent a message to Aeolus, who would draw his sword and stab the side of the mountain, making a hole big enough for the wind to fly through. If the north wind were wanted, he stabbed the north side of the mountain, its east slope for the east wind, and so on. When the storm was done, he would whistle the wind home, and the huge brawling gale, broken by its imprisonment, would crawl back whimpering to its hole.

Aeolus was an enormously fat demigod with a long wind-tangled beard and a red wind-beaten face. He loved to eat and drink, and fight, play games, and hear stories. Twelve children he had, six boys and six girls. He sent them out one by one, riding the back of the wind around the world, managing the weather for each month.

And it was in the great castle of Aeolus that Ulysses and his men found themselves when they awoke from their enchanted sleep. Invisible hands held torches for them, guided them to the baths, anointed them with oil, and gave them fresh clothing. Then the floating torches led them to the dining hall, where they were greeted by Aeolus and his twelve handsome children. A mighty banquet was laid before them, and they ate like starved men.

Then Aeolus said, "Strangers, you are my guests—uninvited—but guests all the same. By the look of you, you have had adventures and should have fine stories to tell. Yes, I love a tale full of fighting and blood and tricks, and if you have such to tell, then I shall entertain you royally. But if you are such men as sit dumb, glowering, unwilling to please, using your mouths only to stuff food into—then—well, then you are apt to find things less pleasant. You, Captain!" he roared, pointing at Ulysses. "You, sir—I take you for the leader of this somewhat motley crew. Do you have a story to tell?"

"For those who know how to listen, I have a tale to tell," said Ulysses.

"Your name?"

"Ulysses—of Ithaca."

"Mmm—yes," said Aeolus. "I seem to recognize that name—believe I heard it on Olympus while my uncles and aunts up there were quarreling about some little skirmish they had interested themselves in. Near Troy I think it was. . . . Yes-s-s. . . . Were you there?"

"I was there," said Ulysses. "I was there

The wall of bronze on the island of Aeolus. It was the gold-bronze coloration of the wall that the ancients recognized as Aeolus' famed wall of fire. Photo by Erich Lessing

for ten years, dear host, and indeed took part in some of that petty skirmishing that will be spoken of by men who love courage when this bronze wall and this island, and you and yours, have vanished under the sea and have been forgotten for a thousand years. I am Ulysses. My companions before Troy were Achilles, Menelaus, Agamemnon, mighty heroes all, and, in modesty, I was not least among them."

"Yes-s-s. . . . " said Aeolus. "You are bold enough. Too bold for your own good, perhaps. But you have caught my attention, Captain. I am listening. Tell on. . . . "

Then Ulysses told of the Trojan War; of the abduction of Helen, and the chase, and the great battles; the attacks, the retreats, the separate duels. He spoke of Achilles fighting Hector, and killing him with a spear thrust, of Paris ambushing Achilles; and, finally, how he himself had made a great hollow wooden horse and had the Greek armies pretend to leave, only to sneak back and hide in the belly of the horse. He told how the Trojans had dragged the horse within their gates, and how the Greek warriors had crept out at night and taken the city and slaughtered their enemies.

Aeolus shouted with laughter. His face blazed and his belly shook. "Ah, that's a trick after my own heart!" he cried. "You're a sharp one, you are. . . . I knew you had a foxy look about you. Wooden horse—ho ho! Tell more! Tell more!"

Then Ulysses told of his wanderings after the fall of Troy, of his adventure in Lotusland, and what had happened in the Cyclops's cave. And when Aeolus heard how he had outwitted Polyphemus and blinded his single eye, he struck the table with a mighty blow of his fist, and shouted, "Marvelous! A master stroke! By the gods, you are the bravest, craftiest warrior that has ever drunk my wine." He was especially pleased because he had always hated Polyphemus. He had no way of knowing, of course, that the blinded Cyclops had prayed to his father and had laid a curse on Ulysses, and that he, Aeolus, was being made the instrument of that curse. He did not know this, for the gods move in mysterious ways. And so he roared with laughter, and shouted, "You have pleased me, Ulysses. You have told me a brave tale, a tale full of blood and tricks. . . . And now I shall grant you any favor within my power. Speak out, Ulysses. Ask what you will."

"But one thing I seek, generous Aeolus," said Ulysses, "your help. I need your help in getting home. For it has been a long weary time since we saw our homes and our families. Our hearts thirst for the sight of Ithaca."

"No one can help you better than I," said Aeolus. "You sail on ships, and I am Keeper of the Winds. Come with me."

He led Ulysses out into the night. A hot orange moon rode low in the sky, and they could see without torches. Aeolus led him to the mountain, carrying his sword in one hand and a great leather bag in the other. He stabbed the side of the mountain. There was a rushing, sobbing sound; he clapped his leather bag over the hole, and Ulysses, amazed, saw the great bag flutter and fill. Aeolus held its neck closed, strode to the east face of the mountain, and stabbed again. As the east wind rushed out, he caught it in his sack. Then he stomped to the south slope and stabbed again, and caught the south wind in the sack. Now, very carefully, he wound a silver wire about the neck of the sack. It was full now, swollen, tugging at his arm like a huge leather balloon, trying to fly away.

He said, "In this bag are the north wind, the south wind, and the east wind. You must keep them prisoner. But if you wish to change course—if a pirate should chase you, say, or a sea monster, or if an adventure beckons, then you open the bag very carefully—you and you alone, Captain—and whistle up the wind you wish, let just a breath of it out, close the bag quickly again, and tie it tight. For winds grow swiftly—that is their secret—and so they must be carefully guarded."

"I shall not change course," said Ulysses. "No matter what enemy threatens or what adventure beckons, I sail straight for Ithaca. I shall not open your bag of winds."

"Good," said Aeolus. "Then bind it to your mast, and guard it yourself, sword in hand; let none of your men approach, lest they open it unwittingly. In the meantime, I will send the gentle west wind to follow your ship and fill your sails and take you home."

"Thank you, great Aeolus, thank you, kindly keeper of the winds. I know now that the gods have answered my prayers, and I shall be able to cease this weary heartbreaking drifting over the face of the sea, having my men killed and eaten, my ships destroyed, and my hopes shattered. I will never cease thanking you, Aeolus, till the day I die."

"May that sad occasion be far off," said Aeolus politely. "Now, sir, much as I like your company, you had better gather your men and go. I shall be uneasy now until my winds return to me and I can shut them in the mountain again."

Ulysses returned to the castle and called together his men. Gladly they trooped down to the ships and went aboard. Ulysses bound the great leather sack to the mast and warned his crew that no man must touch it on pain of death. Then he himself stood with naked sword under the mast, guarding the sack.

"Up anchor!" he cried.

The west wind rolled off the mountain and filled their sails. The black ships slipped out of the harbor. Away from the island they sailed, away from the mountain and the castle, toward the wall of bronze. When they reached the wall, the great gate swung open and they sailed eastward over water oily with moonlight. Eastward they sailed for nine days and nine nights. In perfect weather they skimmed along, the west wind hovering behind them, keeping their sails full, pushing them steadily home.

And for nine nights and nine days, Ulysses did not sleep; he did not close his eyes or sheathe his sword. He kept his station under the mast—food and drink were brought to him there—and never for an instant stopped guarding the sack.

Then, finally, on the morning of the ninth day, he heard the lookout cry, "Land Ho!" and strained his eyes to see. What he saw made his heart swell. Tears coursed down his face, but they were tears of joy. For he saw the dear familiar hills of home. He saw the brown fields of Ithaca, the twisted olive trees, and, as he watched, he saw them even more clearly, saw the white marble columns of his own castle on the cliff. And his men, watching, saw the smoke rising from their own chimneys.

When Ulysses saw the white columns of his palace, he knew that unless the west wind failed, they would be home in an hour, but the friendly wind blew steadily as ever. Ulysses heaved a great sigh. The terrible tension that had kept him awake for nine days and nights eased its grip. He raised his arms and yawned. Then he leaned against the mast and closed his eyes, just for a minute.

Two of the men, standing in the bow, saw him slump at the foot of the mast, fast asleep. Their eyes traveled up the mast to the great leather bag, plump as a balloon, straining against its bonds as the impatient winds wrestled inside. Then Poseidon, swimming invisibly alongside, clinked his golden armlets. The men heard the clinking, and thought it came from the bag.

One man said to the other: "Do you hear that? Those are coins, heavy golden coins, clinking against each other. There must be a fortune in that sack."

The other man said, "Yes, a fortune that should belong to all of us by rights. We shared the danger and should share the loot."

"It is true," said the first, "that he has always been generous. He shared the spoils of Troy."

"Yes, but that was then. Why does he not divide this great sack of treasure? Aeolus gave it to him, and we know how rich he is. Aeolus gave it to him as a guest gift, and he should share it with us."

"He never will. Whatever is in that bag, he does not mean for us to see it. Did you not observe how he has been guarding it all these nights and all these days, standing there always, eating and drinking where he stands, never sheathing his sword?"

"It is in his sheath now," said the second sailor. "And his eyes are closed. Look—he sleeps like a babe. I doubt that anything would wake him."

"What are you doing? What are you going to do with that knife? Are you out of your mind?"

"Yes—out of my mind with curiosity, out of my mind with gold fever, if you must know. Ulysses lies asleep. His sword sleeps in its sheath. And I mean to see what is in that bag."

"Wait, I'll help you. But you must give me half."

"Come then. . . . "

Swiftly and silently the two barefooted sailors padded to the mast, slashed the rope that bound the bag to the spar, and bore it away.

"Hurry—open it!"

"I can't. This wire's twisted in a strange knot. Perhaps a magic knot. It won't come out."

"Then we'll do it this way!" cried the sailor with the knife, and struck at the leather bag, slashing it open. He was immediately lifted off his feet and blown like a leaf off the deck and into the sea as the winds rushed howling out of the bag and began to chase each other around the ship. The winds screamed and jeered and laughed, growing, leaping, reveling in their freedom, roaring and squabbling, screeching around and around the ship. They fell on their gentle brother, the west wind, and cuffed him mercilessly until he fled; then they chased each other around the ship again, spinning it like a cork in a whirlpool.

Then, as they heard the far summoning whistle of the Keeper of the Winds—far, far to the west on the Aeolian Island—they snarled with rage and roared boisterously homeward, snatching the ships along with them, ripping their sails to shreds, snapping their masts like twigs, and hurling the splintered hulls westward over the boiling sea.

Ulysses awoke from his sleep to find the blue sky black with clouds and his home island dropping far astern, out of sight. He saw his crew flung about the deck like dolls, and the tattered sails and the broken spars, and he did not know whether he was awake or asleep—whether this was some nightmare of loss, or whether he was awake now and had slept before, dreaming a fair dream of home. Whichever it was, he began to understand that he was being made the plaything of great powers.

With the unleashed winds screaming behind him at gale force, the trip back to where they had started took them only two days. And once again the black ships were hurled onto the island of the winds. Ulysses left his crew on the beach and went to the castle. He found Aeolus in his throne room, and stood before him, bruised, bloody, clothes torn, eyes like ashes.

"What happened?" cried Aeolus. "Why have you come back?"

"I was betrayed," said Ulysses. "Betrayed by sleep—the most cruel sleep of my life— and then by a wicked foolish greedy crew who released the winds from the sack and let us be snatched back from happiness even as we saw the smoke rising from our own chimneys."

"I warned you," said Aeolus, "I warned you not to let anyone touch that bag."

"And you were right, a thousand times right!" cried Ulysses. "Be generous once again. You can heal my woes, you alone. Renew your gift. Lend me the west wind to bear me home again, and I swear to you that this time I shall do everything you bid."

"I can't help you," said Aeolus. "Whom the gods detest, no one can help. And they detest you, man—they hate you. What you call bad luck is their hatred, turning gifts into punishment, fair hopes into nightmares. And bad luck is very catching. So please go. Get on your ship and sail away from this island, and never return."

"Farewell," said Ulysses, and strode away.

He gathered his weary men and made them board again. The winds were pent in their mountain. The sea was sluggish. A heavy calm lay over the harbor. They had to row on their broken stumps of oars, crawling like beetles over the gray water. They rowed away from the island, through the bronze gate, and out upon the sullen sea.

And Ulysses, heartbroken, almost dead of grief, tried to hide his feelings from the men; he stood on deck, barking orders, making them mend sail, patch hull, rig new spars, and keep rowing. He took the helm himself and swung the tiller, pointing the bow eastward toward home, which once again lay at the other end of the sea.

THINK AND DISCUSS

Understanding

1. Describe the design of Ulysses' ships. What makes them unsuitable for long sea voyages?
2. How does Ulysses free himself and his men from Morpheus's spell?
3. By what schemes does Ulysses escape from Polyphemus's cave with his men?
4. Describe the sequence of events that brings Ulysses back to the island of the winds.
5. Why does Aeolus refuse to aid him a second time?

Analyzing

6. Ulysses' dreams in Lotusland foreshadow (hint at) future events. From these dreams what experiences appear to await him?
7. By the end of "Keeper of the Winds," what can you conclude about Ulysses' character?
8. What can you conclude about the nature of the gods?

Extending

9. To what extent, if any, do you believe human life is "fated"? What role, if any, does luck play in human affairs?
10. Would Ulysses agree with the statement, "Heroes are made, not born"?

REVIEWING: Figurative language HŻ
See Handbook of Literary Terms, p. 638.

Figurative language is language expanded beyond its ordinary literal meaning. It uses comparisons to achieve new effects, to provide fresh insights, or to express a fitting relationship between things essentially unlike.

Reread "The Cyclops's Cave," pages 554–559, and list as many examples as you can find of figurative language used to describe Polyphemus. Which descriptions seem especially fresh, original, and appropriate? Explain your choices.

READING LITERATURE SKILLFULLY

Graphic Aids

Ulysses often did not know where he was or where he next would be. As you can see from the map on pages 544–545, the voyage from Troy (1) to Ithaca (16), his homeland, should not have been a long one. But since Ulysses and his men were in the power of the gods, they were frequently blown off course and spent years trying to reach their final destination. You are more fortunate than they, for you have been furnished a map charting their wanderings.

With the map open before you, answer the following questions.

1. What happened at number 5 on the map?
2. Is Tartarus the nearest or most distant point from Troy?
3. Which number designates the land in which Ulysses' men fell into a drugged sleep?
4. Is the island of the Cyclopes closer to Phaeacia or to Thrinacia?
5. What happened at number 6 on the map?

VOCABULARY
Inflected Forms

The past and past participle forms of many verbs are made by adding -d or -ed. An additional change is made in the endings of others, such as doubling the t in *abetted*. These forms are called inflected forms.

The inflected forms of some verbs are made by a change within the word. For example, *swim* is changed to *swam* and *swum*. Dictionaries and glossaries show such irregular forms in the entry for the root word (*swim*) and also include separate entries for them. If you look up *swam*, for example, you are referred to *swim* because the definition or definitions are given in the entry for the root word.

Use the Glossary to find the root form of each italicized verb below. On your paper, write a sentence about something in *The Adventures of Ulysses*, using that root form. Be prepared to read your sentences aloud.
1. The ships had *spun* around each other.
2. The people *withdrew* into the hills.
3. Polyphemus has *struck* the goats.
4. Ulysses *strode* across the deck.
5. Aeolus *bade* Ulysses to follow him.

COMPOSITION
Narrating an Adventure

Though none of us is Ulysses, all of us have had adventures. In two to four paragraphs, relate for your classmates an adventure that you have had. The experience might have been one that frightened you, excited you, disappointed you, amused you, or filled you with wonder. Before writing, jot down notes on *what* happened, *who* was involved, and *where*, *when*, *how*, and *why* it happened.

From your notes, decide what you most want to emphasize in each paragraph about your adventure.

Summarizing an Event

Assume that you are one of the two men who, along with Ulysses, survived the trip to the land of the Cyclopes. After you rejoin the fleet, one of your fellow crewmen asks you what happened on shore. In three to four paragraphs, summarize your experiences. To organize, you may wish to consider these questions: How did you happen to find yourself inside Polyphemus's cave? How did the Cyclops look and behave? How did Ulysses free you from the giant?

ENRICHMENT
Researching the Greek and Roman Gods

In the Introduction on pages 542–543 you read about a number of the gods and goddesses of ancient Greece, but there were more, many more. Further, the Romans later took for their own the major Greek gods and goddesses, changing their names and occasionally some of their functions. Zeus, for example, became Jove or Jupiter.

To become better acquainted with some of the principal gods and goddesses of ancient Greece and Rome, look through books on mythology in your school and public libraries. Read to learn about a god or goddess, one mentioned in the Introduction or another that interests you. Then write a brief report telling the Greek and Roman names and main responsibility of the god or goddess, as well as a myth connected with him or her. Add the name of your source or sources.

Writer's Craft

Use Precise, Active Verbs

Good writers know that using precise, active verbs is the best way to keep a story moving and create excitement. They choose verbs that will give the reader a clear picture of how an action or event takes place. For example, compare "John went home" with "John raced home." The second sentence is more vivid because it uses a precise, active verb. *Raced* tells not only what happened, but how it happened.

All of the stories in this unit retell the adventures of Ulysses. Though these tales are thousands of years old, it is easy to imagine this ancient hero's brave deeds because of the action-packed verbs. In the following passage from "The Ciconians," consider how the verbs suggest the noise and violence of a battle.

> Ulysses raged among his men, slapping them with the flat of his sword, driving the fumes of wine out of their heads. His great racketing battle cry roused those he could not whip with his sword.
>
> (page 550, column 1)

Later the author uses precise verbs to show specifically the losses Ulysses and his men suffered.

> Their hulls had been battered by axes and flung spears, and they had sprung small leaks. The wind had faded to a whisper, and the men were forced to row with water sloshing around their ankles.
>
> (page 550, column 1)

Good writers often use several verbs in order to emphasize or heighten a dramatic moment. Notice the active verbs used in one sentence to describe what happened to Ulysses' ships as they passed through the gate in "Keeper of the Winds."

> The shrouds snapped, the sails bulged, the masts groaned, and all three ships of the fleet were blown through the gate, which immediately clanged shut behind them.
>
> (page 560, column 1)

More activity, more energy, and more excitement are what an author achieves by using verbs effectively. You can achieve these things in your own writing by choosing lively verbs.

When you read, notice precise verbs. When you write, use precise verbs.

CIRCE

Of the three crews, but one was left. Ulysses found himself with only forty-five men. He was determined to bring these men home safely, or die himself.

They were sailing northward again, and on the third day came in sight of land, low lying, heavily wooded, with a good sheltering harbor. Although they had met terrible treatment everywhere they had landed since leaving Troy, they were out of food, water was running low, and once again they would have to risk the perils of the land.

Ulysses was very cautious. He moored the ship off shore, and said to the crew:

"I shall go ashore myself—alone—to see what there is to see, and make sure there are no terrible hosts, giants, man-eating ogres, or secret sorceries. If I am not back by nightfall, Eurylochus will act as captain. Then he will decide whether to seek food and water here, or sail onward. Farewell."

He lowered a small boat and rowed toward the island, all alone. He beached his skiff and struck inland. The first thing he wanted to do was find out whether he was on an island, or the spur of a mainland. He climbed a low hill, then climbed to the top of a tree that grew on the hill. He was high enough now for a clear view, and he turned slowly, marking the flash of the sea on all sides. He knew that once again they had landed on an island and that the ship was their only means of escape if danger should strike.

Something caught his eye. He squinted thoughtfully at what looked like a feather of smoke rising from a grove of trees. The trees were too thick for him to see through. He climbed down and picked his way carefully toward the smoke, trying to make as little noise as possible. He came to a stand of mighty trees—oak trees, thick and tall with glossy leaves. Glimmering through the trees he saw what looked like a small castle made of polished gray stone. He did not dare go near, for he heard strange howling sounds, a pack of dogs, perhaps, but different from any dogs he had ever heard. So he left the grove and made his way back toward the beach, thinking hard, trying to decide whether to sail away immediately or take a chance on the inhabitants being friendly. He did not like the sound of that howling. There was something in it that froze his marrow. He decided that he would not risk his men on the island, but that he would return to the ship, raise anchor, and sail away to seek food elsewhere.

Just then a tall white deer with mighty antlers stepped across his path. The great stag had a bearing proud as a king, and did not deign to run, but walked on haughtily as if he knew no one would dare to attack him. Unfortunately for the stag, however, Ulysses was too hungry to be impressed by any animal's own opinion of himself. The warrior raised his bronze spear and flung it with all the power of his knotted arm. It sang through the air, pierced the stag's body, and nailed him to a tree. The stag died standing up, still in his pride. He was a huge animal, so large that Ulysses feared he could not carry him back to the ship unaided. But then he remembered how hungry his men were, and he decided to try. He picked weeds and wove a rope which he twisted and twisted again until it was as strong as a ship's line. Then he bound the stag's legs together, swung the great carcass up onto his back, and staggered off using his spear as a cane.

He was at the end of his strength when he reached the beach, and let the deer slip to the sand. He signaled to his men, who left the ship moored and came ashore on five small boats. They raised a mighty shout of joy when they saw the dead stag. All hands fell to. In a twinkling the deer was skinned and cut up. Fires were lighted, and the delicious smell of roasting meat drew the gulls to the beach, screaming and dipping, begging for scraps.

The men gorged themselves, then lay on the sand to sleep. Ulysses, himself, kept guard. All that night he stood watch, leaning on his spear, looking at the moon which hung in the sky like an orange, and paled as it climbed. As he watched, he turned things over in his mind, trying to decide what to do. While he was still bothered by the eerie howling of the mysterious animals at the castle, now, with his belly full, he felt less gloomy. The more he thought about it the wiser it seemed to explore the island thoroughly and try to determine whether it was a friendly place or not. For never before had he seen a deer so large. If there was one, there must be more; and with game like that the ship could be provisioned in a few days. Also the island was full of streams from which they could fill their dry casks with pure water.

"Yes," he said to himself, "perhaps our luck has changed. Perhaps the god that was playing with us so spitefully has found other amusements. Yes, we will explore this island, and see what there is to see."

Next morning he awakened his men and divided them into two groups, one led by himself, the other by Eurylochus. He said to Eurylochus, "There is a castle on this island. We must find out who lives there. If he be friendly, or not too strong a foe, we will stay here and hunt and lay in water until the hold be full; then we will depart. Now choose, Eurylochus. Would you rather stay here with your men and guard the ship while I visit the castle—or would you rather I keep the beach? Choose."

"O Ulysses," Eurylochus said. "I am sick of the sight of the sea. Even as my belly hungers for food, so do my eyes hunger for leaves and trees which might recall our dear Ithaca. And my foot longs to tread something more solid than a deck—a floor that does not pitch and toss and roll. Pray, gentle Ulysses, let me and my men try the castle."

"Go," said Ulysses. "May the gods go with you."

So Eurylochus and twenty-two men set out, while Ulysses guarded the ship. As the band of warriors approached the castle, they too heard a strange howling. Some of them drew their swords. Others notched arrows to their bowstrings. They pressed on, preparing to fight. They passed through the grove of oak trees, and came to where the trees thinned. Here the howling grew louder and wilder. Then, as they passed the last screen of trees and came to the courtyard of the shining gray castle, they saw an extraordinary sight—a pack of wolves and lions running together like dogs—racing about the courtyard, howling.

When they caught sight of the men, the animals turned and flung themselves upon the strangers, so swiftly that no man had time to use his weapon. The great beasts stood on their hind legs and put their forepaws on the men's shoulders, and fawned on them, and licked their faces. They voiced low muttering growling whines. Eurylochus, who stood half-embracing a huge tawny lion, said, "Men, it is most strange. For these fearsome beasts greet us as though we were lost friends. They seem to be trying to speak to us. And look—look—at their eyes! How intelligently they gleam, how sadly they gaze. Not like beasts' eyes at all."

"It is true," said one of the men. "But perhaps there is nothing to fear. Perhaps there is reason to take heart. For if wild beasts are so tame and friendly, then perhaps the master of the castle, whoever he is or whatever he is, will be friendly too, and welcome us, and give us good cheer."

"Come," said Eurylochus.

When they reached the castle gate, they stopped and listened. For they heard a woman singing in a lovely deep full-throated voice, so that without seeing the woman they knew she was beautiful.

Eurylochus said, "Men, you go into the castle and see what is to be seen. I will stay here, and make sure you are not surprised."

"What do you mean? You come with us. Listen to that. There can be no danger where there is such song."

"Yes, everything seems peaceful," said Eurylochus. "The wild animals are friendly. Instead of the clank of weapons, we hear a woman singing. And it may be peaceful. But something says to me, be careful, take heed. Go you, then. I stay on guard. If I am attacked, and you are unharmed, come to my aid. If anything happens to you, then I shall take word back to Ulysses."

So Eurylochus stood watch at the castle gate—sword in one hand, dagger in the other, bow slung across his back—and the rest of the men entered the castle. They followed the sound of singing through the rooms and out onto a sunny terrace. There sat a woman weaving. She sat at a huge loom, larger than they had ever seen, and wove a gorgeous tapestry. As she wove, she sang. The bright flax leaped through her fingers as if it were dancing to the music in her voice. The men stood and stared. The sun seemed to be trapped in her hair, so bright it was; she wore it long, falling to her waist. Her dress was as blue as the summer sky, matching her eyes. Her long white arms were bare to the shoulders. She stood up and greeted them. She was very tall. And the men, looking at her, and listening to her speak, began to believe that they were in the presence of a goddess.

She seemed to read thoughts too, for she said, "No, I am not a goddess. But I am descended from the Immortals. I am Circe, granddaughter of Helios, a sun-god, who married Perse, daughter of Oceanus. So what

Circe offers Ulysses the
magic potion. Attic black-
figured lekythos by the
Athene-painter, from Eretria
on the island of Euboea.
First quarter of the fifth
century B.C. Athens,
National Museum.
Photo by Erich Lessing

The *lekythos* is a bottle for
holding bath oil or perfume.
Eretria, a city of ancient
Greece, is on the Aegean
Sea.

am I—wood nymph, sea nymph, something
of both? Or something more? I can do simple
magic and prophecy, weave certain homely
enchantments and read dreams. But let us
not speak of me, but of you, strangers. You
are adventurers, I see, men of the sword,
men of the black-prowed ships, the hawks of
the sea. And you have come through sore,
sad times, and seek a haven here on this western isle. So be it. I welcome you. For the
sweetest spell Circe weaves is one called hospitality. I will have baths drawn for you,
clean garments laid out. And when you are
refreshed, you shall come and dine. For I
love brave men and the tales they tell."

When the men had bathed and changed,
Circe gave them each a red bowl. And into
each bowl she put yellow food—a kind of
porridge made of cheese, barley, honey, and
wine plus a few secret things known only to
herself. The odor that rose from the red
bowls was more delicious than anything they
had ever smelled before. And as each man ate
he felt himself sinking into his hunger, *be-*

coming his hunger—lapping, panting, grunting, snuffling. Circe passed among them, smiling, filling the bowls again and again. And the men, waiting for their bowls to be filled, looking about, seeing each other's face smeared with food, thought, "How strange. We're eating like pigs."

Even as the thought came, it became more true. For as Circe passed among them now she touched each one on the shoulder with a wand, saying "Glut and swink, eat and drink, gobble food and guzzle wine. Too rude, I think, for humankind, quite right, I think, for *swine!*"

As she said these words in her lovely laughing voice, the men dwindled. Their noses grew wide and long, became snouts. Their hair hardened into bristles; their hands and feet became hooves, and they ran about on all fours, sobbing and snuffling, searching the floor for bones and crumbs. But all the time they cried real tears from their little red eyes, for they were pigs only in form; their minds remained unchanged, and they knew what was happening to them.

Circe kicked them away from the table. "To the sties!" she cried. She struck them with her wand, herding them out of the castle into a large sty. And there she flung them acorns and chestnuts and red berries, and watched them grubbing in the mud for the food she threw. She laughed a wild, hard, bright laugh, and went back into the castle.

While all this was happening, Eurylochus was waiting at the gate. When the men did not return he crept up to a bow slit in the castle wall and looked in. It was dark now. He saw the glimmer of torchlight, and the dim shape of a woman at a loom, weaving.

He heard a voice singing, the same enchanting voice he had heard before. But of his men he saw nothing. Nor did he hear their voices. A great fear seized him. He raced off as fast as he could, hoping against hope that the beasts would not howl. The wolves and lions stood like statues, walked like shadows. Their eyes glittered with cold moonlight, but none of them uttered a sound.

He ran until the breath strangled in his throat, until his heart tried to crack out of his ribs, but he kept running, stumbling over roots, slipping on stones. He ran and ran until he reached the beach and fell swooning in Ulysses' arms. Then with his last breath he gasped out the story, told Ulysses of the lions and the wolves, of the woman singing in the castle, and how the men had gone in and not come out. And then he slipped into blackness.

Ulysses said to his men, "You hear the story Eurylochus tells. I must go to the castle and see what has happened to your companions. But there is no need for you to risk yourselves. You stay here. And if I do not return by sunfall tomorrow, then you must board the ship and sail away, for you will know that I am dead."

The men wept and pleaded with him not to go, but he said, "I have sworn an oath that I will never leave another man behind if there is any way I can prevent it. Farewell, dear friends."

It was dawn by the time he found himself among the oak trees near the castle. He heard the first faint howling of the animals in the courtyard. And as he walked through the rose and gray light, a figure started up before him—a slender youth in golden breastplates and golden hat with wings on it, holding a golden staff. Ulysses fell to his knees.

"Why do you kneel, venerable sir?" said the youth. "You are older than I, and a mighty warrior. You should not kneel."

"Ah, pardon," cried Ulysses. "I have sharp eyes for some things. Behind your youth—so fair—I see time itself stretching to the beginning of things. Behind your slenderness I sense the power of a god. Sweet youth, beautiful lad, I know you. You are Hermes, the swift one, the messenger god. I pray you have come with good tidings for me because I fear that I have offended the gods, or one of them anyway, and he has vowed vengeance upon me."

"It is true," said Hermes. "Somebody up there doesn't like you. Can't say who, not ethical, you know. But if you *should* suspect that he may have something to do with the management of sea matters, well, you're a good guesser, that's all."

"Poseidon . . . I have offended Poseidon," muttered Ulysses, "the terrible one, the earth-shaker."

"Well," said Hermes, "what do you expect? That unpleasant Cyclops whom you first blinded, then taunted is Poseidon's son, you know. Not a son to be proud of, but blood is thicker than water, as they say, even in the god of the sea. So Polyphemus tattled to his father, and asked him to do dreadful things to you, which, I'm afraid, he's been doing. Now, this castle you're going to is Circe's and she is a very dangerous person to meet—a sorceress, a doer of magical mischief. And she is waiting for you, Ulysses. She sits at her loom, weaving, waiting. For you. She has already entertained your shipmates. Fed them. Watched them making pigs of themselves. And, finally, helped them on their way a bit. In brief, they are now in a sty, being fattened. And one day they will make a most excellent meal for someone not too fussy. Among Circe's guests are many peculiar feeders."

"Thunder and lightning!" cried Ulysses. "What can I do!"

"Listen and learn," said Hermes. "I have come to help you. Poseidon's wrath does not please all of us, you know. We gods have our moods, and they're not always kind, but somehow or other we must keep things balanced. And so I have come to help you. You must do exactly as I say, or nothing can help you. Now listen closely. First, take this."

He snapped his fingers and a flower appeared between them. It was white and heavily scented, with a black and yellow root. He gave it to Ulysses.

"It is called *moly*," he said. "It is magical. So long as you carry it, Circe's drugs will not work. You will go to the castle. She will greet you and feed you. You will eat the food which, to her amazement, will leave you unharmed. Then you will draw your sword and advance upon her as though you meant to kill her. Then she will see that you have certain powers, and will begin to plead with you. She will unveil enchantments more powerful than any she has yet used. Resist them you cannot, nor can any man, nor any god. Nor is there any counterspell that will work against such beauty. But if you wish to see your home again, if you wish to rescue your shipmates from the sty, you must resist her long enough to make her swear the great oath of the immortals—that she will not do you any harm as long as you are her guest. That is all I can do for you. From now on, it is up to you. We shall be watching you with interest. Farewell."

The golden youth disappeared just as a ray of sunlight does when a cloud crosses the face of the sun. Ulysses shook his head, wondering whether he had really seen the god, or imagined him, but then he saw that he was still holding the curious flower, and he knew that Hermes had indeed been there. So he marched on toward the castle, through the pack of lions and wolves, who leaped about him, fawning, looking at him with their great intelligent eyes, and trying to warn him in their snarling, growling voices. He stroked their heads, and passed among them, and went into the castle.

And here, he found Circe, sitting at her loom, weaving and singing. She wore a white tunic now and a flame-colored scarf, and was as beautiful as the dawn. She stood up and greeted him, saying, "Welcome, stranger. I live here alone, and seldom see anyone, and almost never have guests. So you are triply welcome, great sea-stained warrior, for I know that you have seen battle and adventure and have tales to tell."

She drew him a warm perfumed bath, and her servants bathed and anointed him, and gave him clean garments to wear. When he came to her, she gave him a red bowl full of yellow food, and said, "Eat." The food smelled delicious; its fragrance was intoxicating. Ulysses felt that he wanted to plunge his face into it and grub it up like a pig, but he held the flower tightly, kept control of himself, and ate slowly. He did not quite finish the food.

"Delicious," he said. "Your own recipe?"

"Yes," she said. "Will you not finish?"

"I am not quite so hungry as I thought."

"Then, drink. Here's wine."

She turned her back to him as she poured the wine, and he knew that she was casting a powder in it. He smiled to himself and drank off the wine, then said: "Delicious. Your own grapes?"

"You look weary, stranger," she said. "Sit and talk with me."

"Gladly," said Ulysses. "We have much to speak of, you and I. I'm something of a farmer myself. I breed cattle on my own little island of Ithaca, where I'm king—when I'm home. Won't you show me your livestock?"

"Livestock? I keep no cattle here."

"Oh, do you not? I fancied I heard pigs squealing out there. Must have been mistaken."

"Yes," said Circe. "Badly mistaken."

"But you do have interesting animals. I was much struck by the wolves and lions who course in a pack like dogs—very friendly for such savage beasts."

"I have taught them to be friendly," said Circe. "I am friendly myself, you see, and I like all the members of my household to share my goodwill."

"Their eyes," said Ulysses. "I was struck by their eyes—so big and sad and clever. You know, as I think of it, they looked like . . . human eyes."

"Did they?" said Circe. "Well—the eyes go last."

She came to him swiftly, raised her wand, touched him on the shoulder, and said: "Change, change, change! Turn, turn, turn!"

Nothing happened. Her eyes widened when she saw him sitting there, unchanged, sniffing at the flower he had taken from his tunic. He took the wand from her gently, and snapped it in two. Then drawing his sword he seized her by her long golden hair and forced her to her knees, pulling her head until her white throat was offered the blade of the sword. Then he said, "You have not asked me my name. It is Ulysses. I am an unlucky man, but not altogether helpless. You have changed my men into pigs. Now I will change you into a corpse."

She did not flinch before the blade. Her great blue eyes looked into his. She took the sharp blade in her hand, stroked it gently, and said, "It is almost worth dying to be overcome by so mighty a warrior. But I think living might be interesting too, now that I have met you."

He tried to turn his head, but sank deeper into the blueness of her eyes.

"Yes, I am a sorceress," she murmured, "a wicked woman. But you are a sorcerer too, are you not? Changing me more than I have changed your men, for I changed only their bodies and you have changed my soul. It is no longer a wicked plotting soul, but soft and tender, full of love for you."

Her voice throbbed. He raised her to her feet, and said, "You are beautiful enough to turn any man into an animal. I will love you. But even before I am a man, I am a leader. My men are my responsibility. I must ask you to swear the great oath that you will not harm me when I am defenseless, that you will not wound me and suck away my blood as witches do, but will treat me honestly. And

that, first of all, you will restore my men to their own forms, and let me take them with me when I am ready to leave."

"I will try to see that you are never ready," said Circe softly.

Circe kept her promise. The next morning she took Ulysses out to the sty and called the pigs. They came trotting up, snuffling and grunting. As they streamed past her, rushing to Ulysses, she touched each one on the shoulder with her wand. As she did so, each pig stood up, his hind legs grew longer, his front hooves became hands, his eyes grew, his nose shrank, his quills softened into hair, and he was his human self once more, only grown taller and younger.

The men crowded around Ulysses, shouting and laughing. He said to them: "Welcome, my friends. You have gone a short but ugly voyage to the animal state. And while you have returned—looking very well—it is clear that we are in a place of sorceries and must conduct ourselves with great care. Our enchanting hostess, Circe, has become so fond of our company that she insists we stay awhile. This, indeed, is the price of your release from hogdom. So you will now go down to your shipmates on the beach, and tell them what has happened. Ask them to secure the ship and then return here with you to the castle. It is another delay in our journey, but it is far better than what might have been. Go, then."

The men trooped happily down to the harbor and told the others what had happened. At first, Eurylochus protested. "How do I know," he said, "that you are not still under enchantment? How do I know that this is not

Companion of Ulysses, changed into a pig. Attic red-figured lekythos from Eretria, Euboea. 485–475 B.C. Athens, National Museum.
Photo by Erich Lessing

some new trick of the sorceress to get us all into her power, turn us all to pigs, and keep us in the sty forever?"

But the other men paid no heed to his warning. They were eager to see the castle and the beautiful witch, to taste the delicious food, and enjoy all the luxuries their friends had described. So they obeyed Ulysses' commands. They dragged the ship up on the beach, beyond reach of the tide, upstepped its mast, then marched off laughing and singing toward the castle, carrying mast and oars and folded sail. Eurylochus followed, but he was afraid.

For some time, things went well. The men were treated as welcome guests. They feasted for hours each night in the great dining hall. And as they ate, they were entertained by minstrels singing, by acrobats, dancing bears, and dancing girls. During the day they swam in the ocean, hunted wild boar, threw the discus, had archery and spear-throwing contests, raced, jumped, and wrestled. Then as dusk drew in they returned to the castle for their warm perfumed baths and bowls of hot wine before the feasting began again.

As for Ulysses he found himself falling deeper under Circe's spell every day. Thoughts of home were dim now. He barely remembered his wife's face. Sometimes he would think of days gone by and wonder when he could shake off this enchantment and resume his voyage. Then she would look at him. And her eyes, like blue flame, burned these pictures out of his head. Then he could not rest until he was within the scent of her hair, the touch of her hand. And he would whimper impatiently like a dog dreaming, shake his head, and go to her.

"It is most curious," she said. "But I love you more than all my other husbands."

"In the name of heaven how many have you had?" he cried.

"Ah, don't say it like that. Not so many, when you consider. I have been a frequent widow, it is true. But, please understand, I am god-descended on both sides. I am immortal and cannot die. I have lived since the beginning of things."

"How many husbands have you buried, dear widow?"

"Buried? Why, none."

"I see. You cremate them."

"I do not let them die. I cannot bear dead things. Especially if they are things I have loved. Of all nature's transformations, death seems to me the most stupid. No, I do not let

them die. I change them into animals, and they roam this beautiful island forevermore. And I see them every day and feed them with my own hand."

"That explains those wolves and lions in the courtyard, I suppose."

"Ah, they are only the best, the cream, the mightiest warriors of ages gone. But I have had lesser husbands. They are now rabbits, squirrels, boars, cats, spiders, frogs, and monkeys. That little fellow there . . ." She pointed to a silvery little ape who was prancing and gibbering on top of the bedpost. " . . . he who pelts you with walnut shells every night. He was very jealous, very busy and jealous, and still is. I picked their forms, you see, to match their dispositions. Is it not thoughtful of me?"

"Tell me," said Ulysses, "when I am used up, will I be good enough to join your select band of wolves and lions, or will I be something less? A toad, perhaps, or a snail?"

"A fox, undoubtedly," she said. "With your swiftness, and your cunning ways—oh, yes, a fox. A king of foxes." She stroked his beard. "But you are the only man who ever withstood my spells," she said. "You are my conqueror, a unique hero. It is not your fate to stay with me. It is not my happy fate to arrange your last hours."

"Is it not?" said Ulysses.

"No," she said. "Unless you can wipe out of your mind all thoughts of home. Unless you can erase all dreams of battle and voyage, unless you can forget your men, and release me from my oath, and let them become animals, contented animals, then and then only, can you remain with me as my husband forever. And I will give you of my immortality.

Yes, that can be arranged. I know how. You will share my immortality and live days of sport and idleness and nights of love. And we will live together always, knowing no other, and we will never grow old."

"Can such a thing be?"

"Yes. But the decision is yours. I have sworn an oath, and cannot keep you against your will. If you choose, you can remain here with me, and make this island a paradise of pleasure. If not, you must resume your voyage, and encounter dangers more dreadful than any you have seen yet. You will watch friends dying before your eyes, have your own life imperiled a hundred times, be battered, bruised, torn, wave-tossed, all this, if you leave me. But it is for you to decide."

Ulysses stood up and strode to the edge of the terrace. From where he stood he could see the light dancing in a million hot little needles on the blue water. In the courtyard he saw the wolves and the lions. Beyond the courtyard, at the edge of the wood, he saw his men, happy looking, healthy, tanned; some were wrestling, some flinging spears, others drawing the bow. Circe had crossed to her loom and was weaving, weaving and singing. He remembered his wife. She also, at home in Ithaca, would sit and weave. But how different she looked. Her hair was no fleece of burning gold, but black. She was much smaller than Circe, and she did not sing.

"I have decided," he said. "I must go."

"Must you?"

"Yes."

"First let me tell you what the gods have decreed. If you sail away from this island, you cannot head for home. First you must go to the Land of the Dead."

"The Land of the Dead?" cried Ulysses. "No! No! It cannot be!"

"To the Land of the Dead. To Tartarus. This is the decree. You must go there with all your men. And there you must consult certain ghosts, of whom you will be told, and they will prophesy for you, and plan your homeward journey. And theirs is the route you must follow if you wish to see Ithaca again."

"The Land of the Dead, dark Tartarus, the realm of torment from which no mortal returns. Must I go there?"

"Unless you stay with me here, in peace, in luxury, in every pleasure but that of adventure."

"It cannot be," said Ulysses. "As you, beautiful sorceress, choose a form for your lovers that matches their natures, and which they must wear when they are no longer men, so the Fates, with their shears, have cut out my destiny.[4] It is danger, toil, battle, uncertainty. And, though I stop and refresh myself now and again, still must I resume my voyage, for that is my nature. And to fit my nature has fate cut the pattern of my days."

"Go quickly," said Circe. "Call your men and depart. For if you stay here any longer, I shall forget all duty. I shall break my oath and keep you here by force and never let you go. Quickly then, brave one, quickly!"

Ulysses summoned his men and led them down to the beach. They stepped the mast, rigged the sails, and sailed away. They caught a northwest puff. The sails filled and

---

4. the Fates . . . have cut out my destiny. Human destiny was thought to be determined by three goddesses called the Fates. One spun the thread of life, the second measured it, and the third cut it.

the black ship ran out of the harbor. Ulysses' face was wet with Circe's last tears and his heart was very heavy. But then spray dashed into his face with the old remembered bright shock, and he laughed.

The last sound the men heard as the ship threaded through the mouth of the harbor and ran for the open sea, was the howling of the lions and wolves who had followed them down to the beach. They stood now breast-deep in the surf, gazing after the white sail, crying their loneliness.

THE LAND OF THE DEAD

In those days men knew that the Ocean Stream was a huge river girdling the earth. Hades' kingdom, dark Tartarus, was presumed to be on the farther shore, over the edge of the visible world. But no one could be certain, for those who went there did not return.

Now it had been foretold by Circe that Ulysses would have to visit the Land of the Dead, and be advised by wise ghosts before he could resume his journey and find his way back to Ithaca. So he turned his bow westward; and a strong east wind caught his white sails and sent the ship skimming toward waters no ship had sailed before.

Night tumbled from the sky and set its blackness on the sea and would not lift. The ship sailed blindly. The men were clamped in a nameless grief. They could hardly bear the sound of their own voices, but spoke to each other in whispers. The night wore on and did not give way to dawn. There were no stars, no moon. They sailed westward and waited for dawn, but no crack of light appeared in the sky. The darkness would not lift.

Once again Ulysses lashed himself to the tiller, and stuck splinters of wood in his eye sockets to prop the weary lids. And, finally, after a week of night, a feeble light did curdle the sky—not a regular dawn, no joyous burst of sun, but a grudging milky grayness that floated down and thickened into fog. Still Ulysses did not dare to sleep, for day was no better than night; no man could see in the dense woolly folds of fog.

Still the east wind blew, pushing them westward through the curdling mist, and still Ulysses did not dare give over the helm. For he had heard that the westward rim of the world was always fog-girt, and was studded by murderously rocky islets, where dwelt the Cimmerians, who waited quietly in the fog for ships to crack upon their shores and deliver to them their natural food, shipwrecked sailors. Finally, Ulysses knew he could not keep awake any longer; yet he knew too that to give over the helm to anyone else meant almost certain death for them all. So he sent a sailor named Elpenor to climb the mast and try to see some distance ahead. No sooner had Elpenor reached the top of the mast than the ship yawed sharply. Ulysses lost his footing and stumbled against the mast.

No one saw Elpenor fall. The fog was too thick. But they heard his terrible scream turned into a choking gurgle. And they knew that he had been shaken from the mast and had fallen into the sea and been drowned. No sooner had his voice gone still than the fog thinned. They could see from one end of the ship to the other—the wet sails, the shining spar, each other's wasted faces. A white gull rose screaming and flew ahead of them.

"Follow that gull," said Ulysses. "He will lead us where we must go."

Then he stretched himself on the deck and went to sleep. Whereupon the crew began to whisper among themselves that the gull was the spirit of their shipmate, Elpenor, and that Ulysses had shaken him from the mast purposely, as you shake fruit from a tree, so that he might fall in the water and be drowned, giving them the white flight of his spirit to follow to Tartarus.

"He has murdered our shipmate," they whispered to each other, "as he will murder us all to gain his ends."

But they did not dare say it loud enough to awaken Ulysses.

All day they sailed, following the white flash of the gull, and when night came there were no stars and no moon, nothing but choking blackness. Ulysses took the helm again. But now the bow tipped forward and the stern arose, and the ship slipped through the water with a rushing rustling speed as if it were sailing downhill. The men clung to the shrouds, and wept and groaned, and pleaded with Ulysses to change course. But he answered them not at all. He planted his feet and gripped the tiller with all his strength, as the deck tilted and the ship slipped down, down. . . .

"Who has ever heard of the sea sloping?" he said to himself. "Truly this must be the waterway to the underworld, and we are the first keel to cut these fathoms. May the gods grant we cross them again going the other way."

There was a roaring of waters. The deck leveled. They sailed out of darkness as through a curtain, and found themselves in a strange place. The sea had narrowed to a river, the water was black, and the sky was black, curving downward like the inside of a bowl; the light was gray. Tall trees grew along the bank of the river—black poplars and white birches. And Ulysses knew that the black river was the Styx, and that he had sailed his ship into the Kingdom of the Dead.

There was no wind, but the sails remained strangely taut, and the ship floated easily into harbor, as if some invisible hand had taken the helm.

Ulysses bade his men disembark. He led them past a fringe of trees to a great meadow where black goats cropped black grass. He drew his sword and scraped out a shallow trench, then had his men cut the throats of two black goats and hold them over the trench until it was filled with blood. For it was ghosts he had come to counsel with, and ghosts, he knew, came only where they could find fresh blood to drink, hoping always to fill their dry veins.

The meadow was still. No birds sang. There was no shrill of insects; the goats did not bleat. The men were too frightened to breathe. Ulysses waited, leaning on his sword, gloomily watching the trench of blood. Then he heard a rustling, and saw the air thicken into spouts of steam. Steamy shapes separated, heads and shoulders of mist leaning over the trench to drink, growing more solid as they drank.

One raised its head and looked at him. He shuddered. It was his mother, Anticleia.

"Greetings, Mother. How do you fare?"

"Poorly, son. I am dead, dead, dead. I kept telling you I would die one day, but you never believed me. Now you see. But do you see? Say you see."

A thin tittering arose from the ghosts, and they spoke in steamy whispers.

"What are you doing here, man? You're still alive. Go and die properly and come back, and we will welcome you."

"Silence!" cried Ulysses. "I come for better counsel than this. I must find my way back to Ithaca, past the mighty wrath of a god who reaches his strong hand and swirls the sea as a child does a mud puddle, dashing my poor twig of a ship from peril to grim peril. I need good counsel to get home. Where is the sage, Teiresias? Why is he not here to greet me?"

"Coming—coming—— He is blind but he smells blood as far as any."

"Do not drink it all. Save some for him."

And Ulysses smote the ghosts with his sword, driving them back, whimpering, from the trench of blood.

But then, striding across the meadow, came certain ghosts in armor. Ulysses bowed low.

"Welcome, O Fox of War," cried the ghost of Achilles. "Tell me, do men remember me in Arcadia?"

"The gods have not allowed me to set foot upon our dear islands," said Ulysses. "But on whatever savage shore I am thrown there are those who know the name of great Achilles. Your fame outshines all warriors who have ever handled weapons. And your son, Neoptolemus, is a hero too."

"Thank you, Ulysses," said the ghost of Achilles. "Your words are fair and courteous, as always. Now, heed this: When you leave this place, you will sail past an island where you will hear the voices of maidens singing. And the sound of their singing will be sweeter than memories of home, and when your men hear them, their wits will be scattered, and they will wish to dive overboard and swim to shore. If they do, they will perish. For these maidens are a band of witch sisters—music-mad sisters—who lure sailors to the rocks so that they may flay them, and make drums of their skin and flutes of their bones. They are the Siren sisters. When you pass their shore, steer clear, steer clear."

"Thank you, great Achilles."

Next to Achilles stood a huge ghost staring at Ulysses out of empty eye sockets. He was a giant skeleton. He wore a cloak of stiffened blood and a red plume upon his skull. His spear and sword were made of bone too. He was Ajax.

"You tricked me, Ulysses," he said. "When great Achilles here fell on the field of battle, you claimed his golden armor by craft, when I should have had it, I . . . I. . . . You took the golden armor that my heart desired and drove me mad with rage, so that I butchered cattle and captives, and then killed myself. I hate you, sly one, and have this bad news for you: If you ever do reach Ithaca, you will find your wife being courted by other men, your son a captive in your own castle, your substance devoured. This is my word to you, Ulysses. So you had simply better fall on your sword now where you stand, and save another trip to Hades."

"Thank you, great Ajax," said Ulysses. "I will remember what you have told me."

"I knew that Penelope was being wooed by other men in your absence," said Ulysses' mother. "I knew it well, but I would not speak evil of your wife, not I, not I. . . ."

"Thank you, Mother," said Ulysses.

Then came a ghost so new that his flesh had not quite turned to mist, but quivered on his bones like a pale jelly. He was Elpenor, who had fallen from the mast and had led them to Tartarus. When Ulysses saw who it was, he was taken by a great dread, and cried, "I did not push you, Elpenor. You fell. It was an accident, I swear."

"Nevertheless," said Elpenor, "my ghost will trouble you until you make my grave."

"How will I do that?"

"The first land you come to, build me a barrow and set thereon my oar. If you forget, I shall scratch at your windows and howl down your chimney and dance in your sleep."

"I will build your grave with my own hands," said Ulysses. "Have you any counsel for me?"

"Yes. Death has cleared my eyes, and I see things I would not have known. I see your ship now sailing in a narrow place between two huge rocks. Beneath the starboard rock is a cave, and in that cave squats Scylla, an unpleasant lady with twelve legs and six heads who cries with the voice of a new-born puppy. If you sail too near that rock, she will seize six sailors to feed her six mouths—"

"Then I will steer away from Scylla—toward the other rock."

"Ah, but under the other rock lurks a strange thirsty monster named Charybdis whose habit it is to drink up a whole tide of water in one gulp, and then spit it out again, making a whirlpool of such terrible sucking force that any ship within its swirl must be destroyed."

"Monster to the right and monster to the left," cried Ulysses. "What can I do then?"

"You must keep to the middle way. But if you cannot—and indeed it will be very difficult, for you will be tacking against head-winds—then choose the right-hand rock where hungry Scylla squats. For it is better to lose six men than your ship and your entire crew."

"Thank you, courteous Elpenor," said Ulysses. "I will heed your words."

Then the air grew vaporous as the mob of ghosts shifted and swayed, making way for one who cleaved forward toward the trench of blood, and Ulysses recognized the one he was most eager to see, the blind woman-shaped ghost of Teiresias, sage of Thebes, expert at disasters, master of prophecy.

"Hail, venerable Teiresias," he cried, "all honor to you. I have journeyed far to make your acquaintance."

Teiresias came silently to the trench, knelt, and drank. He drank until the trench was empty and the misty bladder of his body was faintly pink.

"You honor me by your visit, Ulysses," he said. "Many men sought my counsel when I was alive, but you are the first client to make his way down here. You have heard these others tell you of certain petty dangers which you will do well to avoid, but I have a mighty thing to tell."

"Tell."

"Your next landfall will be Thrinacia, a large island which men shall one day call Sicily. Here the Sun Titan, Hyperion, pastures his herds of golden cattle. Your stores will have been eaten when you reach this place, and your men will be savage with hunger. But no matter how desperate for food they are, you must prevent them from stealing even one beef. If they do, they shall never see home again."

"I myself will guard the herds of the Sun Titan," said Ulysses, "and not one beef shall be taken. Thank you, wise Teiresias."

"Go now. Take your men aboard the ship, and go. Sail up the black river toward the upper air."

"But now that I am here and have come such a long and weary way to get here, may I not see some of the famous sights? May I not see Orion hunting, Minos judging? May I not dance with the heroes in the Fields of Asphodel? May I not see Tantalus thirsting, or my own grandfather, Sisyphus, rolling his eternal stone up the hill?"

"No," said Teiresias. "It is better that you go. You have been here too long already, I fear; too long exposed to these bone-bleaching airs. You may already be tainted with death, you and your men, making your fates too heavy for any ship to hold. Embark then. Sail up the black river. Do not look back. Remember our advice and forget our reproaches, and do not return until you are properly dead."

Ulysses ordered his men aboard. He put down the helm. There was still no wind. But the sails stretched taut, and the ship pushed upriver. Heeding the last words of the old sage, he did not look back, but he heard the voice of his mother calling, "Good-bye . . . good-bye . . ." until it grew faint as his own breath.

THE SIRENS

In the first light of morning Ulysses awoke and called his crew about him.

"Men," he said. "Listen well, for your lives today hang upon what I am about to tell you. That large island to the west is Thrinacia, where we must make a landfall, for our provisions run low. But to get to the island we must pass through a narrow strait. And at the head of this strait is a rocky islet where dwell two sisters called Sirens, whose voices you must not hear. Now I shall guard you against their singing which would lure you to shipwreck, but first you must bind me to the mast. Tie me tightly, as though I were a dangerous captive. And no matter how I struggle, no matter what signals I make to you, *do not release me*, lest I follow their voices to destruction, taking you with me."

Thereupon Ulysses took a large lump of the beeswax which was used by the sail mender to slick his heavy thread, and kneaded it in his powerful hands until it became soft. Then he went to each man of the crew and plugged his ears with soft wax; he caulked their ears so tightly that they could hear nothing but the thin pulsing of their own blood.

Then he stood himself against the mast, and the men bound him about with rawhide, winding it tightly around his body, lashing him to the thick mast.

They had lowered the sail because ships cannot sail through a narrow strait unless there is a following wind, and now each man of the crew took his place at the great oars. The polished blades whipped the sea into a froth of white water and the ship nosed toward the strait.

Siren. Attic red-figured stamnos by the Siren-painter, from Vulci. First quarter of the fifth century B.C. London, British Museum. Photo by Erich Lessing

Ulysses had left his own ears unplugged because he had to remain in command of the ship and had need of his hearing. Every sound means something upon the sea. But when they drew near the rocky islet and he heard the first faint strains of the Sirens' singing, then he wished he had stopped his own ears too with wax. All his strength suddenly surged toward the sound of those magical voices. The very hair of his head seemed to be tugging at his scalp, trying to fly away. His eyeballs started out of his head.

For in those voices were the sounds that men love:

Happy sounds like bird railing, sleet hailing, milk pailing. . . .

Sad sounds like rain leaking, tree creaking, wind seeking. . . .

Autumn sounds like leaf tapping, fire snapping, river lapping. . . .

Quiet sounds like snow flaking, spider waking, heart breaking. . . .

It seemed to him then that the sun was burning him to a cinder as he stood. And the voices of the Sirens purled in a cool crystal pool upon their rock past the blue-hot flatness of the sea and its lacings of white-hot spume. It seemed to him he could actually see their voices deepening into a silvery cool pool, and that he must plunge into that pool or die a flaming death.

He was filled with such a fury of desire that he swelled his mighty muscles, burst the rawhide bonds like thread, and dashed for the rail.

But he had warned two of his strongest men—Perimedes and Eurylochus—to guard him close. They seized him before he could plunge into the water. He swept them aside as if they had been children. But they had held him long enough to give the crew time to swarm about him. He was overpowered— crushed by their numbers—and dragged back to the mast. This time he was bound with the mighty hawser that held the anchor.

The men returned to their rowing seats, unable to hear the voices because of the wax corking their ears. The ship swung about and headed for the strait again.

Louder now, and clearer, the tormenting voices came to Ulysses. Again he was aflame with a fury of desire. But try as he might he could not break the thick anchor line. He strained against it until he bled, but the line held.

The men bent to their oars and rowed more swiftly, for they saw the mast bending like a tall tree in a heavy wind, and they feared that Ulysses, in his fury, might snap it off short and dive, mast and all, into the water to get at the Sirens.

Now they were passing the rock, and Ulysses could see the singers. There were two of them. They sat on a heap of white bones— the bones of shipwrecked sailors—and sang more beautifully than senses could bear. But their appearance did not match their voices, for they were shaped like birds, huge birds, larger than eagles. They had feathers instead of hair, and their hands and feet were claws. But their faces were the faces of young girls.

When Ulysses saw them he was able to forget the sweetness of their voices because their look was so fearsome. He closed his eyes against the terrible sight of these bird-women perched on their heap of bones. But when he closed his eyes and could not see their ugliness, then their voices maddened him once again, and he felt himself straining against the bloody ropes. He forced himself to open his eyes and look upon the monsters, so that the terror of their bodies would blot the beauty of their voices.

But the men, who could only see, not hear the Sirens, were so appalled by their aspect that they swept their oars faster and faster, and the black ship scuttled past the rock. The Sirens' voices sounded fainter and fainter and finally died away.

When Perimedes and Eurylochus saw their captain's face lose its madness, they unbound him, and he signaled to the men to unstop their ears. For now he heard the whistling gurgle of a whirlpool, and he knew that they were approaching the narrowest part of the strait, and must pass between Scylla and Charybdis.

SCYLLA AND CHARYBDIS

Ulysses had been told in Tartarus of these two monsters that guard the narrow waterway leading to Thrinacia. Each of them hid beneath its own huge rock, which stood side by side and were separated only by the width of the strait at its narrowest point.

Charybdis dwelt in a cave beneath the left-hand rock. Once she had been a superbly beautiful naiad, daughter of Poseidon, and very loyal to her father in his endless feud with Zeus, Lord of Earth and Sky. She it was who rode the hungry tides after Poseidon had stirred up a storm, and led them onto the beaches, gobbling up whole villages, submerging fields, drowning forests, claiming them for the sea. She won so much land for her father's kingdom that Zeus became enraged and changed her into a monster, a huge bladder of a creature whose face was all mouth and whose arms and legs were flippers. And he penned her in the cave beneath the rock, saying, "Your hunger shall become thirst. As you once devoured land belonging to me, now you shall drink the tide thrice a day—swallow it and spit it forth again—and your name will be a curse to sailors forever."

And so it was. Thrice a day she burned with a terrible thirst, and stuck her head out of the cave and drank down the sea, shrinking the waters to a shallow stream, and then spat the water out again in a tremendous torrent, making a whirlpool near her rock in which no ship could live.

This was Charybdis. As for Scylla, who lived under the right-hand rock, she too had once been a beautiful naiad. Poseidon himself spied her swimming one day, and fell in love with her, and so provoked the jealousy of his wife, Amphitrite, that she cried, "I will make her the most hideous female that man or god ever fled from!"

Thereupon she changed Scylla into something that looked like a huge fleshy spider with twelve legs and six heads. She also implanted in her an insatiable hunger, a wild greed for human flesh. When any ship came within reach of her long tentacles, she would sweep the deck of sailors, and eat them.

Ulysses stood in the bow as the ship nosed slowly up the strait. The roaring of the waters grew louder and louder, and now he saw wild feathers of spume flying as Charybdis sucked down the tide and spat it back. He looked at the other rock. Scylla was not in sight. But he knew she was lurking underneath, ready to spring. He squinted, trying to measure distances. The only chance to come through unharmed, he saw, was to strike the middle way between the two rocks, just beyond the suction of the whirlpool, and just out of Scylla's reach. But to do this meant that the ship must not be allowed to swerve a foot from its exact course, for the middle way was no wider than the ship itself.

He took the helm, and bade his men keep a perfectly regular stroke. Then, considering further, he turned the helm over to Eurylochus, and put on his armor. Grasping sword and spear, he posted himself at the starboard rail.

"For," he said to himself, "there is no contending with the whirlpool. If we veer off our course it must be toward the other monster. I can fight any enemy I can see."

The men rowed very carefully, very skillfully. Eurylochus chanted the stroke, and the black ship cut through the waters of the strait, keeping exactly to the middle way.

They were passing between the rocks now. They watched in amazement as the water fell away to their left, showing a shuddering flash of sea bed and gasping fish, and then roared back again with such force that the water was beaten into white froth. They felt their ship tremble.

"Well done!" cried Ulysses. "A few more strokes and we are through. Keep the way—the middle way!"

But, when measuring distance, he had been unable to reckon upon one thing. The ship was being rowed, and the great sweep oars projected far beyond the width of the hull. And Scylla, lurking underwater, seized two of the oars, and dragged the ship toward her.

Dumbfounded, Ulysses saw the polished shafts of the oars which had been dipping and flashing so regularly suddenly snap like twigs, and before he knew what was happening, the deck tilted violently. He was thrown against the rail and almost fell overboard.

He lay on the deck, scrambling for his sword. He saw tentacles arching over him; they were like the arms of an octopus, but ending in enormous human hands.

He found his sword, rose to his knees, and hacked at the tentacles. Too late. The hands had grasped six sailors, snatched them screaming through the air, and into the sea.

Ulysses had no time for fear. He had to do a number of things immediately. He roared to the crew to keep the ship on course lest it be swept into the whirlpool. Then he seized an oar himself and rowed on the starboard side where the oars had been broken.

From where he sat he could see Scylla's rock, could see her squatting at the door of her cave. He saw her plainly, stuffing the men into her six bloody mouths. He heard the shrieks of his men as they felt themselves being eaten alive.

He did not have time to weep, for he had to keep his crew rowing and tell the helmsman how to steer past the whirlpool.

They passed through the strait into open water. Full ahead lay Thrinacia with its wooded hills and long white beaches, the Isle of the Sun Titan, their next landfall.

THINK AND DISCUSS

Understanding

1. According to Circe, what experiences await Ulysses once he leaves her island?
2. What warning does Teiresias give to Ulysses?
3. What precautions does Ulysses take to avoid being shipwrecked by the Sirens?
4. In sailing between Scylla and Charybdis, what has Ulysses not been able to reckon upon? What are the consequences for his crew?

Analyzing

5. From Ulysses' encounter with Hermes, what impression do you get of how the gods treat each other?
6. Find two **similes** that appear in the first complete paragraph of page 578. In each, what is being compared? Are the comparisons effective ones?
7. Throughout the adventures, Ulysses reveals that he is a complex **character.** Cite incidents from any of the adventures up to "The Sirens" that show him to be (**a**) strong-willed and able to withstand temptation; (**b**) quick-witted; (**c**) cautious; (**d**) boastful; (**e**) courageous.

Extending

8. What are some of the major problems that a producer and director would encounter in making a film of *The Adventures of Ulysses*?
9. If Ulysses were alive today, what occupations, if any, might interest him?

REVIEWING: Flashback H↗

See Handbook of Literary Terms, p. 639.

A **flashback** is an interruption in the action of a story, play, or work of nonfiction to show an episode that happened at an earlier time. A flashback is used to provide information necessary to understanding the characters or the plot.

Read paragraphs two and three in the second column on page 582. Then answer the questions that follow.

1. Of what does Ajax accuse Ulysses?
2. What does this reveal about Ulysses?
3. How does Ajax feel about Ulysses?
4. What do his feelings lead Ajax to do?

VOCABULARY

Synonyms and Antonyms

A synonym is a word that means the same or almost the same as another word, such as *begin* and *start*. An antonym is a word that means the opposite of another word, such as *tall* and *short*. You can sometimes determine the meaning of an unfamiliar word with the help of a synonym or antonym and context.

Read the following sentences and in each find a synonym or antonym for the italicized word. On your paper, write the numbers of the sentences and after each write the synonym or antonym and tell which it is. Be prepared to explain your answers.

1. The Sirens tempted Ulysses, but he would not be *lured*.
2. The *haughty* princess viewed her humble suitors as unworthy of her.

3. Poseidon vowed to *imperil*, or endanger, Ulysses and his men.
4. The greedy giant could never satisfy his *insatiable* appetite.
5. The *vaporous* air was a shock after sailing through dry breezes.

THINKING SKILLS
Classifying

To classify things is to arrange them into classes or groups according to some system. For example, writings can be classified as prose or poetry; this retelling of *The Adventures of Ulysses* is prose, while the original work was a poem.

Sometimes Ulysses makes his own decision and other times fate determines what will happen to him and his men. Find examples that show Ulysses making a decision and examples in which fate decides the future.

COMPOSITION
Reading/Writing Log

Precise, active verbs help give readers a clear picture of how events happened. Copy the examples below in your **reading/writing log.** Notice the vivid verbs in each. Then reread "Circe," "The Sirens," or "Scylla and Charybdis" to find two more passages that use precise, active verbs. Copy the passages in your **reading/writing log.** Write the page and column where you find each example.

> The warrior raised his bronze spear and flung it with all the power of his knotted arm. It sang through the air, pierced the stag's body, and nailed him to a tree.

> Then he bound the stag's legs together, swung the great carcass up onto his back, and staggered off using his spear as a cane.

(page 570, column 1)

Being a Story Character

Assume that you are a member of Ulysses' crew who has lived through the experience of becoming a pig under Circe's spell. Write three to four paragraphs to a family member or friend about your experience. In your letter you may wish to describe how the event came about, how you felt as you were being transformed, and how you spent your hours in the sty. As the author of *The Adventures of Ulysses* does, use precise, active verbs to tell about your experience. If you are keeping a **reading/writing log,** review it as you plan your letter.

After reading Lesson 11 in the Writer's Handbook, "Writing as a Story Character," begin your letter, "You'll never guess what happened to me!"

Persuading a Friend

A friend of yours shows little interest in reading literature. Write a three- to four-paragraph letter in which you try to persuade him or her to read *The Adventures of Ulysses.* Focus your preplanning notes on what your friend might especially enjoy about the characters, about the conflicts, or about the various settings. If you are keeping a **reading/writing log,** review the passages you copied that use precise, active verbs. Then in your letter use the same sort of vivid verbs to show how exciting and action-packed Ulysses' adventures are.

Before writing the first draft, you should find helpful Lesson 1 in the Writer's Handbook, "Writing About Literature."

THE CATTLE OF THE SUN

Instead of landing on Thrinacia, as the crew expected, Ulysses dropped anchor and summoned his two underchiefs, Eurylochus and Perimedes, to take counsel.

He said, "You heard the warning of old Teiresias down in Tartarus. You heard him say that this island belongs to Hyperion, the Sun Titan, who uses it as a grazing land for his flocks. The warning was most dire: Whosoever of our crew harms these cattle in any way will bring swift doom upon himself, and will never see his home again."

"We all heard the warning," said Eurylochus, "and everyone will heed it."

"How can you be so sure?" said Ulysses. "If this voyage has taught you nothing else, it should have proved to you that there is nothing in the world so uncertain as man's intentions, especially his good ones. No, fair sirs, what I propose is that we change our plans about landing here and seek another island, one where death does not pasture."

"It will never do," said Eurylochus. "The men are exhausted. There is a south wind blowing now, which means we would have to row. We simply do not have the strength to hold the oars."

"Our stores are exhausted too," said Perimedes. "The food that Circe gave us is almost gone. The water kegs are empty. We must land here and let the men rest, and lay in fresh provisions."

"Very well," said Ulysses. "If it must be, it must be. But I am holding you two directly responsible for the safety of the sun-cattle. Post guards at night, and kill any man who goes near these fatal herds."

Thereupon the anchor was raised, and the ship put into harbor, Ulysses did not moor the ship off shore, but had the men drag it up on the beach. He sent one party out in search of game, another to fill the water kegs, and a third to chop down pine trees. From the wood was pressed a fragrant black sap, which was boiled in a big iron pot. Then he had the men tar the ship from stem to stern, caulking each crack.

The hunting party returned, downhearted. There seemed to be no game on the island, they told Ulysses, only a few wild pigs, which they had shot, but no deer, no bear, no rabbits, no game birds. Just the pigs, and great herds of golden cattle.

The water party returned triumphantly, barrels full.

The men were so weary that Ulysses stood guard himself that night. Wrapped in his cloak, naked sword across his knees, he sat hunched near the driftwood fire, brooding into the flames.

"I cannot let them rest here," he said to

himself. "If game is so scarce, they will be tempted to take the cattle. For hungry men the only law is hunger. No, we must put out again tomorrow and try to find another island."

The next morning he routed out the men. They grumbled terribly, but did not dare to disobey. However, they were not fated to embark. A strong south wind blew up, almost gale strength, blowing directly into the harbor. There was no sailing into the teeth of it, and it was much too strong to row against.

"Very well," said Ulysses, "scour the island for game again. We must wait until the wind drops."

He had thought it must blow itself out in a day or so, but it was not to be. For thirty days and thirty nights the south wind blew, and they could not leave the island. All the wild pigs had been killed. The men were desperately hungry. Ulysses used all his cunning to find food. He had the men fish in the sea, dig the beaches for shellfish and turtle eggs, search the woods for edible roots and berries. They tore the clinging limpets off rocks and shot gulls. A huge pot was kept boiling over the driftwood fire, and in it the men threw anything remotely edible—sea polyps, sea lilies, fish heads, sand crabs—vile broth. But most days they had nothing else. And they grew hungrier and hungrier.

For thirty days the strong south wind blew, keeping them beached. Finally, one night when Ulysses was asleep, Eurylochus secretly called the men together, and said, "Death comes to men in all sorts of ways. And however it comes, it is never welcome. But the worst of all deaths is to die of starvation. And to be forced to starve among herds

of fat beef is a hellish torture that the gods reserve for the greatest criminals. So I say to you men that we must disregard the warning of that meddlesome ghost, Teiresias, and help ourselves to this cattle. We can do it now while Ulysses sleeps. And if indeed the Sun Titan is angered and seeks vengeance—well, at least we shall have had one more feast before dying."

It was agreed. They went immediately into the meadow. Now, Hyperion's cattle were the finest ever seen on earth. They were enormous, sleek, broad-backed, with crooked golden horns, and hides of beautiful dappled gold and white. And when the men came among them with their axes, they were not afraid, for no one had ever offered them any harm. They looked at the men with their great plum-colored eyes, whisked their tails, and continued grazing.

The axes rose and fell. Six fine cows were slaughtered. Because they knew they were committing an offense against the gods, the men were very careful to offer sacrifice. Upon a makeshift altar they placed the fat thighbones and burned them as offerings. They had no wine to pour upon the blazing meat as a libation, so they used water instead, chanting prayers as they watched the meat burn.

But the smell of the roasting flesh overcame their piety. They leaped upon the carcasses like wild beasts, ripped them apart with their hands, stuck the flesh on spits, and plunged them into the open fires.

Ulysses awoke from a dream of food. He sniffed the air and realized it was no dream, that the smell of roasting meat was real. He lifted his face to the sky, and said, "O mighty

The cattle of the sun. Caeretan Hydria from Italy, about 550 B.C. The Louvre, Paris. Photo by Erich Lessing

ones, it was unkind to let me fall into sleep. For now my men have done what they have been told they must not do."

He drew his sword and rushed off to the light of the fire.

But just then Zeus was hearing a more powerful plea. For the Sun Titan had been informed immediately by the quick spies that serve the gods, and now he was raging upon Olympus.

"O, Father Zeus," he cried, "I demand vengeance upon the comrades of Ulysses who have slaughtered my golden kine. If they are spared, I will withdraw my chariot from the sky.[5] No longer will I warm the treacherous earth, but will go to Hades and shine among the dead."

"I hear you, cousin," said Zeus, "and promise vengeance."

Ulysses dashed among the feasting crew, ready to cut them down even as they squatted there, eating.

---

5. *withdraw my chariot from the sky.* The sun was thought to be Hyperion's chariot, which he drove daily from horizon to horizon.

"Wait," cried Eurylochus. "Hold your hand. These are not the Sun God's cattle. But six stags we found on the other side of the island."

"Stags?" roared Ulysses. "What kind of monstrous lie is this? You know there are no stags on this island."

"They were there," said Eurylochus. "And now they are here. Perhaps the gods relented, and sent them as food. Come, eat, dear friend, and do not invent misdeeds where none exist."

Ulysses allowed himself to be persuaded, and sat down among the men and began to eat with ravenous speed. But then a strange thing happened. The spitted carcasses turning over the fire began to low and moo as though they were alive, one of the flayed hides crawled over the sand to Ulysses, and he saw that it was dappled gold and white, and knew he had been tricked.

Once again he seized his sword and rushed toward Eurylochus.

"Wait!" cried Eurylochus. "Do not blame me. We have not offended the gods by our trickery. For the south wind has fallen—see? The wind blows from the north now, and we can sail away. If the gods were angry, Ulysses, would they send us a fair wind?"

"To the ship!" shouted Ulysses. "We sail immediately."

The men gathered up the meat that was left, and followed Ulysses to the beached ship. They put logs under it and rolled it down to the sea. Here they unfurled the sail, and slid out of the harbor.

Night ran out and the fires of dawn burned in the sky. The men hurried about their tasks, delighted to be well fed and sailing again, after the starving month on Thrinacia.

But then Ulysses, observing the sky, saw a strange sight. The sun seemed to be frowning. He saw that black clouds had massed in front of it. He heard a rustling noise, and looked off westward, where he saw the water ruffling darkly.

"Down sail!" he shouted. "Ship the mast!"

Too late. A wild west wind came hurtling across the water and pounced on the ship. There was no time to do anything. Both forestays snapped. The mast split and fell, laying its white sail like a shroud over the ship. A lightning bolt flared from the blue sky and struck amidship. Great billows of choking yellow smoke arose. The heat was unbearable. Ulysses saw his men diving off the deck, garments and hair ablaze and hissing like cinders when they hit the water.

He was still shouting commands, trying to chop the sail free and fighting against the gale and fire. But he was all alone. Not one man was aboard. The ship fell apart beneath him. The ribs were torn from the keel. The ship was nothing but a mass of flaming timbers, and Ulysses swam among them. He held on to the mast, which had not burned. Pushing it before him, he swam out of the blazing wreckage. He found the keel floating free. The oxhide backstay was still tied to the head of the mast; with it he lashed mast and keel together into a kind of raft.

He looked about, trying to find someone to pull aboard. There was no one. He had no way of steering the raft, but had to go where the wind blew him. And now, to his dismay, he found the wind shifting again. It blew from the south, which meant that he would be pushed back toward the terrible strait.

All day he drifted, and all night. When dawn came, it brought with it a roaring sucking sound, and he saw that he was being drawn between Scylla and Charybdis. He felt the raft being pulled toward the whirlpool. It was the very moment when Charybdis took her first drink of the day. She swallowed the tide, and held it in her great bladder of a belly. The raft spun like a leaf in the outer eddies of the huge suction, and Ulysses knew that when he reached the vortex of the whirlpool, he and the raft would be drawn to the bottom, and that he must drown.

He kept his footing on the raft until the very last moment, and just as it was pulled into the vortex, he leaped as high as he could upon the naked face of the rock, scrabbling for a handhold. He caught a clump of lichen, and clung with all his strength. He could climb no higher on the rock; it was too slippery for a foothold. All he could do was cling to the moss and pray that his strength would not give out. He was waiting for Charybdis to spit forth the tide again.

The long hours passed. His shoulders felt as though they were being torn apart by red-hot pincers. Finally he heard a great tumult of waters and saw it frothing out of the cave. The waves leaped toward his feet. And then he saw what he was waiting for—his raft came shooting up like a cork.

He dropped upon the timbers. Now he would have some hours of quiet water, he knew, before Charybdis drank again. So he kept to that side of the strait, holding as far from Scylla as he could, for he well remembered the terrible reach of her arms.

He passed safely beyond the rocks and out of the strait. For nine days he drifted under the burning sun, nine nights under the indifferent moon. With his knife he cut a long splinter from the timbers, and shaped it into a lance for spearing fish. He did not get any. Then he lay on his back, pretending to be dead, and gulls came to peck out his eyes. He caught them, and wrung their necks. He ate their flesh and drank their blood, and so stayed alive.

On the tenth day he found himself approaching another island.

He was very weak. The island grew dim as he looked at it. A black mist hid the land, which was odd because the sun was shining. Then the sky tilted, and the black mist covered him.

CALYPSO

When Ulysses awoke he found himself lying on a bed of sweet-smelling grass. The sun shone hotly, but he was in a pool of delicious cool shade under a poplar tree. He was still dizzy. The trees were swaying, and bright flowers danced upon the meadow. He closed his eyes, thinking, "I am dead then. The god that hunts me took pity and shortened my hard life, and I am now in the Elysian Fields."

A voice answered, "You have not died. You are not in the Elysian Fields. You have come home."

He opened his eyes again. A woman was bending over him. She was so tall that he knew she was no mortal woman, but nymph or naiad or demigoddess. She was clad in a short tunic of yellow and purple. Her hair was yellow, and long and thick.

"You are here with me," she said. "You have come home."

"Home? Is this Ithaca? Are you Penelope?"

"This is Ogygia, and I am Calypso."

He tried to sit up. He was too weak. "But Ithaca is my home," he said. "And Penelope is my wife."

"Home is where you dwell. And now you belong to me, because this island and everything on it is mine."

Ulysses went back to sleep. For he believed he was dreaming, and did not wish to wake up again and find himself on the raft. But when he awoke, he was still in his dream. He was strong enough now to sit up and look around. He was in a great grove hemmed by trees—alder and poplar and cypress. Across this meadow four streams ran, crossing each other, making a sound like soft laughter. The meadow was a carpet of wild flowers, violets, parsley, bluebells, daffodils, and cat-faced pansies. His bed had been made in front of a grotto, he saw. Over it a wild grapevine had been trained to fall like a curtain.

The vine curtain was pushed aside, and Calypso came out.

"You are awake," she cried, "and just in time for your wedding feast. The stag is roasted. The wine has been poured. No, don't move. You're still too weak. Let me help you, little husband."

She stooped and lifted him in her great white arms and carried him easily as though he were a child into the grotto, and set him before the hearth. A whole stag was spitted over the flame. The cave was carpeted with the skins of leopard and wolf and bear.

"Lovely and gracious goddess," said Ulysses, "tell me, please, how I came here. The last I remember I was on my raft, and then a blackness fell."

"I was watching for you," said Calypso. "I knew you would come, and I was waiting. Then your raft floated into sight. I saw you slump over and roll off the raft. And I changed you into a fish, for sharks live in this water and they are always hungry. As soon as I turned you into a fish, a gull stooped—and he would have had you—but I shot him with my arrow. Then I took my net and fished you out, restored you to your proper shape, fed you a broth of herbs, and let you sleep. That was your arrival, O man I have drawn from the sea. As for your departure, that will never be. Now eat your meat and drink your wine, for I like my husbands well fed."

Ulysses ate and drank, and felt his strength return.

"After all," he thought, "things could be worse. In fact they have been much worse. This may turn out to be quite a pleasant interlude. She is certainly beautiful, this Calypso. Rather large for my taste, and inclined to be bossy, I'm afraid. But who's perfect?"

He turned to her, smiling, and said, "You say you were waiting for me, watching for my raft. How did you know I would be coming?"

"I am one of the Titan brood," said Calypso. "Daughter of mighty Atlas, who stands upon the westward rim of the world bearing the sky upon his shoulders. We are the elder branch of the gods, we Titans. For us there is no before or after, only now, wherein all things are and always were and always will be. Time, you see, is a little arrangement man has made for himself to try to measure the immeasurable mystery of life. It does not really exist. So when we want to know anything that has happened in what you call 'before,' or what will happen in what you call 'after,' we simply shuffle the pictures and look at them."

"I don't think I understand."

"I have watched your whole voyage, Ulysses. All I have to do is poke the log in a certain way, and pictures form in the heart of the fire and burn there until I poke the log again. What would you like to see?"

"My wife, Penelope."

Calypso reached her long arm and poked the log. And in the heart of the flame Ulysses saw a woman, weaving.

"She looks older," he said.

"You have been away a long time. Only the immortals do not age. I was 2,300 years old yesterday. Look at me. Do you see any wrinkles?"

"Poor Penelope," said Ulysses.

"Don't pity her too much. She has plenty of company. She is presumed to be a widow, you know."

"Has she married again?"

"I weary of this picture. Would you like to see another?"

"My son, Telemachus."

She poked the fire again, and Ulysses saw the flickering image of a tall young man with red-gold hair. He held a spear in his hand and looked angry.

"How he has grown," murmured Ulysses. "He was a baby when I left. He is a young man now, and a fine one, is he not?"

"Looks like his father," said Calypso.

"He seems to be defying some enemy," said Ulysses. "What is happening?"

"He is trying to drive away his mother's suitors, who live in your castle now. She is quite popular—for an older woman. But then, of course, she has land and goods. A rich widow. You left her well provided, O sailor. She has many suitors, and cannot decide among them. Or perhaps she enjoys their courtship too much to decide. But your son is very proud of his father, whom he does not remember, and seeks to drive the suitors from your castle."

"I had better go home and help him," said Ulysses.

"Put that out of your mind. It simply will not happen. Forget Ithaca, Ulysses. You are a hero, a mighty hero, and heroes have many homes, and the last is always the best. Look at this. See some of your exploits. Like many warriors, you were too busy fighting to know what really happened."

She poked the log again and again, and a stream of pictures flowed through the fire. Ulysses saw himself standing on a rock in the Cyclops's cave, holding the white-hot sword above the great sleeping eye, preparing to stab it in. He saw himself wrestling with the leather bag of winds that Aeolus had given him; saw himself running with the wolves and lions who had been Circe's lovers in the dark courtyard of her castle. Then, sword in hand, he saw himself hacking at Scylla's tentacles as she reached across the tilting deck for his men. Going back he saw himself before his homeward voyage crouched in the black belly of the wooden horse he had made. Next, climbing out of that horse after it had been dragged into the city and racing with lifted sword to slaughter the sleeping Trojan warriors. And, as he watched and saw the old battles refought, the men who had been his friends, and the monstrous enemies he had overcome, his heart sang with pride, and a drunken warmth stronger than the fumes of wine rose to his head, drowning out all the pictures of home.

He stood up, and said, "Thank you for showing me myself, Calypso. I do seem to be a hero, don't I? And worthy to love a daughter of the Titans."

"Yes," said Calypso.

Now Calypso had amused herself with shipwrecked sailors before. But she was hard to please, and none of them had lasted very long. When she was tired of someone she would throw him back into the sea. If she were feeling goodnatured she would change him to gull or fish first. Indeed, the trees of the grove were filled with nesting sea birds— gull and heron and osprey and sand owls— who called to her at night, reproaching her.

"What is that clamor of birds?" said Ulysses.

"Just birds."

"Why do they shriek so?"

"They are angry at me for loving you. They were men once, like yourself."

"How did they get to be birds?"

"Oh, well, it's no very difficult transformation, when you know how. I thought they would be happier so."

"They don't sound very happy."

"They have jealous natures."

"You are not unlike Circe in some ways," said Ulysses. "You island goddesses are apt to be abrupt with your former friends. I've noticed this."

"It's a depressing topic, dear. Let's talk about me. Do you find me beautiful today?"

"More beautiful than yesterday, if that is possible. And no doubt will find you even lovelier tomorrow, since you have shown me the penalty of any inattention."

"Do not fear," said Calypso. "You are not like the others. You are bolder and have more imagination. You are a hero."

"Perhaps you could persuade your feathered friends to nest elsewhere? They make me nervous."

"Nothing easier. I shall simply tell them to depart. If they do not, I shall change them all to grasshoppers, all save one, who will eat the rest, and then die of overeating."

"Truly, you are wise and powerful, and fair beyond all women, mortal and immortal."

She smiled. "You have such an apt way of putting things," she said.

So Ulysses made himself at home on the island, and passed the time hunting game, and fishing the sea, and reveling with the beautiful Calypso. He was happy. Thoughts of home grew dim. The nymph taught him how to poke the magic log upon her hearth so that it would cast up fire pictures. And he sat by the hour on the great hearth, reading the flickering tapestry of days gone by and days to come. But she had instructed the log never to show him scenes of Ithaca, for she wished him not to be reminded of his home in any way, lest he be tempted to depart. But Ulysses was as crafty as she was, and after he had poked the log many times, asking it to show him what was happening on his island, and the log had cast up pictures of other times, other places, he realized that Calypso had laid a magic veto upon scenes of home. And this, instead of making him forget, made him more eager than ever to know what was happening to Telemachus and Penelope.

One day he went into the wood, snared a sea crow, and asked, "Can you speak?"

"Yes," said the crow.

"Were you once a man?"

"Once . . . once . . . at the time of your grandfather, Sisyphus. I was a clever man, a spy. That's why Calypso changed me into a crow when she grew weary of me, for of all creatures we are the best for spying and prying and tattling."

"Then you're the bird for me," cried Ulysses. "Listen, I wish you to fly to Ithaca. Go to my castle and see what is happening. Then come back and tell me."

"Why should I? What will you give me?"

"Your life."

"My life? I already have that."

"But not for long. Because if you refuse to do as I ask, I shall wring your neck."

"Hmmm," said the crow. "There is merit in your argument. Very well. I shall be your spy. Only don't let Calypso know. She'll catch me and feed me to the cat before I can report to you. I have a notion she'd like you to forget Ithaca."

"Fly away, little bird," said Ulysses, "and do what you have to do. I'll take care of things here."

The next day, at dusk, as he was returning from the hunt, he heard the crow calling from the depth of an oak tree.

"Greetings," said Ulysses. "Have you done what I asked?"

"I have flown to Ithaca," said the crow. "A rough journey by sea, but not really so far as the crow flies. I flew to your castle, and perched in an embrasure, and watched and watched. Briefly, your son is grieving, your wife is weaving, and your guests are *not* leaving."

"What does my wife weave?"

"Your shroud."

"Has she decided so soon that I am dead? I have been gone scarcely twenty years."

"She is faithful. But the suitors, who are brawling, ill-mannered young men, are pressing her to choose one of them for a husband. However, she refuses to choose until she finishes the shroud. And it has been three years aweaving, for each night she rips up the work she had done by day, so the shroud is never finished. But the suitors grow impatient. They are demanding that she finish her weaving and choose a groom. Your son opposes them. And they threaten to kill him unless he steps aside."

"Thank you, crow," said Ulysses.

"What will you do now—try to escape?"

"Escape? I do not consider myself a captive, good bird. I shall simply inform Calypso that I intend to leave, and ask her to furnish the transportation."

"You make it sound easy," said the crow. "Good luck."

And he flew away.

Ulysses went to Calypso in her grotto, and fell on his knees before her, and said, "Fair and gracious friend, you have made me happier than any man has a right to be, especially an unlucky one. But now I must ask you one last great favor."

Calypso frowned. "I don't like the sound of that," she said. "What do you mean 'last'? Why should I not go on doing you favors?"

"I must go home."

"This is your home."

"No. My home is Ithaca. Penelope is my

Head of Ulysses. Fragment of a marble statue from the cave of Tiberius in Sperlonga, probably from the middle of the first century B.C. Sperlonga Museum. Photo by Erich Lessing

wife. Telemachus is my son. I have enemies. They live in my castle and steal my goods. They wish to kill my son and take my wife. I am a king. I cannot tolerate insults. I must go home."

"Suppose you do go home, what then?"

"I will contend with my enemies. I will kill them or they will kill me."

"You kill them, say—then what?"

"Then I live, I rule. I don't know. I cannot read the future."

"I can. Look."

She poked the magic log. Fire pictures flared. Ulysses saw himself sitting on his throne. He was an old man. Penelope was there. She was an old woman.

"You will grow old . . . old . . . ." Calypso's voice murmured in his ear, unraveling in its rough purring way like raw silk. "Old . . . old. . . . You will live on memories. You will eat your heart out recalling old glories, old battles, old loves. Look . . . look into the fire."

"Is that me?"

"That's you, humping along in your old age among your hills, grown dry and cruel."

She tapped the log and the fire died.

"Do you still want to go back to Ithaca?" she said.

"Will my future be different if I stay here?"

"Certainly. If you stay with me, it will be entirely different. You will no longer be a mortal man. I will make you my eternal consort, make you immortal. You will not die or grow old. This will be your home, not only this island, but wherever the Titans rule."

"Never die, never grow old. It seems impossible."

"You are a man to whom impossible things happen," said Calypso. "Haven't you learned that by now?"

"'Never' . . . ," said Ulysses. "'Always' . . . . These are words I find hard to accept."

"Do not think you will be bored. I am expert at variety. I deal in transformations, you know."

"You are eloquent," said Ulysses. "And you need no eloquence, for your beauty speaks more than any words. Still, I cannot be immortal, never to die, never to grow old. What use is courage then?"

Calypso smiled at him. "Enough discussion for one night. You have time to decide. Take five or ten years. We are in no hurry, you and I."

"Five or ten years may seem little to an immortal," said Ulysses. "But I am still a man. It is a long time for me."

"That's just what I said," said Calypso. "It is better to be immortal. But, think it over."

The next morning, instead of hunting, Ulysses went to the other side of the island and built an altar of rocks and sacrificed to the gods. He poured a libation of unwatered wine, and raised his voice:

"O, great gods upon Olympus— thunder-wielding Zeus and wise Athene, earthshaking Poseidon, whom I have offended, golden Apollo—hear my prayer. For ten years I fought in Troy, and for ten more years have wandered the sea, been hounded from island to island, battered by storms, swallowed by tides. My ships have been wrecked, my men killed. But you have granted me life. Now, I pray you, take back the gift. Let me join my men in Tartarus. For if I cannot return home, if I have to be kept here as a prisoner of Calypso while my kingdom is looted, my son slain, and my wife stolen, then I do not wish to live. Allow me to go home, or strike me dead on the spot."

His prayer was carried to Olympus. Athene heard it. She went to Zeus, and asked him to call the gods into council. They met in the huge throne-room. As it happened, Poseidon was absent. He had ridden a tidal wave into Africa, where he had never been, and was visiting the Ethiopians.

Athene said, "O father Zeus, O brother gods, I wish to speak on behalf of Ulysses, who of all the mighty warriors we sent to Troy shows the most respect for our power, and the most belief in our justice. Ten years after leaving the bloody beaches of Troy he has still not reached home. He is penned now on an island by Calypso, daughter of Atlas, who uses all her Titanic enticements to keep him prisoner. This man's plight challenges our Justice. Let us help him now."

Zeus said, "I do not care to be called unjust. I am forgetful sometimes, perhaps, but then I have much to think of, many affairs to manage. And remember, please, my daughter, that this man has been traveling the sea, which belongs to my brother Poseidon, whom he has offended. Poseidon holds a heavy grudge, as you know; he does not forgive injuries. Ulysses would have been home years ago if he had not chosen to blind Polyphemus, who happens to be Poseidon's son."

"He has paid for that eye over and over again," cried Athene. "Many times its worth, I vow. And the earth-shaker is not here, as it happens. He is off shaking the earth of Africa, which has been too dry and peaceable for his tastes. Let us take advantage of his absence, and allow Ulysses to resume his voyage."

"Very well," said Zeus. "It shall be as you advise."

Thereupon he dispatched Hermes, the messenger god, to Ogygia. Hermes found Calypso on the beach singing a wild sea song, imitating now the voice of the wind, now the lisping scraping sound of waves on a shallow shore, weaving in the cry of heron and gull and osprey, tide suck and drowned moons. Now Hermes had invented pipe and lyre, and loved music. When he heard Calypso singing her wild sea song, he stood upon the bright air, ankle wings whirring, entranced. He hovered there, listening to her sing. Dolphins were drawn by her voice. They stood in the surf and danced on their tails.

She finished her song. Hermes landed lightly beside her.

"A beautiful song," he said.

"A sad song."

"All beautiful songs are sad."

"Yes . . ."

"Why is that?"

"They are love songs. Women love men, and they go away. This is very sad."

"You know why I have come then?"

"Of course. What else would bring you here? The Olympians have looked down and seen me happy for a little while, and they have decreed that this must not be. They have sent you to take my love away."

"I am sorry, cousin. But it is fated that he find his way home."

"Fate . . . destiny . . . what are they but fancy words for the brutal decrees of Zeus. He is jealous, and that is the whole truth of it. He wants us all for himself. Don't deny it. When Eos, Goddess of Dawn, chose Orion for her lover, Zeus had his daughter, Artemis, slay him with her arrows. When Demeter, harvest wife, met Jasion in the ploughed fields, Zeus himself flung his bolt crippling him. It is always the same. He allowed Ulysses to be shipwrecked time and again. When I found him he was riding the timbers of his lost ship and was about to drown. So I took him here with me, and cherished him, and offered to make him immortal. And now Zeus suddenly remembers, after twenty years, that he must go home immediately, because it is ordained."

"You can't fight Zeus," said Hermes gently. "Why try?"

"What do you want me to do?"

"Permit Ulysses to make himself a raft. See that he has provisions. Then let him depart."

"So be it."

"Do not despair, sweet cousin. You are too beautiful for sorrow. There will be other storms, other shipwrecks, other sailors."

"Never another like him."

"Who knows?"

He kissed her on the cheek, and flew away.

INO'S VEIL

In her generous way, Calypso went beyond what the gods had ordered, and provided Ulysses not with a raft, but with a beautiful tight little vessel, sturdy enough for a long voyage, and small enough for one man to sail.

But he would have done just as well with a raft, for his bad luck held. He was seventeen days out of Ogygia, scudding along happily, when Poseidon, on his way back from Africa, happened to notice the little ship.

The sea god scowled, and said, "Can that be Ulysses? I thought I had drowned him long ago. One of my meddlesome relatives up there must be shielding him, and I have a good notion who. Well, I'll give my owlish niece[6] a little work to do."

His scowl deepened, darkening the sun. He shook a storm out of his beard. The winds leaped, the water boiled. Ulysses felt the tiller being torn out of his hand. The boat spun like a chip. The sail ripped, the mast cracked, and Ulysses realized that his old enemy had found him again.

He clung to the splintered mast. Great waves broke over his head, and he swallowed the bitter water. He came up, gasping. The deck broke beneath him.

"Why am I fighting?" he thought. "Why don't I let myself drown?"

But he kept fighting by instinct. He pulled himself up onto a broken plank and clung there. Each boiling whitecap crested over him, and he was breathing more water than air. His arms grew too weak to hold the plank, and he knew that the next wave must surely take him under.

However, there was a nereid near, named Ino, who hated Poseidon for an injury he had done her long before, and now she resolved to balk his vengeance. She swam to Ulysses' timber, and climbed on.

He was snorting and gasping and coughing. Then he saw that he was sharing his plank with a green-haired woman wearing a green veil.

"Welcome, beautiful Nereid," he said. "Are you she who serves Poseidon, ushering drowned men to those caverns beneath the sea where the white bones roll?"

"No, unhappy man," she said. "I am Ino . . . and I am no servant of the windy widow-maker. I would like to do him an injury by helping you. Take this veil. It cannot sink even in the stormiest sea. Strip off your garments, wrap yourself in the veil, and swim toward those mountains. If you are bold, and understand that you cannot drown, then you will be able to swim to the coast where you will be safe. After you land, fling the veil back into the sea, and it will find its way to me."

She unwound the green veil from her body, and gave it to him. Then she dived into the sea.

"Can I believe her?" thought Ulysses. "Perhaps it's just a trick to make me leave the pitiful safety of this timber. Oh, well, if I must drown, let me do it boldly."

---

6. *owlish niece,* a reference to Athene, goddess of wisdom, whose symbol was the owl.

He pulled off his wet clothes and wrapped himself in the green veil and plunged into the sea.

It was very strange. When he had been on the raft, the water had seemed death-cold, heavy as iron, but now it seemed warm as a bath, and marvelously buoyant. He had been unable to knot the veil, but it clung closely to his body. When he began to swim he found himself slipping through the water like a fish.

"Forgive my suspicions, fair Ino," he cried. "Thank you . . . thank you. . . . "

For two days he swam, protected by Ino's veil, and on the morning of the third day he reached the coast of Phaeacia. But he could not find a place to come ashore, for it was a rocky coast, and the water swirled savagely among jagged boulders. So he was in great trouble again. While the veil could keep him from drowning, it could not prevent him from being broken against the rocks.

The current caught him and swept him in. With a mighty effort he grasped the first rock with both hands and clung there, groaning, as the rushing water tried to sweep him on. But he clung to the rock like a sea polyp, and the wave passed. Then the powerful back-tow caught him and pulled him off the rock and out to sea. He had gained nothing. His arms and chest were bleeding where great patches of skin had been scraped off against the rock.

He realized that the only thing he could do was try to swim along the coast until he found an open beach. So he swam and swam. The veil held him up, but he was dizzy from loss of blood. Nor had he eaten for two days. Finally, to his great joy, he saw a break in the reef. He swam toward it, and saw that it was the mouth of a river. Exerting his last strength, he swam into the river, struggled against the current, swimming past the shore where the river flowed among trees. Then he had no more strength. He was exhausted.

He staggered ashore, unwrapped the veil from his body, and cast it upon the river so that it would be borne back to Ino. When he tried to enter the wood, he could not take another step. He collapsed among the reeds.

NAUSICAA

In those days, girls did not find their own husbands, especially princesses. Their marriages were arranged by their parents, and it all seemed to work out as well as any other way. But Nausicaa, sixteen-year-old daughter of the King and Queen of Phaeacia, was hard to please, and had been turning down suitors for two years now. Her father, Alcinous, and her mother, Arete, were becoming impatient. There were several hot-tempered kings and princes who had made offers—for Nausicaa was very lovely—and Alcinous knew that if he kept turning them down he might find himself fighting several wars at once. He was a fine warrior, and enjoyed leading his fleet into battle. Still, he preferred his wars one at a time.

He told the queen that Nausicaa would have to be forced to choose.

"I was very difficult to please, too," said Arete, "but I think you'll admit I married well. Perhaps she too knows in her heart that if she bides her time the gods will send a mighty man to be her husband."

The king smiled. Arete always knew the

right thing to say to him. So the discussion ended for that day. Nevertheless, the queen knew that her husband was right, and that the girl would have to choose.

That night Nausicaa was visited by a dream. It seemed to her that the goddess Athene stood over her bed, tall and gray-eyed, and spoke to her, saying. "How can you have a wedding when all your clothes are dirty? Take them to the river tomorrow and wash them."

The goddess faded slowly until all that was left was the picture on her shield—a snake-haired girl.[7] And it seemed that the snakes writhed and hissed and tried to crawl off the shield to get at the dreamer. Nausicaa awoke, moaning. But she was a brave girl, and went right back to sleep and tried to dream the same dream again, so that she could learn more about the wedding. But the goddess did not return.

The next morning she went to her mother and told her of the dream.

"I don't understand it," she said. "What wedding?"

"Yours, perhaps," said Arete.

"Mine? With whom?"

"The gods speak in riddles. You know that. Especially when they visit us in dreams. So you must do the one clear thing she told you. Take your serving girls to the river, and wash your clothes. Perhaps, if you do that, the meaning will show itself."

Thereupon Nausicaa told her serving girls to gather all the laundry in the castle, and pile it in the mule cart. She also took food, a goat-skin bottle of wine, and a golden flask of oil so that they could bathe in the river. Then they set off in the red cart, and the harness bells jingled as the mules trotted down the steep streets toward the river.

It was a sparkling morning. Nausicaa felt very happy as she drove the mules. They drove past the city walls, and down the hill, and along a road that ran through a wood until they came to the river.

They dumped the clothes in the water, and stamped on them, dancing and trampling and treading them clean. Then they dragged the clothes out, and pounded them on flat stones, afterward spreading them to dry in the hot sun.

They then flung off their garments and swam in the river, scrubbing each other and anointing themselves with oil.

"Well, you look clean enough to get married," cried Nausicaa. "But it's easier to wash than to wed, isn't it, girls?"

The maidens giggled wildly, and Nausicaa shouted with laughter. She was so drunk with sun and water that she felt she could run up the mountain and dance all day and night. It was impossible to sit still. She seized a leather ball from the cart, and flung it to one of her maids, who caught it and threw it back. Then the others joined in, and the girls frisked on the riverbank, tossing the ball back and forth.

Ulysses awoke from a deep sleep. He was still dazed, and could barely remember how he had gotten among the reeds. He peered out, saw the girls playing, and then shrank back, for he did not wish to be seen as he was, naked and bruised.

---

7. *snake-haired girl*. The monsters called Gorgons had snakes in place of hair, and their look turned people to stone.

But Nausicaa threw the ball so hard that it sailed over the heads of the girls and fell near the clump of reeds where Ulysses was hiding. A girl ran to pick it up, then shrank back, screaming.

"A man!" she cried. "A man—all bloody and muddy."

Ulysses reached out and plucked a spray of leaves from a fallen olive branch, and came out of the reeds.

The girls saw a naked man holding a club. His shoulders were bleeding, his legs muddy, and his hair crusted with salt. They fled, screaming. But Nausicaa stood where she was, and waited for him.

Is this why Athene sent me here? she thought. Is this my husband, come out of the river? Is this what I am to take after all the beautiful young men I have refused? "Come back, you silly geese," she shouted to the girls. "Haven't you ever seen a man before?"

Then she turned to Ulysses, who had fallen to his knees before her.

"Speak, grimy stranger," she said. "Who are you, and what do you want?"

"Do not set your dogs upon me," said Ulysses. "I did not mean to surprise you in your glade."

"What talk is this? Are you out of your head?"

"Forgive me, but I know the fate of Actaeon, who came upon you in the wood. You turned him into a stag, and had your hounds tear him to pieces."

"Whom do you take me for?"

"Why you are Artemis, of course, Goddess of the Chase, maiden of the silver bow. I have heard poets praise your beauty, and I know you by your white arms. By your hair, and eyes, and the way you run—like light over water."

"Sorry to disappoint you, but I am not Artemis. I am Nausicaa. My father is king of this island. And I ask again—who are you?"

"An unlucky man."

"Where do you come from?"

"Strange places, princess. I am a sailor, hunted by a god who sends storms against me, wrecks my ships, kills my men. I come now from Ogygia, where I have been held captive by the Titaness, Calypso, who bound me with her spells. But as I was sailing away, a storm leaped out of the blue sky, smashing my boat. And I have been swimming in the sea for more than two days. I was dashed against the rocks of your coast, but managed to swim around it till I found the river. When I came ashore here, I had no strength to go farther, and fell where you found me."

"I suppose no one would look his best after spending two days in the sea and being beaten against rocks. You tell a good story, I'll say that for you. Why don't you bathe in the river now, and try to make yourself look human again. We can give you oil for anointing, and clean garments belonging to my brother. Then you can follow me to the castle and tell your story there."

"Thank you, sweet princess," said Ulysses.

He took the flask of oil, and went into the river and bathed and anointed himself. When he came out, he found clean garments waiting. The serving girls helped him dress, and combed out his tangled hair.

"Well," said Nausicaa, "you look much improved. I can believe you're some kind of chieftain now. Are you married?"

Maiden washing. Attic red-figured pyxis by the vase-painter Aison of Athens. Last quarter of the fifth century B.C. Boston, Museum of Fine Arts. Photo by Erich Lessing.

"Yes."

"Of course. You would have to be, at your age."

"I have not seen my wife for twenty years. She considers herself a widow."

"Has she remarried?"

"Perhaps. I do not know. Last I heard, she was being besieged by suitors."

"I am besieged by suitors too, but haven't found any I like well enough to marry."

As they spoke at the bank of the river, the serving girls had been piling the laundry into the mule cart.

"But I am thoughtless, keeping you here," said Nausicaa. "You need food and rest. You must come to the castle and finish your story there."

"The sight of your beauty is food and drink to me. And the sound of your voice makes me forget my weariness."

She laughed. "Are you courting me, stranger?"

"I am a homeless wanderer. I cannot court a princess. But I can praise her beauty."

"Come along to the castle. I want to introduce you to my father and mother. They are kind to strangers, very partial to brave men, and love to hear stories. And I want to hear more about you, too."

Now, that day, as it happened, King Alcinous had consulted an oracle, who prophesied, saying, "I see danger. I see a mountain blocking your harbor, destroying your commerce. I sense the cold wrath of the god of the sea."

"But the earth-shaker has always favored us," said the king. "He has showered blessings upon this island. Our fleets roam far, return laden. Why should he be angered now?"

"I do not know. It is not clear, it is not clear. But I say to you, O King, beware of strangers, shipwrecks, storytellers. Believe no tale, make no loan, suffer no harm."

"I don't understand."

"Neither do I. But there is no need to understand, only to obey."

The oracle departed, leaving the king very thoughtful.

Just at this time, Nausicaa was leading Ulysses into the courtyard of the castle. She bade her maids take him to the guest house.

"Wait till I send for you," she said. "Food will be brought, and wine."

She raced to her mother's chamber.

"Oh, Mother, Mother," she cried. "I'm so glad I obeyed the dream and went to the river to wash our clothes. What do you think I found there? A man, hiding in the reeds,

naked and wounded. I soon set him right and brought him here. Such an interesting man."

"Brought him here? Here to the castle? Paraded a naked beggar through the streets for the whole town to see? My dear child, haven't you given them enough to gossip about?"

"He's no beggar, Mother. He's a sailor or a pirate or something. Such stories he tells. Listen, he landed on an island once where men eat flowers that make them fall asleep and forget who they are. So they sleep all day and pick flowers all night, and are very happy. This man's crew went ashore and ate the flowers, and forgot who they were and didn't want to go back to the ship, just sleep. But he dragged them back anyway. I'd like to try those flowers, wouldn't you?"

"Who is this man? What's his name?"

"I don't know. He didn't tell me. It's a secret or something."

"Do you believe everything he tells you?"

"Oh, yes. He's not exactly handsome, but very strong-looking, you know. Too old though, much too old. And married, of course. But I don't think he gets along with his wife. You can see he has suffered. You can see by his eyes."

"Where is he now?"

"In the guest house. Don't you think we should have a banquet for him tonight? He's a distinguished visitor, isn't he—all those things he did?"

"We don't quite know what he is, do we, dear? I think I had better meet him myself first. Your father's in a funny mood. Met with the oracle today, and something went wrong, I think."

"Yes, yes, I want you to meet him before

Father does. I want to know what you think. Shall I fetch him?"

"I'll send a servant, child. You are not to see him again until I find out more about him. Do you understand?"

"Oh, yes, find out, find out! Tell me everything he says."

Queen Arete spoke with Ulysses, and then went to her husband, the king, and told him of their visitor. She was amazed to see his face grow black with rage.

"By the gods," he cried. "These are foul tidings you bring. Only today the oracle warned against strangers, shipwrecks, and storytellers. And now you tell me our daughter has picked up some nameless ruffian who combines all three—a shipwrecked stranger telling wild tales. Precisely what is needed to draw upon us the wrath of the sea god. I shall sacrifice him to Poseidon, and there will be an end to it."

"You may not do that," said Arete.

"Who says 'may not' to me? I am king."

"Exactly why you may not. Because you are king. The man comes to you as a supplicant. He is under your protection. If you harm him, you will bring down upon yourself the wrath of all gods—not just one. That is the law of hospitality."

So the king ordered a great banquet that night to honor his guest. But certain young men of the court who were skilled at reading the king's moods knew that he was displeased, and decided to advance themselves in his favor by killing the stranger, and making it seem an accident.

"We will have games in the courtyard," said Euryalus their leader. "We will hurl discus and javelin, shoot with the bow, wrestle, and challenge him to take part. And, when he does, it may be that some unlucky throw of javelin, or misshot arrow, will rid us of his company. Or, perchance, if he wrestles, he will find his neck being broken. It looks to be a thick neck, but he has been long at sea and is unused to such exercises."

So the young men began to hold their contests in the courtyard. When Ulysses stopped to watch them, Euryalus stepped forth, and said, "There is good sport here, stranger, if you care to play."

"No, thank you," said Ulysses. "I'll just watch."

"Yes, of course," said Euryalus. "These games are somewhat dangerous. And one can see that you are a man of prudence. But then, of course, you are rather old for such sports, aren't you?"

He laughed sneeringly, picked up the heavy discus, whirled, and threw. It sailed through the air and landed with a clatter far away. All the young men laughed and cheered.

"Where I come from," said Ulysses, "such little discs are given babies to teethe on. The grown men need a bit more to test them."

He strode over to a battle chariot, and broke off one of its wheels at the axle. It was a very heavy wheel, of oak bound with brass.

He hefted it, and said, "A little light, but it will do."

For he was filled with the wild rage that makes a man ten times stronger than he really is. He cradled the great wheel, whirled, and threw. It flew through the air, far past where the discus had landed, and thudded against the inner wall of the courtyard, knocking a hole in it. He turned to the others, who were paralyzed with amazement.

"Poor throw," he said. "But then, as you say, I'm rather old for such sport. However, since we are gathered here in this friendly fashion, let us play more games. If any of you would like to try me with sword or spear or dagger, or even a simple cudgel, let him step forth. Or, perchance, there is one who would prefer to wrestle?"

"That is well thrown, stranger," said Euryalus. "What is your name?"

"I do not choose to tell you my name, O athlete."

"You are not courteous."

"If you care to teach me manners, young sir, I offer again. Sword, spear, cudgel—any weapon you choose. Or no weapon at all except our hands."

"We are civilized here in Phaeacia," said Euryalus. "We do not fight with our guests. But I cannot understand why you refuse to tell us your name."

"A god hunts me. If I say my name, it may attract his notice."

The young men nodded. For this is what was believed at that time. But Euryalus ran to tell the king.

"I knew it," said Alcinous. "He carries a curse. He is the very man the oracle warned me against. I must get rid of him. But the law of hospitality forbids me to kill him under my roof. So tonight we entertain him at a banquet. But tomorrow he leaves this castle, and we shall find a way to see that he does not return."

"He is no weakling, this old sailor," said Euryalus. "He throws the discus almost as well as I."

Now, all this time, Nausicaa had been thinking about the stranger, and weaving a plan, for she was determined to find out who he was. She visited the old bard who had taught her to play the lyre, and whose task it was to sing for the guests at the royal feasts. She spoke and laughed with the old man and fed him undiluted wine until he lost his wits. Then she locked him in the stable, where he fell fast asleep on a bundle of straw, and she departed with his lyre.

At the banquet that night, when the king called for the bard to sing his tales, Nausicaa said, "The old man is ill and cannot come. However, if you permit, I shall sing for your guests."

The king frowned. But Ulysses said, "This illness is a blessing, King. I think I should rather hear your black-haired daughter sing than the best bard who ever plucked a lyre."

The king nodded. Nausicaa smiled, and began to sing. She sang a tale of heroes. Of those who fought at Troy. She sang of fierce Achilles and mighty Ajax. Of Menelaus and his shattering war-cry. Of brave Diomedes, who fought with Ares himself when the war god came in his brazen chariot to help the Trojans.

She watched Ulysses narrowly as she sang. She saw his face soften, and his eyes grow dreamy, and she knew that he had been there, and that she was singing of his companions. But she still did not know his name.

Then she began to sing of that master of strategy, the great trickster, Ulysses. She sang of the wooden horse, and how the warriors hid inside while the Trojans debated outside, deciding what to do. Some of them wanted to chop it to pieces; others wished to take it to a cliff and push it off; still others wanted to bring it within the city as an offering to the gods—which, of course, was what Ulysses wanted them to do. She told of the men hiding in the belly of the horse, listening to their fate being debated, and of the fierce joy that flamed in their hearts when they heard the Trojans decide to drag the horse within the walls. And of how, in the blackness of the night, they came out of the horse, and how Ulysses led the charge. She sang of him fighting there by the light of the burning houses, knee-deep in blood, and how he was invincible that night and carried everything before him.

And as she sang, she kept watching the stranger's face. She saw tears steal from between his clenched eyelids and roll down his cheeks. Amazed, the banqueters saw this hard-bitten sailor put his head in his hands and sob like a child.

He raised his streaming face, and said, "Forgive me, gracious king. But the wonderful voice of your daughter has touched my heart. For you must know that I am none other than Ulysses, of whom she sings."

A great uproar broke out. The young men cheered. The women wept. The king said, "My court is honored, Ulysses. Your deeds are known wherever men love courage. Now that I know who you are, I put all my power and goods at your disposal. Name any favor you wish, and it shall be yours."

Ulysses said, "O King, if I were the age I was twenty years ago when the ships were launched at Aulis, then the favor I would ask is your daughter's hand. For surely I have traveled the whole world over without seeing her like. I knew Helen whose beauty kindled men to that terrible war. I knew the beauties of the Trojan court whom we took captive and shared among us. And, during my wanderings I have had close acquaintance with certain enchantresses whose charms are more than human, namely Circe and Calypso. Yet never have I seen a girl so lovely, so witty, so courteous and kind as your young daughter. Alas, it cannot be. I am too old. I have a wife I must return to, and a kingdom, and there are sore trials I must undergo before I can win again what belongs to me. So all I ask of you, great king, is a ship to take me to Ithaca, where my wife waits, my enemies wait, my destiny waits."

Arete whispered to the king:

"Yes . . . yes . . . give him his ship tomorrow. I wish it could be tonight. See how your daughter looks at him; she is smitten to the heart. She is sick with love. Let him sail tomorrow. And be sure to keep watch at the wharf lest she stow away."

"It shall be as you say, mighty Ulysses," said the king. "Your ship will sail tomorrow."

So Ulysses departed the next day on a splendid ship manned by a picked crew, laden with rich goods the king had given him as hero gifts.

It is said that Athene drugged Poseidon's cup at the feast of the gods that night, so that he slept a heavy sleep and did not see that Ulysses was being borne to Ithaca. But Poseidon awoke in time to see the ship sailing back, and understood what had happened. In a rage he snatched Athene's Gorgonhead shield, the sight of which turns men to stone, and flashed it before the ship just as it was coming into port after having left Ulysses at his island. The ship and all its crew turned to stone, blocking the harbor, as the oracle had foretold.

It is said too that Nausicaa never accepted any of the young men who came awooing, announcing that she was wedded to song. She became the first woman bard, and traveled all the courts of the world singing her song of the heroes who fought at Troy, but especially of Ulysses and of his adventures among the terrible islands of the Middle Sea.

Some say that she finally came to the court of Ithaca to sing her song, and there she stayed. Others say that she fell in love with a blind poet who took all her songs and wove them into one huge tapestry of song.

But it all happened too long ago to know the truth of it.

THINK AND DISCUSS
Understanding
1. What number on the map (pages 544–545) designates the island owned by Hyperion?
2. What argument does Eurylochus use to persuade Ulysses' men to kill the forbidden cattle?
3. How does Calypso rescue Ulysses?
4. Why and how does Ino help Ulysses?
5. By what means does Nausicaa get Ulysses to reveal his identity?

Analyzing
6. Explain what Ulysses means by telling Calypso, "I cannot be immortal, . . . What use is courage then?"
7. In what ways are Circe and Calypso alike?
8. In what ways are Circe and Calypso different?
9. Why do the attitudes of King Alcinous and Arete change toward Ulysses?

Extending
10. If, like Ulysses, you had the opportunity to see into your own future, would you choose to do so? Why or why not?

REVIEWING: Imagery H⫝̸
See Handbook of Literary Terms, p. 641.

Imagery consists of concrete words or details that appeal to the sense of sight, sound, touch, smell, and taste, or to internal feelings. It is language that causes a scene to flash before the reader's eye, or that summons up a sudden sound or smell or feeling, or that gives reality to a written work.
1. To which senses and feelings do the images in the third complete paragraph in the second column on page 594 appeal?
2. Are the images in the whole passage primarily appealing to sight or sound?
3. What sounds are presented or suggested?
4. What image evokes both the sense of smell and of taste?
5. What images evoke the sense of touch?

VOCABULARY
Dictionary

Every occupation throughout history has developed its own vocabulary. In *The Adventures of Ulysses* there are words from the occupations of sailing, farming, fighting (warfare), and manufacturing. All the words listed below are taken from the story, and each is related to one of these four occupational categories. Write the four categories across the top of your paper. Then look up each word in the Glossary, determine in which category it belongs, and write it in that column. Be prepared to answer the following questions.

fortress	sty	armory
guild	keel	smith
dungeon	moor	besiege
buoyant	byre	

1. Would you be more likely to find bullets in a sty or in an armory?
2. Would a ship more likely remain buoyant if it had a hole in its sail or in its keel?
3. Would an army be more likely to besiege a fortress or a byre?
4. Would a dungeon be a suitable place for a guild to hold a meeting?
5. Would a smith or a sailor be more skilled at mooring?

THINKING SKILLS
Generalizing

To generalize is to draw a general statement from particular information. Think about the gods and goddesses portrayed in *The Adventures of Ulysses*. What can you generalize about how they act when they become angry with each other?

COMPOSITION
Imagining the Future

In his dreams and in the magic log, Ulysses saw his future. Now imagine a day in your future. Assume that you keep a diary and that the date is May 3, 2018. It is now 11:00 P.M. You sit down to write three paragraphs about how you spent the day. First you review by asking yourself some questions: How did I spend the morning? the afternoon? the early evening? Whom or what did I see? for what purpose? Where did I go? Why? How was the weather? Is what I wore important?

Retitling an Author's Work

Titles like "The Ciconians" fail to capture the excitement and adventure in the chapters they head. Write three or four paragraphs in which you recommend new titles for some of the chapters you have read. First decide which chapter titles you would change. Then choose new titles. Devote each of your paragraphs to a chapter you believe needs retitling.

Before writing your first draft, you may wish to read Lesson 2 in the Writer's Handbook, "Supporting Your Ideas."

ENRICHMENT
Illustrating Ulysses' Adventures

The author of *The Adventures of Ulysses* provides vivid word pictures of the characters and events. Try your hand at an illustration for the story. Choose a character or characters, such as Morpheus, Aeolus, or Circe's enchanted animals, or a scene, such as Nausicaa singing about the heroes of the Trojan War, and illustrate it. Write a brief caption for your picture.

Comment

English Borrowings from Greek

What is your *Achilles' heel?* When Achilles was a baby, the story goes, his mother dipped him in the River Styx to make him safe from all mortal wounds. However, the heel by which she held him was not touched by the magic waters. It remained his one vulnerable spot. He was killed at Troy by being struck in that heel. And to this day, the band of tissue in your heel is known as your *Achilles' tendon,* and a person's weak point is called his or her *Achilles' heel.*

The term *Trojan horse* still means something that betrays and destroys from within. An *odyssey* is still a long series of wanderings and adventures.

Ulysses' adventures were first written almost twenty-eight centuries ago, but the tales were being told or sung for unknown years before. In one form or another, they have excited listeners and readers for thousands of years.

Ancient Greece has influenced our culture greatly. About ten percent of our English words are borrowed from Greek or use Greek roots and affixes. There are many more borrowed expressions, such as saying "That's fate" when a situation cannot be helped. Here are some others:

Mount Olympus is an actual mountain in Greece, thought by the ancients to be the home of the gods. Nearby, contests in athletics, poetry, and music were held every four years in honor of Zeus. These Olympic Games were revived in modern times, with athletes from all over the world participating. The word *Olympian* means "majestic; like a god."

Hypnos was the Greek god of sleep, so it is not surprising that *hypnotism* was named after him. Throughout history, it has been a great problem of medicine to get patients to relax or sleep so that treatment could be administered. Then in 1805 a drug was found that was a powerful painkiller and anesthetic. Since Morpheus was the god of dreams, *morphine* was named after him.

Atlas was one of the Titans—giants who ruled the earth before the gods of Olympus. (*Titanic* still means "gigantic; having great strength or power.") For his part in the War of the Gods, he was punished by having to support the heavens on his shoulders. A picture of Atlas was used in the sixteenth century for the cover of a collection of maps; such a book is still called an *atlas* to this day.

King Tantalus, as punishment for revealing some of Zeus's secrets, was made to stand in the underworld in water up to his chin, under branches laden with fruit. Every time Tantalus wanted to eat or drink, however, the fruit and the water would recede. To *tantalize* now means to torment a person with things that cannot be obtained.

The word *nymph* is sometimes applied to any graceful young woman, but it is used as well for certain insects in their stage of development preceding the adult form. *Siren,* besides meaning an attractive but dangerous woman, also means a loud, piercing alarm whistle (usually a warning, unlike the Sirens' singing). No one is sure, however, how *calypso* came to mean an improvised jazz song from the West Indies.

THE RETURN

Ulysses had landed on a lonely part of the shore. His enemies were in control of the island, and it was death to be seen. He stood on the empty beach and saw the Phaeacian ship depart. He was surrounded by wooden chests, leather bags, great bales—the treasure of gifts he had been given by Alcinous.

He looked about, at the beach and the cliff beyond, the wooded hills, the color of the sky. He was home after twenty years, but it did not seem like home. It seemed as strange and unfriendly as any of the perilous isles he had landed on during his long wanderings. And he knew that Ithaca would not be his again until he could know it as king, until he had slain his enemies and regained his throne.

His first care was to find a cave in the cliffside, and there stow all his treasure. He moved swiftly now; he had planned his first moves on his homeward trip. It had helped him keep his thoughts away from Nausicaa. He took off his rich cloak and helmet and breastplate, and hid them in the cave he had found, then laid his sword and spear beside them. He tore his tunic so that it hung in rags. He scooped up mud and smeared his face and arms and legs. Then he huddled his shoulders together and practiced a limping walk. Finally he was satisfied, and began to hump away along the cliff road, no longer a splendid warrior, but a feeble old beggar.

He made his way to the hut of his swineherd, Eumaeus, a man his own age, who had served him all his life, and whom he trusted. Everything was the same here, he saw. The pigs were rooting in the trampled earth. There were four lanky hounds who started from their sleep and barked as he came near.

A man came out of the hut, and silenced the dogs. Ulysses felt the tears well in his eyes. It was Eumaeus, but so old, so gray.

"What do you want?" said the swineherd.

"Food, good sir. Such scraps as you throw to the hogs. I am not proud. I am hungry."

"Are you a native of these parts?" said Eumaeus.

"No. I come from Crete."

"A long way for a beggar to come."

"I was not always a beggar. I was a sailor once . . . yes, and a captain of ships. I have seen better days."

"That's what all beggars say."

"Sometimes it's true. I once met a man from Ithaca, a mighty warrior, and the most generous man I have ever met. He gave me a good opinion of Ithaca. It is a place, I know, where the hungry and helpless are not spurned."

"I suppose this man you met was named Ulysses."

"Why, yes. How did you guess?"

"Because I have heard that tale so many times. Do you think you're the first beggar to come slinking around, pretending to have news of our king? Everyone knows that he vanished on his journey home from Troy. Beggars swarm all over us trying to get some supper by telling lies."

"Then you will give me no food?"

"I didn't say that. Even liars have to eat. Ulysses never turned a beggar away, and neither will I."

The swineherd fed Ulysses, and then let him rest by the fire. Ulysses pretended to sleep, but watched his host through half-closed eyes, and saw that the man was staring at him. He stretched and yawned.

"Are you sure you're a stranger to this island?" said Eumaeus. "Seems to me I've seen you before."

"No," said Ulysses. "You are mistaken. What shall I do now? Have I worn out my welcome, or may I sleep on your hearth tonight?"

"What will you do tomorrow?"

"Go to the castle and beg."

"You will not be welcome there."

"Why not? I will tell them how I met your king, and how kind he was to me. That should make them generous."

"It won't," said Eumaeus. "It will probably get you killed. Those who hold the castle now want to hear nothing about him—except the sure news of his death."

"How is that?"

"They hate him, because they do him harm. There are more than a hundred of them—rude brawling young princes from neighboring islands and thievish young nobles of this island. They dwell in his castle as if they had taken it after a siege and seek to marry his wife, Penelope, refusing to leave until she accepts one of them. They drink his wine, devour his stores, break up the furniture for firewood, roister all night, and sleep all day. Do you know how many hogs I have to bring them? Fifty a day. That is how gluttonous they are. My herds are shrinking fast, but they say they will kill me the first day I fail to bring them fifty hogs."

"I heard he had a grown son. Why does he not defend his father's goods?"

"He's helpless. There are too many of them."

"Is he at the castle now?"

"No one knows where he is. He slipped away one night. Just as well. They were planning to kill him. The rumor is that he took ship and crew and went to seek his father. I hope he stays away. They will surely kill him if he returns."

"I go there tomorrow," said Ulysses. "It sounds like splendid begging. Such fiery young men are frequently generous, especially with other people's goods."

"You don't know them," said Eumaeus. "They are like wild beasts. But you cannot keep a fool from his folly. Go, if you must. In the meantime, sleep."

Now upon this night Telemachus was at sea, sailing toward Ithaca. He had found no news of his father and was coming home with a very heavy heart. He would have been even more distressed had he known that a party of wicked suitors was lying in wait for him aboard a swift ship full of fighting men. The ship was hidden in a cove, and the suitors meant to pounce upon him as he put into port.

But Athene saw this and made a plan. She went to Poseidon, and said, "I know you are angry with me, Uncle, for helping Ulysses. But now I wish to make it up to you. See, down there is a ship from Ithaca." She pointed to the suitors' vessel. "No doubt it holds friends of Ulysses, sailing out to meet their king. Why not do them a mischief?"

"Why not?" growled Poseidon.

And he wound a thick black mist about the suitors' ship so that it was impossible for the helmsman to see.

"Nevertheless," he said to Athene. "I still

The farm of Eumaeus. The plateau of Marathia, in the south of Ithaca, supposed to be the place where Eumaeus, Ulysses' faithful swineherd, kept his herds. Photo by Erich Lessing

owe Ulysses himself a great mischief. I have not forgotten. In the meantime, let his friends suffer a bit."

The suitors' ship lay helpless in the mist, and Telemachus sailing past them, ignorant of danger, put into port and disembarked.

Athene then changed herself into a young swineherd, and hailed Telemachus on the beach:

"Greetings, my lord. I am sent by your servant, Eumaeus, to beg you to come to his hut before you go to the castle. He has important news to tell."

The lad set off, and Telemachus followed him toward the swineherd's hut.

Ulysses, dozing by the fire, heard a wild clamor of hounds outside, then a ringing young voice calling to them. He listened while the snarls turned to yaps of pleasure.

"It is my young master," cried Eumaeus, springing up. "Glory to the gods—he has come safely home."

Telemachus strode in. He was flushed from his walk. His face and arms were wet with the night fog, and his red-gold hair was webbed with tiny drops. To Ulysses he looked all aglitter, fledged by firelight, a golden lad. And Ulysses felt a shaft of wild joy pierce him like a spear, and for the first time he realized that he had come home.

But Telemachus was displeased to see the old beggar by the fire, for he wished to speak to Eumaeus privately to ask him how matters stood at the castle and whether it was safe for him to return.

"I do not wish to be discourteous, old

man," he said, "but would you mind very much sleeping in the pig byre? You can keep quite warm there, and there are secret matters I wish to discuss."

"Be not wroth, my lord, that I have given this man hospitality," said Eumaeus. "He claims to have met your father once. A pitiful beggar's tale, no doubt, but it earned him a meal and a bed."

"Met my father? Where? When? Speak!"

But at the word "father," Ulysses could not endure it any longer. The voice of the young man saying that word destroyed all his strategies. The amazed Eumaeus saw the old beggar leap from his stool, lose his feebleness, grow wider, taller, and open his arms and draw the young man to him in a great bear hug.

"Dearest son," said the stranger, his voice broken with tears. "I am your father, Ulysses."

Telemachus thought he was being attacked, and tensed his muscles, ready to battle for his life. But when he heard these words and felt the old man's tears burning against his face, then his marrow melted, and he laid his head on his father's shoulder and wept.

Nor could the honest old swineherd say anything; his throat was choked with tears, too. Ulysses went to Eumaeus and embraced him, saying, "Faithful old friend, you have served me well. And if tomorrow brings victory, you will be well rewarded."

Then he turned to his son, and said, "The goddess herself must have led you here tonight. Now I can complete my plan. Tomorrow we strike our enemies."

"Tomorrow? Two men against a hundred? These are heavy odds, even for Ulysses."

"Not two men—four. There is Eumaeus here, who wields a good cudgel. There is the neatherd whom we can count on. And, no doubt, at the castle itself we will find a few more faithful servants. But it is not a question of numbers. We shall have surprise on our side. They think I am dead, remember, and that you are helpless. Now, this is the plan. You must go there in the morning, Telemachus, pretending great woe. Tell them you have learned on your journey that I am indeed dead, and that now you must advise your mother to take one of them in marriage. This will keep them from attacking you—for a while anyway—and will give us the time we need. I shall come at dusk, just before the feasting begins."

"What of my mother? Shall I tell her that you are alive?"

"By no means."

"It is cruel not to."

"It will prove a kindness later. Bid her dress in her finest garments, and anoint herself, and be as pleasant as she can to the suitors, for this will help disarm them. Understand?"

"I understand."

"Now, mark this well. You will see me being insulted, humiliated, beaten perhaps. Do not lose your temper and be drawn into a quarrel before we are ready to fight. For I must provoke the suitors to test their mettle, and see where we should strike first."

Telemachus knelt in the firelight, and said, "Sire, I shall do as you bid. I don't see how we can overcome a hundred strong men, but to die fighting at your side will be a greater glory than anything a long life can bestow.

Thank you, Father, for giving me this chance to share your fortune."

"You are my true son," said Ulysses, embracing the boy tenderly. "The words you have just spoken make up for the twenty years of you I have missed."

Eumaeus banked the fire, and they all lay down to sleep.

Ulysses came to the castle at dusk the next day and followed Eumaeus into the great banquet hall which was thronged with suitors. He humped along behind the swineherd, huddling his shoulders, and limping. The first thing he saw was a dog lying near a bench. By its curious golden color he recognized it as his own favorite hunting hound, Argo. It was twenty-one years old, incredibly old for a dog, and it was crippled and blind and full of fleas. But Telemachus had not allowed it to be killed because it had been his father's.

As Ulysses approached, the dog's raw stump of a tail began to thump joyously upon the floor. The tattered old ears raised. The hound staggered to his feet, let out one wild bark of welcome and leaped toward the beggar. Ulysses caught him in his arms. The dog licked his face, shivered, and died. Ulysses stood there holding the dead dog.

Then Antinous, one of the most arrogant of the suitors, who fancied himself a great jokester, strode up and said, "What are you going to do with that dead dog, man, eat him? Things aren't that bad. We have a few scraps to spare, even for a scurvy old wretch like you."

Ulysses said, "Thank you, master. I am grateful for your courtesy. I come from Crete, and—"

"Shut up!" said Antinous. "Don't tell me any sad stories. Now take that thing out and bury it."

"Yes, gracious sir. And I hope I have the honor of performing a like service for you one day."

"Oho," cried Antinous. "The churl has a tongue in his head. Well, well. . . . "

He seized a footstool and smashed it over Ulysses' back. Telemachus sprang forward, blazing with anger, but Eumaeus caught his arm.

"No," he whispered. "Hold your peace."

Ulysses bowed to Antinous, and said, "Forgive me, master. I meant but a jest. I go to bury the dog."

As soon as he left the room, they forgot all about him. They were agog with excitement about the news told by Telemachus, that Ulysses' death had been confirmed, and that Penelope would now choose one of them to wed. They crowded about Telemachus, shouting questions.

He said, "Gently, friends, gently. My mother will announce her choice during the course of the night. But first she desires that you feast and make merry."

The young men raised a great shout of joy, and the feasting began. Ulysses returned and went the round of the suitors, begging scraps of food. Finally he squatted near Eurymachus, a fierce young fellow whom he recognized to be their leader. Eurymachus scowled at him, but said nothing.

Into the banquet hall strode another beggar—a giant shaggy man. He was a former smith who had decided that it was easier to beg than to work at the forge. He was well liked by the suitors because he wheedled and flattered them, and ran their errands. He swaggered over to Ulysses and grasped him by the throat.

"Get out of here, you miserable cur," he said. "Any begging around here to do, I'll do it. I, Iros."

He raised his huge meaty fist and slammed it down toward Ulysses' head. But Ulysses, without thinking, butted the man in the stomach, knocking him back against the wall.

"Look at that," cried Eurymachus. "The old souse has a head like a goat. For shame, Iros, you ought to be able to squash him with your thumb."

"Exactly what I intend to do," said Iros, advancing on Ulysses.

"A fight! A fight!" cried the suitors. "A beggar-bout. Good sport."

They crowded around the beggars, leaving just space enough for them to move.

Ulysses thought quickly. He could not risk revealing himself for what he was, yet he had to get rid of the fellow. So he shrank into his rags, as though fearful, allowing Iros to approach. Then, as the great hands were reaching for him and the suitors were cheering and jeering, he swung his right arm, trying to measure the force of the blow exactly. His fist landed on the smith's chin. The suitors heard a dry cracking sound, as when you snap a chicken bone between your fingers, and they knew that their man's jaw was broken. He fell to the floor, unconscious, blood streaming from mouth and nose. Ulysses stooped and hoisted him over his shoulder and marched out of the banquet room, saying, "I'd better let him bleed outside. It will be less unpleasant for you gentlemen."

He draped the big man over a stile, and came back.

"Well struck, old bones," said Eurymachus. "You fight well for a beggar."

"A beggar?" said Ulysses. "What is a beggar, after all? One who asks for what he has not earned, who eats others' food, uses their goods? Is this not true? If so, young sir, I think you could become a member of our guild tomorrow."

Eurymachus carefully wiped the knife which he had been using to cut his meat, and held the point to Ulysses' throat.

"Your victory over that other piece of vermin seems to have given you big ideas," he said. "Let me warn you, old fool, if you say one word more to me that I find unfitting, I will cut you up into little pieces and feed you to the dogs. Do you understand?"

"I understand, master," said Ulysses. "I meant but a jest."

"The next jest will be your last," growled Eurymachus.

Telemachus stepped between them and said, "Beggar, come with me to my mother. She has heard that you are a voyager, and would question you about the places you have seen."

"What?" cried Eurymachus. "Take this stinking bundle of rags to your mother? She will have to burn incense for hours to remove the stench."

"You forget yourself, sir," said Telemachus. "You have not yet been accepted by my mother. She is still free to choose her own company."

Eurymachus played with his knife, glaring at Telemachus. He was angry enough to kill, but he did not wish to lose his chance with

Penelope by stabbing her son. So he stepped aside, and let Telemachus lead the old beggar out of the hall.

"You have done well," whispered Ulysses. "Another second and I would have been at the cur's throat, and we would have been fighting before we were ready. Besides, it is time I spoke to your mother. She enters our plans now."

When he was alone with Penelope, he sat with his face lowered. He did not wish to look at her. For her presence set up a great shuddering tenderness inside him, and he knew that he had to keep himself hard and cruel for the work that lay ahead.

"In this chamber, you are not a beggar, you are a guest," said Penelope. "So take your comfort, please. Be at ease here with me, and tell me your tidings. I understand you met my husband Ulysses once upon your voyages."

"Beautiful queen," said Ulysses. "I knew him well. Better than I have admitted. I am a Cretan. I was a soldier. When the war with Troy started I went as part of a free-booting band to sell our swords to the highest bidder. We took service with your husband, Ulysses, and I fought under his banner for many years. Now his deeds before Troy have become famous in the time that has passed since the city was destroyed. Bards sing them from court to court all over the lands of the Middle Sea. Let me tell you a little story, though, that has never been told.

"I lay with him in that famous wooden horse, you know. We crouched in the belly of the horse which was dragged into Troy and set before the altar as an offering to the gods. The Trojans were crowding around, looking at this marvelous wooden beast, wondering at it, for such a thing had never been seen. But Queen Helen knew the truth somehow and, being a mischief-loving lady always, tapped on the belly of the horse, imitating the voices of the heroes' wives. She did it so cunningly that they could have sworn they heard their own wives calling to them, and were about to leap out of the horse too soon, which would have been death.

"Now, Helen saved your voice till last. And when she imitated it, I heard Ulysses groan, felt him tremble. He alone was clever enough to know it was a trick, but your voice, even mimicked, struck him to the heart. And he had to mask his distress, and use all his force and authority to keep the others quiet. A tiny incident, madame, but it showed me how much he loved you."

Penelope said, "Truly, this is a story never told. And yet I think that of all the mighty deeds that are sung, I like this one best."

Her face was wet with tears. She took a bracelet from her wrist and threw it to him, saying, "Here is a gift. Small payment for such a tale."

"Thank you, Queen," said Ulysses. "My path crossed your husband's once again. My ship sailed past the Island of the Dawn. We had run out of water and were suffering from thirst, and there we saw a marvelous thing: A fountain of water springing out of the sea, pluming, and curling upon itself. We tasted it, and it was fresh, and we filled our water barrels. When I told about this in the next port, I learned how such a wonder had come to be. The enchantress, Circe, most beautiful of the daughters of the gods, had loved your husband and sought to keep him with her.

But he told her that he must return to his wife, Penelope. After he left, she wept such tears of love as burned the salt out of the sea and turned it into a fountain of pure water."

Penelope took a necklace from her neck, and said, "I liked the first story better, but this is lovely, too."

Ulysses said. "Thank you, Queen. I have one thing more to tell. Your husband and I were talking one time around the watch fire on a night between battles, and he spoke, as soldiers speak, of home. He said that by the odds of war, he would probably leave you a widow. And, since you were beautiful, you would have many suitors, and would be hard put to decide. Then he said, 'I wish I could send her this advice: Let her take a man who can bend my bow. For that man alone will be strong enough to serve her as husband, and Ithaca as king.' "

"Did he say that—truly?"

"Truly."

"How can I ask them to try the bow? They will jeer at me. They may feel offended, and do terrible things."

"Disguise your intention. Tell them you cannot decide among such handsome charming suitors. And so you will let their own skill decide. They are to hold an archery contest, using the great bow of Ulysses, and he who shoots best to the mark will win you as wife. They cannot refuse such a challenge; their pride will not permit them to. Now, good night, lady. Thank you for your sweet company. I shall see you, perchance, when the bow is bent."

"Good night, old wanderer," said Penelope. "I shall never forget the comfort you have brought me."

As Ulysses was making his way through the dark hallway, something clutched his arm and hissed at him.

"Ulysses . . . Ulysses . . . My master, my king . . . my baby . . . my lord . . ."

He bent his head and saw that it was an old woman, and recognized his nurse, Eurycleia, who had known him from the day he was born, and who had tended him through his childhood.

"Dear little king," she wept. "You're back . . . you're back. I knew you would come. I told them you would."

Very gently he put his hand over her mouth, and whispered, "Silence. . . . No one must know, not even the queen. They will kill me if they find out. Silence . . . silence . . ."

She nodded quickly, smiling with her sunken mouth, and shuffled away.

Ulysses lurked outside the banquet hall until he heard a great roar from the suitors, and knew that Penelope had come among them. He listened outside and heard her announce that she would choose the man, who, using her husband's great bow, would shoot best to the mark. He heard young men break into wild cheers. Then he hid himself as Telemachus, leading the suitors into the courtyard, began to set out torches for the shooting. Then it was that he slipped unnoticed into the castle and went to the armory where the weapons were kept. He put on a breastplate, and arranged his rags over it so that he looked as he had before. Then he went out into the courtyard.

All was ready for the contest. An avenue of torches burned, making it bright as day. In the path of light stood a row of battle-axes driven into the earth, their rings aligned. Each archer would attempt to shoot through those rings. Until now only Ulysses himself had been able to send an arrow through all twelve axe-rings.

Now, Penelope, followed by her servants, came down the stone steps carrying the great bow. She handed it to Telemachus, saying, "You, son, will see that the rules are observed." Then, standing tall and beautiful in the torchlight, she said, "I have given my word to choose as husband him who best shoots to the mark, using this bow. I shall retire to my chamber now, as is fitting, and my son will bring me the name of my next husband. Now, may the gods reward you according to your deserts."

She turned and went back into the castle. The noise fell. The young men grew very serious as they examined the great bow. It was larger than any they had ever seen, made of dark polished wood, stiffened by rhinoceros horn, and bound at the tips by golden wire. Its arrows were held in a bull-hide quiver; their shafts were of polished ash, their heads of copper, and they were tailed with hawk feathers.

Ulysses squatted in the shadows and watched the suitors as they crowded around Telemachus, who was speaking.

"Who goes first? Will you try, sir?"

Telemachus handed the bow to a prince of Samos, a tall brawny man, and a skilled archer. He grasped the bow in his left hand and the dangling cord in his right, and tugged at the cord in the swift sure movement that is used to string a bow. But it did not bend. He could not make the cord reach from one end to the other. He put one end of the bow on the ground and grasped the other end and put forth all his strength. His back muscles glistened like oil in the torchlight. The bow bent a bit under the enormous pressure, and a low sighing sound came from the crowd, but when he tugged on the cord, the bow twisted in his hand as if it were a serpent, and leaped free. He staggered, and almost fell. An uneasy laugh arose. He looked wildly about, then stomped away, weeping with rage.

Telemachus picked up the bow, and said, "Next."

One by one they came; one by one they fell back. Not one of them could bend the bow. Finally, all had tried but Antinous and Eurymachus. Now Antinous was holding the bow.

He shook his head, and said, "It is too stiff; it cannot be bent. It has not been used for twenty years. It must be rubbed with tallow, and set by the fire to soften."

"Very well," said Telemachus.

He bade a servant rub the bow with tallow and set it near the fire. Ulysses kept out of sight. As they were waiting, Telemachus had a serving girl pass out horns of wine to the suitors. The men drank thirstily, but there was no laughter. They were sullen. Their hearts were ashen with hatred; they did not believe the bow could be softened. And Ulysses heard them muttering to each other that the whole thing was a trick.

Finally, Antinous called for the bow. He tried to string it. He could not.

"It cannot be done," he cried.

"No," said Eurymachus. "It cannot be done. I will not even try. This is a trick, another miserable deceitful trick. Shroud that is never woven, bow that cannot be bent, there is no end to this widow's cunning. I tell you she is making fools of us. She will not be taken unless she be taken by force."

A great shouting and clamor arose. The suitors pressed close about Telemachus, hemming him in so tightly he could not draw his sword.

"Stop!" shouted Ulysses.

He cried it with all his force, in the great bellowing clanging battle voice that had rung over spear shock and clash of sword to reach the ears of his men on so many fields before Troy. His great shout quelled the clamor. The amazed suitors turned to see the old beggar stride out of the shadows into the torchlight. He came among them, and grasped the bow, and said, "I pray you, sirs, let me try."

Antinous howled like a wolf and sprang toward Ulysses with drawn sword. But Telemachus stepped between them, and shoved Antinous back.

"My mother watches from her chamber window," he said. "Shall she see you as cowards, afraid to let an old beggar try what you cannot do? Do you think she would take any of you then?"

"Yes, let him try," said Eurymachus. "Let the cur have one last moment in which he pretends to be a man. And when he fails, as fail he must, then we'll chop his arms off at the shoulders so that he will never again be tempted to draw bow with his betters."

"Stand back," cried Telemachus. "Let him try."

The suitors fell back, their swords still drawn. Ulysses held the bow. He turned it lightly in his hands, delicately, tenderly, like a bard tuning his lyre. Then he took the cord and strung the bow with a quick turn of his wrist, and as the suitors watched, astounded, he held the bow from him and plucked the cord, making a deep vibrating harp note. Dumbfounded, they saw him reach into the quiver, draw forth an arrow, notch it, then bend the bow easily, powerfully, until the arrowhead rested in the circle of his fingers, just clearing the polished curve of the bow.

He stood there for a second, narrowing his eyes at the mark, then let the arrow fly. The cord twanged, the arrow sang through the air, and passed through the axe-rings, all twelve of them.

Then, paralyzed by amazement, they saw him calmly sling the quiver over his shoulder, and straighten up so that his breastplate gleamed through the rags. He stood tall and, throwing back his head, spoke to the heavens:

"So the dread ordeal ends, and I come to claim my own. Apollo, dear lord of the silver bow, archer-god, help me now to hit a mark no man has hit before."

"It is he!" cried Antinous. "Ulysses!"

He died, shouting. For Ulysses had notched another arrow, and this one caught Antinous full in the throat. He fell, spouting blood.

No suitor moved. They looked at the twitching body that had been Antinous, and felt a sick fear, as if Apollo himself had come to loose his silver shaft among them.

Eurymachus found his tongue, and cried, "Pardon us, great Ulysses. We could not know you had returned. If we have done you

Ulysses and Penelope.
Melian terracotta relief, 460–
450 B.C. The Louvre, Paris.
Photo by Erich Lessing

evil, we will repay you, but hold your hand."

"Too late," said Ulysses. "Your evil can be repaid only by death. Now fight, or flee."

Then Eurymachus raised his sword and called to the suitors, "Up, men! Rouse yourselves, or he will kill us all as we stand here. Let us kill him first."

And he rushed toward Ulysses, and fell immediately with an arrow through his chest. But he had roused them out of their torpor. They knew now that they must fight for their lives, and they charged across the yard toward Ulysses in a great half-circle.

Ulysses retreated slowly, filling the air

with arrows, dropping a suitor with each shaft. But still they kept coming through the heaped dead. Now he darted backward suddenly, followed by Telemachus and Eumaeus, the swineherd, who had been protecting him with their shields. They ran into the dining hall and slammed the great portal, which immediately began to shake under the axe blows of the suitors.

"Overturn the benches," cried Ulysses. "Make a barricade."

The neatherd had joined them. And now Telemachus and the two men overturned the heavy wooden benches, making a barricade. They stood behind the wall of benches and watched the huge door splintering.

It fell. The suitors poured through. Now Ulysses shot the rest of his arrows so quickly that the dead bodies piled up in the doorway making a wall of flesh through which the suitors had to push their way.

His quiver was empty. Ulysses cast the bow aside, and took two javelins. But he did not throw. For the suitors were still too far away, and he had to be sure of killing each time he threw.

A suitor named Agelaus had taken charge now, and he motioned to his men, "Let fly your spears—first you, then you, then the rest. And after each cast of spears let us move closer to the benches."

The long spears hurtled past the rampart. One grazed Telemachus's shoulder, drawing blood. And Ulysses, seeing the blood of his son, lost the battle-coldness for which he was famous among warriors. For the first time he felt the wild hot curdling rage rising in him like wine, casting a mist of blood before his eyes. Without making a decision to move, he felt his legs carrying him toward the great hearth. There he knelt, and grasped the ring of the firestone—a huge slab of rock, large enough for a roasting ox. The suitors, charging toward the wall of benches, saw him rise like a vision of the past, like some Titan in the War of the Gods holding an enormous slab of rock over his head.

They saw their danger and tried to draw back, tried to scatter. But Ulysses had hurled the slab. It fell among the suitors and crushed them like beetles in their frail armor.

Only four of the suitors were left alive. Now Ulysses and Telemachus and the two servants were upon them—one to each and each killed his man. Then Ulysses and Telemachus raised a wild exultant yell. Dappled with blood, they turned to each other, and Ulysses embraced his son.

"Well struck," he said. Then, to Eumaeus, "Thank you, good friend. Now go tell your queen, Penelope, that the contest has been decided, and the winner claims her hand."

"Father," said Telemachus. "When I reach my full strength, shall I be able to bend the great bow?"

"Yes," said Ulysses. "I promise you. I will teach you everything you have to know. I have come home."

Penelope heard her son shouting. "Mother! Mother! It's Father! He's come home!"

Slowly she descended the great stairway and entered the throne-room. She looked at the man who had slain her suitors.

He arose and said, "I greet you, Penelope. I am Ulysses, your husband."

Comment

Uncovering the Real Troy

One morning in 1873, Heinrich Schliemann (shlē′män) was excavating a large mound of earth and stone called Hissarlik (hi sär lik′) in Turkey. As he carefully lifted a large copper shield he had just unearthed, he saw something gleaming underneath. He called his wife, Sophia, who was directing her own digging crew nearby. She joined him in the twenty-eight-foot trench, and together they lifted out piece after piece of gold and silver jewelry, dishes, and household articles, in addition to pottery, tools, and weapons. To Heinrich Schliemann, this breathtaking find offered proof that he had discovered Troy.

About 800 B.C. the Greek poet Homer wrote the two book-length poems called the *Iliad* (il′ē əd), the story of the Trojan War, and the *Odyssey* (od′ə sē), of which *The Adventures of Ulysses* is a retelling. For centuries these poems have been read for enjoyment and for insight into ancient times. But few people seriously considered the poems as *history*. Some claimed that Homer never existed—that the poems were really collections of songs made by many poets over the years.

Heinrich Schliemann first heard the stories as told by his father in their village in Germany. The tales of adventure in ancient Greece inflamed his imagination. Young Schliemann decided for himself that they were not just fanciful tales of a heroic age, but that they were true—and that he was going to be the one to locate the long-lost city of Troy.

Schliemann did not receive training as an archaeologist. Instead, he worked at a variety of jobs in Germany, Holland, Russia, and the United States, learning ten languages and building a fortune. At the age of forty-seven, with money to finance his own expeditions, he went to Greece to start digging, guided by his copy of the *Iliad*. There he met and married Sophia.

When the Schliemanns first announced their discovery of the city of Troy, professional archaeologists became angry. For Schliemann, in his eagerness to find treasures, had gone about his digging in a careless and unscientific way. He had destroyed layers of evidence not as spectacular as gold but every bit as important to the science of archaeology.

Later expeditions uncovered not one, but nine separate cities on the same spot. Troy had been destroyed and rebuilt on its own ruins many times, from 3000 B.C. to A.D. 400. Troy VII, the seventh layer from the bottom, was the Troy of Homer's heroes.

The Schliemanns and others after them excavated many other sites associated with ancient Greece. Such discoveries tell us a great deal about people who lived so long ago. Their weapons, tools, and household utensils fill in details of their lives, details which agree largely with Homer's descriptions, proving that the poet was far more accurate than supposed.

THINK AND DISCUSS
Understanding
1. What does Ulysses learn from Eumaeus about conditions at the castle?
2. What does Athene do to assist Telemachus?
3. What part does Telemachus play in Ulysses' plan to get rid of his enemies?
4. How does Penelope participate unknowingly in furthering the plan?
5. What final act in his plan does Ulysses keep for himself?

Analyzing
6. Upon arriving in Ithaca, why does Ulysses disguise himself as a beggar?
7. Eurymachus offers to repay whatever evil the suitors had done Ulysses. Would acceptance of this offer be consistent with what you know of Ulysses' character? Explain.
8. Does *The Adventures of Ulysses* have a happy ending? Explain.

Extending
9. Can individuals be heroic without risking their lives? Explain.
10. If Ulysses were to be suddenly transported from ancient Ithaca to a modern American city, what might he find most frightening? most puzzling? most amusing? most familiar?

READING LITERATURE SKILLFULLY
Cause/Effect Relationships
Events in literature occur for reasons. Ulysses is not able to sail directly to Ithaca because he offends Poseidon by blinding the god's son Polyphemus. Ulysses' remaining crewmen die because they kill and eat cattle of the Sun God. Just as events occur for reasons, characters behave as they do for reasons. Calypso instructs the magic log not to show Ulysses scenes of Ithaca because she wants him to forget his wife and home. Ino gives Ulysses her veil because she hates Poseidon for an injury he has done her.

To test your understanding of the causes for characters' actions, answer the following questions.

1. Why does Poseidon turn Alcinous's men and ship to stone?
2. Why is Telemachus's ship not attacked by the suitors?
3. Why does Ulysses reveal himself to Telemachus?
4. Why does Eurymachus allow Ulysses to visit Penelope?
5. Why does Ulysses throw the firestone at the remaining suitors?

COMPOSITION
Writing Dialogue

Imagine the conversation between Penelope and Ulysses immediately after the aging warrior greets his wife. Write two to three minutes of dialogue between the two. First make notes on possible topics of their conversation: how Penelope has spent her time in his absence, what adventures Ulysses has undergone, and how husband and wife look to each other after twenty years. Try to keep the tone of the dialogue consistent with what you know about the characters.

Before you begin to write, you will want to read Lesson 8 in the Writer's Handbook, "Writing Dialogue."

Comparing or Contrasting

Write two to four paragraphs for your classmates in which you compare or contrast *The Adventures of Ulysses* to *The Adventures of Tom Sawyer, Treasure Island,* or some other novel of adventure you have read. To focus your paper, you will want to concentrate on only one of the following: how the major characters, the adventures, or the settings are alike or different in the two selections. For example, your opening sentence might be "Tom Sawyer and Ulysses are quite unlike." You might then proceed to discuss the differences in the characters' ages and physical appearances, the differences in the way they confront problems, and the differences in their values. On the other hand, if you wrote "Tom Sawyer and Ulysses have much in common," you might wish to discuss how each is loyal to his companions and how each uses intelligence and cunning to get himself out of difficulties.

Before you begin to write, you will want to consult Lesson 4 in the Writer's Handbook, "Writing to Compare and Contrast."

ENRICHMENT
Interviewing Ulysses

Assume that you are the host of a radio talk show and that Ulysses is to be your guest. First prepare a paragraph in which you introduce the hero to listeners by providing them with interesting biographical information. Then compose six to ten questions that you intend to ask your guest during the course of the interview. After you have finished writing, pair up with a classmate. One of you will assume the role of Ulysses and be responsible for answering the other's questions. When you finish, reverse roles for a second interview.

If tape recorders are available, you may wish to record the interviews for later playback.

THINKING CRITICALLY
ABOUT LITERATURE

UNIT 8 EPIC The Adventures of Ulysses

■ CONCEPT REVIEW

Notice how the literary terms you have reviewed in this unit can be applied with the two poems. The notes in the margins and the questions that follow the poems are designed to help you think critically about your reading. Page numbers in the notes refer to a review. A more complete explanation and examples are in the Handbook of Literary Terms.

Penelope

Dorothy Parker

In the pathway of the sun,
   In the footsteps of the breeze,
Where the world and sky are one,
   He shall ride the silver seas,
5   He shall cut the glittering wave.
I shall sit at home, and rock;
Rise, to heed a neighbor's knock;
Brew my tea, and snip my thread;
Bleach the linen for my bed.
10   They will call him brave.

■ **Figurative language** (page 566): The breeze can literally take footsteps.
■ **Imagery** (page 612): Notice the visual image in line 4.

■ Notice the images that appeal to the senses of sound and taste in lines 7 and 8.

An Ancient Gesture

Edna St. Vincent Millay

I thought, as I wiped my eyes on the corner of my apron:
Penelope did this too.
And more than once: you can't keep weaving all day
And undoing it all through the night;
5 Your arms get tired, and the back of your neck gets tight;
And along towards morning, when you think it will never be light,
And your husband has been gone, and you don't know where,
    for years,
Suddenly you burst into tears;
There is simply nothing else to do.

10 And I thought, as I wiped my eyes on the corner of my apron:
This is an ancient gesture, authentic, antique,
In the very best tradition, classic, Greek;
Ulysses did this too.
But only as a gesture,—a gesture which implied
15 To the assembled throng that he was much too moved to speak.
He learned it from Penelope. . . .
Penelope, who really cried.

■ **Imagery** (page 612):
Note the visual image.

■ **Imagery:** The words
help you feel as Penelope
did.

■ **authentic:** worthy of
acceptance, trust, or belief

■ **implied:** The speaker
suggests that Ulysses'
actions are not honest.
■ Notice the speaker's
comparison of Ulysses and
Penelope.

From *Collected Poems*, Harper & Row. Copyright 1954 by Norma Millay Ellis.

THINK AND DISCUSS
Understanding
1. How will the speaker in "Penelope" pass the time?
2. In "An Ancient Gesture," what has the speaker been doing as the poem begins?
3. Who else in the poem did what the speaker has been doing?

Analyzing
4. In the first poem, how does Penelope compare Ulysses' experiences with her own?
5. In "An Ancient Gesture" what might the references to "weaving" and "undoing" represent beyond the actual act of weaving and unraveling?

6. Contrast the way Ulysses is reported to behave before the "assembled throng" with the way he behaves before Alcinous's court as Nausicaa sings of his deeds. (pages 610–611)

Extending

7. Why do you think Ulysses' heroic deeds are not mentioned in either poem?

REVIEWING LITERARY TERMS
Imagery

1. In line 9 of "Penelope," to what sense does the image appeal?

2. What senses are appealed to in line 8 of "An Ancient Gesture"?

3. To what sense do the words in line 10 appeal?

Figurative Language

4. What two things are compared in line 3 of "Penelope"?

■ CONTENT REVIEW
THINKING SKILLS
Classifying

1. Head two columns *Caused by Ulysses or His Men* and *Caused by a God or Goddess*. Write at least five events from *The Adventures of Ulysses* under each heading. For example, the battle with the Ciconians was caused by Ulysses and his men.

Generalizing

2. An *epic* may be defined as a "story or series of events telling the adventures of a great hero." Using specific examples, tell why *The Adventures of Ulysses* is considered an epic.

3. Recall Ulysses' contests with the young men at Alcinous's court and with Penelope's suitors. How important does

athletic skill seem to have been in ancient Greece?

Synthesizing

4. One interesting characteristic of the gods in the Greek myths is that they have human favorites whom they help and defend against other gods. Which of the Greek gods or goddesses would you most like to have on your side? Identify and explain your choice. Be sure to tell what powers interested you and what aid you would request.

Evaluating

5. The Greeks considered Ulysses a hero. Do you? Explain.

■ COMPOSITION REVIEW
Supporting an Idea

Consider Penelope and Ulysses as they are portrayed in *The Adventures of Ulysses* and the two poems. Do you think that Penelope, in her own way, was as brave as Ulysses, or was Ulysses' bravery far greater? Write a paragraph or two in which you tell who you think was the braver of the two. Give reasons to support your idea.

Reviewing Writer's Craft: Use Precise, Active Verbs

In this unit you have seen how important it is to use precise, active verbs in your writing. Now **try your hand** by writing a brief adventure story. Choose something exciting that has happened to you, or something about which you have read in a newspaper account. Keep your story moving by using active verbs. After you have written a first draft, go back and circle each verb. Can you think of even better ones for your revised story?

Will Barnet, *Introspection—Maine*, 1980, Private Collection

HANDBOOK OF LITERARY TERMS

■ ALLITERATION

When I was down beside the sea
A wooden spade they gave to me
   To dig the sandy shore.

Robert Louis Stevenson
from "At the Sea-Side"

What is the most common sound in the lines above? If you said *s*, you were correct. *Alliteration*, the repetition of consonant sounds, is common in everyday language as well as in poetry. "Safe and sound," "grand and glorious," and "fancy free" are everyday expressions.

Usually, the repeated or alliterative sounds occur at the beginnings of words, but sometimes they are found within words as well, as is the *s* sound in the word *beside* at the top of the page. Note the repetition of *l* in these lines:

I should *l*ike to rise and go
Where the go*l*den app*l*es grow;—
Where be*l*ow another sky
Parrot is*l*ands anchored *l*ie. . . .

Robert Louis Stevenson
from "Travel"

Alliteration in poetry helps create melody, sounds that are pleasant to hear. It can also help call attention to important words.

*P*raise ye the Lord:
For it is *g*ood to sing *p*raises unto our *G*od;
For it is *p*leasant; and *p*raise is comely.
*G*reat is our Lord, and of *g*reat power:

Psalm 147

Alliteration should always be appropriate to the meaning of a poem—the sounds should echo the sense. What sort of mood do the repeated sounds create here? Does the sound echo the sense?

Slowly

Slowly the tide creeps up the sand,
Slowly the shadows cross the land.
Slowly the cart-horse pulls his mile,
Slowly the old man mounts the stile.

5 Slowly the hands move round the clock,
Slowly the dew dries on the dock.
Slow is the snail—but slowest of all
The green moss spreads on the old
   brick wall.

James Reeves

■ ALLITERATION
(ə lit′ə rā′shən)

Repeated consonant sounds occurring at the beginning of words or within words. Alliteration is used to create melody, establish mood, and call attention to important words.

"Slowly" from *The Wandering Moon* by James Reeves. Copyright © by James Reeves. Reprinted by permission of The James Reeves Estate.

■ Apply to **Sarah Cynthia Sylvia Stout** on page 302.

■ CHARACTERIZATION

An author can use several methods to create a fictitious character, and the better an author is at using these techniques, the more a character comes alive. Read the lines below. These lines and the examples that follow are from *National Velvet* by Enid Bagnold.

> Velvet was fourteen. Velvet had short pale hair, large, protruding teeth, a sweet smile, and a mouthful of metal.

What do you know about Velvet from this passage? If you were an artist, what would you include in a drawing of her? What else might you want to know?

Obviously this is only a physical description of Velvet, and it is one method by which authors tell you what a character is like.

Another method by which authors create characters is that of having the characters speak. In the passage below, Velvet is walking beside an elderly neighbor.

> . . . They walked on again, he in his black hat and black waistcoat and shirt-sleeves.
>
> "Going to the stables," said he. "Why, are you fond of horses?"
>
> There was something about him that made Velvet feel he was going to say good-bye to her. She fancied he was going to be carried up to heaven like Elisha.[1]
>
> "Horses," he said. "Did you say you had horses?"
>
> "Only an old pony, sir."
>
> "All my life I've had horses. Stables full of them. You like 'em?"
>
> "I've seen your chestnut," said Velvet. "Sir Pericles. I seen him jump."

> "I wish he was yours, then," said the old gentleman, suddenly and heartily. "You said you rode?"
>
> "We've on'y got Miss Ada. The pony. She's old."
>
> "Huh!"
>
> "Not so much *old,*" said Velvet hurriedly. "She's obstinate."
>
> He stopped again.
>
> "Would you tell me what you want most in the world? . . . would you tell me that?"
>
> He was looking at her.
>
> "Horses," she said, "sir."
>
> "To ride on? To own for yourself?"
>
> He was still looking at her, as though he expected more.
>
> "I tell myself stories about horses," she went on, desperately fishing at her shy desires. "Then I can dream about them. Now I dream about them every night. I want to be a famous rider; I should like to carry dispatches. I should like to get a first at Olympia; I should like to ride in a great race; I should like to have so many horses that I could walk down between the two rows of loose boxes and ride what I chose. I would have them all under fifteen hands. I like chestnuts best, but bays are lovely too. . . ."
>
> She ran out the words and caught her breath and stopped.

What does this excerpt reveal about Velvet? Is she tactful? polite? ambitious? imaginative? Refer to lines or words in the example to support your answers. In what manner do you suppose Velvet speaks her last long speech about horses? Do you

---

1. *Elisha* (i lī′shə), probably a reference to Elijah (i lī′jə), Hebrew prophet of the 800s B.C. who was carried up in a whirlwind to heaven (2 Kings 2:11).

HANDBOOK OF LITERARY TERMS

think she is looking at the old gentleman when she speaks these lines? Is there any physical description of Velvet here? of the old man?

The next passage shows another technique an author uses to create a character.

. . . They all went up to the field to try the horses.

Velvet mounted Sir Pericles. She had ridden Miss Ada for eight years, hopped her over bits of brushwood and gorse-bushes, and trotted her round at the local gymkhana.[2] Once she had ridden a black pony belonging to the farmer at Pendean. She had a natural seat, and her bony hands gathered up the reins in a tender way. But she had never yet felt reins that had a trained mouth at the end of them, and, as she cantered up the slope of the sunny field with the brow of the hill and the height of the sky in front of her, Sir Pericles taught her in three minutes what she had not known existed. Her scraggy, childish fingers obtained results at a pressure. The living canter bent to right or left at her touch. He handed her the glory of command.

When she slid to the ground by the side of the head groom she was speechless, and leant her forehead for a second on the horse's flank.

What does this excerpt describe? What information does it give about Velvet? How does this riding experience differ from a ride on Miss Ada?

Here the author has, for the most part, described Velvet's actions, both in the past and at the present, and you are able to come to several more conclusions about Velvet.

Sometimes an author reveals directly what a character is thinking, as in the passage that follows. Velvet's father has just protested the expenses required to feed and care for a group of horses.

. . . Velvet was conscious of her father's case. It was a good one. There was no benefit to him in the horses. The lovely creatures ate, and were sterile. They laboured not, and ate and ate, and lost their shoes. Velvet had no answers and no comfort to offer.

What is Velvet concerned about?

Finally, an author may tell about one character by showing you what another character thinks.

"If she were a boy . . ." he said longingly to himself. With that light body and grand heart he would get her into a racing stable. He knew of many up North. He had friends here and there. She'd be a great jockey some day. Fancy wasting those hands and that spirit and that light weight on a girl. "No more'n a skeleton," he said. "An' never will be, likely. She'd ride like a piece of lightning. No more weight'n a piece of lightning."

What additional things do you learn about Velvet? Is Velvet a likeable character? If you were drawing a picture of Velvet now, what things would you include?

■ CHARACTERIZATION

The methods an author uses to create a fictional person. An author may develop a character through describing the character's physical appearance, speech, actions, and inner thoughts or through revealing attitudes and reactions of other characters.

---

2. *gymkhana* (jim kä′nə), sports contest or meeting.

■ Apply to **Gentleman of Río en Medio** on page 37.

■ CONNOTATION/ DENOTATION

Emily walked to the desk which sat directly under a sign with the neatly printed words "Motorcoach Tours." She waited for the man sitting at the desk to look up. He smiled and asked, "May I help you?" Emily shyly gestured toward the sign.

"Excuse me," she began, "but what is a 'Motorcoach Tour'?" The man's eyebrows lifted.

"Well," he said, "it's a *bus* tour!"

Emily thought about his answer for a moment.

"Then," she murmured, "—can I ask a question? Why doesn't the sign say 'Bus Tours'?"

"Easy. More people like *motorcoach* tours."

"Are they different from bus tours?"

"Nope. We use the same buses," the man declared, "but people just won't buy tickets for *bus* tours the way they'll buy tickets for *motorcoach* tours!"

The words *bus* and *motorcoach* mean the same thing. The literal meaning of a word— the exact dictionary meaning—is called the *denotation* of the word. The man talking to Emily recognizes, however, that many words have *connotations*—emotional and cultural associations and added meanings that affect the way people respond to words.

Personal reactions to words are also called connotations. These are added meanings and associations that occur to individuals as they hear or read certain words. Write the words *homesick*, *breeze*, and *old*. After each, write the first word you associate with it. Chances are, you and your classmates will find that you wrote different words, because we all react in our own ways.

Think about the word *homesick*, for instance. Can you remember the first time you were homesick? Where were you? How old were you? Did you feel homesick for a long time? The interpretation you bring to a word like *homesick* is the connotation of the word.

Read the dictionary entry for *cat* below and then notice how the speaker in the poem expresses the connotations that a particular cat has for him.

cat (kat), *n.* a small, furry, four-footed, carnivorous mammal, often kept as a pet or for catching mice and rats.

What Could It Be?

I really do not like that cat;
I don't know why, perhaps it's that
She's vicious, cruel, rude, ungrateful,
Smelly, treacherous, and hateful,
5 Supercilious, stupid, eerie;
Thoroughly boring, dull, and dreary,
Scheming, cold, and unproductive,
Inconvenient and destructive—
But most, I've just a *feeling* that
10 I *really* do not like that cat!

William Cole

■ CONNOTATION/ DENOTATION

Connotation: **the associations and added meanings surrounding a word that are not part of its literal dictionary meaning.**
Denotation: **the exact dictionary meaning of a word.**

"What Could It Be?" From *A Book of Animal Poems* by William Cole. Copyright © 1973 by William Cole. Reprinted by permission of the author.

■ Apply to **Business** on page 288.

■ FIGURATIVE LANGUAGE

The hair on her head was dark brown streaked with gray. Her old fur hat was gray, and it clung to the back of her neck—a squirrel with its furry back bent almost double in an effort to hold on. Her blue raincoat hung nearly to the ground in front and was several inches shorter in the back. She carried a shopping bag in each hand. In that city neighborhood, she was a sign of spring. Like a battered crocus or a soot-sprinkled daffodil planted too near the sidewalk, she shrugged off the dirt and burst forth each year. But she was a thorny flower. And none ventured too near, for she mumbled as she trudged from trash basket to trash basket, and anybody—child or adult—who got too close was liable to be jabbed with words that stung like sharp, prickly spines.

In your own words, describe the person in the paragraph above. Is your retelling more or less interesting than the paragraph?

The author of the paragraph has combined ideas, images, and facts in such a way as to make it vivid and forceful. The descriptions are not to be taken literally. The old hat is not really a squirrel, the woman is not a thorny flower, and she did not literally jab people. The writer has used *figurative language* to make meaning more vivid and more interesting. Whenever we use words in nonliteral ways we are using *figures of speech*. Two things that seem unlike each other are compared in a figure of speech, and the reader suddenly sees similarities between them.

Appropriate figurative language has a quality of freshness about it. Poets, especially, use figurative language to suggest an idea in a few words.

Below are some excerpts. Read each one and then answer the questions.

I saw you toss the kites on high
And blow the birds about the sky;
And all around I heard you pass,
Like ladies' skirts across the grass—
5 O wind, a-blowing all day long,
   O wind, that sings so loud a song!

Robert Louis Stevenson
from "The Wind"

1. What human characteristics does the poet give the wind?
2. How do you know whether the wind is gentle or violent?

The moon, like to a silver bow
new-bent in heaven.

William Shakespeare
from *A Midsummer Night's Dream*

3. What two things are being compared?
4. Is the moon full?

Like a lobster boiled, the morn
From black to red began to burn.

Samuel Butler
from *Hudibras*

5. What kind of day is suggested?
6. Explain the meaning of the second line.

■ FIGURATIVE LANGUAGE

Language expanded beyond its ordinary literal meaning. It uses comparisons to achieve new effects, to provide fresh insights, or to express a relationship between things essentially unlike.

■ Apply to **Nancy** on page 343.

■ FLASHBACK

Below is part of a short story. As you read, pay particular attention to the order of events.

The day had been one of those unbearable ones, when every sound had set her teeth on edge like chalk creaking on a blackboard, when every word her father or mother said to her or did not say to her seemed an intentional injustice. And of course it would happen, at the end to such a day, that just as the sun went down back of the mountain and the long twilight began, she noticed that Rollie was not around.

Tense with exasperation—she would simply explode if Mother got going—she began to call him in a carefully casual tone: "Here Rollie! He-ere, boy! Want to go for a walk, Rollie?" Whistling to him cheerfully, her heart full of wrath at the way the world treated her, she made the rounds of his haunts; the corner of the woodshed, where he liked to curl up on the wool of Father's discarded old windbreaker; the hay barn, the cow barn, the sunny spot on the side porch—no Rollie.

Perhaps he had sneaked upstairs to lie on her bed where he was not supposed to go—not that *she* would have minded! That rule was a part of Mother's fussiness, part too of Mother's bossiness. It was *her* bed, wasn't it? But was she allowed the say-so about it? Not on your life. They told her she could have things the way she wanted in her own room, now she was in her teens, but—her heart raged against unfairness as she took the stairs stormily, two steps at a time, her pigtails flopping up and down on her back. If Rollie was on her bed, she was just going to let him stay right there, and Mother could shake her head and frown all she wanted to.

But he was not there. . . .

Before she would let her father and mother know she had lost sight of him, forgotten about him, she would be cut into little pieces. They would not scold her, she knew. They would do worse. They would look at her. And in their silence she would hear droning on reproachfully what they had repeated and repeated when the sweet, woolly collie-puppy had first been in her arms and she had been begging to keep him for her own.

How warm he had felt! Astonishing how warm and alive a puppy was compared to a doll! She had never liked her dolls much, after she had held Rollie, feeling him warm against her breast, warm and wriggling, bursting with life, reaching up to lick her face—he had loved her from that first instant. As he felt her arms around him, his beautiful eyes had melted in trusting sweetness. . . .

Even then, at the very minute when as a darling baby dog he was beginning to love her, her father and mother were saying, so cold, so reasonable—gosh! how she *hated* reasonableness!——"Now Peg, remember that, living where we do, with sheep on the farms around us, it is a serious responsibility to have a collie dog. If you keep him, you've got to be the one to take care of him. You'll have to be the one to train him to stay at home. We're too busy with you children to start bringing up a puppy, too." Rollie, nestling in her arms, let one hind leg drop awkwardly. It must be uncomfortable. She looked down at him tenderly, tucked his dangling leg up under him and gave him a hug. He laughed up in her face—he really did laugh, his mouth stretched wide in a cheerful grin.

All the time her parents kept hammering away: "If you want him, you can have him. But you must be responsible for him. If he gets to running

---

"The Apprentice" from *A Harvest of Stories* by Dorothy Canfield Fisher, copyright 1947 by Curtis Publishing Company; renewed © 1975 by Downe Publishing, Inc. Reprinted by permission of Harcourt Brace Jovanovich, Inc.

sheep, he'll just have to be shot, you know that."

And now, this afternoon, when he was six months old, tall, rangy, powerful, standing up far above her knee, nearly to her waist, she didn't know where he was. But of course he must be somewhere around. He always was. She composed her face to look natural and went downstairs to search the house.

Dorothy Canfield Fisher
from "The Apprentice"

Following is a list of events in the order they are mentioned in the excerpt above. Rearrange these items in the order in which they actually occurred.

a. Peg discovers that Rollie is missing.
b. Peg searches outside.
c. Peg looks in her bedroom for Rollie.
d. Peg thinks about how her parents will react to Rollie's absence.
e. Peg falls in love with the puppy and wants to keep it.
f. Peg's parents warn her of the responsibility of keeping a collie.
g. Peg continues to look for Rollie.

You have rearranged the events in *chronological order,* the order in which events occur in time. In the story, which events are *not* mentioned in chronological order?

A *flashback* is an interruption in the narrative to show a scene or scenes that occurred earlier. A flashback allows the author to include an incident from the past that helps a reader or viewer better understand events or personalities in the present.

1. Find the words or phrases in this excerpt that alert you to the beginning of the flashback.

2. What would happen if the flashback were simply removed?
3. If the author had not used a flashback, how might she have presented the same information to the reader?

Often an author wants a story to cover a limited span of time. A flashback may then be used to fill in background or to make the characters or the situation more understandable. In this selection, Peg's concern about Rollie's absence would not mean nearly so much if the reader were unaware of her parents' earlier warnings.

Instead of showing how Peg and her parents reacted to the puppy, the author might merely have said the following: "Six months earlier, Peg's parents had allowed her to keep Rollie, who was then a puppy. At that time, they warned her of the responsibility involved in keeping a collie in sheep country."

Although this statement provides the same information, it is not a flashback.

■ FLASHBACK

An interruption in the action of a story, play, or work of nonfiction to show an episode that happened at an earlier time. A flashback is used to provide background information necessary to understanding the characters or the plot.

■ Apply to **Last Cover** on page 392.

■ IMAGERY

When you consider what words suggest, you form pictures and sense impressions in your imagination. Such pictures or sense impressions are called *images*.

When writers present what can be seen, heard, touched, tasted, smelled, as well as what can be felt inside (joy, pain, fear), they are using images or *imagery*. Images help to create or re-create an experience so that readers can respond as participants in the event.

> The sun is up today. Water drips from the eaves of the house. Icicles melt into water and drip-drip from nine in the mornin' till three in the evenin'. White clouds scud the sky. Winter has started breakin' up. Warm thaw winds blow through the bare Kentucky trees. One can feel them, warm soft winds, winds that remind one of rain.
>
> *Jesse Stuart*
> **from "Dark Winter"**

1. What sounds are presented?
2. What visual images appear in the passage?
3. What image appeals to the sense of touch?

Good writers choose images with care and try to make those images as specific as possible. Consider the following lines, in which the writer describes a young girl's impressions of her first days in school.

> At last February came. She learned the secret behind the black iron fence, the tall stone walls. High windows laced with steel net. The big, dark basement with white circles painted on the black floors.

The long tables and the smell of vegetable soup as the women cooked for four hundred children. There were long corridors, as in a dream with a thousand doors, each door numbered. Room 126 the blue letters on her door. She watched her teacher, Mrs. Plotkin, a young woman with deep black hair. Who wore crisp blouses. Sometimes the bright sun outside shined in her face. Bright snow edged the window ledge. Other times were winter dull, with only the school lights to brighten the room filled with brown wooden desks, black inkwells, black children.

> *Ellease Southerland*
> **from *Let the Lion Eat Straw***

4. What visual images are most clear?
5. Do any images appeal to the sense of smell? Do any suggest the inner feelings of the girl?
6. The writer might have said, "She began to attend school in February. Everything was new to her." In what ways is the above description more effective?

Notice how the writer of the following poem presents changes in a student.

Foreign Student

In September she appeared
   row three, seat seven,
   heavy pleated skirt,
   plastic purse, tidy notepad,
5 there she sat,
silent,

(continued)

Jesse Stuart. "Dark Winter" from *A Jesse Stuart Harvest*. New York: Dell Publishing Co., Inc., 1936.

From *Let the Lion Eat Straw* by Ellease Southerland. Charles Scribner's Sons, 1979, pp. 18–19.

"Foreign Student" by Barbara Robinson from *English Journal*, May 1976. Copyright © 1976 by the National Council of Teachers of English. Reprinted by permission of the publisher and the author.

straight from Taipei,[1]
and she bowed
when I entered the room.
10 A model student
I noticed,
    though she walked
      alone through the halls,
every assignment neat,
15 on time, complete,
and she'd listen
when I talked.

But now it's May
and Si Lan
20 is called Lani.
She strides in
with Noriyo, and Lynne
and Natavidad.
She wears slacks.
25 Her gear is crammed
into a macramé
shoulder sack.
And she chatters with Pete
during class
30 and
I'm glad.

Barbara B. Robinson

What has happened to Si Lan between September and May? What are some images that reveal change?

■ IMAGERY

Concrete words or details that appeal to the senses of sight, sound, touch, smell, and taste, or to internal feelings.

1. *Taipei* (tī′pā′), capital of Taiwan, an island off southeast China.

■ Apply to **Oranges** on page 279.

■ INFERENCE

Suppose you know that your older sister was to find out if she got a job today. She comes home looking sad. What do you think must have happened? When you draw a reasonable conclusion based on the evidence at hand, you are making an *inference*.

Writers very often expect you to make inferences about setting, characters, and action. To understand fully what you read, you must be alert to what words imply; you have to be able to read between the lines and draw logical inferences from clues an author provides.

Laura and Mary were up next morning earlier than the sun. They ate their breakfast of cornmeal mush with prairie-hen gravy, and hurried to help Ma wash the dishes. Pa was loading everything else into the wagon and hitching up Pet and Patty.

When the sun rose, they were driving on across the prairie. There was no road now. Pet and Patty waded through the grasses, and the wagon left behind it only the tracks of its wheels.

Before noon, Pa said, "Whoa!" The wagon stopped.

"Here we are, Caroline!" he said. "Right here we'll build our house."

Laura and Mary scrambled over the feedbox and dropped to the ground in a hurry. All around them there was nothing but grassy prairie spreading to the edge of the sky.

Laura Ingalls Wilder
from *Little House on the Prairie*

Laura Ingalls Wilder, *Little House on the Prairie*. New York: Harper & Row, Publishers, 1953.

1. Do you think this story takes place before 1920? Why?
2. What kind of wagon do you think these people have?
3. Who are Pet and Patty?
4. Who is Caroline? Who are Laura and Mary?

From the limited information given, you can make several general inferences. You can infer, for instance, that Pet and Patty are pulling the wagon, but you cannot tell whether they are horses or oxen. You can infer that Laura and Mary are children, since there is a woman called "Ma" whom they help with the dishes. Their scrambling from the wagon suggests the high spirits of children. You cannot tell from this passage, however, how old they are. You can tell that the weather is fair, but you can't tell whether it's spring, summer, or fall.

Read the story excerpt below and decide whether the inferences that follow are correct or incorrect. Be ready to support your answers.

"Little Man, would you come on? You keep it up and you're gonna make us late."

My youngest brother paid no attention to me. Grasping more firmly his newspaper-wrapped notebook and his tin-can lunch of cornbread and oil sausages, he continued to concentrate on the dusty road. He lagged several feet behind my other brothers, Stacey and Christopher-John, and me, attempting to keep the rusty Mississippi dust from swelling with each step and drifting back upon his shiny black shoes and the cuffs of his corduroy pants by lifting each foot high before setting it gently down again. Always meticulously neat, six-year-old Little Man never allowed dirt or tears or stains to mar anything he owned. Today was no exception.

"You keep it up and make us late for school, Mama's gonna wear you out," I threatened, pulling with exasperation at the high collar of the Sunday dress Mama had made me wear for the first day of school—as if that event were something special. It seemed to me that showing up at school at all on a bright August-like October morning made for running the cool forest trails and wading barefoot in the forest pond was concession enough; Sunday clothing was asking too much. Christopher-John and Stacey were not too pleased about the clothing or school either. Only Little Man, just beginning his school career, found the prospects of both intriguing.

"Y'all go ahead and get dirty if y'all wanna," he replied without even looking up from his studied steps. "Me, I'm gonna stay clean."

"I betcha Mama's gonna 'clean' you, you keep it up," I grumbled.

"Ah, Cassie, leave him be," Stacey admonished, frowning and kicking testily at the road.

"I ain't said nothing but——"

Staccy cut me a wicked look and I grew silent. His disposition had been irritatingly sour lately. If I hadn't known the cause of it, I could have forgotten very easily that he was, at twelve, bigger than I, and that I had promised Mama to arrive at school looking clean and ladylike. "Shoot," I mumbled finally, unable to restrain myself from further comment, "it ain't my fault you gotta be in Mama's class this year."

Stacey's frown deepened and he jammed his fists into his pockets, but said nothing.

Christopher-John, walking between Stacey and me, glanced uneasily at both of us but did not interfere. A short, round boy of seven, he took little interest in troublesome things, preferring to remain on good terms with everyone. Yet he was

HANDBOOK OF LITERARY TERMS

always sensitive to others and now, shifting the handle of his lunch can from his right hand to his right wrist and his smudged notebook from his left hand to his left armpit, he stuffed his free hands into his pockets and attempted to make his face as moody as Stacey's and as cranky as mine. But after a few moments he seemed to forget that he was supposed to be grouchy and began whistling cheerfully. There was little that could make Christopher-John unhappy for very long, not even the thought of school.

I tugged again at my collar and dragged my feet in the dust, allowing it to sift back onto my socks and shoes like gritty red snow. I hated the dress. And the shoes. There was little I could do in a dress, and as for shoes, they imprisoned freedom-loving feet accustomed to the feel of the warm earth.

"Cassie, stop that," Stacey snapped as the dust billowed in swirling clouds around my feet. I looked up sharply, ready to protest.

Mildred Taylor
from *Roll of Thunder, Hear My Cry*

1. The narrator is a girl.
2. The children's mother is a teacher.
3. Little Man's corduroy pants are new.
4. The story takes place in Georgia.
5. The children attend a country school.
6. Cassie understands the reason for Stacey's mood.
7. The weather is crisp and cool.
8. Cassie is bossy and in a bad mood.

■ INFERENCE

A reasonable conclusion drawn by the reader or viewer from hints, or implications, provided by the author.

■ Apply to **The Day the Sun Came Out** on page 386.

■ IRONY

Verbal Irony

"What a nice person you are," Tom told his sister when she slammed the screen door in his face.

Tom's comment is an example of *verbal irony*. In verbal irony speakers say the opposite of what they really mean or what they think is true. All of us speak ironically at times: if you say "What a great day!" when the temperature is 106 degrees in the shade, you are using verbal irony. You indicate what you really mean by the expression on your face and by your tone of voice.

In literature, verbal irony may include the author's attitude toward a subject. In such cases the writer's real attitude contrasts with the attitude he or she pretends to have. What is *ironic* about the following lines?

Tribute

I do not mind my neighbor's dog,
In fact I love the cur;
I like the way he curls his lip,
I like his mottled fur.

5 I like his bark at 3 A.M.,
I like his throaty growls,
I treasure every playful nip
And both his quivering jowls.

His body scarred and overfed,
10 His baleful eye, his groans and sighs,
All strike in me a keen delight
As on my chest he lies.

Understanding irony requires experience in reading. An inexperienced reader might be misled into thinking that the writer is truly fond of the neighbor's dog. What words tell you that this is not the case?

Irony of Situation

Irony of situation is the term given to a happening that is the opposite of what one would expect. It is an ironic situation if you take a winter vacation to a tropical island to enjoy the sun, and it rains all the time you are there. In literature very often an ironic twist does not come until the end of a poem, a story, or a play. What is ironic in the following poem?

The Rich Man

The rich man has his motor-car
  His country and his town estate.
He smokes a fifty-cent cigar
  And jeers at Fate.

5 He frivols through the livelong day,
  He knows not Poverty, her pinch.
His lot seems light, his heart seems gay;
  He has a cinch.

Yet though my lamp burns low and dim,
10   Though I must slave for livelihood—
Think you that I would change with him?
  You bet I would!

Franklin P. Adams

Dramatic Irony

Sometimes the words or actions of a character in a play or story carry meaning significant to the audience or reader but not to the character. This is called *dramatic irony*. For instance, a character may discuss her plans for the future while the audience or reader knows that several things will prevent her from carrying out those plans. The purpose of dramatic irony may be to elicit sympathy for a character, to build suspense, or create a comic effect.

In the cartoon below, what is the reader aware of that the man and woman watching television are not?

© 1983 United Feature Syndicate, Inc.

"Nothing much . . . just an elephant missing from the circus!"

■ IRONY

A contrast between what appears to be and what really is.

Verbal irony **occurs when what one says or writes is the opposite of the intended meaning.**

Irony of situation **exists when an event is contrary to what is expected or appropriate.**

Dramatic irony **occurs when the reader or spectator knows more about the true state of affairs than a character does.**

"The Rich Man" from *Tobogganing on Parnassus* by Franklin P. Adams. Copyright 1911 by Doubleday & Company, Inc. Reprinted by permission.

■ Apply to **A Man Who Had No Eyes** on page 333.

■ METAPHOR

Broken Sky

The sky of gray is eaten in six places,
    Rag holes stand out.
It is an army blanket and the sleeper
    Slept too near the fire.

Carl Sandburg

The poet says the sky is an army blanket. What are the similarities between this sky and an army blanket? What do the "rag holes" represent?

A weather forecaster might have made a literal statement: "The sky is partly cloudy." Sandburg chose to describe the sky figuratively by comparing it to a ragged blanket.

Writers often compare two things that are basically unlike but with some similarities. When the figurative comparison uses the words *like* or *as*, it is called a *simile*.

The hungry girl ate like a wolf.

When the comparison does not use *like* or *as*, and is therefore implied, it is called a *metaphor*.

The hungry girl wolfed her food.

A metaphor is a type of FIGURATIVE LANGUAGE. Metaphors are used not to make writing more difficult to read but to communicate a fresh way of looking at a common object, person, scene, event, or emotion. What is "every man" compared to in the following example?

No man is an island, entire of itself; every man is a piece of the continent, a part of the main.

John Donne
from *Meditation 17*

When a comparison pleases or surprises or stimulates a new way of looking at something, then the metaphor is effective. What two things are being compared in the following metaphor? Do you think the comparison is effective?

Fame Is a Bee

Fame is a bee.
    It has a song—
It has a sting—
    Ah, too, it has a wing.

Emily Dickinson

1. What is the song of a bee? What might the speaker mean by saying that fame has a song?
2. A bee can sting. How do you think fame could sting?
3. What does a bee do with its wings? What is suggested by saying that fame, too, has a wing?

■ METAPHOR

A figure of speech that involves an implied comparison between two basically unlike things.

■ Apply to **Fog** on page 298.

■ MOOD

Does the photograph evoke a feeling of peacefulness? hopelessness? loneliness? terror? happiness?

In this picture a special atmosphere, or *mood*, is created by the windowless and partially destroyed house, the littered ground, and the bare trees. Writers create mood through their choice of details.

The kitchen had a cold stone floor. The walls, also of stone, were slightly damp to the touch. Above the stove—itself a hulking black creature— an unpainted shelf held misshapen clay pots and jars ranging in color from dirty gray to blood red. A bench, hard and uninviting, ran along one wall.

1. Is the kitchen a cheery room? a comfortable room? Find words in the passage to support your answer.
2. Are the pots and jars pleasant to look at? Why?

3. Which of these two passages makes the better closing for the paragraph? Why?

A. In a corner near the stove on a piece of warm plaid flannel, a brown setter lay peacefully asleep with a litter of puppies nestled around her. A cat, fat in its puffy winter coat, curled up near the fire.

B. In the corner near the stove lurked a huge, liver-colored dog surrounded by a horde of squealing puppies. A cat, scrawny and ill-tempered, paced the littered floor.

■ MOOD

The atmosphere or feeling within a work of art. The choice of setting, objects, details, images, and words all contribute to create a specific mood.

■ Apply to **The Monsters Are Due on Maple Street** on page 131.

■ PERSONIFICATION

Theme in Yellow

I spot the hills
With yellow balls in autumn.
I light the prairie cornfields
Orange and tawny gold clusters
5 And I am called pumpkins.
On the last of October
When dusk is fallen
Children join hands
And circle round me
10 Singing ghost songs
And love to the harvest moon;
I am a jack-o'-lantern
With terrible teeth
And the children know
15 I am fooling.

Carl Sandburg

1. Who is speaking in the poem?
2. What human characteristic does the
   poet give to the pumpkins in line 13?

In his description, the poet makes use of
a figure of speech called *personification*.
Through the use of personification,
nonhuman things or inanimate objects are
given human characteristics. We often use
personification in our daily speech. We
may speak of angry clouds or a raging
river, for example.

Personification is an effective device in
poetry for it enables the poet to present
events, ideas, or objects in human terms,
thus making them more vivid and
understandable. When the poet William
Wordsworth wrote "the green field sleeps
in the sun" and "Like an army defeated/
The snow hath retreated, ..." he used
personification. To what is each thing
compared in these personifications? Is the
comparison appropriate in each case?

■ PERSONIFICATION
(pər son′ə fə kā′shən)

**A figure of speech in which human
characteristics are assigned to nonhuman
things.**

■ Apply to **Four Little Foxes** on page 306.

"Theme in Yellow" from *Chicago Poems* by Carl Sandburg,
copyright 1916 by Holt, Rinehart and Winston, Inc.; renewed 1944
by Carl Sandburg. Reprinted by permission of Harcourt Brace
Jovanovich, Inc.

■ PLOT

Read the following short story.

Take Over, Bos'n

1 Hour after hour I kept the gun pointed at the other nine men. From the lifeboat's stern, where I'd sat most of the twenty days of our drifting, I could keep them all covered. If I had to shoot at such close quarters, I wouldn't miss. They realized that. Nobody jumped at me. But in the way they all glared I could see how they'd come to hate my guts.

2 Especially Barrett, who'd been bos'n's[1] mate; Barrett said in his harsh, cracked voice, "You're a dope, Snyder. Y-you can't hold out forever! You're half asleep now!"

3 I didn't answer. He was right. How long can a man stay awake? I hadn't dared shut my eyes in maybe seventy-two hours. Very soon now I'd doze off, and the instant that happened they'd pounce on the little water that was left.

4 The last canteen lay under my legs. There wasn't much in it after twenty days. Maybe a pint. Enough to give each of them a few drops. Yet I could see in their bloodshot eyes that they'd gladly kill me for those few drops. As a man I didn't count any more. I was no longer third officer of the wrecked *Montala*. I was just a gun that kept them away from the water they craved. And with their tongues swollen and their cheeks sunken, they were half crazy. . . .

5 The way I judged it, we must be some two hundred miles east of Ascension. Now that the storms were over, the Atlantic swells were long and easy, and the morning sun was hot—so hot it scorched your skin. My own tongue was thick enough to clog my throat. I'd have given the rest of my life for a single gulp of water.

6 But I was the man with the gun—the only authority in the boat—and I knew this: once the water was gone we'd have nothing to look forward to but death. As long as we could look forward to getting a drink later, there was something to live for. We had to make it last as long as possible. If I'd given in to the curses and growls, if I hadn't brandished the gun, we'd have emptied the last canteen days ago. By now we'd all be dead.

7 The men weren't pulling on the oars. They'd stopped that long ago, too weak to go on. The nine of them facing me were a pack of bearded, ragged, half-naked animals, and I probably looked as bad as the rest. Some sprawled over the gunwales, dozing. The rest watched me as Barrett did, ready to spring the instant I relaxed.

8 When they weren't looking at my face they looked at the canteen under my legs.

9 Jeff Barrett was the nearest one. A constant threat. The bos'n's mate was a heavy man, bald, with a scarred and brutal face. He'd been in a hundred fights, and they'd left their marks on him. Barrett had been able to sleep—in fact, he'd slept through most of the night—and I envied him that. His eyes wouldn't close. They kept watching me, narrow and dangerous.

10 Every now and then he taunted me in that hoarse, broken voice:

11 "Why don't you quit? You can't hold out!"

12 "Tonight," I said. "We'll ration the rest of the water tonight."

13 "By tonight some of us'll be dead! We want it now!"

14 "Tonight," I said.

15 Couldn't he understand that if we waited until night the few drops wouldn't be sweated out of us so fast? But Barrett was beyond all reasoning. His mind had already cracked with thirst. I saw him begin to rise, a calculating look in his eyes. I aimed the gun at his chest—and he sat down again.   (continued)

---

1. *Bos'n* (bō′sn), boatswain, a ship's officer in charge of the anchors, ropes, rigging, and so on.

"Take Over, Bos'n" by Oscar Schisgall originally appeared in *This Week Magazine*, 1950. Reprinted by permission of the author.

16 I'd grabbed my Luger on instinct, twenty days ago, just before running for the lifeboat. Nothing else would have kept Barrett and the rest away from the water.

17 These fools—couldn't they see I wanted a drink as badly as any of them? But I was in command here—that was the difference. I was the man with the gun, the man who had to think. Each of the others could afford to think only of himself; I had to think of them all.

18 Barrett's eyes kept watching me, waiting. I hated him. I hated him all the more because he'd slept. He had the advantage now. He wouldn't keel over.

19 And long before noon I knew I couldn't fight any more. My eyelids were too heavy to lift. As the boat rose and fell on the long swells, I could feel sleep creeping over me like paralysis. It bent my head. It filled my brain like a cloud. I was going, going . . .

20 Barrett stood over me, and I couldn't even lift the gun. In a vague way I could guess what would happen. He'd grab the water first and take his gulp. By that time the others would be screaming and tearing at him, and he'd have to yield the canteen. Well, there was nothing more I could do about it.

21 I whispered, "Take over, bos'n."

22 Then I fell face down in the bottom of the boat. I was asleep before I stopped moving . . .

23 When a hand shook my shoulder I could hardly raise my head. Jeff Barrett's hoarse voice said, "Here! Take your share o' the water!"

24 Somehow I propped myself up on my arms, dizzy and weak. I looked at the men, and I thought my eyes were going. Their figures were dim, shadowy; but then I realized it wasn't because of my eyes. It was night. The sea was black; there were stars overhead. I'd slept the day away.

25 So we were in our twenty-first night adrift—the night in which the tramp *Groton* finally picked us up—but now as I turned my head to Barrett there was no sign of any ship. He knelt, beside me, holding out the canteen, his other hand with the gun steady on the men.

26 I stared at the canteen as if it were a mirage. Hadn't they finished that pint of water this morning? When I looked up at Barrett's ugly face, it was grim. He must have guessed my thoughts.

27 "You said, 'Take over, bos'n,' didn't you?" he growled. "I been holdin' off these apes all day." He hefted the Luger in his hand. "When you're bossman," he added with a sheepish grin, "in command and responsible for the rest—you—you sure get to see things different, don't you?"

Oscar Schisgall

The following discussion covers *conflict, details, pattern of events, climax,* and *conclusion,* all of which are elements of *plot.*

Conflict

1. What is the source of the disagreement between Snyder and Barrett? Against what force or forces are Snyder and the other men struggling?
2. What feelings does Snyder have to combat in deciding to wait to share the water?

Most stories, novels, and plays are built around a *conflict* or struggle. The conflict may be fairly simple: the hero, who stands for the forces of good, fights the villain, who represents the forces of evil. Usually, however, a work of fiction will be built around a more complicated struggle, and more than one struggle may take place at the same time. For example, in "Take Over, Bos'n," Snyder must fight Barrett and the other men to keep them from drinking the water. Snyder and the other men must combat nature in the form of the weather and the sea. Finally, Snyder must also struggle with himself: although he believes in his responsibility as leader, he, too, is thirsty.

A conflict in which the main character (or group) struggles with other characters, society, or nature is called an *external conflict*. A conflict in which the main character struggles with his or her own beliefs or feelings is called an *internal conflict*.

Details

3. At the beginning of "Take Over, Bos'n," how long has the lifeboat been adrift?
4. How long has it been since Snyder has slept?
5. What is the weather like?

In answering the questions above, you selected *details* provided in the story. Is each of these details important? Explain.

From all the things that might be said about a subject, a capable author chooses only those details that help to develop the conflict. Schisgall provides a description of the weather because the heat serves to intensify the men's desire for water and Barrett's determination to take the canteen.

Pattern of Events

6. Arrange the following incidents in the order in which they occurred in the story.
   a. Snyder tells Barrett to take over and then falls asleep.
   b. Snyder points the gun at Barrett's chest.
   c. Barrett takes the gun and guards the water until nightfall.
   d. Barrett sits down and waits for Snyder to fall asleep.
   e. Barrett moves toward Snyder and the canteen.

f. Snyder guards the canteen with the last of the water in it.

When you arranged the events above in the order in which they occurred, you organized them according to a cause-effect relationship. An author chooses events to form a pattern in which each event grows out of the one that happened before, and all events lead to a conclusion.

Climax and Conclusion

7. At what point in the story do you know that a major change is about to occur in the situation aboard the lifeboat?
8. What happens to Barrett once he has the gun? Why?

In a work of literature the *climax* is the turning point in the conflict. A character may do something to cause a change, or events may dictate that some change must take place. Once Snyder falls asleep, you know that conditions on board the boat cannot remain as they had been.

The *conclusion*, or ending, is the solution of the conflict. When Barrett takes over the care of the water supply, the conflict between him and Snyder no longer exists.

■ PLOT

A pattern of related events selected by the author to present and resolve some internal or external conflict. In a carefully constructed plot, each event is important: the incidents are arranged in a cause-effect relationship, with each incident becoming a necessary link leading to the climax and conclusion of the work.

■ Apply to **The Widow and the Parrot** on page 13.

■ POINT OF VIEW

Read the following passages.

A. I had never seen my family look so stern. Oh, maybe I'd seen one or two of them look that way at the same time, but never the whole crew. And with mom and dad and—including me—six girls, we do make up a crew.

I played with my food, trying not to look at anybody, especially Karen Beth, who wasn't even pretending to eat. There really wasn't anything to say or do—to her or anybody else. I'd been the one to sneak Furface into the room I share with Karen Beth. And I'd been the one to leave the closet door open even though I knew Furface was looking for a place to have her kittens. So when the cat pulled Karen's red velvet party dress off the hanger and made it a nest for herself and six newborn kittens, who could be blamed but me?

B. The parents and their six daughters sat around the dinner table in silence. Beverly pushed the food around on her plate and wondered for the hundredth time how she could have been foolish enough to let a cat due to have kittens at any moment into the bedroom she shared with Karen Beth, her sister.

C. Nobody seemed to be eating much; all eight members of the family sat looking serious. Beverly continued to scold herself silently. She should have known that Furface would make a nest in the closet—and what would make a better nest than Karen's red velvet dress?

Karen Beth couldn't have cared less about the velvet dress. It could be a permanent nest as far as she was concerned. She and Bulldog Hershbine had broken up that morning after English class; she'd have no need for a party dress this Christmas.

Mr. Anderson struggled to keep his face from betraying his true feelings. Although the family

myth was that she belonged to the girls, Furface was really his cat, and everybody knew it. Privately he thought there was no prettier picture than the long-haired white cat and six varicolored kittens lying against the red velvet.

1. Each of the accounts above describes the same basic situation. Using as few words as possible, summarize that situation.
2. What is the main difference between passage **A** and passages **B** and **C**?
3. What is the main difference between **B** and **C**?
4. In which account are you given the most information?

All writing is told, or narrated, by someone. That someone is called the *narrator*. In poetry that someone is more frequently called the *speaker*. It is important that you do not confuse the narrator or speaker with the author or poet, who may or may not agree with what the narrator or speaker says. The angle from which an account is told is called its *point of view*.

First-Person Point of View

The narrator may be a character in the narrative, as in passage **A**. In this first-person account the narrator, using the pronoun *I*, can tell the reader what she sees and hears and also what she is thinking. However, she cannot see into the minds of others to tell the reader what they are thinking or feeling; she can only report what they say and do. An author may use the first-person point of view to create an element of surprise or discovery that helps the reader experience the same things as the narrator. For example, what did you learn about Karen Beth in passage **C** that you did not learn in passage **A?** If the first-person account were continued using the events in passage **C,** how would the author reveal the true feelings of Karen Beth and her father to both Beverly and the reader?

Third-Person Limited Point of View

The narrator of passage **B** is an outsider, not a character in the story. Because the narrator refers to Beverly as *she,* this account is said to be written in the third person. The narrator sees into the mind of only one character. Passage **B** is written from a third-person limited point of view.

Third-Person Omniscient (om nish′ənt) Point of View

The narrator of passage **C** is able to see into the minds of all of the characters. Like a superhuman being, this narrator is omniscient, or all-knowing. The reader of an account written from this point of view finds a certain satisfaction in being "in on" what all the characters are thinking and feeling.

Through the selection of point of view, an author can control the development of a story.

■ POINT OF VIEW

The relationship between the narrator and the story. The author's choice of narrator determines the amount of information a reader will be given. Three major points of view are first person, third-person limited, and third-person omniscient.

■ Apply to **Hunger** on page 183.

■ RHYME

Minnie Morse

Of all the problems no one's solved
The worst is Minnie Morse's;
I mean why Minnie's so involved
With horses.

5 Since Minnie bought a horse this spring
(An animal named Mable)
She doesn't care to do a thing
But hang around the stable.

In school, she'll never ever pass.
10 She fills her notebook spaces
And messes up her books in class
By drawing horses' faces.
Last week our teacher, Miss McGrew,
Made Minnie stand—and said
15 She didn't mind a sketch or two
But now please write instead.
And Minnie sat again, and drew
Another horse's head.

"I said to *write*," cried Miss McGrew,
20 "Does someone have to force you?"
At which point, Minnie stomped her shoe
As if she wore a horseshoe,
And tossing back her mane of hair
While all the class just waited,
25 She said that horses didn't *care*
If girls got educated.

Well, if a horse is what you've got,
It's fine to want to please one;
But what I brood about a lot
30 Is Minnie acts like *she's* one.

(continued)

"Minnie Morse" from *Don't Ever Cross a Crocodile* by Kaye Starbird. Copyright © 1963 by Kaye Starbird. Reprinted by permission of Ray Lincoln Literary Agency, 4 Surrey Road, Melrose Park, PA, 19126.

HANDBOOK OF LITERARY TERMS

In fact, the way she is today,
You can't get far with Minnie
Unless you live on oats and hay—
And whinny.

Kaye Starbird

In the first stanza of "Minnie Morse,"
what words rhyme at the ends of lines? In
the second stanza what words rhyme?

Ending two or more lines of poetry with
words that sound alike is called *end
rhyming;* end words that share a particular
sound are called *end rhymes.*

When they are used in a poem, end
rhymes set up a pattern of sounds called a
rhyme scheme. You can chart a rhyme
scheme with letters of the alphabet by
using the same letter for end words that
rhyme. Read the following poem.

Beetle Bemused

With careful tread, through dim green-
    pillared halls,
Inch by long inch the purblind beetle crawls.
I watch, my forehead tickled by the grasses;
    Time passes.
5 Beetle, bemused, where every way's the same,
Turns and sets back along the road he came.
I roll upon my side and break my glasses;
    Time passes.

R. P. Lister

1. If the last word of the first line were
   labeled *a,* what other word or words
   at the ends of lines would also be
   labeled *a?*
2. If the last word of line 3 were labeled *b,*
   what other word or words at the ends of
   lines would also be labeled *b?*

3. With what letter would you label line 5?
   Why?

The rhyme scheme for the poem is
aabb ccbb. The *a*'s represent the rhymes in
lines 1 and 2, the *b*'s represent the rhymes
in lines 3 and 4, the *c*'s represent the
rhymes in lines 5 and 6, and the *b*'s
represent the rhymes in lines 7 and 8
because they are like those in lines 3 and
4. If the poem had two more lines that
rhymed with sounds unlike any of those
before, what letter would represent those
sounds?

4. On a sheet of paper, chart the rhyme
   scheme for "Minnie Morse."

A poem does not have to contain a
rhyme scheme, but end rhyme does serve a
purpose in poetry. The sound of rhyming
words can be pleasant to hear. And end
rhyme may help to divide a poem into
stanzas, as it does in "Beetle Bemused,"
where each of the two stanzas ends in *bb.*
In "Minnie Morse" end rhyme also
contributes to the amusing effect of the
poem. (Note especially the two-syllable
rhymes in lines 20 and 22 and again in
lines 28 and 30.)

■ RHYME

**The repetition of syllable sounds. End
words that share a particular sound are
called *end rhymes.* The pattern of end
rhymes in a poem is called a *rhyme
scheme.***

■ Apply to **The Hunter** on page 270.

■ RHYTHM

Read the lines below aloud.

It was the schooner Hesperus,
    That sailed the wintry sea;
And the skipper had taken his little
        daughter,
    To bear him company. . . .

5 The skipper he stood beside the helm,
    His pipe was in his mouth,
And he watched how the veering flaw[1] did
        blow
    The smoke now West, now South.

Then up and spake an old Sailor,
10   Had sailed to the Spanish Main,
"I pray thee, put into yonder port,
    For I fear a hurricane.

"Last night the moon had a golden ring,
    And tonight no moon we see!"
15 The skipper, he blew a whiff from his pipe,
    And a scornful laugh laughed he.

Henry Wadsworth Longfellow
from "The Wreck of the Hesperus"

Did you notice that as you read you automatically stressed some words and syllables more than others? This pattern of stressed and unstressed words or syllables is called *rhythm.*

We respond to rhythm because it is enjoyable, but poets have other reasons for using rhythm, beyond the important one of creating a poem with a pleasing beat. Rhythm allows a poet to fit the movement of the poem to the MOOD.

Some poets try to avoid regular rhythm because it may lead to drowsiness in the reader, or it may actually take the inexperienced reader *away* from the meaning. Read the lines below. The syllables that are emphasized, or stressed, are in capital letters.

Had I but PLENty of MONey, MONey eNOUGH
    and to SPARE,
The HOUSE for ME, no DOUBT, were a HOUSE in
    the CITY SQUARE;
Ah, SUCH a LIFE, SUCH a LIFE, as one LEADS at
    the WINdow THERE!

Robert Browning
from "Up at a Villa—Down in the City"

1. How many stressed syllables are there in the first line? in the second? in the third?
2. Where is the first pause? the second pause? Where is the longest pause before the end of the last line?
3. Where does the "I" in the poem want to live? Why? What prevents his or her living there?

Rhythm can also be used to emphasize important words in a poem.

When the green woods laugh with the voice of
    joy,
And the dimpling stream runs laughing by;
When the air does laugh with our merry wit,
And the green hill laughs with the noise of it.

William Blake
from "Laughing Song"

Notice how many times the words *laugh* or *laughing* are stressed here. What other stressed words contribute to an atmosphere of merriment?

---

1. *flaw,* a gust of wind.

Many poems do not have a regular pattern of sound throughout. All poems have rhythm, however, since there are always some words that are stressed more than others. Read the lines below, being careful not to pause unless the punctuation indicates that there should be a pause. Which words do you think the poet wants stressed?

Trees and Evening Sky

I saw the black trees leaning
In different ways, their limbs
Tangled on the mottled clouds,
The clouds rolling on themselves:
5 A wide belt of four colors,
Yellow, orange, red, and black;
And stars in the tangled limbs.

N. Scott Momaday

■ RHYTHM

The arrangement of stressed and unstressed sounds in writing and speech. The rhythm in a poem may have a regular beat, or it may be varied within the poem to fit different moods or to emphasize certain words.

"Trees and Evening Sky" by N. Scott Momaday from *Carriers of the Dream Wheel* published by Harper & Row, 1975. Reprinted by permission of the author.

■ Apply to **Almost Perfect** on page 256.

■ SETTING

The year my brother Joseph went to Vietnam as a fighter pilot, I was sent to live with my Aunt Harriet. I spent the first weeks there being dreadfully homesick and trying to act as if I weren't. Even after school started, I found myself lonely and almost totally friendless. I spent my evenings shooting baskets in Aunt Harriet's driveway, or lying moodily in the hammock under the orange tree in the backyard, or baking cookies to send to Joseph.

1. The paragraph above is the beginning of a short story. The story takes place in the (**a**) 1860s; (**b**) 1920s; (**c**) 1940s; (**d**) 1960s. How do you know?
2. Aunt Harriet lives in (**a**) a high-rise apartment in the city; (**b**) a mountain cabin; (**c**) a house in town. What details helped you decide?
3. The story probably takes place in (**a**) New York; (**b**) Florida; (**c**) Illinois; (**d**) Oregon. On what did you base your answer?
4. The conditions under which the narrator lives might best be described as (**a**) poverty-stricken; (**b**) comfortable; (**c**) humiliating; (**d**) unhealthy.

Setting is the word used to indicate the time, the location, and the general environment. The time setting might be a particular day, a season of the year, or a period in history. The place might be one room, a city, or the countryside. The environment, or general conditions surrounding the characters, may be one of affluence and joy, poverty and despair, or anything in between.

An author may directly state the setting.

Usually, though, the author informs readers about the background of the story through scattered details that hint at time and location.

Sometimes setting also aids understanding of people in a story.

Thad Lemonovich left work at the usual time and returned to the rented room he had occupied ever since he'd finished college.

Like most furnished rooms, this one contained the bare necessities: a narrow bed with a headboard of painted wood, a dresser and chest that matched neither the bed nor each other, an armchair, and a small metal bookcase.

But Thad had added his own touches, and the room was like no other in Mrs. Glott's rooming house. Arranged on the wall above the bed were three felt pennants—a little faded, perhaps, but still bright enough to stand out against the pale green wall. All three were from the college Thad had attended twenty years before. Another wall held an assortment of framed photographs and yellowed newspaper clippings, also in frames. "Lemonovich Clicks as Soph at State" one headline read. Another announced that "Star Quarterback Lemonovich Leads State to Victory." Some of the photos were of the whole team. Others were of Thad alone: throwing a pass, running with the ball into the end zone, unhelmeted and grinning at a mob of fans clustered around him.

The bookcase was empty except for four college yearbooks, but the tops of both the dresser and the chest were covered with trophies and more photos.

5. What was Thad's main interest when he was in college? How do you know?
6. Describe the room as it would look without Thad's belongings in it.
7. What kind of person do you think Thad is now? How can you tell?

At times setting may be vital to the development of the plot.

The elevator held six people. The two young men who had just visited the Statue of Liberty for the first time talked of their adventure; the middle-aged couple stood silently, each of them balancing a sack stuffed full of groceries on the rail at the back of the car; the jogger stood panting and dripping from his run through the park under a relentless sun; and Luis carefully held the box containing his sister's birthday cake that he'd carried all the way from Harlem.

They were between floors when the blackout began. The elevator stopped with a soft bump. At the same time the lights went out and the piped-in music died.

The little group was silent for the several seconds it took for the unwelcome truth to dawn on them.

One of the young men was the first to speak. "Ah, is this a . . . well, is this . . ." he tried to stop his voice from shaking, ". . . is this one of your famous New York blackouts? H-How do we get out of here?"

8. In what city does the action occur?
9. What time of year is it?
10. Where are the people?
11. How do you think the setting will influence the behavior of the characters?

An author may also use details of setting to create a particular atmosphere or MOOD.

■ SETTING

The time, place, and general environment in which the events of a narrative occur. Details of setting may be either stated or suggested.

■ Apply to **Rikki-tikki-tavi** on page 60.

■ SIMILE

Shooting Star Love

It's only one of a kind
The love that comes
Like a shooting star
Entering space with
5 Flare, and warmth, and flourish
But leaving on its demise
Only traces of dust
And tear-stained, crumpled faces.

Maria Herrera-Sobek

1. By comparing love to a shooting star, what does the speaker tell you about love?
2. What is the same about both?
3. What is the result of both when they are over?
4. In describing the speaker's thoughts, the writer might have said, "Once love ends, the people involved are left sad and tearful." Which of the two descriptions is more effective? Why?

In the poem above, Herrera-Sobek has used a *simile*. A simile directly states a comparison between two basically dissimilar objects by using the word *like* or *as*. A figurative comparison that does not use *like* or *as* is called a METAPHOR. If the poet had said, "Love *is* a shooting star," she would have been using a metaphor.

Similes are common in everyday speech, and some similes are used so often that they become stale and lifeless:

The cake was as light as a feather.
George shook like a leaf in a storm.

Writers attempt to create fresh images by using comparisons that help you look at things in a new way.

Read the following poem.

Train of Thought

Wisps of memory
are like train whistles
heard from afar
drifting
5 across the prairie.
But the sudden
reminder of
a promise unkept
bursts upon the mind
10 like a locomotive
screeching, shuddering
into the station.

5. To what are wisps of memory compared?
6. To what is the sudden reminder of an unkept promise compared?
7. Do you agree that these comparisons offer fresh ways of "looking at" memory? Why or why not?
8. To what other things might wisps of memory and sudden reminders be compared?

■ SIMILE (sim′ə lē)

A comparison in which the word *like* or *as* is used to point out a similarity between two basically unlike things.

"Shooting Star Love" by Maria Herrera-Sobek from *Hispanics in the United States,* edited by Gary D. Keller and Francisco Jiménez. Copyright © 1980 by Bilingual Press. Reprinted by permission of Bilingual Review/Press.

■ Apply to **I'm Nobody** on page 292.

■ STEREOTYPE

Marvin Gregg laughed wildly and clutched his hair, pulling it until it stood straight out on either side of his head. Then, mumbling and chuckling to himself, he again leaned over the test tube.

Smoke poured from one corner of the lab; somebody knocked on the door; the telephone rang and rang. Gregg never took his eyes off the thick green liquid in the test tube.

His chuckles became groans as the liquid stopped bubbling and became once again the clear water with which he had started the experiment. With an anguished cry, he smashed the test tube against the far wall and ran out of the laboratory.

In the passage above, Marvin Gregg is presented as an intense, highly emotional, and perhaps even slightly mad person. If the story were continued and Marvin bumped into a fellow scientist in the hall, would he be more likely to stop and apologize or turn away, still muttering to himself?

In fiction a *stereotype* is a character that embodies only those traits that are most commonly expected from members of the group to which the character belongs. The stereotype of the mad scientist is founded on the assumption that anyone so wrapped up and emotionally involved in work that most of us cannot understand must be out of his or her mind. When a character is presented as a stereotype, the qualities that make that character an individual are ignored. Stereotypes may embody either favorable or unfavorable qualities. The kindly, overworked country doctor, the hot-tempered redhead, and the shrewd, tough private detective are all familiar stereotypes.

Can you name other stereotypes? (Consider the stereotypes you see every day in television commercials: the warm-hearted grandparent, the dignified medical expert, the perfectly conditioned athlete, and others.)

Stereotypes are used in fiction because they are easily recognized by the reader, who already has a knowledge of what such people are like and how they will behave. Because stereotypes permit authors to sketch certain characters quickly, they serve as a type of fictionalized shorthand. But because they lack individualizing qualities, stereotyped characters do not present people as they are in real life. In addition to using stereotypes, capable authors also create characters who, like real people, are complicated and many-sided.

Read the following passages.

A. Professor Townley put on his glasses, grabbed his tweed coat from the back of a chair, and rushed downstairs.

"I completely forgot about my eight o'clock class," he told Joanie, his wife.

"You've been meeting that class for a whole term now." Joanie smiled and went back to her toast and tea.

"Where are my books?"

"Right where you left them, on the table by the door," Joanie replied.

"Have you seen the car keys?"

"You left them in the car when you came home yesterday." Joanie reached for the newspaper. "I put them on the hook in the kitchen."

Professor Townley dashed about gathering books and keys. Joanie sighed as she heard him run back upstairs and begin to search the bedroom. She abandoned her breakfast and paper and slowly climbed the stairs.

"Now what is it?"

"Joanie," he rushed up to her, "have you seen my glasses?"

"Yes. In fact, dear, I'm looking right at them."

B. Kimmie's hair was dark and curly, too curly as far as Kimmie was concerned. Heat and dampness made it curl even more, and the day was nothing if not hot and damp.

Kimmie wriggled her shoulders to shift the weight of the pack strapped to her back and wondered why she'd ever agreed to a hike on such a day. She dreaded the climb ahead of her, and she was sorry that in her enthusiasm yesterday she had volunteered to cook dinner for the group. Cooking stew over a campfire no longer seemed such a good way to end the day.

1. Which of the passages does not contain a stereotype?
2. Can you name the stereotype found in the other passage?

In a *stereotyped plot* the action follows a familiar and predictable pattern. A talented understudy who suddenly becomes a star, the lady in distress who is rescued by a handsome man with whom she falls in love, the millionaire who leaves all his money to a poor orphan—all are examples of stereotyped plots.

■ STEREOTYPE (ster′ē ə tīp′)

A character in fiction that fits a standardized mental picture of what members of a certain group are like, or a plot in which the action follows a predictable pattern.

■ Apply to **The Storyteller** on page 380.

■ SYMBOL

What does each of the following suggest to you?

a red paper heart
a handshake
a red cross
a bright yellow sports car
the American flag

Each of the above has some special meaning to most people. The meaning may be the same for everyone: a red paper heart, for example, almost always suggests love. Or the meaning may vary from person to person, as is the case with the sports car. The sports car might represent either glamor and wealth or the competitive and dangerous life of a racer.

The paper heart, the sports car, and the rest of the items listed above are *symbols*. A symbol may be an object, a person, an action, a situation—anything that has a meaning of its own but suggests other emotional meanings as well.

In addition to the symbols we share with others, most of us have private symbols to which we attach values and meanings that others do not see in them. Read the following account.

With increasing uneasiness, Karina searched the top of the dresser. She was sure she had left the coin—a shiny half dollar—in the little china dish. Still, she lifted the hand mirror and a vase of flowers to be sure the coin wasn't hidden under one of them.

She thought of the day nearly two years ago when she won the half dollar in the race at the Sons of Italy picnic. At thirteen, Karina had been the youngest in the race. That was the first time in her life that she had won anything—and the first time she had seen any advantage in having such long legs.

Since then, she had run every evening after supper. Her posture was better now that she didn't mind being tall. She won other and better prizes, but she intended to keep the half dollar forever.

Until yesterday Karina hadn't told anyone else about the coin; she'd kept it in a little velvet box in the bottom drawer. But yesterday she had shown it to her new friend Jennifer and then left it in the china dish on the dresser. With increased concern, she began to search the floor. . . .

"It's not like I've stolen anything," Karina's little brother Jeff assured himself as he went into the store. "She won't care that I didn't ask, and I can return it all tomorrow when I get my allowance. In fact, I can give part of it back this afternoon." Having convinced himself, he marched up to the counter, slapped down the half dollar, and ordered one scoop of bubble gum fudge ice cream in a sugar cone.

1. What does the coin symbolize to Karina?
2. How does Jeff view the coin?

Characters in fiction can have their own private symbols. You can usually recognize literary symbols by paying careful attention to the objects, persons, or situations for which a character has special feelings. By analyzing the character's attitude toward these objects, persons, or situations, you

can infer what they mean to that character. This knowledge may help you to understand the character more fully.

Try to find the symbol in the following excerpt from a short story.

She hadn't seen her for two years, but Kelly knew that when Aunt Kathy came back next week, everything at the farm was going to be different. Kelly remembered each detail of the last visit—how her aunt had come breezing in carrying two heavy suitcases as if they didn't weigh an ounce and how lovely her suit had been and how she had started to laugh and talk to all of them almost before she'd gotten through the door.

Kelly had been ten then, but Aunt Kathy (against Kelly's parents' polite objections) had included her in the adult conversation. The two of them had had lunch at a restaurant in town, where her aunt had told Kelly all about the city and her apartment and her job. That whole week Kelly sailed through her chores, hurrying back to the house where her mother and aunt visited. Her bedtimes were ignored as the whole family sat up talking and laughing.

3. From the description, what can you tell about Kelly's day-to-day life?
4. How was life different during Aunt Kathy's visit?
5. Kelly obviously is fond of her aunt, but—in addition to that—what might Aunt Kathy symbolize to Kelly?

■ SYMBOL

A person, place, event, or object that has a meaning in itself but suggests other meanings as well.

■ Apply to **The Hundredth Dove** on page 369.

HANDBOOK OF LITERARY TERMS

■ THEME

For an Old Man

I wish I had listened then. When you began
Those long old stories, I was bored and ran
Outdoors to play; or, older, tactfully drew
The talk away to light immediate things . . .
5 And all the while your generation lay
Behind your baffled eyes and wistful speech
Groping toward mine: and I can never reach
It now. The things you did not say
Are buried with you, and the bright thin line
10 Of contact broken. For I closed a door
And let you go away, your stories all untold:
I wish I had listened more.

Floris Clark McLaren

1. How did the speaker react to the old man's stories as a child? after growing older?
2. What did the old man hope to accomplish by telling his stories? What lines in the poem tell you this?
3. Now that the old man is dead, how does the speaker feel about his or her behavior toward him?
4. Do you think the speaker is the only person who has had an experience like this? Why or why not?
5. Which of the following best expresses the underlying meaning of the poem? (a) A young person who has never been willing to take the time to establish communication with an old man regrets that behavior after the old man dies. (b) Be nice and pay attention to old people or you will feel guilty when they die. (c) Youth may not appreciate the value of communication between generations until it is no longer possible.

The *theme* of a work of literature is the underlying meaning of the selection. Statement **c** above expresses the theme of "For an Old Man."

While the subject of a work is the topic on which an author has chosen to write, the theme makes some statement about or expresses some opinion on that topic. The topic of "For an Old Man" is youth and age. The theme is that youth may not place enough value on contact and communication with old people until the opportunity for such sharing is gone.

Statement **b** gives a moral rather than a theme. A moral is a lesson or a rule to live by: its purpose is to change human behavior. Although the speaker in this poem expresses regret for his or her behavior, he or she does not tell readers what they should do in a similar situation.

Statement **a** tells what happens in "For an Old Man." It gives the PLOT, or pattern of events that make up the poem. The theme of the poem states the significance of the plot. The reader must often examine the pattern of events in a work in order to determine its theme.

A work of literature does not have to contain a theme. Works written purely for entertainment—mystery stories, for example—may not have themes.

■ THEME

The underlying meaning of a literary work. A theme may be directly stated, but more often it is implied.

"For an Old Man" from *The Dalhousie Review*. Reprinted by permission.

■ Apply to **The Fallen Angel** on page 80.

■ TONE

Don't you dare move an inch before I tell you
to!
Please stay right there until I come back.

1. How are the two statements above
similar? How are they different?
2. Read each statement aloud as you think
it might be spoken.

Read through the following, paying
careful attention to the way the authors use
words.

Dear Son,

Now that you have left home for school, our
house seems empty and lonely. Mom and I cheer
ourselves up every evening remembering the good
times we had when you were little. Do you remember the time we played Easter Bunny when
you were five, and I had to hop around the house
wiggling my ears, and you wouldn't let me eat
anything but carrots and lettuce for three days?
Remember how we used to spread the funnies out
on the living room rug and read them together
every Sunday morning? And how you used to
sneak up and sock me in the stomach just for the
fun of it? And how funny you were when Mr.
Nash would come to visit and you used to climb
all over him? I suppose he loved every minute of
it, although he was too shy ever to say so.

Well, we miss you, sonny boy. You're on your
own now in the big, wide world, and we know
you'll do well. Write right away and tell us how
things are starting off at your new school.

Love, Dad

Let's straighten this out, my little man,
And reach an agreement if we can.
I entered your house an honored guest.
My shoes were shined and my trousers are
pressed,
5 And I won't stretch out and read you the
funnies.
And I won't pretend that we're Easter
bunnies. . .
You may take a sock at your daddy's tummy
Or climb all over your doting mummy,
But keep your attention to me in check
10 Or, sonny boy, I will wring your neck. . .

Ogden Nash,
**from "To a Small Boy Standing on My
Shoes While I Am Wearing Them"**

3. To whom is the speaker in each
selection talking?
4. What two very different attitudes are
expressed in these selections?

From "To a Small Boy Standing on My Shoes While I Am Wearing
Them" from *Family Reunion* (British title: *I Wouldn't Have Missed
It*) by Ogden Nash. Copyright 1931 by Ogden Nash. Reprinted by
permission of Little, Brown and Company and Andre Deutsch Ltd.

Tone 663

5. Point out words and phrases that helped you determine the speaker's attitude in each.

Everything ever said is expressed in some tone of voice. The tone in which you speak helps listeners understand your feelings on the subject you are talking about.

An author also expresses a *tone* in writing. Sometimes an author will write in anger, and the choice of short, tense-sounding words, such as *fret*, *rush*, or *hit* will indicate tone. Or, in order to ridicule a situation, a writer may say the opposite of what is meant. In short, a tone may be despairing, triumphant, admiring, affectionate, defiant, resentful, sarcastic, happy, or amused—it may reflect a wide variety of emotions.

Tone in literature has much the same purpose as tone of voice: it helps readers understand an author's attitude toward the subject. To interpret a work of literature accurately, a reader must sense its tone.

To determine the tone of a selection, analyze the words and details used by the author to describe setting, to portray characters, and to present events. For example, a paragraph containing words such as *grim*, *gray*, *bleak*, *dejected*, and *beaten* might have an unhappy or despairing tone. A description like "unique as a snowflake" or "graceful as a gazelle" might convey the author's admiration for the subject.

■ TONE

An author's expressed attitude toward the subject in a literary work. Tone is conveyed through the author's particular choice of words and details in describing setting, portraying characters, and presenting events.

■ Apply to **The Pasture** on page 311.

Rembrandt van Rijn, *Titus at His Desk*, 1655, Rotterdam, Museum Boymans-van Beuningen

WRITER'S HANDBOOK

Writing About Literature

Writing about a literature selection is similar to many other kinds of writing you do. First of all, you need to make sure you understand the assignment. Then you must plan your paper carefully in order to include the necessary information. The Writer's Handbook gives guidelines and models to help you communicate effectively when you write about literature and when you write your own stories and poems. The first article is about three important steps—prewriting, writing, and revising.

PREWRITING

Sample Assignment

Whatever became of Cutie Pie? Write a brief news story to explain what might have happened to Cutie Pie after the spaceship landed in the story beginning on page 3 of this book. First reread and take notes. Look for answers that tell who did what, when, and where. Why are these events of interest to readers?

Follow these guidelines whenever you write about a literature selection.

1. Determine Your Purpose and Audience

First make sure you understand exactly what you are to do. Look for words that set the purpose for your writing.

compare: point out how two or more things are alike

contrast: point out how two or more things are different

convince: persuade by argument or proof

create: produce from one's imagination

describe: give a picture of something

explain: make something clear

imagine: form an image or idea; put yourself in a new situation

summarize: give the main points

support: prove ideas, inferences, or opinions

Before you begin to write, consider your audience. It may be a specific person, as when you are to write a letter, or it may be a wide and varied group, as when you write a news story. Knowing your audience will help you decide what and how much information to give as well as what words to use.

Assignments requiring only one paragraph can be developed around a topic sentence, a sentence stating the main idea of the paragraph. A thesis statement may be needed for a longer composition. It explains the topic of the paper in one or more sentences and may also express your attitude toward the subject.

2. Take Effective Notes

For the assignment to write a news story about what became of Cutie Pie, begin by reviewing the story and taking notes. Look for answers that tell who did what, when and where. Why are these events of interest to readers?

3. Organize Your Notes

Make an outline with the headings *Who, What, Where, When,* and *Why.* Compare the news story on the next page with the notes that were prepared for it. Forms such as charts and cluster diagrams can also be used to organize notes.

WRITING

As you write your first draft, concentrate on getting your ideas on paper quickly, without paying much attention to correct form. Write as if you were talking to someone, clearly and to the point. If you can't think of a first sentence, leave it for later. Begin with your second sentence.

Change words and move sentences around as you write. Don't be discouraged if your first draft is less than perfect. Your ideas are down on paper, and you will have a chance to revise them later.

Here is the way one writer developed a news story about what became of Cutie Pie.

```
Whatever Became of Cutie Pie?
    As everyone knows, Cutie Pie, the colorful
little creature from another planet, escaped from
his glass cage and seemed to disappear. Yesterday
an alien spaceship was reportedly sighted near
Herts Village. Scientists believe Cutie Pie
returned to his home aboard that spaceship. They
had observed that he was unhappy and sick here on
Earth, in spite of their attempts to create an
environment like the one on his home planet.
```

```
Headline
1. Who—Cutie Pie
2. What—escaped
   and seemed to
   disappear; may
   have returned
   home
3. When—yesterday,
   after sighting
   of alien
   spaceship
4. Where—near
   Herts Village
5. Why—he was
   unhappy and ill
   on Earth
```

REVISING

If possible, set aside your first draft for a few days. Do your ideas still make sense? It is often useful to read your draft to a partner or group for help before revising. Use the following checklist.

Content and Organization Questions
• Is the topic of each paragraph developed fully with examples or reasons?
• Does each sentence in a paragraph relate to its topic sentence?
• Are the ideas presented in a reasonable order?

• Are transitional words used within and between paragraphs?
• Should any information be added?
• Should some information be dropped or moved?
• Does the concluding paragraph provide a good ending?

Style Questions
• Is the language simple and direct?
• Are the point of view and tone consistent?
• Is there a variety of sentence types?

- Are too many *and*'s used when other ways of combining sentences are appropriate?
- Are the verbs active rather than passive?
- Are the tenses of the verbs consistent?
- Are the pronoun references clear?
- Are there overused words, such as *nice* and *good*, that should be changed?

Mechanical Questions
- Is each paragraph indented?
- Are words correctly spelled?
- Are capital letters used correctly?
- Is punctuation used correctly?
- Are there sentence fragments that need to be revised?

Supporting Your Ideas

When your assignment is to support an idea, your main task is to convince your readers that your idea is sound, or valid. To do this, you need to gather evidence in much the same way that a detective gathers evidence to solve a crime.

PREWRITING

Sample Assignment

After reading "The Widow and the Parrot," what idea do you have about the kind of person Mrs. Gage is? Write a short description of her. Give examples from the story to support your ideas.

Here are some guidelines to help you with the sample assignment.

1. Go to the Source

First go back and reread the story. As you do this, make notes about Mrs. Gage's appearance, sayings, and beliefs. Include examples of how she affects others.

Consider using **direct quotations** from the story to provide specific examples. In a direct quotation, the writer copies exact words from the selection, in the exact order in which they are presented. The quote is enclosed in quotation marks.

You will also want to **paraphrase,** or state in your own words, examples from the story. In a paraphrase the writer tells something about a character or an event but changes the exact wording.

2. Choose Your Examples

Now look over your notes and select only the strongest and most convincing items. Ask yourself: Is this evidence convincing to me? Will it convince my readers? If you want to prove that Mrs. Gage demonstrates kindness to animals, what examples would you use to support your idea? Your strongest evidence would be clear details that directly relate to the point—she feeds her dog well, even though she is low on money. Your weakest evidence would be unsupported opinions— she seems like a nice person; therefore, she probably is kind to animals. Watch for statements that are true but have nothing to do with the point you want to make—

the clergyman thought Mrs. Gage was wandering in her mind. Such examples hurt your argument not only because they can be dismissed easily, but also because they distract your readers from the evidence that does support your idea.

3. Arrange Your Examples

Go over your examples and arrange them in an order that makes sense. One good way to present evidence is in the reverse order of importance, saving the best for last. This allows you to leave your readers with a strong final impression.

If time is an important element in the selection, you may want to arrange your examples chronologically. If cause-and-effect relationships are important, you may want to show how one event causes another, which in turn causes another.

WRITING

4. Explain Your Idea

State your idea in the first sentence or two. Follow it with your examples. Be sure to explain how each piece of evidence relates to your idea.

5. End Forcefully

After presenting your last piece of evidence, bring your composition to a quick and forceful conclusion. You might summarize your evidence and restate your main point, rewording it slightly.

REVISING

When you have completed your first draft, evaluate it by using the checklist of content and organization, style, and mechanical questions on pages 667–668. In addition, look for the following.

- Is the idea stated clearly?
- Do the examples support the stated idea?
- Does the paper end with a summary of the evidence and a restatement of the main idea?

You will find this article helpful in completing the assignments on pages 22, 160, 291, 530, and 613.

Writing a Clear Description

Suppose your assignment is to write a description of a favorite pet, a character in a story, the setting of a novel, your best friend, or your worst enemy. How can you find just the right words for the "picture" you hope to "paint"? Where should you begin? What should you say?

PREWRITING

Sample Assignment

Describe Rikki-tikki-tavi. Tell about his physical appearance, his fighting style, and the attitudes of the other characters toward him.

1. Form a Picture in Your Mind

Visualize what you are going to describe. Imagine the character, the scene, and the mood.

2. Decide What Main Impression You Want to Create

What makes the character in the story memorable? Why is the place special? Consider how you want your readers to picture what you are describing.

3. Choose Details and Arrange Them

Remember that the reader can't see your picture without your help. As you form the picture in your mind, jot down all the details that come to mind. If you are writing about a literary selection, reread to find details. For example, if your assignment is to describe Rikki-tikki-tavi, you might review the story and list these details:

Rikki-tikki-tavi
like a little cat in fur and tail
eyes and nose pink
could scratch himself anywhere with any leg
fluffs up tail to look like a bottle brush

---

4. Choose a Way to Present Your Details

You can arrange them according to any of several patterns. If you are describing Rikki-tikki-tavi, you might begin with his physical appearance, move on to his behavior in a fight, and conclude with his relationship to the other animals and people in the story.

If you are describing a house, you might use a spatial pattern, moving from the outside of the house to the inside or from the roof to the basement. Look over the details you want to use and select a pattern that fits those details.

WRITING

5. Create a Picture

Use words that appeal to the senses of sight, sound, touch, taste, or smell. If you are writing about an abandoned house at night, don't list as a detail that the building is frightening. Instead show the fear with your choice of details.

---

sight: broken windows; shadows; darkness
sound: shutters striking the side of the
   house; wind blowing; creaky doors
smell: musty furniture; dampness
touch: dust; cobwebs; cold air

One way to add spark to writing is to use precise, forceful words. Fire doesn't just *burn;* it *crackles, snaps, smolders, dances,* or *hisses.* Listen and observe carefully. Be specific.

Use comparisons to help make your description vivid. Instead of "My aunt stood motionless," try "My aunt stood as motionless as a petrified tree."

6. Round Off Your Description

End your description with a sentence or two that gives your composition a sense of completeness. Some closing sentences summarize. Others express an opinion, pose a question, express wonder, or share a memory.

REVISING

In addition to the checklist questions on pages 667–668, ask yourself:
- Does the description create a main impression?
- Does it show rather than tell?
- Are the words and comparisons precise and forceful?

You will find this article helpful in completing the assignments on pages 72, 129, 289, 332, 363, and 379.

Writing to Compare and Contrast

Many writing assignments require you to make **comparisons** or **contrasts.** How do you begin to discuss likenesses and differences between two or more characters, events, objects, or ideas? Here are some basic guidelines.

PREWRITING
Sample Assignment

Compare Mrs. Wang in "The Old Demon" and Don Anselmo in "Gentleman of Río en Medio." Write two or three paragraphs in which you tell ways they are alike and ways they are different. Consider their families and how they feel about them.

1. List Points of Comparison

Whether your assignment is general, as "Compare Mrs. Wang and Don Anselmo," or specific, as "Compare the family relationships of Mrs. Wang and Don Anselmo," take time to list points of comparison.

For example, if you are comparing the family relationships of two characters in stories, your points of comparison might be as follows:

attitude of character toward family
attitude of family toward character
how character is related to others
size of family

As you study your selections, you will probably drop some points of comparison and add others. Having some ideas down on paper will help you get organized.

2. Make Charts

Study your characters and jot down your notes in separate columns for each subject. As the example shows, your lists won't always be equal in the number of items included in each column.

Mrs. Wang	Don Anselmo
thinks dead husband was careless and a "silly fellow," but still works to get him out of purgatory appreciates the concern shown for her by grandson's wife cares more for grandson's unborn child than for self sad to learn of loss of one living brother	considers everyone in his village a descendant shows care for family by planting a tree each time a child is born shows value of family over money by refusing to take payment for trees

3. Form an Opinion

Write your opinion on the comparison or contrast of your subjects in one or two sentences. For example, you might say that Don Anselmo and Mrs. Wang differ in the number of living relatives in their families and that they live in different countries during different times. On the other hand, the two are alike in that both seem to value family relationships. You might use the statement to begin your paper, or you may not use it at all. Establishing your opinion at this point will help you choose details to use in shaping your paper.

4. Choose a Pattern for Presenting the Details

There are a number of ways to arrange details in a composition about likenesses and differences. One method is to compare or contrast your subjects point by point, writing a sentence or two for each item. For example, in contrasting Stephen Malone and the Pioche Kid in "One Night Stand," you might write that the two men are at opposite extremes in their experience with guns. While Malone has never fired a gun, the Pioche Kid has killed four men.

A second pattern is to discuss one of your subjects first and then turn to the other subject. If you use this method, remember to keep your discussions balanced, devoting about the same amount of space to each one and covering the same points.

A third method is to explain the likenesses of your subjects in one section and the differences in another section.

WRITING

5. Write Your Composition

Begin with a sentence that clearly identifies the subjects you will compare or contrast and your purpose in doing so. Then follow the pattern you have chosen to present your details.

6. Use Words That Signal

Use connecting words and phrases to help show how your examples are related to the subject. To signal likenesses, use words such as these: *comparably, alike, similarly,* and *both.* The following words and phrases signal differences: *but, yet, on the other hand,* and *in contrast.*

7. Conclude Your Paper

There are a variety of ways to round out your composition. You can restate your purpose, briefly summarize the points of comparison, use your last example as the basis for a concluding remark, or offer your own opinion about the comparisons or contrasts shown.

REVISING

In addition to using the checklist on pages 667–668, consider the following questions.
- Are my points of comparison clear?
- Is my organization pattern consistent?
- Have I used words that emphasize likenesses and differences?

You will find this article helpful in completing the assignments on pages 53, 72, 205, 337, 421, 444, 530, and 629.

WRITER'S HANDBOOK

Writing to Summarize

You will need to know how to write a summary for most book reports and for composition assignments that require a summary of a story or play. Remember that a summary is a brief statement. It gives only the main points about the selection.

PREWRITING

Sample Assignment

Summarize the story "Raymond's Run." Include only the main events and omit any unimportant details.

Understanding a Summary

A summary should, first of all, be short. For a short story, a summary should be no longer than a paragraph. If you are summarizing an entire book, you may need to write two or three paragraphs, but no more.

A summary must also be accurate. Be sure that your facts are correct. If you can't remember a character's name or the spelling of it, look back and find it.

Newspaper reporters use the five Ws—*who* did *what, when, where,* and *why.* Using these one-word questions will help you choose and organize the important points in your summary.

A summary of a short story or novel usually follows the plot line and includes only the main events. A summary of nonfiction is made up of the main ideas. In summarizing nonfiction, it will help you to watch for the following clues.

bold lettering
words in italic type
repeated words and phrases
first and last sentences of paragraphs

WRITING

Here are two summaries of the short story "Raymond's Run." The first is too long. It tells too much of the story, and it includes too many details. In the second summary, the writer omitted unimportant details and combined sentences. Notice that the summaries are written in the present tense. Follow this convention when you summarize.

Squeaky lives with her family in New York City. She runs fast. She is faster than anyone in her neighborhood. She is proud of her running ability. It doesn't matter that her father really is faster because only the two of them know this fact. Her family responsibility is Raymond, her brother, who needs constant care and attention. Squeaky practices all the time, taking Raymond along with her. One day she meets Gretchen, Rosie, and Mary Louise while she is practicing. Rosie insults Raymond. On Field Day, Mr. Pearson, who pins numbers on the racers, asks Squeaky if she plans to give someone else a chance this year. Some people think Gretchen might win the race. Just before the race begins she tells herself she must win. During the race she notices Raymond running in his own style along beside her, on the other side of the fence. All at once she realizes that even if she loses the race this year everything will be fine. Her new goal will be coaching Raymond. In the end Gretchen smiles at her.

Squeaky runs faster than anyone in her neighborhood, and she is proud of her ability. At home her only responsibility is Raymond, her brother. While running in an important Field Day race, she notices Raymond running along beside her, on the other side of the fence. All at once she realizes that even if she loses the race this year her new goal will be coaching Raymond.

REVISING

In addition to reviewing the checklist on pages 667–668, ask yourself these questions.
• Have I included only the main ideas or the main events in the plot line?
• Does the summary tell who did what, when, where, and why?
• Is the summary short?
• Is it accurate?
• Have I used present tense verbs?
• Have I combined sentences?

You will find this article helpful in completing the assignments on pages 129, 145, 260, 315, 434, and 567.

Writing About Plot

The **plot** of a story consists of a series of related events that presents a problem or conflict, leads to the climax or point at which the conflict is resolved, and finally results in a resolution of the conflict. For more details, see the article on plot in the Handbook of Literary Terms.

Composition assignments about plot may require you to discuss the plot as a whole or to look at only one aspect of it. Either way, you will have to understand the story well and probably also reread at least parts of it.

PREWRITING
Sample Assignment

Here is a sample assignment about plot based on the story "One Night Stand" on page 29.

Does "One Night Stand" have an effective plot? In a three- or four-paragraph composition point out the strengths or weaknesses of the plot.

Recall that for a story to have an effective plot, suspense must be created through a conflict or problem. The events should be linked in a cause-and-effect pattern with the events leading to a turning point in the action and finally concluding the story in a satisfactory way.

The following points may help you with composition assignments about plot.

1. Think It Through

Ask yourself questions, such as the following.

What is the conflict? How does it create suspense? Review your Glossary of Literary Terms for a definition of *suspense*.

Are the events linked together in a cause-and-effect relationship? Does the turning point follow the events naturally, or does it seem forced?

Is the conclusion satisfactory?

2. Trace the Plot

Here is how you might chart the skeleton of the plot of "One Night Stand."

Sequence of Main Events: Malone overhears a conversation between Brady and Else. Malone offers to play the role of Hickok in front of the Pioche Kid, who has come to town to murder Brady. The Kid enters the bar. Malone enters the bar. Malone offers to pay two men for a digging job. Malone leaves the bar.	**Conflict:** There is an external conflict between Malone and the Pioche Kid. **Climax:** The Pioche Kid walks to the door and sees Malone with his back to him. **Resolution:** The Kid leaves town and Malone admits he has blanks in his gun.

WRITING

Here is an example of the first paragraph in a composition written about the plot of "One Night Stand."

The story "One Night Stand" by Louis L'Amour has an effective plot because there is suspense created by a conflict between characters. The events are linked together naturally in a cause-and-effect pattern. The turning point in the action leads to a satisfactory conclusion of the story.

In the remaining paragraphs of the composition, you would need to explain the various points made in this paragraph. Deal with the points in the order in which they are given in the assignment.
—the conflict
—the development of suspense
—a cause-and-effect pattern of events
—the turning point
—the conclusion

Include examples to support each point you make about the effectiveness, or lack of effectiveness, of the plot.

REVISING

When you have completed your first draft, evaluate it with the checklist on pages 667–668.

Here are some specific points that you should also check.
• Is the connection between events clear?
• Have I used examples from the selection to support my judgment about the effectiveness of the plot?

You will find this article helpful in completing the assignment on page 391.

WRITER'S HANDBOOK

Writing About Characters

As a reader, you have no doubt met fictional characters who seem as real as people you know. Consider, for example, Squeaky in "Raymond's Run," Mrs. Wang in "The Old Demon," and Anthony Mullins in "The Fallen Angel." The authors of these stories have used certain methods to bring their characters to life. Other characters are not memorable at all. You can scarcely remember their names—let alone anything unusual about them. Where did the writer fail?

PREWRITING
Sample Assignment

When you are asked to write about a character or characters for a composition assignment, review the story with the specific assignment in mind.

Choose a character from one of the stories in this book. Describe that character from the information given by the author. Explain what methods of characterization the author uses to picture the character.

1. Think It Through

You will usually have to consider the following questions when writing about characters.

Who are the major characters and who are the minor ones? Most of the attention in a story will be centered on the main character or characters. Recall that in "The Fallen Angel" the main characters are Anthony Mullins and Sam Angeli. Minor characters, though not fully developed, may make a crucial difference in the action of the story, as Sue Ellen plays an important part in what happens to Angeli in the conclusion of the story.

How does an author create characters on paper? Recall that authors reveal characters through physical description, the character's actions and words, the character's inner thoughts and feelings, and what other characters in the story say and think. Consider these methods as you review a story. It is a good idea to make notes of examples that you may use in your composition.

Do the character's motives seem to suit the person portrayed in the story? Well-developed characters act in certain ways for reasons. When writing about a literary selection, try to figure out what motivates each character. Are the character's actions consistent with the person created by the author?

Are the characters stereotypes or are they unique individuals? Story characters come to life for readers when they seem to be real. What makes Anthony Mullins seem like a real person? What is special about Mrs. Wang in "The Old Demon"?

2. Organize Character Details

If you were to choose to write about Ch-stal in "Cutie Pie," you might begin by

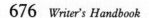

reviewing the story and making notes similar to the ones in this chart. Other details from the story could be added to the chart. In addition, columns could be included for Ch-stal's motivations and his attitude toward others.

Physical Description	Actions	Inner Thoughts	Attitudes of Others
iridescent feathers curved, cozy, rounded body dark, liquid eyes gentle mouth busy hands whiskers	hides after escaping searches for a friend communicates with a baby	knows the scientists don't mean to hurt him realizes that even if he can escape he will be powerless without whiskers	the world says, "too sweet to *live*" scientists are sympathetic but annoyed by his sickness

WRITING

Here is one way you might begin an assignment in which you describe Ch-stal and explain the methods of characterization used by the author of "Cutie Pie."

The events in "Cutie Pie" could not happen in the world today, but Ch-stal, the main character in the story, is clearly pictured by the author. One way readers learn about Ch-stal is through the vivid words used to describe his physical appearance. For example, he has feathers of changing colors and whiskers that allow him to communicate. Human beings think Ch-stal is "cute." The author shows why people on Earth are so delighted with Ch-stal in the following example from the story: "Human hearts doted on his dark, liquid eyes; on the gentle mouth that seemed to smile; . . ." (page 3)

In other paragraphs about the character of Ch-stal, you would need to develop the ideas listed under the columns headed "Actions," "Inner Thoughts," and "Attitudes of Others" in the chart.

REVISING

When you have completed the first draft of your composition, evaluate it, either alone or with others, by going through the checklist on pages 667–668. Here are some other points about characters to check.
• Is the character portrayed accurately, as he or she appears in the story?
• Are there examples from the story to support the character traits discussed?

You will find this article helpful in completing the assignments on pages 91, 187, 197, 257, 332, and 444.

Writing Dialogue

A dialogue is a conversation between two or more people. While a story or a novel usually includes some dialogue, a play will consist almost entirely of conversations among the characters. Nonfiction will generally have less dialogue than fiction. A poem sometimes will include dialogue for a special reason.

PREWRITING
Sample Assignment

Suppose Wild Bill Hickok comes into town just after the final scene of "One Night Stand." Write a dialogue that might occur between him and Stephen Malone.

Think It Through

As you read literary selections, notice these important points about dialogue. When you are assigned to write dialogue, try to follow the same guidelines.

Dialogue imitates the way people talk in real life. People often leave out a word or speak in incomplete sentences, as in the following conversation between Stephen Malone and the bartender in "One Night Stand."

> "That's right. I want two men to dig a hole about—" he turned deliberately and looked right at the Kid, "—six feet long, six feet deep, and three wide."
> "Whereabouts you want it dug?"
> "On Boot Hill."
> "A grave?"
> "Exactly."

Dialogue should suit the person who is speaking. Note that Malone, the out-of-work actor in "One Night Stand," speaks in a somewhat formal manner, in keeping with his profession.

> "I am grateful for your concern but this will be the first time I have been offered one thousand dollars for a single performance."

Dialogue advances the story. Any conversation between characters should move along the action of the story or reveal information needed for the unfolding of the plot. Note that the dialogue at the beginning of "One Night Stand" introduces the main character and provides the setting and conflict of the story. In "The Hummingbird That Lived Through Winter" Dikran's words advance the plot.

> "Put a tablespoonful of honey over the gas fire and pour it into my hand, but be sure it is not too hot."

Dialogue is indicated with the use of quotation marks. Whenever a character speaks, quotation marks are placed around the exact words of the speaker. A new paragraph is used to show a change in speaker. Plays are an exception, since they consist almost entirely of dialogue. Instead of quotation marks, the speaker's name is printed at the left of the words spoken. The reader of a play is alerted to the change in speakers by the name.

WRITING

Here is the way one writer began the assignment to create a dialogue between Wild Bill Hickok and Stephen Malone. Are Malone's words consistent with the way he is shown in the story?

Wild Bill Hickok walked into Brady's room through the open door and said, "I just saw the Pioche Kid riding off in a cloud of dust. What happened? Why are *you* dressed to look like *me?*"

Stephen Malone replied, "Someone had to deal with the Pioche Kid, and I needed money—desperately."

To complete the assignment, the writer would need to explain why Malone needs money, what kind of costume he put together in order to look like Hickok, and what Malone's thoughts and feelings were during his encounter with the Kid.

REVISING

When you have completed the first draft of your dialogue, use the checklist on pages 667–668. In addition, consider the following:

- Are the exact words enclosed in quotation marks?
- Are the words spoken consistent with the character in the story, or with the character created by the writer of the dialogue?
- Is each change of speaker indicated by a new paragraph?

You will find this article helpful in completing the assignments on pages 145, 264, 337, 425, and 629.

Writing Your Own Story

Ideas for stories come from many sources, including conversations, newspaper accounts, dreams, memories, and books. Some writers first imagine characters, develop them in detail to get to know them, and then let the characters move the story along. Other writers start with a conflict that determines who the characters will be and what events will occur.

PREWRITING
Sample Assignment

Think about Hugh in "The Hundredth Dove" and the things in which he takes pride. When is pride good and when can it blind people so that they lose sight of the difference between right and wrong? Write a brief story of your own about a character who suffers from too much pride.

No matter how you begin writing, you first need to make some basic decisions about plot, characters, and setting. You will also want to determine whether the story should be told from the first-person or third-person point of view.

1. Outline Your Plot

What will be the main conflict? Usually a short story will have only one major conflict. It may be an external conflict in which a character struggles with another character, society, or nature, or it may be an internal conflict where the character struggles with his or her own beliefs or feelings.

What events will occur as a result of the conflict? List them and show how they will lead to the climax, or turning point, and conclusion. These events should be interesting, and they should keep the plot moving.

Work for a smooth ending to the conflict, one that is true to life and not too farfetched. Remember that ". . . and they lived happily ever after" endings are not necessarily realistic.

2. Describe Your Main Characters

What kind of person is this individual? Draw on your observations of people and on characters in books you have read. Choose a name. Describe the character's appearance. How will this person think, talk, and act? How will your character interact with others? What will be others' reactions to your character?

3. Determine an Appropriate Setting

Choose a time and a place for your story. It is easier to write convincingly about your own time period and a place you know well, but you can use another time and place if you do some background research before you begin to write. The importance of setting varies from one story to another. It is up to you as writer to determine the amount of information about setting that readers of your story need.

4. Decide Who Will Narrate the Story

One of the characters in the story might relate the events using the first-person point of view, or the narrator could be an outsider who is not a character in the story. If the outsider sees into the mind of only one character, the point of view is third-person limited. If the narrator sees into the minds of all of the characters, the point of view is third-person omniscient. Refer to the article on point of view in the Handbook of Literary Terms, if necessary.

Review the plots, characters, and settings of stories you have read to get ideas for your own stories. On the next page is a chart with examples based on stories in this book. You will probably recognize many of the conflicts, characters, and settings listed. Make your own chart. Use other selections in this book and your own experiences.

WRITING

Recall that the bachelor in "The Storyteller" uses a simple, familiar plot but gives the story a new twist by changing the ending. You can follow a similar pattern in writing your own story. Use the basic conflict of a well-known story but make your writing unique by changing the characters and conclusion.

One writer began a story about a character who suffers too much pride with the following paragraph.

        Once, long ago and in a
    faraway country known as
    Outer Marsland, Queen Tess
    ruled a kingdom that
    stretched for hundreds of
    miles in all directions from
    her palace. She took great
    pride in the size of the
    kingdom. Although it was
    already the largest in the
    world, she wanted to make it

Ideas for Stories

Conflicts	Characters	Settings
wanting to win a race but facing a new and challenging competitor meeting an enemy face to face finding something of value but knowing it should be returned to the owner facing an obstacle or physical handicap wanting to keep a wild animal that needs to be free	a teenager, slim, athletic, a strong competitor a widow, lame, nearsighted, kind to animals, poor a widow, strong, courageous, persistent, unselfish an actor, talented, brave, clever a cowboy, outwardly brave but a coward inside a mongoose, furry, curious, a fighter a blind person, successful in business	a large city a small town another planet a faraway country a drugstore a train a mining town current times an imagined future time a past time

even greater by taking over the neighboring lands ruled by King Nicholas.

Notice that the first paragraph introduces two characters, identifies the setting, and suggests the beginning of a conflict. The story will be narrated from the third-person point of view.

REVISING

When you have finished your first draft, evaluate it with the checklist on pages 667– 668. You should also look for the following things.

- Is the conflict well developed through the pattern of events?
- Is there a clear turning point in the action and a satisfying conclusion for the story?
- Does the main character come alive?
- If the time and place are important, are they explained?

You will find this article helpful in completing the assignments on pages 341, 385, and 468.

WRITER'S HANDBOOK

Writing a Poem

A poem is an arrangement of words designed to express a feeling or to describe an object or an experience. It is like a telegram in that it gives a message in a few words. Every poem will have rhythm, whether it is regular in beat or not, since there are always some words that are stressed more than others. Elements of literature often found in poems include rhyme, imagery, simile, metaphor, and personification.

PREWRITING

Sample Assignment

Recall that a poem is an attempt to re-create an experience. Write a brief poem of not more than six lines. Use an image to appeal to one or more of the senses.

Whenever your assignment is to write a poem, follow these guidelines.

1. Choose a Subject

Subjects of poems range from spiders to rusty automobiles to love. The well-known poet William Carlos Williams chose such subjects as a red wheelbarrow, plums in a refrigerator, and a number on a fire engine. The subject can be whatever captures your interest and imagination.

2. Use Appropriate Rhythm

Rhythm is the arrangement of stressed and unstressed sounds. It can be regular, or it may be varied to suit the mood or to emphasize certain words.

3. Decide Whether or Not to Use Rhyme

Rhyme is the repetition of syllable sounds. Although rhyme is important in many poems, it is not essential to poetry. In fact, some kinds of poems, such as haiku, should not rhyme.

4. Choose Appropriate Images

Concrete words that appeal to the senses of sight, sound, smell, touch, and taste are frequently used in poetry. Carefully chosen **imagery** helps create or re-create experiences to which readers or listeners can respond.

5. Consider Using Figurative Language

Language expanded beyond its ordinary literal meaning provides fresh insights or expresses a fitting relationship between things basically unlike. A comparison of two essentially unlike things is a **metaphor.** A comparison that uses the word *like* or *as* is a **simile.** Another device often used by poets is **personification,** in which human traits are given to nonhuman objects.

6. Consider the Form of the Poem

Some kinds of poems, like haiku, must follow a strict form, but most often the form is determined by the effect the poet wants to achieve.

Generally each line of a poem begins with a capital letter, but, again, there are exceptions to this convention. As a beginning poet, try to follow the usual style.

The use of commas, periods, and other marks of punctuation helps the reader follow the meaning of a poem. Try to use punctuation that will communicate your ideas effectively.

WRITING

Suppose you decide to write a haiku for the sample assignment. A haiku is a verse in three lines. The lines should not rhyme. The first and third lines have five syllables each; the second line has seven syllables. A haiku usually gives a sudden glimpse of nature, and the first line often suggests a season of the year. Since a haiku almost always includes an image that appeals to the senses, it is a suitable choice for the sample assignment.

The chart shows various ideas considered by one person who chose to write a haiku.

Seasons of the Year	Possible Subjects	Glimpses of Nature
spring summer autumn winter	wild flowers families of ducks falling leaves songbird	patches of color swimming on ponds red and yellow snowy branch

Note how the writer chose from the possibilities listed in the chart to create the following haiku.

On a snowy branch
A feathered cardinal sings—
Red against the white.

REVISING

After you have written your poem, evaluate it according to the following list.
- Do the words create an experience to which readers will respond?
- Is the rhythm appropriate to the subject and mood of the poem?

Writing as a Story Character

Have you ever dreamed about what it would be like to be someone else? When you were a child, you may have played at being a movie star or hero of the wild West. Doing a writing assignment that asks you to express someone else's opinion or to relate events from that person's point of view requires playing such a role. You will need to put yourself in that character's place—to think, react, and speak as that character does.

PREWRITING
Sample Assignment

Assume you are Mrs. Gage in "The Widow and the Parrot" and have just arrived home after your trip to Rodmell. After collecting your thoughts, you take out your diary. Write three or four paragraphs from Mrs. Gage's point of view. Tell what happened and how you feel about it.

Here are some suggestions to help you write as a story character.

1. Familiarize Yourself with the Character

Learn everything you can about the person you are asked to become. If the assignment involves a character in a story, read the story carefully and jot down any details that might help you understand that character better. What does the person look like? Is he or she young, old, tall, short, overweight, attractive, sickly? How does the character speak? It might be in a mumble, with a stutter, or in dialect. Note how the person feels about himself or herself and what other characters think and say. Is the character shy, bold, friendly, fearful? Is he or she well liked, despised, trusted, honored? Finally, consider the situation the person is in at the moment in the story. Is the situation dangerous, emotionally upsetting, happy?

2. Study the Assignment

Make sure you understand the purpose of the writing assignment. Sometimes you will be given specific instructions. For example, for the assignment "Being a Story Character" on page 28, you are to imagine you are Gretchen B. Lewis and write a diary entry. You are specifically asked to include what the girls' actions at the end of the story show about their feelings. For this assignment, you will need to reread at least the ending of the story and probably the part in which the girls meet earlier as well. As you read, make notes on exactly what happens.

Other assignments may give you more freedom in choosing what you will say.

You might be asked, for instance, to imagine what Gretchen would say and do if she were to run into Squeaky five years later. In this assignment, you can be creative and let your imagination take over. Gretchen might say and do almost anything, as long as it is consistent with her character in "Raymond's Run."

3. Use the First-Person Point of View

When you write as a story character, use the pronoun *I*. Express the feelings and words of that character. If there is dialogue in the story, study your character's words. For example, Mrs. Gage in "The Widow and the Parrot" is apt to exclaim "Lawk a mussy" at times when she is nervous or excited.

WRITING

Note how one writer began a diary entry for the day Mrs. Gage returned to Spilsby after her trip to Rodmell.

> Today I came home to Spilsby. Lawk a mussy, what a trip it was! First I thought old brother Joseph left me a fortune. Then Mr. Stagg informed me there was no trace of the three thousand pounds. I just knew old Joseph did this express to plague me. All the time, my poor old leg was troubling me. It's not easy moving around when you're lame and don't see well either.

To continue the diary entry for the sample assignment, the writer would need to include what Mrs. Gage would say about the fire, finding the coins, and the parrot.

REVISING

Use the checklist on pages 667–668 to evaluate your work. In addition, ask

yourself the following questions.
- Does the character sound like the person portrayed in the story? Are the ideas and emotions consistent with what I know about the character?

- Did I use the first-person point of view?
- Have I followed the assignment exactly?

You will find this article helpful in completing the assignments on pages 159, 181, 220, 233, 368, and 590.

Writing to Persuade

You are sometimes asked to express and defend a viewpoint about a literature selection. There are certain techniques you can use to persuade others to your way of thinking. To be convincing, you need to organize your argument logically, present the facts clearly, and give supporting examples.

PREWRITING
Sample Assignment

Is Don Anselmo in "Gentleman of Río en Medio" truly a gentleman, or is he pretending to be something other than he really is? Find examples to support your opinion.

Use these guidelines when you are asked to express and defend an opinion.

1. State Your Opinion in a Sentence

If you are writing that Don Anselmo is, or is not, truly a gentleman, you may want to begin by checking the definition of *gentleman* in a dictionary. One dictionary defines a gentleman as "a man of good family; a well-bred man; a man of fine feelings or instincts, shown by his behavior and his consideration of others." Review the story and decide if Don Anselmo is a gentleman.

Write your idea as clearly and as forcefully as you can. Your tone will help

persuade your readers. Sound confident and avoid saying "I think."

2. Reread the Selection

Look for facts, details, and examples that support your idea. Do you still believe your conclusion is true? If you do, go on. If you don't think it is valid, change your opinion to one that is supported by examples in the story.

3. Make Notes

Jot down the evidence that supports your opinion. For example, your definition suggests that to persuade your readers Don Anselmo is a gentleman you need examples showing him as a man of good family, well bred, who has fine feelings and shows consideration for others.

> *good family:* he lives in a town where his people have been for hundreds of years; he is proud of his large family
> *well bred:* he bows when he enters the room and removes his hat and gloves;

he makes polite conversation about the weather before getting to the business matters

a man of fine feelings and instincts: he refuses more money for his land because he has made an agreement to sell for a certain price; he cares about his family and plants a tree for every person born in the town; he refuses to sell what he feels he doesn't own

4. Make Sure Your Opinion Is Sound

Find three or four strong points to back up your opinion. Your most solid evidence will be factual details about which there can be no disagreement.

When Don Anselmo refuses to sell his land for more money than was first offered, the narrator says, "Finally he signed the deed and took the money but refused to take more than the amount agreed upon." (page 38, column 1)

Look for evidence that supports the opposite viewpoint. If you find it, your argument may not be as strong as it should be. Although Don Anselmo wears worn-out clothing and has little money, there is no evidence in the story that he ever acts in less than a gentlemanly manner.

Avoid words and phrases that signal weak evidence—words such as *always, every, never, none, everyone realizes,* and *it's always true.* These words are used to make the evidence seem more convincing than it is.

5. Arrange Your Evidence

Save your strongest reasons for first and last. Give a paragraph to each main point you make. Use a topic sentence to let your readers know what each point is. For your concluding paragraph, you may want to restate your idea.

WRITING

The first two paragraphs of one writer's paper about Don Anselmo are shown below.

Don Anselmo is pictured as a true gentleman in the story. One dictionary defines a gentleman as a man of good family who is well bred and whose behavior shows consideration for others. Don Anselmo possesses all of these qualities.

The author portrays Don Anselmo as a man of some social standing in the town of Río en Medio. He lives in the place where his people have lived for hundreds of years. On the day of the sale of his land, he talks about his family and shows his pride in them.

The remaining paragraphs for this paper would state that Don Anselmo is well bred and that he is a man of fine feelings and instincts. These statements would need to be supported by examples from the story.

REVISING

Test your first draft. Is your evidence convincing? Be objective.
- Does the first sentence of each paragraph express the main idea of the paragraph?
- Are there examples to back up each of your main ideas?
- Does the last paragraph restate the viewpoint of the first paragraph?

You will find this article helpful in completing the assignments on pages 277 and 590.

WRITER'S HANDBOOK

GLOSSARY OF LITERARY TERMS

Words in SMALL CAPITAL LETTERS refer you to other entries in the Glossary of Literary Terms.

alliteration (ə lit′ə rā′shən), the REPETITION of consonant sounds at the beginnings of words or within words. (See the Handbook of Literary Terms.)

biography (bī og′rə fē), any account of a real person's life. The excerpt from *Harriet Tubman* on page 188 is biography. *Autobiography* is the story of part or all of a person's life written by the person who lived it.

characterization (kar′ik tər ə zā′shən), the methods an author uses to acquaint a reader with the characters in a work. (See the Handbook of Literary Terms.)

connotation (kon′ə tā′shən), the emotional associations surrounding a word, as opposed to its literal meaning. (See the Handbook of Literary Terms.)

denotation (dē′nō tā′shən), the strict, literal meaning of a word; the definition in a dictionary. (See the Handbook of Literary Terms.)

dialogue, the conversation between one or more people in a literary work.

drama, a composition in prose or verse written to be acted on a stage or before motion-picture or television cameras, or in front of a microphone.

end rhyme, the rhyming of words at the ends of lines of poetry. "Under the Mistletoe," page 275, has end rhyme. (See Handbook of Literary Terms.)

epic (ep′ik), a long NARRATIVE poem dealing with great heroes and adventures, written in a majestic style, and often expressing the ideals of a people. *The Adventures of Ulysses*, page 542, is based on an epic.

essay, a brief composition that presents a personal point of view. "Thank You," page 215, is an essay.

fable, a brief TALE, in which the characters are often animals, told to point out a moral truth. There are fables in Unit 6.

fantasy/science fiction. Both fantasy and science fiction are works set wholly or partly in an unreal world. Often, at least one character is unlike a human being. Frequently, the plot concerns events that cannot be scientifically explained. "Cutie Pie," page 3, is an example of science fiction. "The Hundredth Dove," page 369, is an example of fantasy.

fiction, a story, novel, or play about imagined people and events.

figurative language, language expanded beyond its ordinary literal meaning. (See the Handbook of Literary Terms.)

flashback, an interruption in the action of a story, play, or piece of nonfiction to show an episode that happened at an earlier time. (See the Handbook of Literary Terms.)

foreshadowing, a hint given to the reader of what is to come. In *The Monsters Are Due on Maple Street*, page 131, strange events are foreshadowed when the electricity goes off and the telephones stop working in Act One.

free verse, a type of poetry that is "free" from a fixed pattern of RHYTHM or RHYME. "Words," page 290, and "Oranges," page 279, are examples of free verse.

genre (zhän′rə), a form or type of literary work.

hero/heroine, the main character in a literary work.

humor, a literary work that is funny or amusing. "Almost Perfect," page 256, is an example of humor.

hyperbole (hī pėr′bə lē), an exaggerated statement, sometimes involving FIGURATIVE LANGUAGE. The descriptions of the garbage in "Sarah Cynthia Sylvia Stout . . . ," page 302, are hyperbole.

imagery (im′ij rē), concrete words or details that appeal to the senses of sight, sound, touch, smell, taste, and to internal feelings. (See the Handbook of Literary Terms.)

irony (ī′rə nē), a contrast between what appears to be and what really is. (See the Handbook of Literary Terms.)

legend, a story by an unknown author, handed down through the years.

light verse, short poems written chiefly to amuse or entertain. "The Hunter," page 270, and "Jabberwocky," page 272, are light verse.

limerick, a five-line humorous poem. The first, second, and fifth lines rhyme and the third and fourth lines rhyme. Limericks usually are about the manners and peculiarities of people.

metaphor (met′ə fôr), a figure of speech that involves an implied comparison between two basically unlike things. (See the Handbook of Literary Terms.)

mood, the atmosphere or feeling within a work of art. (See the Handbook of Literary Terms.)

moral, the lesson or teaching in a fable or story. Aesop's fables, pages 426–427, contain morals.

myth (mith), a traditional story connected with the religion or beliefs of a people, usually attempting to account for something in nature. "How the Animals Got Their Color," page 423, is a myth.

narrative, a story or account of an event or a series of happenings. It may be true or fictional.

narrator, the teller of a story. The teller may be a character in the story, as in "Last Cover," page 392, or someone outside the story, as in "Cutie Pie," page 3.

nonfiction, literature about real people and events rather than imaginary ones. Nonfiction can be history, biography, essay, or article.

novel/novella, long works of FICTION dealing with characters, situations, and settings that copy those of real life. A novella (nō vel′ə) is a short novel. *Kävik, the Wolf Dog,* page 454, is a novel.

onomatopoeia (on′ə mat′ə pē′ə), words used to imitate the sound of a thing. *Hiss, smack, buzz,* and *hum* are examples of words whose sounds suggest their sense.

personification (pər son′ə fə kā′shən), a figure of speech or FIGURATIVE LANGUAGE in which human characteristics are given to nonhuman things. (See the Handbook of Literary Terms.)

play, see DRAMA.

plot, a series of happenings in a literary work. Plot consists of these elements: a conflict, a pattern of events, a climax, and a conclusion. (See the Handbook of Literary Terms.)

poetry, composition in verse. The words in poetry are arranged in lines that have rhythm and, sometimes, rhyme.

point of view, the relationship between the NARRATOR of a story and the characters and action in it. (See the Handbook of Literary Terms.)

repetition, word or phrase used over and over again for emphasis, especially in poetry but also sometimes in folk tales.

resolution (rez′ə lü′shən), the tying up of the PLOT; the conclusion, where the complications in a plot are resolved.

rhyme, the REPETITION of syllable sounds. End words that share a particular sound are called END RHYMES. (See the Handbook of Literary Terms.)

rhyme scheme (skēm), the pattern of END RHYMES in a poem.

rhythm (riᴛн′əm), the arrangement of stressed and unstressed sounds in writing and speech. (See the Handbook of Literary Terms.)

satire, a kind of writing that makes fun of something, often some human weakness. "Almost Perfect," page 256, is satirical (sə tir′ə kəl).

science fiction, see FANTASY/SCIENCE FICTION.

setting, the time and place in which the events in a NARRATIVE occur. (See the Handbook of Literary Terms.)

short story, a story shorter than a NOVEL. Although it generally describes just one event, it must have a beginning, a middle, and an end. The characters are usually fewer in number and not as fully developed as those in a novel.

simile (sim′ə lē), a comparison in which the word *like* or *as* is used to point out a similarity between two basically unlike things. (See the Handbook of Literary Terms.)

speaker, the same as a NARRATOR. Often the narrator of a poem is called the speaker.

stanza, a group of lines set off visually from the other lines in a poem. "The Chipmunk's Day," page 296, has five stanzas.

suspense, the method or methods an author uses to maintain a reader's interest.

symbol, a person, place, event, or object that has a meaning in itself but also suggests other meanings. (See the Handbook of Literary Terms.)

tale, a spoken or written account of some happening. It is usually less complicated than a short story. Unit 6 contains tales.

theme, the main idea or underlying meaning of a literary work. (See the Handbook of Literary Terms.)

tone, an author's attitude toward the subject of a literary work or toward the reader. (See the Handbook of Literary Terms.)

GLOSSARY

Full pronunciation key

The pronunciation of each word is shown just after the word, in this way: **ab bre vi ate** (ə brē′vē āt). The letters and signs used are pronounced as in the words below. The mark ′ is placed after a syllable with primary or heavy accent, as in the example above. The mark ′ after a syllable shows a secondary or lighter accent, as in **ab bre vi a tion** (ə brē′vē ā′shən).

Some words, taken from foreign languages, are spoken with sounds that do not otherwise occur in English. Symbols for these sounds are given in the key as "foreign sounds."

a	hat, cap	j	jam, enjoy	u	cup, butter
ā	age, face	k	kind, seek	ù	full, put
ä	father, far	l	land, coal	ü	rule, move
		m	me, am		
b	bad, rob	n	no, in	v	very, save
ch	child, much	ng	long, bring	w	will, woman
d	did, red			y	young, yet
		o	hot, rock	z	zero, breeze
e	let, best	ō	open, go	zh	measure, seizure
ē	equal, be	ô	order, all		
ėr	term, learn	oi	oil, voice	ə	represents:
		ou	house, out		a in about
f	fat, if				e in taken
g	go, bag	p	paper, cup		i in pencil
h	he, how	r	run, try		o in lemon
		s	say, yes		u in circus
i	it, pin	sh	she, rush		
ī	ice, five	t	tell, it		
		th	thin, both		
		ŦH	then, smooth		

foreign sounds

Y as in French *du.* Pronounce (ē) with the lips rounded as for (ü).

à as in French *ami.* Pronounce (ä) with the lips spread and held tense.

œ as in French *peu.* Pronounce (ā) with the lips rounded as for (ō).

N as in French *bon.* The N is not pronounced, but shows that the vowel before it is nasal.

H as in German *ach.* Pronounce (k) without closing the breath passage.

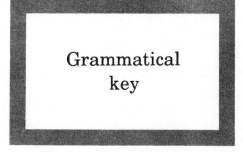

Grammatical key

adj.	adjective	*prep.*	preposition
adv.	adverb	*pron.*	pronoun
conj.	conjunction	*v.*	verb
interj.	interjection	*v.i.*	intransitive verb
n.	noun	*v.t.*	transitive verb
sing.	singular	*pl.*	plural
pt.	past tense	*pp.*	past participle

ab do men (ab′də mən, ab dō′mən), *n.* **1** the part of the body of mammals between the thorax and the pelvis, containing the major digestive organs. **2** the posterior of the three parts of the body of an insect or a crustacean. [<Latin]

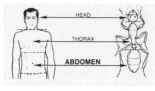

a bet (ə bet′), *v.t.,* **a bet ted, a bet ting. 1** encourage by aid or approval in doing something wrong. **2** urge on or assist in any way. [< Old French *abeter* arouse < *a-* to + *beter* to bait] **—a bet′ment,** *n.* **—a bet′tor, a bet′ter,** *n.*

-able, *suffix forming adjectives from verbs and nouns.* **1** that can be ___ed: *Enjoyable = that can be enjoyed.* **2** giving ___; suitable for ___: *Comfortable = giving comfort.* **3** inclined to ___: *Peaceable = inclined to peace.* **4** deserving to be ___ed: *Lovable = deserving to be loved.* **5** liable to be ___: *Breakable = liable to be broken.* [< Old French < Latin *-abilem*]

a breast (ə brest′), *adv., adj.* **1** side by side. **2** up with; alongside of: *Keep abreast of what is going on.*

ab sorb (ab sôrb′, ab zôrb′), *v.t.* **1** take in or suck up (a liquid or gas): *The sponge absorbed the spilled milk.* **2** take in and make a part of itself; assimilate: *The United States has absorbed millions of immigrants.* **3** take in without reflecting: *Rugs absorb sounds and make a house quieter. Dark surfaces absorb light and convert its energy to heat.* **4** take up all the attention of; interest very much: *Building a dam in the brook absorbed the girl.* **5** grasp with the mind; understand: *absorb the full meaning of a remark.*

ab stract (ab′strakt, ab strakt′), *adj.* thought of apart from any particular object or actual instance; not concrete: *Sweetness is an abstract quality.*

a byss (ə bis′), *n.* **1** a bottomless or very great depth; chasm. **2** anything too deep or great to be measured; lowest depth. **3** the chaos before the Creation. [< Late Latin *abyssus* < Greek *abyssos* < *a-* without + *byssos* bottom]

ac cede (ak sēd′), *v.i.,* **-ced ed, -ced ing. 1** give in; agree; consent *(to): Please accede to my request.* **2** become a party *(to): Our government acceded to the treaty.*

ac cel e rate (ak sel′ə rāt′), *v.,* **-rat ed, -rat ing.** —*v.t.* **1** cause (anything in motion or process) to go or move faster; speed up: *accelerate a train.* **2** cause to happen sooner; hasten: *Rest often accelerates a person's recovery from sickness.* **3** change the speed or velocity of (a moving object). —*v.i.* **1** become or go faster: *accelerate in one's studies.* **2** change in velocity.

ac cord (ə kôrd′), *v.i.* be in harmony; agree; correspond; harmonize *(with): Her report accords with yours.* —*v.t.* **1** give wholeheartedly; grant freely or readily; award: *Accord her praise for her good work.* **2** reconcile.

ac curs ed (ə kėr′sid, ə kėrst′), *adj.* **1** annoying and troublesome; hateful. **2** under a curse; doomed. ARCHAIC, **accurst.**

ac cus tomed (ə kus′təmd), *adj.* **1** usual; customary. **2 accustomed to,** used to; in the habit of: *The farmer was accustomed to hard work. She is accustomed to jogging daily.*

ac rid (ak′rid), *adj.* **1** sharp, bitter, or stinging to the mouth, eyes, skin, or nose. **2** irritating in manner; acrimonious.

ac tiv i ty (ak tiv′ə tē), *n., pl.* **-ties. 1** condition of being active; use of power; movement: *physical activity, mental activity.* **2** action; doing: *the activities of enemy spies.* **3** vigorous action; liveliness: *the activity of children playing.* **4** thing to do; pursuit: *a student's outside activities.* **5** normal function: *The study of the activities of a living being is called its physiology.* **6** radioactivity. [< Latin *actus* a doing, and *actum* (thing) done; both < *agere* do] **—act′a ble,** *adj.*

ad he sion (ad hē′zhən), *n.* **1** act or condition of adhering; sticking fast. **2** faithfulness; adherence. **3** the molecular attraction exerted between the surfaces of unlike bodies in contact, as a solid and a liquid. **4** a growing together of body tissues that are normally separate, especially after surgery.

ad just ment (ə just′mənt), *n.* **1** act or process of adjusting. **2** process by which a person adapts to the surrounding natural or social conditions. **3** means of adjusting one thing to another.

ad mon ish (ad mon′ish), *v.t.* **1** advise against something; warn: *admonish a person of danger.* **2** scold gently; reprove: *admonish a student for careless work.* **3** urge strongly; advise earnestly; exhort: *admonish one to be more careful.* **4** recall to a duty overlooked or forgotten; remind. [<*admonition*] **—ad mon′ish er,** *n.* **—ad mon′ish ing ly,** *adv.* **—ad mon′ish ment,** *n.*

a droit (ə droit′), *adj.* **1** resourceful in reaching one's objective; ingenious; clever. **2** skillful in the use of the hands or body; dexterous. **—a droit′ly,** *adv.*

af front (ə frunt′), *n.* **1** word or act that openly and purposely expresses disrespect; open insult: *To be called a coward is an affront.* **2** a slight or injury to one's dignity. —*v.t.* **1** insult openly; offend purposely and to one's face. **2** face courageously and defiantly; confront.

af ter math (af′tər math), *n.* result or consequence, especially of something destructive.

ag gra vate (ag′rə vāt), *v.t.,* **-vat ed, -vat ing.** INFORMAL. annoy; irritate; exasperate.

a ghast (ə gast′), *adj.* struck with surprise or horror; filled with shocked amazement.

ag i tate (aj′ə tāt), *v.t.,* **-tat ed, -tat ing. 1** move or shake violently: *A sudden wind agitated the surface of the river.* **2** disturb or upset very much: *They were agitated by the news of their friend's illness.* **3** argue about; discuss vigorously and publicly.

-al¹, *suffix forming adjectives from nouns.* of; like; having the nature of: *Ornamental = having the nature of ornament.* Also, **-ial.** [< Latin *-alem*]

-al², *suffix forming nouns from verbs.* act of ___ing: *Refusal = act of refusing.* [< Latin *-alia,* neuter plural of *-alem*]

al cove (al′kōv), *n.* **1** a small room opening out of a larger room. **2** recess or large, hollow space in a wall.

a lign (ə līn′), *v.t.* bring (anything) into line; adjust to a line: *align the sights of a gun.*

al le vi ate (ə lē′vē āt), *v.t.,* **-at ed, -at ing. 1** make easier to endure (suffering of the body or mind); relieve; mitigate: *Heat often alleviates pain.* **2** lessen or lighten; diminish.

al lot (ə lot′), *v.t.,* **-lot ted, -lot ting. 1** divide and distribute in parts or shares: *The profits have all been allotted.* **2** give as a share, task, duty, etc.; assign: *The dance chairman allotted responsibility for tickets, refreshments, and decorations.*

al lure (ə lür′), *v.,* **-lured, -lur ing,** *n.* —*v.t.* tempt or attract very strongly; fascinate; charm: *City life allured her with its action and excitement.* —*n.* great charm; fascination. [< Middle French *alurer* < *a* -to + *leurre* lure]

al lure ment (ə lür′mənt), *n.* **1** charm; fascination. **2** thing that allures; temptation; attraction.

a loof (ə lüf′), *adv.* away at some distance but within view; apart.

am ber (am′bər), *n.* **1** a hard, translucent, yellow or yellowish-brown fossil resin, easily polished and used for jewelry, in making pipe stems, etc. **2** the color of amber; yellow or yellowish brown. —*adj.* **1** made of amber. **2** yellow or yellowish-brown.

am ble (am′bəl), *n., v.,* **-bled, -bling.** —*n.* **1** gait of a horse or mule when it lifts first the two legs on one side and then the two on the other. **2** an easy, slow pace in walking. —*v.i.* **1** (of a horse or mule) go with such a gait. **2** walk at an easy, slow pace.

a mi a ble (ā′mē ə bəl), *adj.* having a good-natured and friendly disposition; pleasant and agreeable. **—a′mi a bly,** *adv.*

am i ca ble (am′ə kə bəl), *adj.* having or showing a friendly attitude; peaceable: *settle a quarrel in an amicable way.* **—am′i ca ble ness,** *n.* **—am′i ca bly,** *adv.*

a mid (ə mid′), *prep.* in the middle of; surrounded by; among.

a mid ship (ə mid′ship), *adv.* in or toward the middle of a ship; halfway between the bow and stern.

an-¹, *prefix.* **1** not: *anastigmatic = not astigmatic.* **2** without: *Anhydrous = without water.* Also, **a-,** before consonants except *h.* [< Greek]

an-², *prefix.* form of **ad-** before *n,* as in *annex.*

-an, *suffix forming adjectives and nouns, especially from proper nouns.* **1** of or having to do with ___: *Mohammedan = of or having to do with Mohammed.* **2** of or having to do with ___ or its people: *Asian = of or having to do with Asia or its people.* **3** native or inhabitant of ___: *American = native or inhabitant of America.* **4** person who knows much about or is skilled in ___: *Magician = person skilled in magic. Historian = person who knows much about history.* Also, **-ian, -ean.** [< Latin *-anus*]

a nal y sis (ə nal′ə sis), *n., pl.* **-ses** (-sēz′). **1** a breaking up of anything complex into its various simple elements. **2** this process as a method of studying the nature of a thing or of determining its essential features. An analysis can be made of a book, a person's character, a situation, etc.

-ance, *suffix forming nouns chiefly from verbs.* **1** act or fact of ___ing: *Avoidance = act or fact of avoiding.* **2** quality or state of being ___ed: *Annoyance = quality or state of being annoyed.* **3** thing that ___s: *Conveyance = thing that conveys.* **4** what is ___ed: *Contrivance = what is contrived.* **5** quality or state of being ___ant: *Importance = quality or state of being important.* [< Old French < Latin *-antia, -entia*]

an guish (ang′gwish), *n.* **1** severe physical pain; great suffering: *the anguish of an unrelieved toothache.* **2** extreme mental pain or suffering: *the anguish of despair.*

a noint (ə noint′), *v.t.* **1** apply an ointment, oil, or similar substance to; cover or smear with oil, etc.

ant-, *prefix.* form of **anti-** before vowels and *h,* as in *antacid.*

-ant, *suffix forming adjectives and nouns from verbs.* **1** that ___s; ___ing: *Compliant = that complies or complying.* **2** one that ___s: *Assistant = one that assists.* [< Old French < Latin *-antem*]

an tag o nism (an tag′ə niz′əm), *n.* activity or relation of contending parties or conflicting forces; active opposition; hostility.

ante-, *prefix.* **1** before: *Antedate = to date before.* **2** in front of: *Anteroom = a room in front of (another).* [< Latin]

anti-, *prefix.* **1** against ___; opposed to ___: *Antiaircraft = against aircraft.* **2** not ___; the opposite of ___: *Antisocial = the opposite of social.* **3** rival ___: *Antipope = rival pope.* **4** reducing or counteracting ___: *Antifriction = reducing or counteracting friction.* **5** preventing, curing, or alleviating ___: *Antiscorbutic = preventing or curing scurvy.* Also, **ant-** before vowels and *h.* [< Greek]

ap pall ing (ə pô′ling), *adj.* causing consternation and horror; dismaying; terrifying. **—ap pall′ing ly,** *adv.*

ap pre ci a tive (ə prē′shē ā′tiv, ə prē′shə tiv), *adj.* feeling or showing appreciation: *appreciative of the smallest kindness.* **—ap pre′ci a′tive ly,** *adv.* **—ap pre′ci a′tive ness,** *n.*

ap pre hen sive (ap′ri hen′siv), *adj.* afraid that some misfortune is about to occur; anxious about the future; fearful. **—ap′pre hen′sive ly,** *adv.* **—ap′pre hen′sive ness,** *n.*

ar mor (är′mər), *n.* **1** a covering, usually of metal or leather, worn to protect the body in fighting. **2** any similar type of protective covering, such as a diver's suit or the scales of a fish. **3** armor plate. **4** the armored forces and equipment, such as the tanks, of a military unit. **—v.t., v.i.** cover or protect with armor. Also, BRITISH **armour.** [< Old French *armeüre* < Latin *armatura* < *armare* to arm. Doublet of ARMATURE.] **—ar′mor like′,** *adj.*

ar mor y (är′mər ē), *n., pl.* **-mor ies.** **1** place where weapons are kept; arsenal. **2** place where weapons are manufactured. **3** a building with a drill hall, offices, etc., for militia. **4** ARCHAIC. armor; arms.

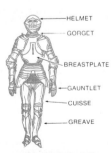

armor (def. 1) of the 1400's, weighing about 65 pounds (29.5 kg.)

Labels: HELMET, GORGET, BREASTPLATE, GAUNTLET, CUISSE, GREAVE

a hat	i it	oi oil	ch child		⎧ a in about
ā age	ī ice	ou out	ng long		⎪ e in taken
ä far	o hot	u cup	sh she	ə = ⎨ i in pencil
e let	ō open	u̇ put	th thin		⎪ o in lemon
ē equal	ô order	ü rule	ᴛʜ then		⎩ u in circus
ėr term			zh measure		< = derived from

ar ray (ə rā′), *v.t.* **1** put in order for some purpose; marshal: *array troops for battle.* **2** dress in fine clothes; adorn. [< Anglo-French *arayer* < Old French *a-* to + *rei* order] **—ar ray′er,** *n.*

ar rest (ə rest′), *v.t.* **1** seize (a person) and keep in custody by legal authority; apprehend: *The police arrested the woman for shoplifting.* **2** cause to stop (in a course of action); halt: *A fallen tree arrested traffic on the road.* **3** attract and hold (the attention of a person): *They were arrested by an unusual sound.*

ar ro gant (ar′ə gənt), *adj.* excessively proud and contemptuous of others.

-ary, *suffix forming nouns and adjectives.* **1** place for ___: *Infirmary = place for the infirm.* **2** collection of ___: *Statuary = collection of statues.* **3** person or thing that ___s: *Boundary = thing that bounds.* **4** of or having to do with ___: *Legendary = of legend.* **5** being; having the nature of ___: *Secondary = being second.* **6** characterized by ___: *Customary = characterized by custom.* [< Latin *-arium*]

ash cake (ash′kāk), *n.* a corn meal cake baked in hot ashes.

a skance (ə skans′), *adv.* **1** with suspicion or disapproval: *The students looked askance at the suggestion for having classes on Saturday.* **2** to one side; sideways. [origin uncertain]

as phalt (as′fôlt), *n.* **1** a dark, waterproof substance much like tar, found in natural beds in various parts of the world or obtained by refining petroleum. **2** mixture of this substance with crushed rock or sand, used to pave streets, etc.

a sphyx i ate (a sfik′sē āt), *v.t., v.i.,* **-at ed, -at ing.** produce asphyxia in; suffocate. **—a sphyx′i a′tion,** *n.*

as pire (ə spīr′), *v.i.,* **-pired, -pir ing.** have an ambition for something; desire earnestly; seek.

as sail (ə sāl′), *v.t.* **1** attack repeatedly with violent blows. **2** attack with hostile words, arguments, or abuse.

as sent (ə sent′), *v.i.* express agreement; agree; consent: *Everyone assented to the plans for the dance.* **—n.** acceptance of a proposal, statement, etc.; agreement.

-ate¹, *suffix forming adjectives, verbs, and nouns.* **1** of or having to do with ___: *Collegiate = having to do with college.* **2** having or containing ___: *Compassionate = having compassion.* **3** having the form of; like ___: *Stellate = having the form of a star.* **4** become ___: *Maturate = become mature.* **5** cause to be ___: *Alienate = cause to be alien.* **6** produce ___: *Ulcerate = produce ulcers.* **7** supply or treat with ___: *Aerate = treat with air.* **8** combine with ___: *Oxygenate = combine with oxygen.* [< Latin *-atus, -atum,* past participle endings]

-ate², *suffix forming nouns.* office, rule, or condition of ___: *Caliphate = rule of a caliph.* [< Latin *-atus*]

-ation, *suffix forming nouns chiefly from verbs.* **1** act or process of ___ing: *Admiration = act or process of admiring.* **2** condition or state of being ___ed: *Cancellation = condition or state of being canceled.* **3** result of ___ing: *Civilization = result of civilizing.* [< Latin *-ationem*]

au di ble (ô′də bəl), *adj.* that can be heard; loud enough to be heard. [< Latin *audire* hear] **—au′di bly,** *adv.*

aus cul tate (ôs′kəl tāt), *v.t., v.i.,* **-tat ed, -tat ing.** examine by auscultation. [back-formation < *auscultation*]

aus cul ta tion (ôs′kəl tā′shən), *n.* a listening to sounds within the human body, especially with a stethoscope, to determine the condition of the heart, lungs, or abdominal organs. [< Latin *auscultationem* a listening < *auscultare* listen]

az ure (azh′ər), *n.* the clear blue color of the unclouded sky; sky blue. **—adj.** sky-blue.

bade (bad, bād), v. a pt. of **bid**.

baf fle (baf′əl), v., **-fled, -fling,** n. —v.t. **1** hinder (a person) by being too hard to understand or solve; perplex: *This puzzle baffles me.* **2** control or regulate by a baffle. –n. wall, screen, or other device for controlling the flow of air, water, or sound waves by hindering its movement or changing its course.

bale (bāl), n., v., **baled, bal ing.** —n. a large bundle of merchandise or material closely pressed, tightly corded or hooped, and (sometimes) wrapped or bound for shipping or storage. —v.t. make into bales; tie in large bundles.

bale ful (bāl′fəl), adj. **1** full of hurtful or deadly influence; destructive. **2** full of misfortune; disastrous. —**bale′ful ly,** adv.

balk (bôk), v.i. **1** stop short and stubbornly refuse to go on: *My horse balked at the fence.* **2** (in baseball) make a balk. —v.t. **1** check, hinder, or thwart (a person or his or her actions); frustrate: *The police balked the robber's plans.* **2** fail to use; let slip; miss. —n. **1** a hindrance, check, or defeat. **2** a blunder or mistake. **3** a ridge between furrows; strip left unplowed.

ball bearing, **1** bearing in which the shaft revolves upon a number of freely moving, very smooth steel balls which are contained in a channel or groove around the shaft. Ball bearings are used to lessen friction. **2** one of these steel balls.

ban dan na or **ban dan a** (ban dan′ə), n. a large, gaily colored kerchief or handkerchief, often worn on the head or neck. [< Hindustani *bāndhnū* way of tying cloth so as to produce designs when dyed]

ban gle (bang′gəl), n. **1** a small ornament suspended from a bracelet. **2** a bracelet or anklet without a clasp. [< Hindustani *bangrī* glass bracelet]

ban ish (ban′ish), v.t. **1** compel (a person) to leave a country by order of political or judicial authority; exile. **2** drive away; dismiss; expel: *banish all cares.*

bard (bärd), n. **1** a Celtic minstrel and poet who from earliest times to the Middle Ages sang his own poems, usually to harp accompaniment, celebrating martial exploits, etc. **2** any poet.

bed lam (bed′ləm), n. noisy confusion; uproar.

be guile (bi gīl′), v.t., **-guiled, -guil ing.** **1** trick or mislead (a person); deceive; delude: *Your flattery beguiled me into thinking that you were my friend.* **2** take away from deceitfully or cunningly. **3** win the attention of; entertain; amuse. **4** while away (time) pleasantly.

bel la don na (bel′ə don′ə), n. **1** a poisonous plant of the nightshade family of Europe and Asia with black berries and red, bell-shaped flowers; deadly nightshade. **2** drug made from this plant; atropine.

bel low (bel′ō), v.i. **1** (of an animal, especially of a bull) make a loud, roaring noise, as when excited or enraged. **2** shout loudly, angrily, or with pain. **3** make a loud, deep noise; roar. —v.t. shout in a loud and deep voice; roar. —n. **1** the roar of a bull. **2** any noise made by bellowing; loud, deep noise; roar. [Old English *bylgian*] —**bel′low er,** n.

be mused (bi myüzd′), adj. **1** confused; bewildered; stupefied. **2** absorbed in reverie or thought.

be nef i cence (bə nef′ə səns), n. **1** a doing of good; kindness. **2** a kindly act; gift.

be nev o lence (bə nev′ə ləns), n. desire to promote the happiness of others; goodwill; kindly feeling.

be queath (bi kwēᴛʜ′, bi kwēth′), v.t. **1** give or leave (especially money or other personal property) by a will. **2** hand down or leave to posterity; pass along.

be siege (bi sēj′), v.t., **-sieged, -sieg ing.** **1** surround by armed forces in order to compel surrender; lay siege to: *For ten years the Greeks besieged the city of Troy.* **2** crowd around.

bid (bid), v.t., **bade, bid,** or (ARCHAIC) **bad, bid den** or **bid, bid ding,** **1** tell (someone) what to do, where to go, etc.; command; order: *Do as I bid you. You bade me forget what is unforgettable. They were bidden to assemble.* **2** say or tell (a greeting, etc.); wish: *My friends came to bid me good-by.* [Old English *biddan* ask; meaning influenced by *bēodan* to offer, command]

bil low (bil′ō), n. **1** a great, swelling wave or surge of the sea. **2** a great rolling or swelling mass of smoke, flame, air, etc. —v.i. **1** rise or roll in big waves; surge. **2** swell out; bulge: *The sheets on the clothesline billowed in the wind.*

bi o log i cal (bī′ə loj′ə kəl), adj. **1** of living organisms. **2** having to do with biology. **3** for use in or prepared by a biological laboratory: *biological serums.* **4** involving the use of disease germs, viruses, or other living organisms: *biological insecticides.* —n. drug prepared from living tissue. —**bi′o log′i cal ly,** adv.

bland (bland), adj. **1** gentle or soothing; balmy: *a bland summer breeze.* **2** smoothly agreeable and polite: *a bland smile.* **3** soothing to the palate or digestive tract; not irritating: *a bland diet of baby food.* [< Latin *blandus* soft] —**bland′ly,** adv.

blind (blīnd), adj. **1** not able to see; sightless. **2** difficult to see; hidden: *a blind curve on a highway.* **3** without the help of sight; by means of instruments instead of the eyes: *blind flying of an aircraft at night.* **4** without thought, judgment, or good sense: *blind fury, a blind guess.* —n. **1** something that keeps out light or hinders sight, as a window shade or shutter. **2** anything that conceals an action or purpose; pretext. **3** a hiding place for a hunter.

blood line (blud′līn′), n. **1** series of ancestors in a pedigree. **2** pedigree, family, or strain (applied especially to animals).

blow hole (blō′hōl′), n. **1** nostril or hole for breathing, in the top of the head of whales, porpoises, and dolphins. **2** hole in the ice to which whales, seals, etc., come to breathe.

board (bôrd, bōrd), v.t. **1** cover, enclose, or close with boards. **2** provide with regular meals, or room and meals, for pay. **3** get on (a ship, train, bus, airplane, etc.).—n. meals.

boat (bōt), n. **1** a small, usually open vessel for traveling on water, propelled by oars, sails, or motor. **2** ship. **3 in the same boat,** in the same position or condition; taking the same chances.

body (bod′ē), v.t. **bod ied, bod y ing.** provide with a body; give substance to; embody. [Old English *bodig*]

bog (bog, bôg), n. piece of wet, spongy ground, consisting chiefly of decayed or decaying moss and other vegetable matter, too soft to bear the weight of any heavy body on its surface; marsh; swamp.

bois ter ous (boi′stər əs), adj. rough and noisy; clamorous: *a boisterous child.* [Middle English *boistrous*] —**bois′ter ous ly,** adv.

bond (bond), n. **1** anything that binds or fastens, as a rope, cord, or other band. **2** any force or influence that serves to unite.

booking (bük′ing), n. a contract, engagement, or scheduled performance of an entertainer.

boor ish (bür′ish), adj. like a boor; rude or rustic. —**boor′ish ly,** adv. —**boor′ish ness,** n.

bore (bôr, bōr), v., **bored, bor ing,** n. —v.i. **1** make a hole by means of a tool that keeps turning, or by penetrating as a worm does in fruit; pierce; perforate; drill. **2** be bored; be suited for boring: *This wood bores easily.* **3** force a way through; push forward. —v.t. **1** make (a hole, passage, entrance, etc.) by pushing through or digging out. **2** bore a hole in; hollow out evenly. —n. hole made by boring.

bore dom (bôr′dəm, bōr′dəm), n. a bored condition; weariness caused by dull, tiresome people or things.

brack en (brak′ən), n. **1** a large, coarse fern common on hillsides, in woods, etc. **2** thicket of these ferns.

brand (brand), n. **1** the quality or kind (of goods) as indicated by a mark, stamp, or label; a certain kind, grade, or make. **2** a piece of wood that is burning or partly burned on the hearth. [Old English]

breast plate (brest′plāt′), n. armor for the chest. See **armor** for picture.

bris tle (bris′əl), v.i., **-tled, -tling.** **1** stand up straight: *The angry dog's hair bristled.* **2** have one's hair stand up straight: *The frightened kitten bristled when it saw the dog.* **3** show that one is aroused and ready to fight.

broach (brōch), v.t. begin conversation or discussion about; introduce: *broach a subject.*

broke (brōk), v. **1** pt. of **break.** *She broke her doll.*
2 ARCHAIC. a pp. of **break.** —*adj.* INFORMAL. **1** without
money; bankrupt. **2 go broke,** become financially ruined or
bankrupt.

bronze (bronz), n., adj., **bronzed, bronz ing.** —*n.* **1** a
brown metal, an alloy of copper and tin. **2** a similar alloy of
copper with zinc or other metals. **3** statue, medal, disk, etc.,
made of bronze. **4** a yellowish brown or reddish brown.
—*adj.* **1** made of bronze. **2** yellowish-brown or reddish-
brown.

bru tal i ty (brü tal′ə tē), n., pl. **-ties. 1** brutal conduct;
cruelty; savageness. **2** a cruel or savage act. **3** coarse behavior.

bull ock (bùl′ək), n. **1** a castrated bull; ox; steer. **2** (originally) a young bull. [Old English *bulluc* bull calf]

bun ga low (bung′gə lō), n. a small house, usually of one
story or a story and a half, with low, sweeping lines. [< Hindustani *banglā* of Bengal]

buoy ant (boi′ənt, bü′yənt), adj. **1** able to float: *Wood and
cork are buoyant in water; iron and lead are not.* **2** able to
keep things afloat or aloft: *Air is buoyant; helium-filled balloons
float in it.* **3** tending to rise. **4** cheerful; lighthearted.

bur row (bėr′ō), n. **1** hole dug in the ground by woodchucks,
rabbits, and various other animals for refuge or shelter. **2** a
similar dwelling, shelter, or refuge.

bush pilot, pilot who flies a small plane over relatively unsettled country, such as parts of Alaska and northern Canada.

byre (bī′ər), n. a stable for cows or pigs.

cache (kash), n. **1** a hiding place, especially of goods, treasure, food, etc. **2** the store of food or supplies hidden.

ca coph o ny (kə kof′ə nē), n., pl. **-nies.** succession of
harsh, clashing sounds; dissonance; discord.

ca jole (kə jōl′), v.t., **-joled, -jol ing.** persuade by pleasant
words, flattery, or false promises; coax.—**ca jol ing ly,** adv.

ca lam i ty (kə lam′ə tē), n., pl. **-ties. 1** a great misfortune,
such as a flood, a fire, the loss of one's sight or hearing.
2 serious trouble; misery. [< Latin *calamitatem*]

cal dron (kôl′drən), n. a large kettle or broiler.

cal lous (kal′əs), adj. **1** hard or hardened, as parts of the skin
that are exposed to pressure and friction. **2** unfeeling; insensi-
tive.

cam ou flage (kam′ə fläzh), n. **1** a disguise or false appearance serving to conceal. **2** (in warfare) the act or practice of
giving things a false appearance to deceive the enemy. **3** materials or other means by which this is done.

can ner y (kan′ər ē), n., pl. **-ner ies.** factory where food is
canned.

cant (kant), n. **1** a sloping, slanting, or tilting position; inclination. **2** a sudden pitch which causes a person or thing to overturn or fall. **3** a turning or tilting movement.

ca per (kā′pər), v.i. leap or jump about playfully.

cap i tal ist (kap′ə tə list), n. **1** person whose money and property are used in carrying on business. **2** a wealthy person.
3 person who favors or supports capitalism.

ca rafe (kə raf′), n. a glass bottle for holding water, wine, etc.

cash (kash), n. **1** money in the form of coins and bills.
2 money, or something equivalent to money, such as a bank
check.

caulk (kôk), v.t. fill up (a seam, crack, or joint) so that it will
not leak; make watertight. Sailors caulk wooden boats with
oakum and tar. Plumbers caulk joints in pipe with lead. Also,
calk.

caus tic (kô′stik), adj. **1** that burns or destroys flesh; corro-
sive. Lye is caustic soda or caustic potash. **2** very critical or
sarcastic; stinging; biting: *The coach's caustic remarks made
the football players angry.* —**caus′ti cal ly,** adv.

cease less (sēs′lis), adj. going on all the time; never stopping;
continual. —**cease′less ly,** adv. —**cease′less ness,** n.

chi nook (shə nùk′, chə nük′), n. a warm, moist wind blowing
from the sea to the land in winter and spring on the northern
Pacific Coast. Also, **Chinook.**

a hat	i it	oi oil	ch child		⎧ a in about
ā age	ī ice	ou out	ng long		e in taken
ä far	o hot	u cup	sh she	ə =	i in pencil
e let	ō open	ù put	th thin		o in lemon
ē equal	ô order	ü rule	ŦH then		⎩ u in circus
ėr term			zh measure		< = derived from

chor tle (chôr′tl), v., **-tled, -tling,** n. —*v.i., v.t.* chuckle or
snort with glee. —*n.* a gleeful chuckle or snort. [blend of
chuckle and *snort;* coined by Lewis Carroll] —**chor′tler,** n.

chron ic (kron′ik), adj. **1** lasting a long time: *Rheumatism is
often a chronic disease.* **2** suffering long from an illness: *a
chronic invalid.* **3** never stopping; constant; habitual: *a chronic
liar.*

churl (chėrl), n. **1** a rude, surly person; boor. **2** person of low
birth; peasant. **3** person stingy in money matters; miser.

ci ca da (sə kā′də, sə kä′də), n. a large insect, commonly
called a locust, with two pairs of thin, transparent wings. The
male produces a loud, shrill sound in hot, dry weather by vibrating membranes on the abdomen. [< Latin]

cir cuit (sėr′kit), n. **1** a going around; a moving around: *It
takes a year for the earth to make its circuit of the sun.* **2** route
over which a person or group makes repeated journeys at certain
times.

cir cum vent (sėr′kəm vent′), v.t. **1** get the better of or defeat
by trickery; outwit: *circumvent the law.* **2** go around.

clad (klad), v. a pt. and a pp. of **clothe.**

claim (klām), n. **1** demand for something due; assertion of a
right. **2** right or title to something; right to demand something.
3 something that is claimed. **4** piece of public land which a
settler or prospector marks out for possession.

claim ant (klā′mənt), n. person who makes a claim.

clam ber (klam′bər), v.i., v.t. climb, using both hands and
feet; climb awkwardly or with difficulty; scramble.

clam or (klam′ər), n. **1** a loud noise or continual uproar;
shouting. **2** a shout; outcry. **3** a noisy demand or complaint.

clan (klan), n. **1** group of related families that claim to be
descended from a common ancestor. **2** group of people closely
joined together by some common interest.

clar et (klar′ət), n. **1** kind of red wine. **2** a dark purplish red.

cleave (klēv), v., **cleft** or **cleaved** or **clove, cleft** or **cleaved** or
clo ven, cleav ing. —*v.t.* **1** cut, divide, or split open. **2** pass
through; pierce; penetrate: *The airplane cleft the clouds.*
3 make by cutting: *They cleft a path through the wilderness.*
—*v.i.* **1** split, especially into layers. **2** pass; penetrate. [Old
English *clēofan*] —**cleav′a ble,** adj.

clog (klog), n. **1** anything that hinders or interferes. **2** any
weight, such as a block of wood, fastened to the leg of an
animal to hinder motion. **3** shoe with a thick, wooden sole.

clothe (klōŦH), v.t., **clothed** or **clad, cloth ing. 1** put clothes
on; cover with clothes; dress. **2** provide with clothes.

clout (klout), v.t. INFORMAL. hit with the hand; rap; knock;
cuff. —*n.* **1** INFORMAL. a hit with the hand; rap; knock; cuff.
2 INFORMAL. political force, power, or influence. **3** a white
cloth target used in archery. **4** shot that hits this. **5** ARCHAIC.
a cloth or rag. **b** garment. [Old English *clūt* small piece of
cloth or metal]

co-, prefix. **1** with; together: *Coexist = exist together or with.*
2 joint: *Coauthor = joint author.* **3** equally: *Coextensive =
equally extensive.* [< Latin, variant of *com-*]

col league (kol′ēg′), n. fellow worker; fellow member of a
profession, organization, etc.; associate.

com-, prefix. with; together; altogether: *Commingle = mingle
with one another. Compress = press together.*

com mend (kə mend′), v.t. **1** speak well of; praise. **2** recommend.

com mis sion (kə mish′ən), n. **1** a written order giving certain
powers, privileges, and duties. **2** a written order giving rank
and authority as an officer in the armed forces. **3** rank and
authority given by such an order. **4** a giving of authority. **5**

GLOSSARY

authority, power, or right given. **6** thing for which authority is given; task entrusted to a person.

com mon denominator, **1** a common multiple of the denominators of a group of fractions: *12 is a common denominator of* $\frac{1}{2}$, $\frac{2}{3}$, *and* $\frac{3}{4}$. **2** quality, attribute, opinion, etc., shared by all in a group.

com mo tion (kə mō′shən), *n.* **1** violent movement; agitation; turbulence: *the commotion of the storm.* **2** bustle or stir; confusion.

com pas sion (kəm pash′ən), *n.* feeling for another's sorrow or hardship that leads to help; sympathy; pity. [< Latin *compassionem* < *compati* suffer with < *com-* with + *pati* suffer]

com pas sion ate (kəm pash′ə nit), *adj.* desiring to relieve another's suffering; sympathetic; pitying.

com pla cent (kəm plā′snt), *adj.* pleased with oneself or what one has; self-satisfied. —**com pla′cent ly,** *adv.*

com plaint (kəm plānt′), *n.* **1** a complaining; finding fault. **2** accusation; charge. **3** a cause for complaining. **4** illness; ailment: *A cold is a very common complaint.*

com ple ment (kom′plə mənt), *n.* **1** something that completes or makes perfect. **2** number required to fill: *The plane had its full complement of passengers; all seats were taken.*

com pul sor y (kəm pul′sər ē), *adj.* compelled; required: *Attendance at school is compulsory for children.*

con-, *prefix.* form of **com-** before *n,* as in *connote,* and before consonants except *b, h, l, m, p, r, w,* as in *concern.*

con dem na tion (kon′dem nā′shən), *n.* a condemning; an expression of disapproval.

Con es to ga wagon (kon′ə stō′gə), a covered wagon with broad wheels, used especially by the American pioneers for traveling on soft ground or on the prairie. [< *Conestoga* Valley, Pennsylvania, where they were first built]

con fec tion er y (kən fek′shə ner′ē), *n., pl.* **-er ies.** candies or sweets; confections.

con found (kon found′, kən found′), *v.t.* **1** confuse; mix up: *The shock confounded me.* **2** surprise and puzzle. **3** ARCHAIC. make uneasy and ashamed. **4** ARCHAIC. defeat; overthrow. [< Old French *confondre* < Latin *confundere* pour together, mix up, confuse] —**con found′er,** *n.*

con front (kən frunt′), *v.t.* **1** meet face to face; stand facing. **2** face boldly; oppose. **3** bring face to face; place before. —**con′fron ta′tion,** *n.*

con jure (kon′jər, kun′jər), *v.,* **-jured, -jur ing.** —*v.t.* **1** compel (a spirit, devil, etc.) to appear or disappear by a set form of words. **2** cause to appear or happen as if by magic: *conjure up a whole meal in a jiffy.* **3** cause to appear in the mind: *conjure a vision.* —*v.i.* **1** summon a devil, spirit, etc. **2** practice magic. **3** perform tricks by skill and quickness in moving the hands.

con scious ness (kon′shəs nis), *n.* **1** condition of being conscious; awareness. People and animals have consciousness; plants and stones do not. **2** all the thoughts and feelings of a person or group of people: *the moral consciousness of our generation.* **3** awareness of what is going on about one: *A severe emotional shock can make a person lose consciousness for a time.*

con sen sus (kən sen′səs), *n.* general agreement; opinion of all or most of the people consulted.

con so la tion (kon′sə lā′shən), *n.* **1** a consoling. **2** a being consoled. **3** a comforting person, thing, or event.

con sol i date (kən sol′ə dāt), *v.,* **-dat ed, -dat ing.** —*v.t.* **1** combine into one; unite: *The small farms were consolidated for greater efficiency.* **2** make solid or firm; solidify. **3** make secure; strengthen: *The political party consolidated its power by winning many state elections.*

con sort (kon′sôrt), *n.* husband or wife. The husband of a queen is sometimes called the prince consort.

con ster na tion (kon′stər nā′shən), *n.* great dismay; paralyzing terror: *To our consternation the child darted out in front of the speeding car.*

con sti tu tion (kon′stə tü′shən, kon′stə tyü′shən), *n.* way in which a person or thing is organized; nature; makeup: *A person with a good constitution is strong and healthy.*

con stric tion (kən strik′shən), *n.* **1** a constricting; compression; contraction. **2** a feeling of tightness; constricted condition: *a constriction in one's chest.* **3** a constricted part.

con tem plate (kon′təm plāt), *v.,* **-plat ed, -plat ing.** —*v.t.* **1** look at for a long time; gaze at. **2** think about for a long time; study carefully. **3** have in mind; consider; intend: *She is contemplating a trip to Europe.* —*v.i.* be absorbed in contemplation; meditate.

con tempt (kən tempt′), *n.* **1** the feeling that a person, act, or thing is mean, low, or worthless; scorn; despising; disdain: *We feel contempt for a cheat.* **2** a being scorned; disgrace.

con temp tu ous (kən temp′chü əs), *adj.* showing contempt; scornful: *a contemptuous look.*

con tort (kən tôrt′), *v.t.* twist or bend out of shape; distort: *The clown contorted his face.*

con tract (kən trakt′), *v.t.* **1** draw together; make shorter, narrower, or smaller: *contract a muscle. The earthworm contracted its body.* **2** shorten (a word, phrase, etc.) by omitting some of the letters or sounds: *In talking and writing we often contract ''do not'' to ''don't.''* **3** bring on oneself; get; form: *contract bad habits, contract a disease.*

con verge (kən vėrj′), *v.i.,* **-verged, -verg ing.** **1** tend to meet in a point: *The sides of a road seem to converge in the distance.* **2** turn toward each other: *If you look at the end of your nose, your eyes converge.* **3** come together; center: *The interest of all the students converged upon the celebration.*

con vic tion (kən vik′shən), *n.* **1** act of proving or declaring guilty. **2** condition of being proved or declared guilty. **3** act of convincing (a person). **4** a being convinced. **5** firm belief.

con viv i al (kən viv′ē əl), *adj.* fond of eating and drinking with friends; jovial; sociable.

con vul sive (kən vul′siv), *adj.* **1** violently disturbing. **2** having convulsions. **3** producing convulsions. —**con vul′sive ly,** *adv.*

cop pice (kop′is), *n.* copse; thicket of small trees, bushes, shrubs, etc.

cor re spond ing (kôr′ə spon′ding, kor′ə spon′ding), *adj.* **1** similar; matching. **2** in harmony. —**cor′re spond′ing ly,** *adv.*

cor rob o rate (kə rob′ə rāt′), *v.t.,* **-rat ed, -rat ing.** make more certain; confirm; support: *Eyewitnesses corroborated my testimony in court.*

cos set (kos′it), *n.* a pet lamb; a pet. —*v.t.* treat as a pet; pamper. [origin uncertain]

cot (kot), *n.* **1** a narrow, light bed. A cot is sometimes made of canvas stretched on a frame that folds together. **2** BRITISH. a child's crib. [< Hindustani *khāt*]

court yard (kôrt′yärd′, kōrt′yärd′), *n.* space enclosed by walls, in or near a large building.

cow er (kou′ər), *v.i.* **1** crouch in fear or shame. **2** draw back tremblingly from another's threats, blows, etc.

cre vasse (krə vas′), *n.* a deep crack or crevice in the ice of a glacier, or in the ground after an earthquake.

crev ice (krev′is), *n.* a narrow split or crack; fissure.

crow (krō), *n.* any of several large, glossy, black birds that have a harsh cry or caw.

crow's nest (krōz′nest′), *n.* a small, enclosed platform near the top of a ship's mast, used by the lookout.

crys tal lize (kris′tl īz), *v.,* **-lized, -liz ing.** —*v.i., v.t.* **1** form into crystals; solidify into crystals: *Water crystallizes to form snow.* **2** form into definite shape.

cu bi cle (kyü′bə kəl), *n.* a very small room or compartment.

cue (kyü), *n.* **1** action, speech, or word which gives the signal for an actor, singer, musician, etc., to enter or to begin. **2** hint or suggestion as to what to do or when to act.

cul ti vate (kul′tə vāt), *v.t.,* **-vat ed, -vat ing.** **1** prepare and use (land) to raise crops by plowing it, planting seeds, and taking care of the growing plants; till. **2** help (plants) grow by labor and care. **3** loosen the ground around (growing plants) to kill weeds, etc. **4** improve or develop (the body, mind, or manners) by education or training. **5** give time, thought, and effort to; practice.

cun ning (kun′ing), *adj.* **1** clever in deceiving; sly: *a cunning fox, a cunning thief.* **2** skillful; clever: *The old watch was a fine example of cunning workmanship.* —*n.* **1** slyness in getting what one wants; cleverness in deceiving one's enemies: *The fox has a great deal of cunning.* **2** skill; cleverness.

cu po la (kyü′pə lə), *n.* **1** a rounded roof; dome. **2** a small dome or tower on a roof.

cur dle (kėr′dl), *v.t., v.i.,* **-dled, -dling. 1** form into curds: *Milk curdles when kept too long.* **2** thicken.

cus to di al (ku stō′dē əl), *adj.* having to do with custody or custodians.

custom (kus′təm), *n.* **1** any usual action or practice; habit. **2 customs,** *pl.* **a** taxes paid to the government on things brought in from foreign countries. **b** department of the government that collects these taxes.

cut a way (kut′ə wā′), *n.* man's coat for formal daytime wear with the lower part cut back in a curve or slope from the waist in front to the tails in back.

dal ly (dal′ē), *v.,* **-lied, -ly ing.** —*v.i.* **1** act in a playful manner. **2** talk, act, or think about without being serious; trifle: *For over a month she dallied with the idea of buying a new car.* **3** linger idly; loiter. —*v.t.* waste (time); idle: *dally the afternoon away.*

dank (dangk), *adj.* unpleasantly damp or moist: *The cave was dark, dank, and chilly.* —**dank′ly,** *adv.* —**dank′ness,** *n.*

de cap i tate (di kap′ə tāt), *v.t.,* **-tat ed, -tat ing.** cut off the head of; behead.

de ceit ful (di sēt′fəl), *adj.* **1** ready or willing to deceive. **2** meant to deceive; deceiving; misleading. —**de ceit′ful ly,** *adv.* —**de ceit′ful ness,** *n.*

de con tam i nate (dē′kən tam′ə nāt), *v.t.,* **-nat ed, -nat ing. 1** make free from poison gas or harmful radioactive agents. **2** free from any sort of contamination. —**de′con tam i na′tion,** *n.*

de co rum (di kôr′əm, di kōr′əm), *n.* proper behavior; good taste in conduct, speech, dress, etc.

de duce (di düs′, di dyüs′), *v.t.,* **-duced, -duc ing.** reach (a conclusion) by reasoning; infer from a general rule or principle.

de fi ant (di fī′ənt), *adj.* showing defiance; openly resisting.

deft (deft), *adj.* quick and skillful in action; nimble: *the deft fingers of a surgeon.* —**deft′ly,** *adv.* —**deft′ness,** *n.*

deg ra da tion (deg′rə dā′shən), *n.* **1** a degrading. **2** a being degraded. **3** a degraded condition; debasement; degeneracy.

de hy drate (dē hī′drāt), *v.,* **-drat ed, -drat ing.** —*v.t.* take water or moisture from; dry: *dehydrate vegetables.* —*v.i.* lose water or moisture. [< *de-* remove + Greek *hydōr* water]

deign (dān), *v.i.* think fit; condescend. —*v.t.* condescend to give (an answer, a reply, etc.).

de jec tion (di jek′shən), *n.* lowness of spirits; sadness; discouragement: *Her face showed her dejection at missing the airplane.*

de lir i ous (di lir′ē əs), *adj.* **1** temporarily out of one's senses; wandering in mind; raving. **2** wildly enthusiastic.

del uge (del′yüj), *v.t.,* **-uged, -ug ing. 1** flood or overflow. **2** overwhelm. [< Old French < Latin *diluvium* < *diluere* wash away < *dis-* away + *luere* to wash]

dem i god (dem′i god′), *n.* a god who is partly human. Hercules was a demigod.

de par ture (di pär′chər), *n.* **1** act of going away; leaving. **2** a turning away; change: *a departure from our old custom.* **3** a starting on a new course of action or thought.

de plor a ble (di plôr′ə bəl, di plōr′ə bəl), *adj.* **1** that is to be deplored; regrettable; lamentable: *a deplorable accident.* **2** wretched; miserable. —**de plor′a bly,** *adv.*

de prav i ty (di prav′ə tē), *n., pl.* **-ties. 1** a being depraved; corruption. **2** a corrupt act; bad practice.

a hat	i it	oi oil	ch child		a in about
ā age	ī ice	ou out	ng long		e in taken
ä far	o hot	u cup	sh she	ə =	i in pencil
e let	ō open	ů put	th thin		o in lemon
ē equal	ô order	ü rule	ŦH then		u in circus
ėr term			zh measure	< = derived from	

dep re cate (dep′rə kāt), *v.t.,* **-cat ed, -cat ing. 1** express strong disapproval of: *Lovers of peace deprecate war.* **2** depreciate; belittle: *Don't deprecate the abilities of your classmates.* [< Latin *deprecatum* pleaded in excuse, averted by prayer < *de-* + *precari* pray] —**dep′re cat′ing ly,** *adv.* —**dep′re ca′tion,** *n.*

de pres sion (di presh′ən), *n.* **1** a depressed condition. **2** a low place; hollow: *depressions in the ground.*

de prive (di prīv′), *v.t.,* **-prived, -priv ing. 1** take away from by force; divest: *deprive a dictator of his power* **2** keep from having or doing: *Worrying deprived me of sleep.*

des o la tion (des′ə lā′shən), *n.* **1** act of making desolate; devastation. **2** a ruined, lonely, or deserted condition. **3** a desolate place. **4** lonely sorrow; sadness.

des pe ra tion (des′pə rā′shən), *n.* **1** a hopeless and reckless feeling; readiness to run any risk: *They jumped out of the window in desperation when they saw that the stairs were on fire.* **2** despair.

de tach (di tach′), *v.t.* loosen and remove; unfasten; separate: *She detached the trailer from the car.*

de test a ble (di tes′tə bəl), *adj.* deserving to be detested; hateful. —**de test′a ble ness,** *n.* —**de test′a bly,** *adv.*

de vour (di vour′), *v.t.* **1** eat (usually said of animals): *The lion devoured the zebra.* **2** eat like an animal; eat very hungrily: *The hungry hikers devoured the meal.*

dic tum (dik′təm), *n., pl.* **-tums** or **-ta. 1** a formal comment; authoritative opinion: *The dictum of the critics was that the play was excellent.* **2** maxim; saying.

dic (dī), *v.i.,* **died, dy ing. 1** stop living; become dead. **2** lose force or strength; come to an end; stop: *My sudden anger died.*

dif fi dent (dif′ə dənt), *adj.* lacking in self-confidence; shy. —**dif′fi dent ly,** *adv.*

di lem ma (də lem′ə), *n.* situation requiring a choice between two alternatives, which are or appear equally unfavorable; difficult choice. [< Greek *dilēmma* < *di-* two + *lēmma* premise]

di min ish (də min′ish), *v.t.* **1** make smaller; lessen; reduce. **2** lessen the importance, power, or reputation of; belittle. **3** (in architecture) to cause to taper. —*v.i.* **1** become smaller; lessen; decrease. **2** (in architecture) to taper.

dire (dīr), *adj.,* **dir er, dir est.** causing great fear or suffering; dreadful. [< Latin *dirus*] —**dire′ly,** *adv.* —**dire′ness,** *n.*

di rect (də rekt′, dī rekt′), *v.t.* **1** instruct to do something; order: *We were directed to include return addresses on our applications.* **2** tell or show (a person) the way; inform or guide as to the right way or road: *Can you direct me to the airport?* [< Latin *directum* led straight < *dis-* + *regere* to guide]

dis-, *prefix.* **1** opposite of; lack of; not: *Dishonest = not honest; opposite of honest. Discomfort = lack of comfort.* **2** do the opposite of: *Disentangle = do the opposite of entangle.* **3** apart; away, as in *dispel.*

dis cern (də zėrn′, də sėrn′), *v.t.* see clearly; perceive the difference between (two or more things); distinguish or recognize: *We discerned the island through the mist.*

dis close (dis klōz′), *v.t.,* **-closed, -clos ing. 1** open to view; uncover: *The window disclosed a beautiful landscape.* **2** make known; reveal: *This letter discloses a secret.*

dis con cert (dis′kən sėrt′), *v.t.* **1** disturb the self-possession of; embarrass greatly; confuse: *I was disconcerted to find that I was wearing two different shoes.* **2** upset or frustrate (plans, etc.). —**dis′con cert′ing ly,** *adv.*

dis con so late (dis kon′sə lit), *adj.* **1** without hope; forlorn; unhappy: *disconsolate over the death of a friend.* **2** causing discomfort; cheerless: *a long, disconsolate day.* [< Medieval Latin *disconsolatus* < Latin *dis-* + *consolari* to console] —**dis con′so late ly**, *adv.*

dis count (dis′kount, dis kount′) *v.t.* **1** deduct (a certain percentage) of the amount or cost: *The store discounts 2 percent on all bills paid when due.* **2** allow for exaggeration, prejudice, or inaccuracy in (a statement, etc.); believe only part of. **3** leave out of account; disregard: *In his plans he discounted the expense.*

dis course (dis′kôrs, dis′kōrs) —*n.* **1** a formal or extensive speech or writing: *Lectures and sermons are discourses.* **2** talk; conversation.

dis cre tion (dis kresh′ən), *n.* **1** quality of being discreet; great carefulness in speech or action; good judgment; wise caution: *Use your own discretion.* **2** freedom to decide or choose.

dis cus (dis′kəs), *n.* a heavy, circular plate, often of wood with a metal rim, thrown for distance in an athletic contest or as an exercise. [< Latin < Greek *diskos.* Doublet of DAIS, DESK, DISH, and DISK.]

dis dain (dis dān′), *v.t.* think unworthy of oneself or one's notice; regard or treat with contempt; scorn. —*n.* a disdaining; feeling of scorn. [< Old French *desdeignier* < *des-* dis- + *deignier* deign]

dis dain ful (dis dān′fəl), *adj.* feeling or showing disdain; scornful. —**dis dain′ful ly**, *adv.* —**dis dain′ful ness**, *n.*

dis em bod ied (dis′em bod′ēd), *adj.* separated from the body: *Ghosts are usually thought of as disembodied spirits.*

discus—athlete about to throw the discus

di shev eled or **di shev elled** (də shev′əld), *adj.* not neat; rumpled; disordered: *disheveled hair, disheveled appearance.*

dis in te grate (dis in′tə grāt), *v.,* **-grat ed, -grat ing.** —*v.t.* break up; separate into small parts or bits. —*v.i.* become disintegrated; break up.

dis pel (dis pel′), *v.t.,* **-pelled, -pel ling.** drive away and scatter; disperse.

dis pir it (dis pir′it), *v.t.* lower the spirits of; discourage; depress; dishearten. —**dis pir′it ed ly**

dis port (dis pôrt′, dis pōrt′), *v.t., v.i.* amuse or entertain (oneself); play; sport: *bears disporting themselves in the water.* [< Old French *desporter* < *des-* dis- + *porter* carry]

dis po si tion (dis′pə zish′ən), *n.* **1** one's habitual ways of acting toward others or of thinking about things; nature: *a cheerful disposition.* **2** tendency; inclination: *a disposition to argue.*

dis pute (dis pyüt′), *n.* **1** argument; debate. **2** a quarrel.

dis sect (di sekt′, dī sekt′), *v.t.* cut apart (an animal, plant, etc.) in order to examine or study the structure.

dis sen tient (di sen′shənt), *adj.* dissenting from the opinion of the majority. —*n.* person who dissents.

dis sim u late (di sim′yə lāt), *v.,* **-lat ed, -lat ing.** —*v.t.* disguise or hide under a pretense; dissemble. —*v.i.* hide the truth; dissemble. —**dis sim′u la′tion**, *n.* —**dis sim′u la′tor**, *n.*

dis si pate (dis′ə pāt), *v.,* **-pat ed, -pat ing.** —*v.t.* **1** spread in different directions; scatter. **2** cause to disappear; dispel: *The sun dissipated the mist.* **3** spend foolishly; waste on things of little value; squander. —*v.i.* scatter so as to disappear.

di ver sion (də ver′zhən, dī ver′zhən), *n.* **1** distraction from work, care, etc.; amusement; entertainment; pastime: *Baseball is my favorite diversion.* **2** attack or feint intended to distract an opponent's attention from the point of main attack.

di vulge (də vulj′, dī vulj′), *v.t.,* **-vulged, -vulg ing.** make known or tell others (something private or secret); reveal.

-dom, *suffix forming nouns.* **1** (*added to nouns*) position, rank, or realm of a ___: *Kingdom = realm of a king.* **2** (*added to adjectives*) condition of being ___: *Freedom = condition of being free.* **3** (*added to nouns*) all those who are ___: *Heathendom = all those who are heathen.* [Old English *-dōm* state, rank < *dōm* law, judgment]

dom i nate (dom′ə nāt), *v.t.,* **-nat ed, -nat ing.** **1** control or rule by strength or power. **2** rise high above; tower over: *The mountain dominates the city and its harbor.*

don (don), *v.t.,* **donned, don ning.** put on (clothing, etc.): *The knight donned his armor.* [contraction of *do on*]

dor mant (dôr′mənt), *adj.* **1** lying asleep; sleeping or apparently sleeping: *Bears and other animals that hibernate are dormant during the winter.* **2** in a state of rest or inactivity; not in motion, action, or operation; quiescent: *a dormant volcano.* [< Old French, present participle of *dormier* to sleep < Latin *dormire*]

dote (dōt), *v.i.,* **dot ed, dot ing.** **1** be weak-minded and childish because of old age. **2 dote on** or **dote upon,** be foolishly fond of; be too fond of. [Middle English *doten*] —**dot′er**, *n.*

down y (dou′nē), *adj.,* **down i er, down i est.** **1** made or consisting of soft feathers or hair. **2** covered with soft feathers or hair.

draft (draft), *n.* **1** current of air, especially in a confined space, as a room or a chimney. **2** device for controlling a current of air in a furnace, fireplace, stove, etc. **3** plan; sketch. **4** a rough copy: *I made three different drafts of my theme before I had it in final form.* **5** quantity of fish caught in a net at one time. **6** a single act of drinking.

drag gle (drag′əl), *v.,* **-gled, -gling.** —*v.t.* make wet or dirty (a garment, etc.) by dragging it through mud, water, dust, etc. —*v.i.* become wet or dirty by dragging through mud, water, dust, etc.

draught (draft), *n.* draft; a breathing in of air.

droop (drüp), *v.i.* **1** hang down; bend down. **2** become weak; lose strength and energy.

dum found (dum′found′), *v.t.* amaze and make unable to speak; bewilder; confuse. Also, **dumbfound.** [< *dumb* + *(con)found*]

dun geon (dun′jən), *n.* **1** a dark underground room or cell to keep prisoners in. **2** donjon. [< Old French *donjon*]

ear (ir), *n.* **1** the part of the body by which human beings and other vertebrates hear; organ of hearing. **2 play by ear, a** play (a piece of music or a musical instrument) without using written music. **b** handle (a matter) without adequate preparation or guidance. **3 up to the ears,** INFORMAL. thoroughly involved; almost overwhelmed.

eaves (ēvz), *n.pl.* the lower edge of a roof that projects over the side of a building. [Old English *efes* edge]

e bul lience (i bul′yəns), *n.* great enthusiasm. [< Latin *ebullientem* < *ex-* out + *bullire* to boil]

eb ul li tion (eb′ə lish′ən), *n.* **1** a boiling or a bubbling up. **2** outburst (of feeling, etc.).

ec cen tric (ek sen′trik), *adj.* out of the ordinary; not usual; odd; peculiar.

e clipse (i klips′), *n., v.,* **e clipsed, e clips ing.** —*n.* a complete or partial blocking of light passing from one heavenly body to another. —*v.t.* **1** cut off or dim the light from; darken. **2** cast a shadow upon; obscure. **3** surpass; outshine: *Napoleon eclipsed other generals of his time.*

ec sta sy (ek′stə sē), *n., pl.* **-sies.** condition of very great joy; thrilling or overwhelming delight.

-eer, *suffix added to nouns to form nouns and verbs.* **1** person who directs or operates ___: *Auctioneer = person who directs an auction.* **2** person who produces ___: *Pamphleteer = person who produces pamphlets.* **3** be concerned or deal with, as in *electioneer.*

ef fi cient (ə fish′ənt), *adj.* able to produce the effect wanted without waste of time, energy, etc.; capable; competent.

egg (eg), *v.t.* urge or encourage; incite: *We egged the team on when it was behind.*

e late (i lāt′), *v.t.,* **e lat ed, e lat ing.** raise the spirits of, make joyful or proud.

el e gant (el′ə gənt), *adj.* **1** having or showing good taste; gracefully and richly refined; beautifully luxurious: *The palace had elegant furnishings.* **2** expressed with taste; correct and polished in expression or arrangement.

el o quence (el′ə kwəns), *n.* **1** flow of speech that has grace and force. **2** power to win by speaking; the art of using language so as to stir the feelings.

el o quent (el′ə kwənt), *adj.* **1** having eloquence. **2** very expressive: *eloquent eyes.* **—el′o quent ly,** *adv.*

em-¹, *prefix.* form of **en-¹** before *b, p,* and sometimes *m,* as in *embark, employ.*

em-², *prefix.* form of **en-²** before *b, m, p, ph,* as in *emblem, emphasis.*

e ma ci ate (i mā′shē āt), *v.t.,* **-at ed, -at ing.** make unnaturally thin; cause to lose flesh or waste away: *A long illness had emaciated the patient.*

em boss (em bôs′, em bos′), *v.t.* decorate with a design, pattern, etc., that stands out from the surface: *Our coins are embossed with letters and figures.*

em bra sure (em brā′zhər), *n.* **1** an opening in a wall for a gun, with sides that spread outward to permit the gun to fire through a greater arc. **2** a slanting off of the wall at an oblique angle on the inner sides of a window or door. [< French]

embrasure (def. 1)

e merge (i mėrj′), *v.i.,* **e merged, e merg ing.** **1** come into view; come out; come up: *The sun emerged from behind a cloud.* **2** become known: *New facts emerged as a result of a second investigation.* See **issue** for synonym study.

em phat ic (em fat′ik), *adj.* **1** said or done with force or stress; strongly expressed: *Her answer was an emphatic ''No!''* **2** attracting attention; very noticeable; striking: *The club made an emphatic success of its party.* **—em phat′i cal ly,** *adv.*

en-¹, *prefix.* **1** cause to be ___; make ___: *Enfeeble = make feeble.* **2** put in ___; put on ___: *Enthrone = put on a throne.* **3** other meanings, as in *enact, encourage, entwine.* The addition of *en-* rarely changes the meaning of a verb except to make it more emphatic. See also **em-¹.** [< Old French < Latin *in-*]

en-², *prefix.* in; on, as in *energy.* See also **em-².** [< Greek]

-ence, *suffix forming nouns chiefly from verbs.* **1** act or fact of ___ing: *Abhorrence = act or fact of abhorring.* **2** quality or condition of being ___ent: *Prudence = quality of being prudent. Absence = condition of being absent.* Also, **-ency.**

en core (äng′kôr, äng′kōr; än′kôr, än′kōr), *interj., n.,* —*interj.* once more; again. —*n.* a demand by the audience for the repetition of a song, etc., or for another appearance of the performer or performers.

en fold (en fōld′), *v.t.* **1** fold in; wrap up: *enfold oneself in a blanket.* **2** embrace; clasp: *enfold a puppy in one's arms.*

en ig mat ic (en′ig mat′ik, ē′nig mat′ik), *adj.* like an enigma or riddle; baffling; puzzling. **—en′ig mat′i cal ly,** *adv.*

en sconce (en skons′), *v.t.,* **-sconced, -sconc ing.** **1** shelter safely; hid: *We were ensconced in the cellar during the tornado.* **2** settle comfortably and firmly: *The cat ensconced itself in the armchair.* [<*en-¹* + *sconce* fortification, probably < Dutch *schans*]

-ent, *suffix added to verbs.* **1** (*to form adjectives*) that ___s; ___ing: *Absorbent = that absorbs* or *absorbing.* **2** (*to form nouns*) one that ___s: *Correspondent = one that corresponds.* **3** (*to form adjectives*) other meanings, as in *competent, confident.* See also **-ant.**

en ter pris ing (en′tər prī′zing), *adj.* likely to start projects; ready to face difficulties. **—en′ter pris′ing ly,** *adv.*

en tice (en tīs′), *v.t.,* **-ticed, -tic ing.** attract by arousing

a hat	i it	oi oil	ch child	(a in about
ā age	ī ice	ou out	ng long	e in taken
ä far	o hot	u cup	sh she	ə = { i in pencil
e let	ō open	ù put	th thin	o in lemon
ē equal	ô order	ü rule	ᴛʜ then	(u in circus
ėr term			zh measure	< = derived from

hopes or desires; tempt. **—en tice′ment,** *n.*

-er¹, *suffix forming nouns.* **1** (*added to verbs*) person or thing that ___s: *Admirer = a person who admires. Burner = thing that burns.* **2** (*added to nouns*) person living in ___: *New Yorker = a person living in New York. Villager = a person living in a village.* **3** (*added to nouns*) person who makes or works with ___: *Hatter = a person who makes hats.* **4** person or thing that is or has ___: *Six-footer = a person who is six feet tall.* [Old English *-ere,* ultimately < Latin *-arium -ary*]

-er², *suffix forming nouns from other nouns.* person or thing connected with ___: *Officer = person connected with an office.*

-er³, *suffix forming the comparative degree of adjectives and adverbs.* more: *Softer = more soft. Slower = more slow.*

err (ėr, er), *v.i.* **1** go wrong; make a mistake. **2** be wrong; be mistaken or incorrect. **3** do wrong; sin. [< Latin *errare* wander]

es cort (es′kôrt), *n.* **1** person or group of persons going with another to give protection, show honor, etc.: *an escort of several city officials.* **2** one or more ships or airplanes serving as a guard. **3** man who goes on a date with a woman: *Her escort to the party was a tall young man.*

-ess, *suffix forming nouns from other nouns.* female___: *Lioness = female lion.* [< Old French *-esse* < Latin *-issa* < Greek]

es sence (es′ns), *n.* **1** that which makes a thing what it is; necessary part or parts; important feature or features: *Being thoughtful of others is the essence of politeness.* **2** a concentrated substance that has the characteristic flavor, fragrance, or effect of the plant, fruit, etc., from which it is taken.

es ti ma tion (es′tə mā′shən), *n.* **1** judgment or opinion: *In my estimation, your plan will not work.* **2** esteem; respect.

e ther (ē′thər), *n.* a colorless, volatile, flammable, sweet-smelling liquid, produced by the action of sulfuric acid on ethyl alcohol.

e va sion (i vā′zhən), *n.* **1** a getting away from something by trickery; avoiding by cleverness. **2** an attempt to escape an argument, a charge, a question, etc. **3** means of evading; trick or excuse used to avoid something.

e voke (i vōk′), *v.t.,* **e voked, e vok ing.** call forth; bring out; elicit: *A good joke evokes a laugh.*

ex-¹, *prefix.* **1** former; formerly: *Ex-president = former president.* **2** out of; from; out: *Express = press out.* **3** thoroughly; utterly: *Exterminate = terminate (finish or destroy) thoroughly.*

ex-² *prefix.* from; out of, as in *exodus.* Also, **ec-** before consonants. [< Greek]

ex alt (eg zôlt′), *v.t.* **1** make high in rank, honor, power, character, or quality; elevate. **2** fill with pride, joy, or noble feeling. **3** praise; honor; glorify.

ex clu sive (ek sklü′siv, ek sklü′ziv), *adj.* **1** not divided or shared with others; single; sole: *exclusive rights to sell a product.* **2** limited to a single object: *exclusive attention to instructions.* **3** very particular about choosing friends, members, etc. **4** each shutting out the other.—*n.* a news story printed by a single newspaper.

ex ha la tion (eks′hə lā′shən), *n.* a breathing out of air.

ex hil a rate (eg zil′ə rāt′), *v.t.,* **-rat ed, -rat ing.** make merry or lively; put into high spirits; cheer.

ex ot ic (eg zot′ik), *adj.* **1** from a foreign country; not native: *We saw many exotic plants at the flower show.* **2** fascinating or interesting because strange or different: *an exotic island.*

ex traor di nar y (ek strôr′də ner′ē) *adj.* beyond what is ordinary; very unusual or remarkable; exceptional: *Eight feet is an* *extraordinary height for a person.* **—ex traor′di nar′i ly,** *adv.* **—ex traor′di nar′i ness,** *n.*

ex trem i ty (ek strem′ə tē), *n., pl.* **-ties.** **1** the very end; farthest possible place; last part or point. **2** an extreme degree: *Joy is the extremity of happiness.* **3** an extreme action or measure.

ex tri cate (ek′strə kāt), *v.t.,* **-cat ed, -cat ing.** set free (from entanglements, difficulties, embarrassing situations, etc.); release.

ex tro vert (ek′strə vèrt′), *n.* person tending to act rather than think. Extroverts are more interested in what is going on around them than in their own thoughts. [< *extro-* outside (variant of *extra-*) + Latin *vertere* to turn]

ex ult ant (eg zult′nt), *adj.* rejoicing greatly; exulting; triumphant: *an exultant shout.* **—ex ult′ant ly,** *adv.*

fac et (fas′it), *n., v.,* **-et ed, -et ing** or **-et ted, -et ting.** **—n.** any one of the small, polished, flat surfaces of a cut gem. **—v.t.** cut facets on. [< French *facette*]

fag ot (fag′ət), *n.* bundle of sticks or twigs tied together for fuel.

fain (fān), ARCHAIC. **—adv.** gladly; willingly. **—adj.** **1** willing, but not eager. **2** obliged. **3** glad. **4** eager. [Old English *faegen*]

faint (fānt), *adj.* **1** not clear or plain; hardly perceptible; dim; indistinct: *faint colors, a faint idea.* **2** weak; feeble; faltering: *a faint voice.*

fall out (fôl′out′), *n.* the radioactive particles or dust that fall to the earth after a nuclear explosion.

fan cy (fan′sē), *v.t.,* **-cied, -cy ing.** **1** picture to oneself; imagine; conceive: *Can you fancy yourself on the moon?* **2** have an idea or belief; suppose: *I fancy that is right, but I am not sure.* **3** be fond of; like: *I fancy the idea of having a picnic.*

fare (fer, far), *n.* **1** the money paid to ride in a taxi, bus, train, airplane, etc. **2** passenger. **3** food: *dainty fare.* [Old English *faran* go, travel]

fas tid i ous (fa stid′ē əs), *adj.* hard to please; dainty in taste; easily disgusted. [< Latin *fastidiosus* < *fastidium* loathing]

fat u ous (fach′ü əs), *adj.* stupid but self-satisfied; foolish; silly. [< Latin *fatuus*] **—fat′u ous ly,** *adv.*

faun (fôn), *n.* (in Roman myths) a minor god that lived in fields and woods, represented as a man but having the pointed ears, small horns, tail, and sometimes the legs, of a goat.

fawn (fôn), *v.i.* try to get favor or notice by slavish acts: *Many flattering relatives fawned on the rich old woman.*

feign (fān), *v.t.* put on a false appearance of; make believe; pretend: *Some animals feign death when in danger.*

feint (fānt), *n.* movement intended to deceive; sham attack; pretended blow. **—v.i.** make a feint: *The fighter feinted with his right hand and struck with his left.*

fe roc i ty (fə ros′ə tē), *n., pl.* **-ties.** savage cruelty; fierceness.

-ferous, *suffix added to nouns to form adjectives.* producing ___; containing ___; conveying ___: *Metalliferous = containing metal.* [< Latin *-fer* (< *ferre* to bear) + English *-ous*]

fer vent (fèr′vənt), *adj.* showing great warmth of feeling; very earnest; ardent: *fervent devotion.* **—fer′vent ly,** *adv.*

feign
an opossum feigning death

fiend (fēnd), *n.* **1** an evil spirit; devil; demon. **2** a very wicked or cruel person.

fiend ish (fēn′dish), *adj.* very cruel or wicked; devilish: *fiendish tortures, a fiendish yell.* **—fiend′ish ly,** *adv.*

flail (flāl), *v.t.* beat; thrash.

flam beau (flam′bō), *n., pl.* **-beaux** or **-beaus** (-bōz). **1** a flaming torch. **2** a large, decorated candlestick. [< French]

flank (flangk), *n.* the fleshy or muscular part of the side of an animal or person between the ribs and the hip.

flat¹ (flat), *adj.,* **flat ter, flat test.** **1** smooth and level; even; plane: *flat land.* **2** at full length; horizontal: *The storm left the trees flat on the ground.* **3** not very deep or thick.

flat² (flat), *n.* apartment.

flax (flaks), *n.* **1** a slender, upright plant with small, narrow leaves, blue or white flowers, and slender stems about two feet tall. **2** the threadlike fibers into which the stems of this plant separate. Flax is spun into thread and woven into linen.

flay (flā), *v.t.* **1** strip off the skin or outer covering of; skin. **2** scold severely; criticize without pity or mercy.

fleck (flek), *v.t.* mark with spots or patches of color, light, etc.; speckle: *The bird's breast is flecked with brown.* [perhaps < Scandinavian (Old Icelandic) *flekkr*]

fledg ling or **fledge ling** (flej′ling), *n.* a young bird that has just grown feathers needed for flying.

fleet-footed (flēt′fut′id), *adj.* able to run fast.

fleet ing (flē′ting), *adj.* passing swiftly; soon gone; transitory: *a fleeting smile.* **—fleet′ing ly,** *adv.* **—fleet′ing ness,** *n.*

flex i ble (flek′sə bəl), *adj.* **1** easily bent; not stiff; bending without breaking: *Leather, rubber, and wire are flexible.* **2** easily adapted to fit various conditions.

flin ders (flin′dərz), *n. pl.* small pieces; fragments; splinters.

foot hill (fut′hil′), *n.* a low hill at the base of a mountain or mountain range.

ford (fôrd, fōrd), *n.* place where a river or other body of water is shallow enough to be crossed by wading or driving through the water.

fore stay (fôr′stā′, fōr′stā′), *n.* rope or cable reaching from the top of a ship's foremast to the bowsprit. The forestay helps to support the foremast.

forge (fôrj, fōrj), *n., v.,* **forged, forg ing.** **—n.** **1** an open fireplace or hearth with a bellows attached, used for heating metal very hot to be hammered into shape. **2** a blacksmith's shop; smithy. **—v.t.** **1** shape (metal) by heating in a forge and then hammering. **2** make, shape, or form.

for get (fər get′), *v.t.* **-got, -got ten** or **-got, -get ting.** **1** let go out of the mind; fail to remember. **2 forget oneself,** forget what one should do or be; say or do something improper.

for mi da ble (fôr′mə də bəl), *adj.* hard to overcome; hard to deal with; to be dreaded: *a formidable opponent.*

for tress (fôr′tris), *n.* a large, permanently fortified place or building; large fort or fortification. [<Old French *forteresse* < *fort* strong < Latin *fortis*]

foun der (foun′dər), *v.i.* **1** fill with water and sink. **2** fall down; stumble: *The horse foundered.*

fowl er (fou′lər), *n.* person who hunts, shoots, catches, or traps wild birds.

fray (frā), *n.* a noisy quarrel; brawl. [variant of *affray*]

fresh et (fresh′it), *n.* **1** flood caused by heavy rains or melted snow. **2** stream or rush of fresh water flowing into the sea.

frog (frog, frôg), *n.* **1** any of various small, tailless amphibians, having a smooth skin and powerful web-footed hind legs for leaping, and being more aquatic and more agile than a toad. **2 frog in the throat,** slight hoarseness caused by soreness or swelling in the throat.

froth (frôth, froth), *n.* **1** foam. **2** foaming saliva coming from the mouth, caused by disease, exertion, etc. **3** something light or trifling; trivial notions, talk, etc. **—v.i.** give out froth; foam.

fu gi tive (fyü′jə tiv), *n.* **1** person who is fleeing or who has fled from danger, an enemy, justice, etc. **2** exile; refugee.

-ful, *suffix added to nouns to form adjectives or other nouns.* **1** full of ___: *Cheerful = full of cheer.* **2** showing ___: *Careful = showing care.* **3** having a tendency to ___:

Harmful = having a tendency to harm. **4** enough to fill a ___: *Cupful = enough to fill a cup.* **5** that can be of ___: *Useful = that can be of use.*

fur row (fėr′ō), *n.* **1** a long, narrow groove or track cut in the earth by a plow. **2** any long, narrow groove or track.

fur tive (fėr′tiv), *adj.* **1** done quickly and with stealth to avoid being noticed; secret: *a furtive glance into the forbidden room.* **2** sly; stealthy: *a furtive manner.* [< Latin *furtivus* < *furtum* theft < *fur* thief] —**fur′tive ly,** *adv.* —**fur′tive ness,** *n.*

fu tile (fyü′tl, fyü′tīl), *adj.* **1** not successful; useless; ineffectual: *He fell down after making futile attempts to keep his balance.* **2** not important; trifling. [< Latin *futilis* pouring easily, worthless < *fundere* pour] —**fu′tile ly,** *adv.*

-fy, *suffix forming verbs chiefly from adjectives.* **1** make ___; cause to be ___: *Simplify = make simple.* **2** become ___: *Solidify = become solid.*

gait (gāt), *n.* the manner of walking or running.

gal ley (gal′ē), *n., pl.* **-leys. 1** a long, narrow ship propelled by both oars and sails, used in medieval times in the Mediterranean. **2** kitchen of a ship or airplane. **3** (in printing) a long, narrow tray for holding type that has been set. **4** galley proof.

gal lows (gal′ōz), *n., pl.* **-lows es** or **-lows.** a wooden structure usually consisting of a crossbar on two upright posts, used for hanging criminals.

ga lumph (gə lumf′), *v.i.* gallop in a clumsy way: *cows galumphing home.* [perhaps blend of *gallop* and *triumph;* coined by Lewis Carroll]

gal va nize (gal′və nīz), *v.t.,* **-nized, -niz ing.** cover (iron or steel) with a thin coating of zinc to prevent rust.

game (gām), *n.* **1** way of playing; pastime; amusement: *a game of tag.* **2** plan; scheme: *They tried to trick us, but we saw through their game.* **3 the game is up,** the plan or scheme has failed.

garb (gärb), *n.* the way one is dressed; kind of clothing.

gaunt (gônt, gänt), *adj.* **1** very thin and bony; with hollow eyes and a starved look: *Sickness had made him gaunt.* **2** looking bare and gloomy; desolate. [origin uncertain] —**gaunt′ly,** *adv.* —**gaunt′ness,** *n.*

gaunt let (gônt′lit, gänt′lit), *n.* **1** a stout, heavy glove usually of leather covered with plates of iron or steel, that was worn as part of medieval armor. **2** a stout, heavy glove with a wide, flaring cuff often covering part of the arm, used in fencing, riding, etc.

ga zelle (gə zel′), *n., pl.* **-zelles** or **-zelle.** any of a genus of small, swift, graceful antelope of Africa and Asia. [< French < Arabic *ghazāl*] —**ga zelle′like′,** *adj.*

gild (gild), *v.t.,* **gild ed** or **gilt, gild ing. 1** cover with a thin layer of gold or similar material; make golden. **2** make (something) look bright and pleasing. **3** make (something) seem better than it is.

gimp¹ (gimp), *n.* a braidlike trimming used on garments, curtains, furniture, etc. [< French *guimpe*]

gimp² (gimp), *n.* SLANG. **1** a lame step or walk; limp. **2** person who limps. [origin uncertain]

gin ger (jin′jər), *n.* **1** spice made from the pungent root of a cultivated tropical plant. It is used for flavoring and in medicine. **2** its root, often preserved in syrup or candied. **3** the plant. **4** INFORMAL. liveliness; energy. **5** a light reddish or brownish yellow.

gin ger ly (jin′jər lē), *adv.* with extreme care or caution. —*adj.* extremely cautious or wary. —**gin′ger li ness,** *n.*

gird (gėrd), *v.t.,* **gird ed** or **girt, gird ing. 1** put a belt, cord, etc., around. **2** fasten with a belt, cord, etc.: *gird on one's sword.* **3** surround; enclose.

gloss (glôs, glos), *v.t.* put a smooth, shiny surface on.

glow er (glou′ər), *v.i.* stare angrily; scowl fiercely.

glut ton ous (glut′n əs), *adj.* **1** greedy about food; having the habit of eating too much. **2** greedy.

gnarled (närld), *adj.* containing gnarls; knotted; twisted: *The farmer's gnarled hands grasped the plow firmly.*

gnat (nat), *n.* any of various small, two-winged flies.

goad (gōd), *v.t.* drive or urge on; act as a goad to: *Hunger can goad a person to steal.*

gouge (gouj), *v.t.,* **gouged, goug ing. 1** cut with a gouge. **2** dig out; tear out; force out.

grav i ty (grav′ə tē), *n., pl.* **-ties.** seriousness; earnestness.

grille (gril), *n.* an openwork, metal structure or screen, used as a gate, door, window, or to cover the opening in front of the radiator of an automobile; grating. [< French]

gris tly (gris′lē), *adj.,* **-tli er, -tli est.** of, containing, or like gristle; cartilaginous. —**gris′tli ness,** *n.*

grits (grits), *n.pl.* **1** corn, oats, wheat, etc., husked and coarsely ground. Grits are eaten boiled. **2** coarsely ground corn or hominy cooked as a cereal.

grope (grōp), *v.,* **groped, grop ing.** —*v.i.* **1** feel about with the hands: *I groped for a flashlight when the lights went out.* **2** search blindly and uncertainly: *The detectives groped for some clue to the mysterious crime.* —*v.t.* find by feeling about with the hands; feel (one's way) slowly.

grot to (grot′ō), *n., pl.* **-toes** or **-tos.** cave or cavern.

ground (ground), *n.* **1** the solid part of the earth's surface. **2** soil; earth; dirt. **3 grounds,** *pl.* small bits that sink to the bottom of a drink such as coffee or tea; dregs; sediment.

grouse (grous), *n., pl.* **grouse.** any of a family of brown game birds with feathered legs. The prairie chicken, ruffed grouse, and sage grouse are different kinds of grouse. [origin unknown]

guard ed (gär′did), *adj.* careful; cautious: *"Maybe" was the guarded answer to my question.* —**guard′ed ly,** *adv.*

guild (gild), *n.* **1** association or society formed by people having the same interests, work, etc., for some useful or common purpose: *the hospital guild of a church.* **2** (in the Middle Ages) an association of merchants in a town or of persons in a particular trade or craft, formed to keep standards high, promote their business interests, protect themselves, etc.

gut tur al (gut′ər əl), *adj.* **1** of the throat. **2** formed in the throat; harsh: *speak in a deep, guttural voice.* **3** formed between the back of the tongue and the soft palate. The g in go is a guttural sound.

hale (hāl), *adj.,* **hal er, hal est.** free from infirmity; strong and well; healthy. [Old English *hāl*]

half crown, a former coin of Great Britain which was equal to 2½ shillings.

half pen ny (hā′pə nē, hāp′nē), *n., pl.* **half pence** (hā′pəns), **half pen nies,** a former British coin worth half a penny.

hal lu ci na tion (hə lü′sn ā′shən), *n.* **1** a seeing or hearing things that exist only in a person's imagination. Hallucinations may occur as a result of certain mental illnesses, acute alcoholism, the taking of certain drugs, etc. **2** an imaginary thing seen or heard.

ham per (ham′pər), *v.t.* hold back; obstruct in action; hinder; restrain. [Middle English *hampren*]

har bin ger (här′bən jər), *n.* one that goes ahead to announce another's coming; forerunner: *The robin is a harbinger of spring.*

har ass (har′əs, hə ras′), *v.t.* **1** trouble by repeated attacks; harry: *Pirates harassed the villages along the coast.* **2** distress with annoying labor, care, misfortune, etc.; disturb; worry.

har ry (har′ē), *v.,* **-ried, -ry ing.** —*v.t.* **1** raid and rob with violence; lay waste; pillage. **2** keep troubling; worry; torment.

hatch

—*v.i.* make predatory raids. [Old English *hergian* < *here* army]

hatch (hach), *n.* an opening in a ship's deck through which the cargo is loaded.

haugh ty (hô′tē), *adj.,* **-ti er, -ti est.** too proud and scornful of others: *a haughty glance, haughty words.* [Middle English *haute* < Middle French *haut* < Latin *altus* high] —**haugh′ti ly,** *adv.* —**haugh′ti ness,** *n.*

haunch (hônch, hänch), *n.* **1** hip. **2 haunches,** *pl.* the hindquarters of an animal.

haw ser (hô′zər, hô′sər), *n.* a large, stout rope or thin steel cable, used for mooring or towing ships.

haz ard (haz′ərd), *v.t.* **1** take a chance with; risk; venture: *I would hazard my life on his honesty.* **2** expose to risk: *hazard life for a friend.* [< Old French *hasard* game of dice < Arabic *az-zahr* the die]

head wind, wind blowing from the direction in which a ship, etc., is moving.

heark en (här′kən), *v.i.* pay attention to what is said; listen attentively; listen. Also, **harken.** [Old English *heorcnian*]

hear say (hir′sā′), *n.* common talk; gossip or rumor.

hearth (härth), *n.* stone or brick floor of a fireplace, often extending into the room.

heir loom (er′lüm′, ar′lüm′), *n.* any piece of personal property that has been handed down from generation to generation: *This clock is a family heirloom.*

helm (helm), *n.* **1** handle or wheel by which a ship is steered. **2** the steering apparatus of a ship, including the wheel, rudder, and connecting parts.

herb (ėrb, hėrb), *n.* plant whose leaves or stems are used for medicine, seasoning, food, or perfume.

he ret i cal (hə ret′ə kəl), *adj.* **1** of or having to do with an opinion or doctrine opposed to what is accepted as authoritative. **2** containing heresy; characterized by heresy.

her met ic (hər met′ik), *adj.* closed tightly so that air cannot get in or out; airtight. —**her met′i cal ly,** *adv.*

hoard (hôrd, hōrd), *v.t., v.i.* save and store away (money, goods, etc.) for preservation or future use: *A squirrel hoards nuts for the winter.* —*n.* what is saved and stored away for preservation or future use; things stored. [Old English *hordian*] —**hoard′er,** *n.*

hold (hōld), *n.* interior of a ship or airplane where the cargo is carried. A ship's hold is below the deck. [variant of *hole*]

home stead er (hōm′sted′ər), *n.* **1** person who has a homestead. **2** settler granted a homestead by the government.

hos pi ta ble (hos′pi tə bəl, ho spit′ə bəl), *adj.* giving or liking to give a welcome, food and shelter, and friendly treatment to guests or strangers: *a hospitable family.*

hos pi tal i ty (hos′pə tal′ə tē), *n., pl.* **-ties.** friendly reception; generous treatment of guests or strangers.

hos tile (hos′tl; *sometimes* hos′til), *adj.* **1** of an enemy or enemies: *the hostile army.* **2** opposed; unfriendly; unfavorable.

hov er (huv′ər, hov′ər), *v.i.* hang fluttering or suspended in air.

hull (hul), *n.* **1** body or frame of a ship. **2** the main body or frame of a seaplane, airship, etc.

hu mane (hyü mān′), *adj.* not cruel or brutal; kind; merciful.

hu mil i ate (hyü mil′ē āt), *v.t.,* **-at ed, -at ing.** lower the pride, dignity, or self-respect of; make ashamed. [< Latin *humiliare* < *humilis* low.] —**hu mil′i at′ing ly,** *adv.*

hutch (huch), *n.* **1** box or pen for small animals, such as rabbits. **2** hut. **3** box, chest, or bin. **4** cupboard with open shelves on the upper part for holding dishes, etc.

hypodermic syringe, syringe fitted with a hollow needle, used to inject a dose of medicine beneath the skin, or to take out blood or other bodily fluid.

-ial, *suffix.* a form of **-al¹**, as in *adverbial, facial.*

-ian, *suffix.* a form of **-an**, as in *mammalian, Italian.*

-ible, *suffix added to verbs to form adjectives.* that can be ___ed: *Reducible = that can be reduced.* [< Old French < Latin *-ibilis*]

-ic, *suffix added to nouns to form adjectives.* **1** of or having to do with: *Atmospheric = of the atmosphere.* **2** having the nature of: *Heroic = having the nature of a hero.* **3** constituting or being: *Bombastic = constituting bombast.* **4** containing; made up of: *Alcoholic = containing alcohol.*

-ical, *suffix.* **1** -ic, as in *geometrical, parasitical, hysterical.* **2** -ic + -al or -ics + -al, as in *critical, musical, ethical, statistical.*

id i om (id′ē əm), *n.* phrase or expression whose meaning cannot be understood from the ordinary meanings of the words in it. "Hold one's tongue" is an English idiom meaning "keep still."

id i o syn cra sy (id′ē ō sing′krə sē), *n., pl.* **-sies.** a personal peculiarity of taste, behavior, opinion, etc.

i dle (ī′dl), *v.,* **i dled, i dling.** —*v.i.* **1** be idle; do nothing. **2** move or saunter idly. **3** run without transmitting power. The motor of a car idles when out of gear and running slowly. —*v.t.* **1** spend or waste (time). **2** cause (a person or thing) to be idle; take out of work or use. [Old English *īdel*]

i dyll or **i dyl** (ī′dl), *n.* **1** a short poem or piece of prose describing some simple and charming scene or event, especially one connected with country life. **2** a narrative poem treating a historical, romantic, or heroic theme.

ig no ble (ig nō′bəl), *adj.* without honor; disgraceful; base. —**ig no bly,** *adv.*

ig no min i ous (ig′nə min′ē əs), *adj.* shameful; disgraceful.

il-¹, *prefix.* the form of **in-¹** before *l*, as in *illegal, illegible,* etc.

il-², *prefix.* the form of **in-²** before *l*, as in *illuminate.*

il lu mi nate (i lü′mə nāt), *v.t.,* **-nat ed, -nat ing.** light up; make bright: *The room was illuminated by four large lamps.*

im-¹, *prefix.* the form of **in-¹** before *b, m, p,* as in *imbalance, immoral, impatient.*

im-², *prefix.* the form of **in-²** before *b, m, p,* as in *imbibe, immure, impart.*

im mac u late (i mak′yə lit), *adj.* **1** without a spot or stain; absolutely clean. **2** without fault or errors. **3** without sin; pure. [< Latin *immaculatus* < *in-* not + *macula* spot] —**im mac′u late ly,** *adv.* —**im mac′u late ness,** *n.*

im meas ur a ble (i mezh′ər ə bəl, i mā′zhər ə bəl), *adj.* too vast to be measured; very great; boundless.

im merse (i mėrs′), *v.t.,* **-mersed, -mers ing.** **1** dip or lower into a liquid until covered by it. **2** baptize by dipping (a person) completely under water. **3** involve deeply; absorb: *immersed in business, immersed in debts.* [< Latin *immersum* plunged in < *in-* in + *mergere* to plunge]

im mi nent (im′ə nənt), *adj.* likely to happen soon; about to occur: *Black clouds show rain is imminent.*

im mor tal (i môr′tl), *adj.* living forever; never dying.

im per a tive (im per′ə tiv), *adj.* not to be avoided; that must be done; urgent; necessary.

im per i al (im pir′ē əl), *adj.* **1** of an empire or its ruler: *the imperial palace.* **2** supreme; majestic; magnificent. —*n.* a small, pointed beard growing beneath the lower lip.

im per il (im per′əl), *v.t.,* **-iled, -il ing** or **-illed, -il ling.** put in danger; endanger; jeopardize.

im pet u ous (im pech′ü əs), *adj.* **1** acting or done with sudden or rash energy; hasty: *He was so angry that he made an impetuous decision.* **2** rushing with force and violence.

im ple ment (im′plə mənt) *n.* a useful article of equipment; tool; instrument; utensil.

im pli ca tion (im′plə kā′shən), *n.* **1** an implying. **2** a being implied. **3** something implied; indirect suggestion; hint.

im plic it (im plis′it), *adj.* **1** meant, but not clearly expressed or distinctly stated; implied: *implicit consent.* **2** without doubting, hesitating, or asking questions; absolute. —**im plic′it ness,** *n.* —**im plic′ it ly,** *adv.*

im plore (im plôr′, im plōr′), *v.t.,* **-plored, -plor ing.** **1** beg or pray earnestly for. **2** beg (a person) to do something.

im pres sive (im pres′iv), *adj.* able to impress the mind, feelings, conscience, etc.; able to excite deep feeling: *an impressive*

sermon, an impressive storm, an impressive ceremony.
—im pres′sive ly, *adv.* **—im pres′sive ness,** *n.*

in-[1], *prefix.* not; the opposite of; the absence of: *Inexpensive = not expensive. Inattention = the absence of attention.*

in-[2] *prefix.* in; into; on; upon: *Incase = (put) into a case. Intrust = (give) in trust.* See also **il-, im-, ir-.** [< Latin < *in,* preposition]

in-[3] *prefix.* in; within; into; toward: *Indoors = within doors. Inland = toward land.* [Old English]

in ad e quate (in ad′ə kwit), *adj.* not adequate; not enough; not as much as is needed: *inadequate preparation for an examination.* **—in ad′e quate ly,** *adv.* **—in ad′e quate ness,** *n.*

in cen tive (in sen′tiv), *n.* thing that urges a person on; cause of action or effort; motive; stimulus.

in ces sant (in ses′nt), *adj.* never stopping; continued or repeated without interruption; continual. **—in ces′sant ly,** *adv.*

in ci sive (in sī′siv), *adj.* sharp or keen; penetrating.

in com pe tence (in kom′pə təns), *n.* **1** lack of ability, power, or fitness. **2** lack of legal qualification.

in com pre hen si ble (in′kom pri hen′sə bəl), *adj.* impossible to understand.

in cor po rate (in kôr′pə rāt′), *v.t.,* **-rat ed, -rat ing.** **1** make (something) a part of something else; join or combine (something) with something else: *We will incorporate your suggestion in this new plan.* **2** make into a corporation: *When the business became large, the owners incorporated it.*

in cred i ble (in kred′ə bəl), *adj.* hard to believe; seeming too extraordinary to be possible; unbelievable: *incredible bravery.*

in cre du li ty (in′krə dü′lə tē, in′krə dyü′lə tē), *n.* lack of belief; doubt.

in cred u lous (in krej′ə ləs), *adj.* **1** not ready to believe; doubting; skeptical: *If they look incredulous show them the evidence.* **2** showing a lack of belief: *an incredulous smile.* **—in cred′u lous ly,** *adv.*

in crim i nate (in krim′ə nāt), *v.t.,* **-nat ed, -nat ing.** accuse of a crime; show to be guilty: *In a signed confession the thief incriminated two others.*

in cu ba tion (ing′kyə bā′shən, in′kyə bā′shən), *n.* **1** act of incubating. **2** condition of being incubated. **3** stage of a disease from the time of infection until the first symptoms appear.

in cur a ble (in kyùr′ə bəl), *adj.* not capable of being cured or healed: *an incurable invalid.* **—n.** person having an incurable disease. **—in cur′a ble ness,** *n.* **—in cur′a bly,** *adv.*

in de fin a ble (in′di fī′nə bəl), *adj.* that cannot be defined or described exactly.

in del i ble (in del′ə bəl), *adj.* **1** that cannot be erased or removed; permanent: *indelible ink, an indelible impression.* **2** capable of making an indelible mark. **—in del′i bly,** *adv.*

in di cate (in′də kāt), *v.t.,* **-cat ed, -cat ing.** **1** point out; point to: *The arrow on the sign indicates the right way to go.* **2** be a sign or hint of: *Fever indicates illness.* [< Latin *indicatum* pointed out, shown < *in-* in, to + *dicare* make known, proclaim]

in di ca tion (in′də kā′shən), *n.* **1** act of indicating. **2** thing that indicates; sign.

in dif fer ence (in dif′ər əns), *n.* **1** lack of interest or attention. **2** lack of importance.

in dif fer ent (in dif′ər ənt), *adj.* **1** having or showing no interest or attention: *indifferent to an admirer.* **2** not inclined to prefer one person or thing to another; impartial; neutral; fair: *an indifferent decision.* **3** not mattering much; unimportant: *The time for starting is indifferent to me.* **4** neither good nor bad; just fair; mediocre. **5** rather bad; poor. **6** neutral in chemical, electrical, or magnetic quality. **—in dif′fer ent ly,** *adv.*

in dig nant (in dig′nənt), *adj.* angry at something unworthy, unjust, unfair, or mean.

in dom i ta ble (in dom′ə tə bəl), *adj.* that cannot be discouraged, beaten, or conquered; unyielding.

in doors (in′dôrz′, in′dōrz′), *adv.* in or into a house or building: *Go indoors.*

in ert (in ėrt′), *adj.* having no power to move or act; lifeless.

in ev i ta ble (in ev′ə tə bəl), *adj.* not to be avoided; sure to

a hat	i it	oi oil	ch child		a in about
ā age	ī ice	ou out	ng long		e in taken
ä far	o hot	u cup	sh she	ə –	i in pencil
e let	ō open	ù put	th thin		o in lemon
ē equal	ô order	ü rule	ᴛH then		u in circus
ėr term			zh measure		< = derived from

happen; certain to come: *Death is inevitable.*

in fer no (in fėr′nō), *n., pl.* **-nos.** **1** hell. **2** place of torment or intense heat like hell: *a roaring inferno of flames.* [< Italian]

in glo ri ous (in glôr′ē əs, in glōr′ē əs), *adj.* **1** bringing no glory; shameful; disgraceful. **2** having no glory; not famous; obscure. **—in glo′ri ous ly,** *adv.* **—in glo′ri ous ness,** *n.*

in her ent (in hir′ənt, in her′ənt), *adj.* belonging to a person or thing as a permanent and essential quality or attribute; intrinsic. **—in her′ent ly,** *adv.*

i ni ti a tion (i nish′ē ā′shən), *n.* **1** act or process of initiating; beginning. **2** fact of being initiated. **3** formal admission into a group or society. **4** ceremonies by which one is admitted to a group or society.

i ni ti a tive (i nish′ē ə tiv, i nish′ē ā′tiv), *n.* **1** active part in taking the first steps in any undertaking; lead: *A shy person is not likely to take the initiative in making acquaintances.* **2** readiness and ability to be the one to start something; enterprise: *A good leader must have initiative.*

in laid (in′lād′), *adj.* **1** set in the surface as a decoration or design: *The top of the desk had an inlaid design of light wood in dark.* **2** decorated with a design or material set in the surface: *The box had an inlaid cover.* **—v.** pt. and pp. of **inlay.**

in nu mer a ble (i nü′mər ə bəl, i nyü′mər ə bəl), *adj.* too many to count; very many; countless.

in quis i tive (in kwiz′ə tiv), *adj.* **1** asking many questions; curious. **2** prying into other people's affairs; too curious. **—in quis′i tive ly,** *adv.* **—in quis′i tive ness,** *n.*

in sane (in sān′), *adj.* **1** not sane; mentally ill; crazy. **2** characteristic of one who is mentally ill: *an insane laugh.* **3** for insane people: *an insane asylum.* **4** extremely foolish; completely lacking in common sense. **—in sane′ly,** *adv.*

in sa tia ble (in sā′shə bəl), *adj.* that cannot be satisfied; extremely greedy: *an insatiable appetite.*

in so lent (in′sə lənt), *adj.* boldly rude; intentionally disregarding the feelings of others; insulting.

in stan ta ne ous (in′stən tā′nē əs), *adj.* coming or done in an instant. **—in′stan ta′ne ous ly,** *adv.*

in still or **in stil** (in stil′), *v.t.,* **-stilled, -still ing.** **1** put in little by little; cause to enter the mind, heart, etc., gradually: *Reading good books instills a love for fine literature.* **2** put in drop by drop.

in stinct (in′stingkt), *n.* **1** a chain of unlearned, coordinated acts characteristic of a particular species or group of animals; inborn tendency to act in a certain way: *Birds do not learn to build nests but build them by instinct.* **2** a natural tendency or ability; talent.

in stinc tive (in stingk′tiv), *adj.* of or having to do with instinct; caused or done by instinct; born in an animal or person, not learned: *The spinning of webs is instinctive in spiders.* **—in stinc′tive ly,** *adv.*

inter-, *prefix.* **1** one with the other; together: *Intercommunicate = communicate with each other.* **2** between: *Interpose = put between.* **3** between or among a group: *International = between or among nations.* [< Latin < *inter* among, between, during.]

in ter ject (in′tər jekt′), *v.t.* throw in between other things; insert abruptly.

in ter mit tent (in′tər mit′nt), *adj.* stopping for a time and beginning again; pausing at intervals.

in tern (in tėrn′), *v.t.* confine within a country or place; force to stay in a certain place, especially during wartime.

in tern ment (in tėrn′mənt), *n.* **1** an interning. **2** a being interned.

in ter state (in′tər stāt′), *adj.* between persons or organizations in different states; between states, especially of the United States: *an interstate highway.*

in ter val (in′tər vəl), *n.* **1** period of time between; pause: *an interval of a week, intervals of freedom from worry.* **2** space between things; intervening space: *an interval of ten feet between trees.* **3 at intervals. a** now and then. **b** here and there.

in tol er a ble (in tol′ər ə bəl), *adj.* too much to be endured; unbearable: *intolerable pain.*

intra-, *prefix.* within; inside; on the inside, as in *intramural, intrastate.* [< Latin < *intra-* inside of]

in tra ve nous (in′trə vē′nəs), *adj.* **1** within a vein or the veins. **2** into a vein or veins. **—in′tra ve′nous ly,** *adv.*

in tri cate (in′trə kit), *adj.* **1** with many twists and turns; puzzling, entangled, or complicated: *an intricate knot, an intricate plot.* **2** very hard to understand: *intricate directions.*

in trude (in trüd′), *v.,* **-trud ed, -trud ing. —***v.i.* **1** force oneself in; come unasked and unwanted: *If you are busy, I will not intrude.* **2** (in geology) force (molten rock) into fissures or between strata. **—***v.t.* give unasked and unwanted; force in: *intrude one's opinions upon others.* [< Latin *intrudere* < *in-* in + *trudere* to thrust] **—in trud′er,** *n.*

in vin ci ble (in vin′sə bəl), *adj.* unable to be conquered; impossible to overcome; unconquerable.

in vis i ble (in viz′ə bəl), *adj.* not visible; not capable of being seen: *Thought is invisible. Germs are invisible to the naked eye.*

-ion, *suffix forming nouns chiefly from verbs.* **1** act of ___ing: *Attraction = act of attracting.* **2** condition of being ___ed: *Adoption = condition of being adopted.* **3** result of ___ing: *Abbreviation = result of abbreviating.*

ir-¹ *prefix.* the form of **in-¹** before *r,* as in *irrational, irregular.*

ir-², *prefix.* the form of **in-²** before *r,* as in *irrigate.*

ir i des cent (ir′ə des′nt), *adj.* displaying changing colors; changing color when moved or turned.

irk (ėrk), *v.t.* cause to feel disgusted, annoyed, or troubled; weary by being tedious or disagreeable.

irk some (ėrk′səm), *adj.* tiresome; tedious; annoying: *an irksome task.*

ir reg u lar (i reg′yə lər), *adj.* not regular; not according to rule; not the usual order or natural way.

ir res o lute (i rez′ə lüt), *adj.* not resolute; unable to make up one's mind; not sure of what one wants; hesitating; vacillating. **—ir res′o lute ly,** *adv.* **—ir res′o lute ness,** *n.*

ir ri ta bil i ty (ir′ə tə bil′ə tē), *n., pl.* **-ties. 1** a being irritable; impatience. **2** an unnatural sensitiveness of an organ or part of the body.

ir ri ta tion (ir′ə tā′shən), *n.* **1** act or process of irritating; annoyance; vexation. **2** irritated condition.

-ish, *suffix forming adjectives from other adjectives and from nouns.* **1** somewhat ___: *Sweetish = somewhat sweet.* **2** like a ___: *Childish = like a child.* **3** like that of a ___: *Girlish = like that of a girl.* **4** of ᴏʀ having to do with ___: *English = of or having to do with England.*

is sue (ish′ü), *v.,* **-sued, -su ing,** *n.* **—***v.t.* **1** send out; put forth: *The government issues money and stamps.* **2** put into public circulation; put out for sale or distribution; publish: *issue a new edition of a book.* **3** distribute officially to a person or persons: *Each soldier was issued a rifle.* **4** send forth; discharge; emit: *The chimney issues smoke from the fireplace.* **—***v.i.* **1** come out; go out; proceed: *Smoke issues from the chimney.* See synonym study below. **2** be published. **3** emerge. **4** result or end *(in).* **5** result *(from).* **6** be born; be descended; be derived.

Syn. *v.i.* **1 Issue, emerge, emanate** mean to come out. **Issue** is applied chiefly to what can be thought of as flowing out in a mass from a confined space through an opening: *Pus issued from the wound.* **Emerge** is applied to what can be thought of as coming into sight from a place where it has been hidden or covered up: *The train emerged from the tunnel.* **Emanate** means to flow out from a source: *The story emanated from the mayor's office.*

-ist, *suffix forming nouns chiefly from other nouns.* **1** person who does or makes: *Tourist = a person who tours.* **2** an expert in an art or science: *Botanist = an expert in botany.* **3** person who plays a musical instrument: *Organist = person who plays the organ.* **4** person engaged in or working with: *Journalist = a person engaged in journalism.* **5** person who believes in: *Socialist = a person who believes in socialism.* [< Greek *-istēs* < *-izein* *-ize*]

-ity, *suffix forming nouns from adjectives.* quality, condition, or fact of being ___: *Sincerity = quality or condition of being sincere.* Also, **-ty.** [< Old French *-ité* < Latin *-itatem*]

-ive, *suffix forming adjectives from nouns.* **1** of or having to do with, as in *interrogative, inductive.* **2** tending to; likely to, as in *active, appreciative.*

-ize, *suffix forming verbs from adjectives and nouns.* **1** make ___: *Legalize = make legal.* **2** become ___: *Crystallize = become crystal.* **3** engage in or use ___: *Criticize = engage in criticism.* **4** treat or combine with ___: *Oxidize = combine with oxygen.*

jad ed (jā′did), *adj.* **1** worn out; tired; weary. **2** dulled from continual use; surfeited; satiated: *a jaded appetite.*

jaun ty (jôn′tē, jän′tē), *adj.,* **-ti er, -ti est.** easy and lively; sprightly; carefree.

jave lin (jav′lən, jav′ə lin), *n.* a light spear thrown by hand.

jos tle (jos′əl), *v.,* **-tled, -tling, —***v.t.* shove, push, or crowd against; elbow roughly. **—***v.i.* crowd, strike, or push.

jug u lar (jug′yə lər, jü′gyə lər), *adj.* **1** of the neck or throat. **2** of the jugular vein. **—***n.* jugular vein.

keel (kēl), *n.* the main timber or steel piece that extends the whole length of the bottom of a ship or boat. The whole ship is built up on the keel.

keen¹ (kēn), *adj.* **1** so shaped as to cut well: *a keen blade.* **2** sharp; piercing; cutting: *a keen wind, keen hunger, keen wit, keen pain.* **3** strong; vivid: *keen competition.* **4** highly sensitive; able to perceive well; acute: *a keen mind.*

keen² (kēn), *n.* a wailing lament for the dead.—*v.i.* wail; lament. [<Irish *caoine*]

kin dle (kin′dl), *v.,* **-dled, -dling. —***v.t.* **1** set on fire; light. **2** stir up; arouse: *kindle enthusiasm. His cruelty kindled our anger.* **3** light up; brighten: *Pleasure kindled her face.* **—***v.i.* **1** catch fire; begin to burn: *This damp wood will never kindle.* **2** become stirred up or aroused. **3** light up; brighten.

kin dling (kind′ling), *n.* small pieces of wood, etc., that ignite easily for setting fire to larger pieces and other fuel.

kine (kīn), *n.pl.* ᴀʀᴄʜᴀɪᴄ ᴏʀ ᴅɪᴀʟᴇᴄᴛ. cows or cattle.

la dy fin ger (lā′dē fing′gər), *n.* a small sponge cake shaped somewhat like a finger.

la ment (lə ment′), *v.t.* **1** express grief for; mourn for: *lament the dead.* **2** regret: *We lamented his absence.* [< Latin *lamentari* < *lamentum* a wailing]

land fall (land′fôl′), *n.* **1** a sighting of land. **2** the land sighted or reached. **3** approach to land; landing.

lan guor (lang′gər), *n.* **1** lack of energy; weakness; weariness: *A long illness causes languor.* **2** lack of interest or enthusiasm; indifference.

lar der (lär′dər), *n.* **1** place where meat and other foods are kept; pantry. **2** stock of food.

lash (lash), *v.t.* tie or fasten with a rope, cord, etc.

las si tude (las′ə tüd, las′ə tyüd), *n.* lack of energy; weariness; languor. [< Latin *lassitudo* < *lassus* tired]

lat i tude (lat′ə tüd, lat′ə tyüd), *n.* distance north or south of the equator, measured in degrees. A degree of latitude is about 69 miles (111 kilometers).

launch (lônch, länch), *v.t.* **1** cause to slide into the water; set afloat: *A new ship is launched from the supports on which it was built.* **2** push out or put forth into the air: *launch a plane from an aircraft carrier.* **3** set going; set out; start.

lau rel (lôr′əl, lor′əl), *n.* **1** a small evergreen tree of southern Europe, with smooth, shiny leaves; bay; sweet bay. **2** its leaves.

lea (lē), *n.* a grassy field; meadow; pasture. [Old English *lēah*]

league (lēg), *n.* measure of distance, varying at different periods and in different countries, usually about 3 miles (5 kilometers).

le git i mate (lə jit′ə mit), *adj.* **1** allowed or admitted by law; rightful; lawful: *a legitimate claim.* **2** valid; logical; acceptable: *Sickness is a legitimate reason for absence from work.*

len ient (lē′nyənt, lē′nē ənt), *adj.* mild or gentle; not harsh or stern; merciful: *a lenient judge, a lenient punishment.* [< Latin *lenientem* < *lenis* mild] **—len′ient ly,** *adv.*

-less, *suffix forming adjectives from verbs and nouns.* **1** without a ___; that has no ___: *Homeless = without a home.* **2** that does not ___: *Ceaseless = that does not cease.* **3** that cannot be ___ed: *Countless = that cannot be counted.*

leth ar gy (leth′ər jē), *n., pl.* **-gies.** drowsy dullness; lack of energy; sluggish inactivity.

li ba tion (lī bā′shən), *n.* a pouring out of wine, water, etc., as an offering to a god.

li chen (lī′kən), *n.* any of a group of flowerless organisms that look like moss and grow in patches on trees, rocks, etc.

limb (lim), *n.* **1** leg, arm, wing, or other member of an animal body distinct from the head or trunk. **2** a large or main branch of a tree. **3 out on a limb,** in a dangerous or vulnerable position.

lim pet (lim′pit), *n.* a small marine mollusk of the same class as snails, with a conical shell that clings to rocks, etc. Limpets are used for bait and sometimes for food.

list less (list′lis), *adj.* seeming too tired to care about anything; not interested in things; not caring to be active; languid. **—list′less ly,** *adv.* **—list′less ness,** *n.*

livery stable, stable where horses are taken care of for pay or hired out.

lo gis tics (lō jis′tiks), *n.* the planning and carrying out of any complex or large-scale operation.

loi ter (loi′tər), *v.i.* **1** linger idly or aimlessly on one's way; move or go in a slow or lagging manner. **2** waste time in idleness; idle; loaf. *—v.t.* spend (time) idly: *loiter the hours away.* [< Middle Dutch *loteren* be loose] **—loi′ter er,** *n.*

loll (lol), *v.i.* **1** recline or lean in a lazy manner: *loll on a sofa.* **2** hang loosely or droop; dangle.

lon gi tude (lon′jə tüd, lon′jə tyüd), *n.* distance east or west on the earth's surface, measured in degrees from a certain meridian, usually the meridian through Greenwich, England.

loom (lüm), *n.* frame or machine for weaving yarn or thread into cloth.

lu mi nous (lü′mə nəs), *adj.* **1** shining by its own light: *The sun and stars are luminous bodies.* **2** full of light; shining; bright.

lunge (lunj), *n., v.,* **lunged, lung ing.** *—n.* any sudden forward movement, such as a thrust with a sword or other weapon. *—v.i.* move with a lunge; make a sudden forward movement; thrust.

lure (lur), *n., v.,* **lured, lur ing.** *—n.* **1** power of attracting or fascinating; charm; allure; attraction: *the lure of the sea.* **2** something that allures, entices, or tempts. **3** a decoy or bait, especially an artificial bait used in fishing. *—v.t.* **1** lead away or into something by arousing desire; allure; entice; tempt. **2** attract with a bait. [< Old French *leurre*, of Germanic origin]

lush (lush), *adj.* **1** tender and juicy; growing thick and green: *Lush grass grows along the river banks.* **2** characterized by abundant growth; producing abundantly. **3** luxurious. **4** rich in ornament; flowery. [Middle English *lache*]

lus ter (lus′tər), *n.* a bright shine on the surface; sheen: *the luster of pearls.*

lust y (lus′tē), *adj.,* **lust i er, lust i est.** strong and healthy; full of vigor; robust: *a lusty boy.* **—lust′i ly,** *adv.*

-ly¹, *suffix forming adverbs from adjectives.* **1** in a ___ manner: *Cheerfully = in a cheerful manner.* **2** in ___ ways or respects: *Financially = in financial respects.* **3** to a ___ degree or extent: *Greatly = to a great degree.* **4** in, to, or from a ___ direction: *Northwardly = to or from the north.* **5** in a ___ place: *Thirdly = in the third place.* **6** at a ___ time: *Recently = at a recent time.*

-ly² *suffix forming adjectives from nouns.* **1** like a ___: *Ghostly = like a ghost.* **2** like that of a ___; characteristic of a ___: *Brotherly = like that of a brother.* **3** suited to a ___; fit or proper for a ___: *Gentlemanly = suited to a gentleman.* **4** of each or every ___; occurring once per ___: *Daily = of every day.* **5** being a ___; that is a ___: *Heavenly = that is a heaven.*

lyre (līr), *n.* an ancient stringed musical instrument somewhat like a small harp. [< Latin *lyra* < Greek]

ma ca bre (mə kä′brə, mə kä′bər), *adj.* causing horror; gruesome; horrible; ghastly. [< French] **—ma ca′bre ly,** *adv.*

Malacca cane, a light walking stick made of the stem of an East Indian rattan palm.

mal ad just ed (mal′ə jus′tid), *adj.* badly adjusted; not in a healthy relation with one's environment.

mal a mute (mal′ə myüt, mal′ə müt), *n.* **1** Alaskan malamute. **2** any of an Alaskan breed of large, strong dogs having a gray or black and white coat and commonly used for pulling sleds.

mal con tent (mal′kən tent′), *adj.* discontented; rebellious. *—n.* a discontented, rebellious person.

ma lev o lent (mə lev′ə lənt), *adj.* wishing evil to happen to others; showing ill will; spiteful.

ma li cious (mə lish′əs), *adj.* **1** showing active ill will; wishing to hurt or make suffer; spiteful. **2** proceeding from malice: *malicious mischief.* **—ma li′cious ly,** *adv.*

mal nu tri tion (mal′nü trish′ən, mal′nyü trish′ən), *n.* a malnourished condition. Improper food can cause malnutrition.

mal prac tice (mal prak′tis), *n.* criminal neglect or wrong treatment of a patient by a doctor.

mal treat (mal trēt′), *v.t.* treat roughly or cruelly; abuse.

mam mal (mam′əl), *n.* any of a class of warm-blooded, vertebrate animals usually having hair, the females of which secrete milk from mammary glands to nourish their young. Human beings, horses, dogs, lions, bats, and whales are all mammals.

ma neu ver (mə nü′vər), *n.* **1** a planned movement of troops, ships, etc., especially for tactical purposes. **2 maneuvers,** *pl.* a training exercise between two or more military or naval units, simulating combat situations. **3** a skillful plan; clever trick: *a series of political maneuvers to get votes.* **4** an agile or skillful movement made to elude or deceive.

man gle¹ (mang′gəl), *v.t.,* **-gled, -gling.** **1** cut or tear (the flesh) roughly; lacerate. **2** spoil; ruin.

man gle² (mang′gəl), *n., v.,* **-gled, -gling.** —*n.* machine with rollers for pressing and smoothing sheets, towels, and other flat things after washing. —*v.t.* press or make smooth in a mangle.

ma nip u late (mə nip′yə lāt), *v.t.,* **-lat ed, -lat ing.** handle or treat, especially skillfully: *manipulate the controls.*

mar row (mar′ō), *n.* **1** the soft, vascular tissue that fills the cavities of most bones and is the source of red blood cells and many white blood cells. **2** the inmost or essential part.

mas sa cre (mas′ə kər), *n.* the wholesale, pitiless slaughter of people or animals.

mas sive (mas′iv), *adj.* **1** forming a large mass; bulky and heavy; huge: *a massive rock.* **2** giving the impression of being large and broad: *a massive forehead.* **3** imposing; impressive.

ma ter i al ize (mə tir′ē ə līz), *v.,* **-ized, -iz ing.** —*v.i.* **1** become an actual fact; be realized: *Our plans did not materialize.* **2** appear in material or bodily form.

maz y (mā′zē), *adj.,* **maz i er, maz i est.** like a maze; intricate.

-ment, *suffix added to verbs to form nouns.* **1** act, process, or fact of ___ing: *Enjoyment = act of enjoying.* **2** condition of being ___ed: *Amazement = condition of being amazed.* **3** product or result of ___ing: *Pavement = product of paving.* **4** means of or instrument for ___ing: *Inducement = means of inducing.*

mer ry (mer′ē), *adj.,* **-ri er, -ri est.** **1** laughing and happy; full of fun. **2** make merry, laugh and be happy; have fun.

Messrs., the plural of *Mr. (Messrs. Harrison and Smith)* and sometimes, though rarely now in American usage, in addressing firms *(Messrs. Brown, Hubbell, and Company).*

met a mor pho sis (met′ə môr′fə sis), *n., pl.* **-ses** (-sēz′). **1** a marked change in the form, and usually the habits, of an animal in its development after the embryonic stage. Tadpoles become frogs by metamorphosis; they lose their tails and grow legs. **2** change of form, structure, or substance by or as if by witchcraft;

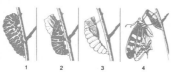

metamorphosis (def. 1) of a butterfly
1 Caterpillar prepares to change form.
2 It sheds skin, exposing chrysalis.
3 Chrysalis is entirely exposed.
4 Adult emerges from the chrysalis.

transformation. **3** form, shape, substance, etc., resulting from any such change. **4** a noticeable or complete change of character, appearance, circumstances, etc. [< Greek *metamorphōsis,* ultimately < *meta-* after + *morphē* form]

me te or (mē′tē ər), *n.* mass of rock or metal that enters the earth's atmosphere from outer space with enormous speed; falling star; shooting star.

meth od (meth′əd), *n.* way of doing something, especially according to a defined plan; mode; manner.

me thod i cal (mə thod′ə kəl), *adj.* done according to a method; systematic; orderly.

met tle (met′l), *n.* **1** quality of disposition or temperament. **2** spirit; courage. **3** on one's mettle, ready to do one's best.

min is tra tion (min′ə strā′shən), *n.* **1** service as a minister of a church. **2** help; aid: *ministration to the poor.*

mis-, *prefix.* **1** bad: *Misgovernment = bad government.* **2** badly: *Misbehave = behave badly.* **3** wrong: *Mispronunciation = wrong pronunciation.* **4** wrongly: *Misapply = apply wrongly.*

mis chance (mis chans′), *n.* bad luck; misfortune.

mis cre ant (mis′krē ənt), *adj.* having very bad morals; wicked; base. —*n.* a base or wicked person; villain.

mon goose or **mon goos** (mong′güs), *n., pl.* **-gooses.** any of several genera of slender, carnivorous mammals of Asia and Africa, especially a species native to India, belonging to the same family as the civet and resembling a ferret. The Indian species has been introduced elsewhere to destroy rats and is noted for its ability to kill cobras and certain other poisonous snakes. [< Marathi (a language of western India) *mangūs*]

mongooses—about 2 ft. (61 cm.) long with the tail

monk (mungk), *n.* man who gives up all worldly things and enters a monastery to live a life devoted to religious duties and contemplation.

moor (mùr), *v.t.* **1** put or keep (a ship, etc.) in place by means of ropes or chains fastened to the shore or to anchors. **2** fix firmly; secure. —*v.i.* **1** moor a ship. **2** be made secure by ropes, anchors, etc. [Middle English *moren*]

morgue (môrg), *n.* place in which the bodies of persons unidentified or killed by accident or violence are temporarily held, for identification and claim or for investigation.

mor sel (môr′səl), *n.* **1** a small portion of food; bite. **2** a small piece, quantity, or amount of anything; fragment; bit. [< Old French, diminutive of *mors* a bite, ultimately < Latin *mordere* to bite]

mor tar¹ (môr′tər), *n.* mixture of lime, cement, sand, and water, placed between bricks or stones to hold them together when it has dried and hardened. —*v.t.* plaster with mortar; fix with mortar. [< Old French *mortier* < Latin *mortarium* mortar²]

mortar² (def. 1)

mor tar² (môr′tər), *n.* **1** bowl of porcelain, glass, or other very hard material, in which substances may be pounded to a powder with a pestle. **2** a very short cannon with a wide, unrifled barrel, used to fire shells at high angles over a short range.

mot ley (mot′lē), *adj.,* made up of parts or kinds that are different or varied: *a motley crowd.*

mot tle (mot′l), *v.t.,* **-tled, -tling,** mark with spots or streaks of different colors or shades.

mul ti tu di nous (mul′tə tüd′n əs, mul′tə tyüd′n əs), *adj.* forming a multitude; very numerous; existing or occurring in great numbers.

mus kel lunge (mus′kə lunj), *n., pl.* **-lunge.** a very large North American pike, valued as a food and game fish.

musk y (mus′kē), *adj.,* **musk i er, musk i est.** of or like musk; a strong, lasting odor.

mus ty (mus′tē), *adj.,* **-ti er, -ti est.** **1** having a smell or taste suggesting mold, damp, poor ventilation, decay, etc.; moldy: *a musty room, musty crackers.* **2** stale; out-of-date: *musty laws about witches.* [perhaps < *moisty* < *moist* + *-y¹*] —**mus′ti ly,** *adv.* —**mus′ti ness,** *n.*

mute (myüt), *adj.* **1** not making any sound; silent: *The little girl stood mute with embarrassment.* **2** unable to speak; dumb. —*n.* person who cannot speak, usually because of deafness, loss of or damage to the tongue, etc.

mu ti nous (myüt′n əs), *adj.* **1** given to or engaged in mutiny; rebellious: *a mutinous crew.* **2** like or involving mutiny; characterized by mutiny: *a mutinous look.* **3** not controllable.

na ta to ri um (nā'tə tôr'ē əm, nā'tə tōr'ē əm), *n., pl.* **-to riums, -to ri a** (-tôr'ē ə, -tōr'ē ə). a swimming pool, especially one in a gymnasium or other building.

nat ur al ist (nach'ər ə list), *n.* person who makes a study of living organisms, especially in their native habitats.

neat herd (nēt'hėrd'), *n.* ARCHAIC. cowherd.

neb u lous (neb'yə ləs), *adj.* hazy; vague; confused.

ne go ti ate (ni gō'shē āt), *v.,* **-at ed, -at ing.** —*v.i.* talk over and arrange terms; confer; consult: *Both countries negotiated for peace.* **—ne go'ti a'tion,** *n.*

-ness, *suffix added to adjectives to form nouns.* **1** quality or condition of being ___: *Preparedness = condition of being prepared.* **2** ___ action: ___ behavior: *Carefulness = careful action; careful behavior.* [Old English *-ness, -niss*]

net tle (net'l), *n.* any of a genus of herbs having sharp hairs on the leaves and stems that sting the skin when touched.

neu rot ic (nù rot'ik, nyù rot'ik), *adj.* having or appearing to have a mental disorder characterized by depression, anxiety, compulsive behavior, etc.

neu tral ize (nü'trə līz, nyü'trə līz), *v.t.,* **-ized, -iz ing.** make no effect by some opposite force; counterbalance. **—neu'tral i za'tion,** *n.*

niche (nich), *n., v.,* **niched, nich ing.** —*n.* **1** recess or hollow in a wall for a statue, vase, etc.; nook. **2** a suitable place or position; place for which a person is suited.

nigh (nī), *adv.* **1** near (in position, time, relationship, etc.). **2** nearly; almost. —*adj.* **1** near; close. **2** (of one of a team of horses) left; near. —*prep.* near.

no ble (nō'bəl), *adj.,* **-bler, -blest. 1** high and great by birth, rank, or title; aristocratic: *a noble family, noble blood.* **2** high and great in character; showing greatness of mind; good; worthy: *a noble deed.* **3** having excellent qualities; fine: *a noble animal.* **4** grand in appearance; splendid; magnificent: *a noble sight.* **—no'ble ness,** *n.* **—no'bly,** *adv.*

non-, *prefix.* not; not a; opposite of; lack of; failure of: *Nonessential = not essential. Nonresident = not a resident. Nonconformity = lack of conformity.* [< Latin < *non* not]

nos tal gia (no stal'jə), *n.* a painful or wistful yearning for one's home, country, city, or for anything far removed in space or time.

o blig ing (ə blī'jing), *adj.* willing to do favors; helpful. **—o blig'ing ly,** *adv.* **—o blig'ing ness,** *n.*

o blique (ə blēk'), *adj.* neither perpendicular to nor parallel with a given line or surface; not straight up and down or straight across; slanting. **—o blique ly,** *adv.*

o bliv i ous (ə bliv'ē əs), *adj.* **1** not mindful; forgetful: *The book was so interesting that I was oblivious of my surroundings.* **2** bringing or causing forgetfulness.

ob scure (əb skyùr'), *adj.,* **-scur er, -scur est,** *v.,* **-scured, -scur ing.** —*adj.* **1** not easily discovered; hidden: *an obscure path, an obscure meaning.* **2** not distinct; not clear: *an obscure shape, obscure sounds.* —*v.t.* **1** hide from view; make obscure; dim; darken: *Clouds obscure the sun.* **2** make dim or vague to the understanding.

ob sess (əb ses'), *v.t.* fill the mind of; keep the attention of to an unreasonable or unhealthy extent; haunt.

o cean og ra phy (ō'shə nog'rə fē), *n.* science that deals with the oceans and seas, including marine life.

of fi cious (ə fish'əs), *adj.* too ready to offer services or advice; minding other people's business; meddlesome. [< Latin *officiosus* dutiful < *officium* service] **—of fi'cious ly,** *adv.*

op pres sive (ə pres'iv), *adj.* **1** hard to bear; burdensome: *The intense heat was oppressive.* **2** harsh; unjust; tyrannical.

-or, *suffix forming nouns from verbs.* person or thing that ___s: *Governor = person who governs. Accelerator = thing that accelerates.*

o ra cle (ôr'ə kəl, or'ə kəl), *n.* (in ancient Greece and Rome) an answer believed to be given by a god through a priest or

priestess to some question. It often had a hidden meaning that was ambiguous or hard to understand.

or gan ic (ôr gan'ik), *adj.* **1** of the bodily organs; affecting an organ: *an organic disease.* **2** of or obtained from living organisms: *organic fertilizer.*

or tho dox (ôr'thə doks), *adj.* **1** generally accepted, especially in religion. **2** approved by convention; usual; customary: *the orthodox Thanksgiving dinner of turkey and pumpkin pie.*

-ous, *suffix forming adjectives from nouns.* **1** full of; having much; having: *Joyous = full of joy.* **2** characterized by: *Zealous = characterized by zeal.* **3** having the nature of: *Idolatrous = having the nature of an idolater.* **4** of or having to do with: *Monogamous = having to do with monogamy.* **5** like: *Thunderous = like thunder.* **6** committing or practicing: *Bigamous = practicing bigamy.*

out ra geous (out rā'jəs), *adj.* very offensive or insulting; shocking. **—out ra'geous ly,** *adv.* **—out ra'geous ness,** *n.*

o ver run (ō'vər run'), *v.t.,* **-ran** (-ran'), **-run, -run ning. 1** spread over and spoil or harm in some way, as weeds, vermin, disease, or invading troops do. **2** spread over; cover pleasingly.

o ver se er (ō'vər sē'ər, ō'vər sir'), *n.* one who oversees others or their work.

o ver whelm (ō'vər hwelm'), *v.t.* **1** overcome completely; crush: *overwhelm with grief.* **2** cover completely as a flood would: *A great wave overwhelmed the boat.*

pa la tial (pə lā'shəl), *adj.* of, like, or fit for a palace; magnificent. **—pa la'tial ly,** *adv.* **—pa la'tial ness,** *n.*

pal ing (pā'ling), *n.* **1** fence of long narrow boards, painted on top. **2** pales collectively, as fencing material. **3** pale in a fence.

pall bear er (pôl'ber'ər, pôl'bar'ər), *n.* one of the people who walk with or carry the coffin at a funeral.

pal let (pal'it), *n.* bed of straw; small or poor bed. [< Old French *paillet* < *paille* straw < Latin *palea*]

pal pi tate (pal'pə tāt), *v.i.,* **-tat ed, -tat ing. 1** beat very rapidly, as from emotion, exercise, or disease; throb: *Your heart palpitates when you are excited.* **2** quiver; tremble.

par a pher nal ia (par'ə fər nā'lyə), *n., pl. or sing.* **1** personal belongings. **2** equipment; outfit.

parch (pärch), *v.t.* **1** dry by heating; roast slightly: *Corn is sometimes parched.* **2** make hot and dry or thirsty: *The fever parched her.* —*v.i.* become dry, hot, or thirsty. *I am parching with the heat.* [Middle English *parchen*]

Par chee si (pär chē'zē), *n.* trademark for a board game developed from pachisi.

pa ro chi al (pə rō'kē əl), *adj.* **1** of or in a parish: *a parochial church.* **2** narrow; limited: *a parochial viewpoint.* [< Late Latin *parochialis* < *parochia* parish.]

pas sive (pas'iv), *adj.* **1** being acted on without itself acting; not acting in return: *a passive mind, a passive disposition.* **2** not resisting; yielding or submitting to the will of another; submissive: *the passive obedience of a slave.*

pa thet ic (pə thet'ik), *adj.* **1** arousing pity; pitiful; pitiable: *the pathetic sight of a crippled child.* **2** full of pathos: *pathetic music.*

path o log i cal (path'ə loj'ə kəl), *adj.* **1** of pathology; dealing or concerned with diseases: *pathological studies.* **2** due to or

GLOSSARY

accompanying a physical disease or mental disorder: *a pathological condition of the blood cells, a pathological liar.*

peace (pēs), *n.* **1** freedom from strife of any kind; condition of quiet, order, and security. **2 hold one's peace** or **keep one's peace,** be silent; keep still.

peer less (pir'lis), *adj.* without an equal; matchless.

pel ar go ni um (pel'är gō'nē əm), *n.* any of a genus of plants of the same family as the geranium, with fragrant leaves and large clusters of showy flowers; geranium.

pelt (pelt), *v.t.* **1** hit with (objects, words, etc.) thrown one after another; attack or assail by throwing things at: *The children were pelting each other with snowballs. The attorney pelted the witness with angry questions.* **2** beat heavily or continuously upon: *Hail pelted the roof.* **3** throw; hurl: *The clouds pelted rain upon us.* —*v.i.* **1** beat heavily or continuously: *The rain came pelting down.* **2** go rapidly; hurry.

pence (pens), *n.* a pl. of **penny.** a former British coin equal to ¹⁄₁₂ of a shilling. Until 1971, 240 pennies made one pound.

pen e trate (pen'ə trāt), *v.t.* **-trat ed, -trat ing. 1** enter into or pass through. **2** pierce through: *Our eyes could not penetrate the darkness.* **3** soak or spread through; permeate: *The odor penetrated the whole house.* **4** see into or through; understand: *I could not penetrate the mystery.*

pen sive (pen'siv), *adj.* **1** thoughtful in a serious or sad way. **2** melancholy. —**pen'sive ly,** *adv.*

per cep tion (pər sep'shən), *n.* **1** act of perceiving: *His perception of the change came in a flash.* **2** power of perceiving: *a keen perception.* **3** understanding that is the result of perceiving: *I now have a clear perception of what went wrong.*

per il ous (per'ə ləs), *adj.* full of peril; dangerous.

per i scope (per'ə skōp), *n.* an optical instrument consisting of an arrangement of prisms or mirrors that reflect light rays down a vertical tube, used in a submarine, trench, etc., to obtain a view of the surface. —**per'i scope like',** *adj.*

per tain (pər tān'), *v.t.* **1** belong or be connected as a part, possession, etc.: *We own the house and the land pertaining to it.* **2** have to do with; be related; refer: *documents pertaining to the case.* **3** be appropriate: *We had turkey and everything else that pertains to Thanksgiving.* [< Old French *partenir* < Latin *pertinere* reach through, connect < *per-* through + *tenere* to hold]

per turb (pər tėrb'), *v.t.* disturb greatly; make uneasy or troubled; distress.

pet u lant (pech'ə lənt), *adj.* likely to have little fits of bad temper; irritable over trifles; peevish.

phlegm (flem), *n.* **1** the thick mucus discharged into the mouth and throat during a cold or other respiratory disease. **2** sluggish disposition or temperament; indifference. —**phlegm'y,** *adj.*

pi az za (pē az'ə *for 1;* pē ät'sə, pē az'ə *for 2*), *n.* **1** a large porch along one or more sides of a house; veranda. **2** an open public square in Italian towns.

pi e ty (pī'ə tē), *n., pl.* **-ties.** a being pious; reverence for God; devotion to religion; godliness; devoutness.

pil ing (pī'ling), *n.* **1** piles or heavy beams driven into the ground. **2** structure made of piles.

pin a fore (pin'ə fôr, pin'ə fōr'), *n.* **1** a child's apron that covers most of the clothes. **2** a light dress without sleeves.

pin ion (pin'yən), *n.* **1** the last joint of a bird's wing. **2** wing. **3** any one of the stiff flying feathers of the wing; quill.

plac ard (plak'ärd), *n.* notice to be posted in a public place; poster.

plac id (plas'id), *adj.* pleasantly calm or peaceful; quiet: *a placid lake, a placid temper.* [< Latin *placidus* < *placere* to please] —**plac'id ly,** *adv.* —**plac'id ness,** *n.*

plague (plāg), *v.t.,* **plagued, pla guing. 1** cause to suffer from a plague. **2** vex; annoy; bother.

plain tive (plān'tiv), *adj.* expressive of sorrow; mournful; sad.

plan tain (plan'tən), *n.* **1** a tropical plant of the same family as the banana. **2** its fruit, longer and more starchy than the banana, eaten cooked. It is one of the chief articles of food in tropical countries. [< Spanish *plátano*]

plas ter (plas'tər), *n.* **1** a soft, sticky mixture of lime, sand, and water that hardens as it dries, used for covering walls, ceilings, etc. **2** plaster of Paris. **3** a medical preparation consisting of some substance spread on cloth, that will stick to the body and protect cuts, relieve pain, etc.

pla teau (pla tō'), *n., pl.* **-teaus** or **-teaux** (-tōz'). **1** plain in the mountains or at a height considerably above sea level; large, high plain; tableland. **2** a level, especially the level at which something is stabilized for a period. [< French < Old French *platel,* diminutive of *plat* flat.]

pleur i sy (plùr'ə sē), *n.* inflammation of the pleura, often marked by fever, chest pains, and difficulty in breathing.

pluck (pluk), *v.t.* **1** pull off; pick: *pluck flowers in the garden.* **2** pull at; pull; tug; jerk: *pluck a person by the sleeve.* **3** pull on (the strings of a musical instrument). —*n.* **1** act of picking or pulling. **2** courage; boldness; spirit. **3** heart, liver, and lungs of an animal killed for food. [Old English *pluccian*]

plum age (plü'mij), *n.* feathers of a bird.

plume (plüm), *n., v.,* **plumed, plum ing.** —*n.* **1** feather, especially a large, long, or conspicuous feather. **2** feather or bunch of feathers, tuft of hair, etc., worn as an ornament on a hat, helmet, etc. **3** any feathered part or formation as of an insect, seed, leaf, etc. **4** ornament or token of distinction or honor. —*v.t.* **1** furnish with plumes. **2** smooth or arrange the feathers of; preen: *The eagle plumed its wing.* **3** show pride in (oneself): *She plumed herself on her skill in dancing.* [< Old French < Latin *pluma*]

pneu mo nia (nü mō'nyə, nyü mō'nyə), *n.* a bacterial or viral disease in which the lung becomes inflamed, often accompanied by chills, a pain in the chest, a hard, dry cough, and a high fever. [< Greek < *pneumōn* lung]

poach (pōch), *v.t.* **1** trespass on (another's land), especially to hunt or fish. **2** take (game or fish) without any right. [< Middle French *pocher* poke out; of Germanic origin]

pol yp (pol'ip), *n.* a small coelenterate attached at the base of its tubular body, with a mouth at the other end surrounded by fingerlike tentacles to gather in food, often growing in colonies, as hydras, corals, sea anemones, etc.

po man der (pə man'dər, pō'man dər), *n.* ball of mixed aromatic substances formerly carried for perfume.

post-, *prefix.* **1** after in time; later: *Postwar = after a war.* **2** after in space; behind: *Postnasal = behind the nasal cavity.*

pot ter (pot'ər), *v.i.* BRITISH INFORMAL. move slowly.

pox (poks), *n.* any disease characterized by eruption of pustules on the skin, such as chicken pox or smallpox.

prac ti tion er (prak tish'ə nər), *n.* person engaged in the practice of a profession: *a medical practitioner.*

pram (pram), *n.* BRITISH INFORMAL. baby carriage; perambulator.

prank (prangk), *n.* piece of mischief; playful trick.

pre-, *prefix.* **1** before in time, rank, etc.: *Precambrian = before the Cambrian.* **2** before in position, space, etc.; in front of: *Premolar = in front of the molars.* [< Latin *prae-, pre-*]

pre car i ous (pri ker'ē əs, pri kar'ē əs), *adj.* **1** not safe or secure; uncertain; dangerous; risky: *Soldiers on the battlefield lead a precarious life.* **2** dependent on chance or circumstance.

pred a to ry (pred'ə tôr'ē, pred'ə tōr'ē), *adj.* living by preying upon other animals. Hawks and owls are predatory birds.

pre des tine (prē des'tən), *v.t.,* **-tined, -tin ing.** determine or settle beforehand; foreordain.

pre lim i nar y (pri lim'ə ner'ē), *adj.* coming before the main business; leading to something more important.

pre miere (pri mir', prə myer'), *n.* a first public performance: *the premiere of a new play.*

pres tige (pre stēzh', pre stēj'), *n.* reputation, influence, or distinction based on what is known of one's abilities, achievements, opportunities, associations, etc.

pri or i ty (prī ôr'ə tē, prī or'ə tē), *n., pl.* **-ties. 1** a being earlier in time. **2** a coming before in order or importance.

priv et (priv'it), *n.* any of several shrubs much used for hedges.

priv y (priv'ē), *n., pl.* **priv ies.** a small outhouse used as a toilet.

prize (prīz), *v.t.*, **prized, priz ing.** raise or move by force; pry.

pro-, *prefix.* **1** before; preceding; prior to, as in *prologue.* **2** in front of; anterior, as in *prothorax, proscenium.* [< Greek]

probe (prōb), *v.t.*, **probed, prob ing. 1** search into; examine thoroughly; investigate: *I probed my memory for her name.* **2** examine with a probe. —*v.i.* search; penetrate: *probe into the causes of a crime.*

proc la ma tion (prok′lə mā′shən), *n.* an official announcement; public declaration: *a proclamation ending the war.*

pro ce dure (prə sē′jər), *n.* **1** way of proceeding; method of doing things: *What is your procedure in making bread?* **2** the customary manners or ways of conducting business: *parliamentary procedure, legal procedure.*

prof fer (prof′ər), *v.t.* offer for acceptance; present; tender: *We proffered regrets at having to leave so early.* [< Anglo-French *proffrir* < Old French *pro-* forth + *offrir* to offer]

pro fu sion (prə fyü′zhən), *n.* great abundance.

pro lif ic (prə lif′ik), *adj.* **1** producing offspring or fruit abundantly: *a prolific garden.* **2** highly productive; fertile: *a prolific imagination, a prolific writer.*

proph e cy (prof′ə sē), *n., pl.* **-cies.** a telling what will happen; foretelling future events.

pros trate (pros′trāt), *adj.* **1** lying flat with face downward: *She was humbly prostrate in prayer.* **2** lying flat: *I stumbled and fell prostrate on the floor.*

prov i dence (prov′ə dəns), *n.* **1** God's care and help. **2** Providence, God. **3** instance of God's care and help.

prow (prou), *n.* the front part of a ship or boat; bow.

pru dence (prüd′ns), *n.* wise thought before acting; good judgment.

pru dent (prüd′nt), *adj.* planning carefully ahead of time; sensible; discreet: *A prudent man saves part of his wages.*

psych (sīk), *n.* INFORMAL. psychology. —*v.t.* SLANG. **1** psychoanalyze. **2** use psychology on.

psych out, SLANG. **a** use psychology on: *psych out an opponent by making false moves.* **b** figure out the intentions of beforehand: *psych out the other player at chess.* **b** confuse or become confused: *So much was happening that the viewers psyched out.*

psy chot ic (sī kot′ik, si kot′ik), *adj.* having a severe form of mental disorder.

ptar mi gan (tär′mə gən), *n., pl.* **-gans** or **-gan.** any of several kinds of grouse which become white in the winter, have feathered feet, and are found in mountainous and cold regions.

punc tu al i ty (pungk′chü al′ə tē), *n.* a being on time.

pur blind (pėr′blīnd′), *adj.* **1** nearly blind. **2** slow to discern or understand; dull; obtuse. [Middle English *pur blind* pure blind] —**pur′blind′ly,** *adv.* —**pur′blind′ness,** *n.*

pur chase (pėr′chəs), *v.*, **-chased, -chas ing,** *n.* —*v.t.* **1** get by paying a price; buy: *purchase a new car.* **2** get in return for something: *purchase safety at the cost of happiness.* **3** hoist, haul, or draw by the aid of some mechanical device. —*n.* **1** act of buying. **2** thing bought. **3** a firm hold to help move something or to keep from slipping: *Wind the rope twice around the tree to get a better purchase.*

purl (pėrl), *v.i.* **1** flow with rippling motions and a murmuring sound. *A shallow brook purls.* **2** pass with a sound like this.

pur pose ful (pėr′pəs fəl), *adj.* **1** having a purpose; intentional: *a purposeful retreat.* **2** having or full of determination; determined: *a purposeful leader.* **3** full of meaning; significant: *a purposeful life.* —**pur′pose ful ly,** *adv.*

purse (pėrs), *v.t.*, **pursed, purs ing.** draw together; press into folds or wrinkles: *She pursed her lips and frowned.*

quaint (kwānt), *adj.* strange or odd in an interesting, pleasing, or amusing way: *Old photographs seem quaint to us today.*

quell (kwel), *v.t.* **1** put down (disorder, rebellion, etc.): *quell a riot.* **2** put an end to; overcome: *quell one's fears.*

queue (kyü), *n.* a line of people, automobiles, etc.: *There was a long queue in front of the theater.*

a hat	i it	oi oil	ch child		a in about
ā age	ī ice	ou out	ng long		e in taken
ä far	o hot	u cup	sh she	ə =	i in pencil
e let	ō open	ù put	th thin		o in lemon
ē equal	ô order	ü rule	₮H then		u in circus
ėr term			zh measure	< = derived from

quiv er (kwiv′ər), *n.* **1** case to hold arrows. **2** supply of arrows in such a case. [< Old French *cuivre*]

ram ble (ram′bəl), *v.i.*, **-bled, -bling,** wander about: *We rambled here and there through the woods.*—*n.* a walk for pleasure, not to go to any special place: *a short ramble.* [origin uncertain]

ram pant (ram′pənt), *adj.* **1** growing without any check: *The vines ran rampant over the fence.* **2** passing beyond restraint or usual limits; unchecked: *Anarchy was rampant after the dictator died.* **3** angry; excited; violent.

ram part (ram′pärt), *n.* **1** a wide bank of earth, often with a wall on top as a fortification, built around a fort to help defend it. **2** anything that defends; defense; protection.

ran cid (ran′sid), *adj.* stale; spoiled: *rancid butter.*

ran dom (ran′dəm), *adj.* without a definite aim, plan, method, or purpose; by chance: *a random guess, random questions, pick a random number.*

rap tur ous (rap′chər əs), *adj.* full of rapture; expressing or feeling rapture. —**rap′tur ous ly,** *adv.*

rar i ty (rer′ə tē, rar′ə tē), *n., pl.* **-ties. 1** something rare: *A person over a hundred years old is a rarity.* **2** fewness; scarcity.

rasp (rasp), *v.i.* make a harsh, grating sound: *The file rasped as she worked.* —*v.t.* **1** utter with a grating sound: *rasp out a command.* **2** have a harsh or irritating effect on; grate on.

rav en ous (rav′ə nəs), *adj.* **1** very hungry. **2** greedy. —**rav′en ous ly,** *adv.*

ra vine (rə vēn′), *n.* a long, deep, narrow gorge eroded by running water. [< French, violent rush]

re-, *prefix.* **1** again; anew; once more: *Reappear = appear again.* **2** back: *Repay = pay back.* Also, sometimes before vowels, **red-.**

re cede (ri sēd′), *v.i.*, **-ced ed, -ced ing. 1** go or move backward. **2** slope backward: *a chin that recedes.* **3** withdraw.

re coup (ri küp′), *v.t.* **1** make up for: *recoup one's losses.* **2** repay: *recoup a creditor.* [< Middle French *recouper* cut back < *re-* back + *couper* to cut]

re crim i na tion (ri krim′ə nā′shən), *n.* an accusing in return; counter accusation.

re cum bent (ri kum′bənt), *adj.* lying down; reclining; leaning.

reg u lar (reg′yə lər), *adj.* fixed by custom or rule; usual; normal: *Six o'clock was her regular hour of rising.*

re luc tant (ri luk′tənt), *adj.* **1** showing unwillingness; unwilling. **2** slow to act because unwilling. —**re luc′tant ly,** *adv.*

re mark (ri märk′), *v.t.* **1** say in a few words; state; comment. **2** notice; observe.

rem i nis cence (rem′ə nis′ns), *n.* a remembering; recalling past persons, events, etc.

re mon strance (ri mon′strəns), *n.* act of remonstrating; protest; complaint.

rend (rend), *v.t.*, **rent, rend ing. 1** pull apart violently; tear: *Wolves will rend a lamb.* **2** split: *Lightning rent the tree.* **3** disturb violently: *a mind rent by doubt.*

ren der (ren′dər), *v.t.* **1** cause to become; make: *Fright rendered me speechless.* **2** give; do: *render a service.*

ren dez vous (rän′də vü), *n., pl.* **-vous** (-vüz), *v.,* **-voused** (-vüd), **-vous ing** (-vü′ing). —*n.* **1** an appointment or engagement to meet at a fixed place or time; meeting by agreement. **2** a meeting place; gathering place: *The family had two favorite rendezvous, the library and the garden.* —*v.i.* meet at a rendezvous. —*v.t.* bring together (troops, ships, space capsules, etc.) at a fixed place.

re nowned (ri nound′), *adj.* having fame; famed.

rent¹ (rent), *n.* **1** a regular payment for the use of property. **2** (in economics) what is paid for the use of natural resources. **3** house or other property for which rent is received. **4 for rent,** available in return for rent paid. —*v.t.* **1** pay at regular times for the use of (property): *We rent a house from them.* **2** receive regular pay for the use of (property): *They rent several other houses.*

rent² (rent), *n.* a torn place; tear; split. —*adj.* torn; split. —*v.* pt. and pp. of **rend.**

re pent ance (ri pen′təns), *n.* **1** sorrow for having done wrong; contrition. **2** sorrow; regret.

re plen ish (ri plen′ish), *v.t.* fill again; provide a new supply for; renew: *replenish one's wardrobe.*

rep re hen si ble (rep′ri hen′sə bəl), *adj.* deserving reproof, rebuke, or blame.

re proach (ri prōch′), *n.* **1** blame or censure. **2** a cause of blame or disgrace; discredit. **3** object of blame, censure, or disapproval. **4** expression of blame, censure, or disapproval. —*v.t.* blame or censure; upbraid.

re pulse (ri puls′), *v.t.,* **-pulsed, -puls ing. 1** drive back; repel. **2** refuse to accept; reject: *She repulsed my invitation.*

res o lute (rez′ə lüt), *adj.* **1** having a fixed resolve; determined; firm. **2** constant in pursuing a purpose; bold. [< Latin *resolutum* resolved] **—res′o lute′ly,** *adv.* **—res′o lute′ness,** *n.*

re sound (ri zound′), *v.i.* **1** give back sound; echo. **2** sound loudly. **3** be filled with sound.

res pi ra tor (res′pə rā′tər), *n.* **1** device worn over the nose and mouth to prevent inhaling harmful substances. **2** device used to give artificial respiration.

re sume (ri züm′), *v.t.,* **-sumed, -sum ing. 1** begin again; go on: *Resume reading where we left off.* **2** get or take again: *Those standing may resume their seats.*

re tal i ate (ri tal′ē āt), *v.i.,* **-at ed, -at ing.** pay back wrong, injury, etc.; return like for like, usually to return evil for evil: *If we insult them, they will retaliate.*

re tort (ri tôrt′), *v.i.* reply quickly or sharply. —*v.t.* **1** say in sharp reply. **2** return in kind; turn back on: *retort insult for insult.*

retro-, *prefix.* backward; back; behind, as in *retrocede.*

rev e la tion (rev′ə lā′shən), *n.* **1** act of making known. **2** the thing made known: *Her true nature was a revelation to me.*

re vive (ri vīv′), *v.i.,* **-vived, -viv ing. 1** come back to life or consciousness. **2** come back to a fresh, lively condition: *Flowers revive in water.*

re weave (rē wēv′), *v.t.,* **re wove, re weaving.** to weave over again.

rheu mat ic (rü mat′ik), *adj.* **1** of or having to do with rheumatism. **2** having or liable to have rheumatism. **3** causing rheumatism. **4** caused by rheumatism. —*n.* person who has rheumatism.

rick (rik), *n.* an outdoor stack of hay, straw, wood, etc., especially one which is covered to protect it from rain.

ri fle (rī′fəl), *v.t.,* **-fled, -fling. 1** search and rob; ransack and rob. **2** take away; steal. **3** strip bare: *rifle an apple tree.*

rill (ril), *n.* a tiny stream; little brook.

rit u al (rich′ü əl), *n.* **1** form or system of rites. The rites of baptism, marriage, and burial are parts of the ritual of most churches. **2** a prescribed order of performing a ceremony or rite.

rois ter (roi′stər), *v.i.* be boisterous; revel noisily; swagger.

Roman road (rō′mən), *n.* a road built by Romans at the time of the ancient Roman Empire.

round a bout (round′ə bout′), *n.* **1** an indirect way, course, or speech. **2** BRITISH. merry-go-round.

rouse (rouz), *v.t.,* **roused, rous ing. 1** wake up: *I was roused by the ring of the telephone.* **2** stir up: *the dogs roused a deer from the bushes.* **3** excite: *be roused to anger by an insult.*

rout (rout), *v.t.* **1** dig (out); get by searching. **2** put (out); force (out): *be routed out of bed at five o'clock.*

row el (rou′əl), *n.* a small wheel with sharp points, attached to the end of a spur.

ruff (ruf), *n.* a collarlike growth of long or specially marked feathers or hairs on the neck of a bird or animal.

rye (rī), *n.* **1** a hardy, annual cereal grass widely grown in northern regions for its grain, and also to protect or improve the soil. **2** its seeds or grain, used for making flour, as food for livestock, and in making whiskey. **3** whiskey distilled from rye or from rye and other grains. —*adj.* made from rye grain or flour: *rye bread.*

sa chet (sa shā′, sash′ā), *n.* **1** a small bag or pad containing perfumed powder. **2** perfumed powder.

sa gac i ty (sə gas′ə tē), *n.* keen, sound judgment; mental acuteness; shrewdness.

sanc tion (sangk′shən), *n.* **1** permission with authority; support; approval: *We have the sanction of the recreation department to play ball in this park.* **2** solemn ratification or confirmation. —*v.t.* **1** authorize; approve; allow: *Her conscience does not sanction stealing.* **2** confirm. [< Latin *sanctionem* < *sancire* ordain] **—sanc′tion er,** *n.*

sanc tu ar y (sangk′chü er′ē), *n., pl.* **-ar ies. 1** place of refuge or protection: *a wildlife sanctuary.* **2** refuge or protection: *The cabin provided sanctuary from the rain.*

sane (sān), *adj.* **1** san er, san est. having a healthy mind.

sar cas tic (sär kas′tik), *adj.* using sarcasm; sneering; cutting. **—sar cas′ti cal ly,** *adv.*

sass (sas), INFORMAL. —*n.* rudeness; back talk; impudence. —*v.t.* be rude or disrespectful to. —*v.i.* talk rudely or impudently.

sa vor (sā′vər), *v.t.* **1** enjoy the savor of; perceive or appreciate by taste or smell: *We savored the soup.* **2** think about with great delight; relish: *I wanted to savor my victory.* **3** give flavor to; season. **4** show traces of the presence or influence of.

scape goat (skāp′gōt′), *n.* person or thing made to bear the blame for the mistakes or sins of others.

scud (skud), *v.i.,* **scud ded, scud ding,** run or move swiftly: *Clouds scudded across the sky driven by the high wind.*

scul ler y (skul′ər ē), *n., pl.* **-ler ies.** a small room where the dirty, rough work of a kitchen is done.

scut tle (skut′l), *v.,* **-tled, -tling,** *n.* —*v.i.* run with quick, hurried steps; scamper; scurry. —*n.* a short, hurried run. [variant of earlier *scuddle,* frequentative of *scud*] **—scut′tler,** *n.*

scythe (sīŦH), *n., v.,* **scythed, scyth ing.** —*n.* a long, thin, slightly curved blade on a long handle, for cutting grass, etc. —*v.t.* cut or mow with a scythe.

sear (sir), *v.t.* **1** burn or char the surface of: *sear a roast.* **2** make hard or unfeeling: *A cruel person must have a seared conscience.* **3** dry up; wither.

se date (si dāt′), *adj.* quiet; calm; serious: *a sedate child who preferred reading to playing.* [< Latin *sedatum,* related to *sedere* sit] **—se date′ly,** *adv.* **—se date′ness,** *n.*

seed y (sē′dē), *adj.,* **seed i er, seed i est. 1** full of seed. **2** gone to seed. **3** no longer fresh or new; shabby, run-down.

semi-, *prefix.* **1** half: *Semicircle = half circle.* **2** partly; incompletely: *Semicivilized = partly civilized.* **3** twice. *Semi___ly* means in each half of a ___, or twice in a ___: *Semiannually = every half year, or twice a year.* [< Latin]

se nil i ty (sə nil′ə tē), *n.* **1** old age. **2** the mental and physical deterioration often characteristic of old age.

sen si tiv i ty (sen′sə tiv′ə tē), *n., pl.* **-ties. 1** quality or condition of being sensitive. **2** capacity to respond to stimuli.

sen try (sen′trē), *n., pl.* **-tries. 1** soldier stationed as a sentinel. **2** stand sentry, watch; guard: *We stood sentry over the sleepers.* [perhaps short for earlier *centrinel,* variant of *sentinel*]

se quin (sē′kwən), *n.* a small spangle used to ornament dresses, scarfs, etc.

se ren i ty (sə ren′ə tē), *n., pl.* **-ties. 1** peace and quiet; calmness. **2** clearness; brightness.

ser i al (sir′ē əl), *n.* story published, broadcast, or televised one part at a time.

shaft (shaft), *n.* **1** the long, slender stem of an arrow, spear, etc. **2** arrow or spear.

sham poo (sham pü′), *v.,* **-pooed, -poo ing;** *n., pl.* **-poos.** —*v.t.* wash with a detergent, soap, or similar preparation. —*n.* **1** a washing of the hair, a rug, etc. **2** preparation used for shampooing. [< Hindustani *champō,* literally, press!]

share crop per (sher′krop′ər, shar′krop′ər), *n.* person who farms land for the owner in return for part of the crops.

sheath (shēth), *n., pl.* **sheaths** (shēTHZ, shēths). **1** case or covering for the blade of a sword, knife, etc. **2** any similar covering, especially on an animal, plant, or other organism.

sheathe (shēTH), *v.t.,* **sheathed, sheath ing. 1** put (a sword, etc.) into a sheath. **2** enclose in a case or covering.

sheep ish (shē′pish), *adj.* awkwardly bashful or embarrassed: *a sheepish smile.* —**sheep′ish ly,** *adv.*

shift less (shift′lis), *adj.* lazy; inefficient.

shil ling (shil′ing), *n.* a former coin of Great Britain, which was equal to 12 pence or ¹⁄₂₀th of a pound. It was replaced by the 5 new pence piece.

ship mate (ship′māt′), *n.* a fellow sailor on a ship.

shoat (shōt), *n.* a young pig that no longer suckles.

short wave (shôrt′wāv′), *n.* a radio wave having a wavelength of 60 meters or less.

shrewd (shrüd), *adj.* **1** having a sharp mind; showing a keen wit; clever. **2** keen; sharp.

shroud (shroud), *n.* **1** cloth or garment in which a dead person is wrapped or dressed for burial. **2** something that covers, conceals, or veils: *The fog was a shroud over the city.* **3** Usually, **shrouds,** *pl.* rope from a mast to the side of a ship. Shrouds help support the mast. **4** one of the lines attached to the canopy of a parachute. —*v.t.* **1** wrap or dress for burial. **2** cover; conceal; veil: *Their plans are shrouded in secrecy.* [Old English *scrūd*] —**shroud′like′,** *adj.*

shrouds (def. 3)

shun (shun), *v.t.,* **shunned, shun ning.** keep away from because of dislike. [Old English *scunian*] —**shun′ner,** *n.*

sil hou ette (sil′ü et′), *n.* **1** an outline portrait, especially in profile, cut out of a black paper or drawn and filled in with some single color. **2** a dark image outlined against a lighter background.

sim u late (sim′yə lāt), *v.t.,* **-lat ed, -lat ing. 1** put on a false appearance of; pretend; feign: *simulate interest.* **2** act like; look like; imitate: *Certain insects simulate flowers or leaves.*

si mul ta ne ous (sī′məl tā′nē əs, sim′əl tā′nē əs), *adj.* existing, done, or happening at the same time: *The two simultaneous shots sounded like one.* —**si′mul ta′ne ous ly,** *adv.*

sin ew (sin′yü), *n.* **1** tendon. **2** strength; energy; force. [Old English *sionu*]

sire (sīr), *n.* **1** a male ancestor. **2** male parent; father: *Lightning was the sire of the racehorse Danger.* **3** title of respect used formerly to a great noble and now to a king.

skiff (skif), *n.* a small, light rowboat.

skir mish (skėr′mish), *n.* **1** a brief fight between small groups of soldiers. **2** a slight conflict, argument, contest, etc.

slack (slak), *adj.* **1** not tight or firm; loose: *a slack rope.* **2** careless: *a slack housekeeper.* **3** slow: *The horse was moving at a slack pace.* **4** not active; not brisk; dull.

sloth (slôth, slōth), *n.* unwillingness to work or exert oneself; laziness; idleness: *His sloth keeps him from engaging in sports.*

slov en ly (sluv′ən lē), *adj.,* **-li er, -li est.** untidy, dirty, or careless in dress, appearance, habits, work, etc.

sluice (slüs), *n.* **1** structure with a gate or gates for holding

---

a hat	i it	oi oil	ch child		a in about
ā age	ī ice	ou out	ng long		e in taken
ä far	o hot	u cup	sh she	ə =	i in pencil
e let	ō open	u̇ put	th thin		o in lemon
ē equal	ô order	ü rule	₮H then		u in circus
ėr term			zh measure		< = derived from

spin

back or controlling the water of a canal, river, or lake. **2** gate that holds back or controls the flow of water. When the water behind a dam gets too high, the sluices are opened. **3** channel for carrying off overflow or surplus water.

smite (smīt), *v.,* **smote, smit ten** or **smote, smit ing.** —*v.t.* **1** give a hard blow to (a person, etc.) with the hand, a stick, or the like; strike. **2** impress suddenly with a strong feeling, sentiment, etc.: *smitten with curiosity.* **3** punish severely; chasten. —*v.i.* deliver a blow or blows, a stroke, etc., with or as with a stick, weapon, etc.; strike.

smith (smith), *n.* **1** worker in metal, especially iron. **2** blacksmith.

smote (smōt), *v.* pt. and a pp. of **smite.**

snuff (snuf), *v.t.* **1** draw in through the nose; draw up into the nose. **2** smell at; examine by smelling: *The dog snuffed the track of the fox.* —*v.i.* **1** draw air, etc., up or in through the nose. **2** sniff, especially curiously as a dog would.

so lic i tous (sə lis′ə təs), *adj.* **1** showing care or concern. **2** desirous; eager. [< Latin *sollicitus* < *sollus* all + *ciere* arouse] —**so lic′i tous ly,** *adv.*

sol i tar y (sol′ə ter′ē), *adj.* **1** alone or single; only: *A solitary rider was seen in the distance.* **2** without companions; away from people; lonely: *lead a solitary life.*

-some, *suffix forming adjectives.* **1** tending to ___: *Meddlesome = tending to meddle.* **2** causing ___: *Troublesome = causing trouble.* **3** ___ to a considerable degree: *Lonesome = lone to a considerable degree.* [Middle English < Old English *-sum*]

sor cer y (sôr′sər ē), *n., pl.* **-cer ies.** magic performed with the supposed aid of evil spirits; witchcraft.

sov er eign (sov′rən), *n.* **1** supreme ruler; king or queen; monarch. **2** person, group, or nation having supreme control or dominion; master: *sovereign of the seas.*

Spanish moss, a mosslike, epiphytic plant of the same family as the pineapple, growing on the branches of certain trees, from which it hangs in gray streamers.

spank ing (spang′king), —*adj.* **1** blowing briskly: *a spanking breeze.* **2** quick and vigorous. **3** INFORMAL. unusually fine, great, large, etc.

spar (spär), *n.* a stout pole used to support or extend the sails of a ship; mast, yard, gaff, boom, etc., of a ship.

spark (spärk), *n.* **1** a lively, showy young man; dandy. **2** beau; lover. —*v.t., v.i.* INFORMAL. court; woo.

spate (spāt), *n.* **1** a sudden outburst: *a spate of words.* **2** a large number; great quantity: *a spate of new books on astronomy.*

spec ta cle (spek′tə kəl), *n.* **1** something presented to the view as noteworthy, striking, etc.; thing to look at; sight: *a charming spectacle of children at play.* **2** a public show or display.

spec u la tion (spek′yə lā′shən), *n.* **1** careful thought; reflection. **2** a guessing; conjecture.

spend thrift (spend′thrift′), *n.* person who spends money extravagantly or wastefully. —*adj.* wastefully extravagant. [< *spend* + *thrift*]

sphinx (sfingks), *n.* **1 Sphinx,** (in Greek myths) a monster with the head of a woman, the body of a lion, and wings. The Sphinx proposed a riddle to every passer-by and killed those unable to answer it. **2** a puzzling or mysterious person; enigma.

spin (spin), *v.t.,* **spun** or (ARCHAIC) **span, spun, spin ning. 1** cause to turn or revolve rapidly; rotate: *spin a top.* **2** draw out and twist (cotton, flax, wool, etc.) into thread, either by hand or by machinery. **3** make (thread, yarn, etc.) by drawing out and

709

GLOSSARY

twisting cotton, flax, wool, etc.

splay (splā), *v.t.* **1** spread out; expand; extend. **2** make slanting; bevel. —*v.i.* **1** have or lie in a slanting direction; slope. **2** spread out; flare.

spoil (spoil), *n.* **1** Often, **spoils,** *pl.* things taken by force; things won; booty; loot: *The victors returned with the spoils of war.* **2 spoils,** *pl.* government offices and positions filled by the political party that has won an election. **3** an object of plundering; prey.

spore (spôr, spōr), *n.* a single-celled reproductive body of fungi, flowerless plants such as ferns, and some protozoans, which is capable of developing into a living organism.

spouse (spous, spouz), *n.* husband or wife.

spume (spyüm), *n., v.,* **spumed, spum ing.** —*n.* frothy matter; foam; froth. —*v.i.* foam or froth. [< Latin *spuma*]

spun (spun), *v.* a pt. and pp. of **spin.**

squan der (skwon′dər), *v.t.* spend foolishly; waste: *squander one's money in gambling.* [origin uncertain]

squash (skwosh), *n.* either of two games somewhat like handball and tennis, played in a walled court with rackets and a rubber ball.

staid (stād), *adj.* **1** having a settled, quiet character; sober; sedate. **2** settled; unchanging; fixed.

stale mate (stāl′māt′), *n.* **1** (in chess) a draw which results when you cannot move any of your pieces without putting your own king in check. **2** any position in which no action can be taken; complete standstill.

stam pede (stam pēd′), *v.i.,* **-ped ed, -ped ing.** **1** scatter or flee in a stampede. **2** make a general rush.

star board (stär′bərd, stär′bôrd, *or* stär′bōrd), *n.* the right side of a ship, boat, or aircraft, when facing forward. —*adj.* on, at, or of the right side of a ship, boat, or aircraft.

stay (stā), *n.* one of the strong ropes, often of wire, by which the mast of a ship is held in position.

stealth y (stel′thē), *adj.,* **stealth i er, stealth i est.** done in a secret manner; secret; sly: *The cat crept in a stealthy way toward the bird.* —**stealth′i ly,** *adv.* —**stealth′i ness,** *n.*

sti fle (stī′fəl), *v.,* **-fled, -fling.** —*v.t.* **1** stop the breath of; smother: *The smoke stifled the firefighters.* **2** keep back; suppress; stop: *stifle a cry, stifle a yawn, stifle business activity, stifle a rebellion.* —*v.i.* **1** be unable to breathe freely: *I am stifling in this hot room.* **2** die or become unconscious by being unable to breathe.

stile (stīl), *n.* **1** step or steps for getting over a fence or wall. **2** turnstile. [Old English *stigel,* related to *stīgan* climb]

stint (stint), *v.t.* limit; restrict: *to stint expenses, to stint oneself on meals.* —*v.i.* be saving; get along on very little.

stile (def. 1)

stir rup (stėr′əp, stir′əp), *n.* loop or ring of metal or wood that hangs from a saddle to support a rider's foot.

stol id (stol′id), *adj.* hard to arouse; not easily excited; showing no emotion; seeming dull; impassive.

stout (stout), *adj.* **1** brave; bold: *a stout heart.* **2** not yielding; stubborn: *stout resistance.* —**stout′ly,** *adv.*

strait (strāt), *n.* a narrow channel connecting two larger bodies of water.

stra tum (strā′təm, strat′əm), *n., pl.* **-ta** or **-tums.** social level; group having about the same education, culture, development, etc.: *rise from a low to a high stratum of society.*

stri a tion (strī ā′shən), *n.* **1** streaked condition or appearance. **2** one of a number of parallel narrow stripes or streaks.

strick en (strik′ən), *adj.* **1** hit, wounded, or affected by (a weapon, disease, trouble, sorrow, etc.): *a stricken deer, a city stricken by fire.* **2 stricken in years.** old. —*v.* a pp. of **strike.**

stride (strīd), *v.,* **strode, strid den, strid ing,** —*v.i.* **1** walk with long steps: *stride rapidly down the street.* **2** pass with one long step: *He strode over the brook.* —*v.t.* **1** walk with long steps: *stride the streets.* **2** go over or across with one long step: *stride a brook.* **3** sit or stand with one leg on each side of: *stride a fence.*

strike (strīk), *v.,* **struck, struck** or **strick en, strik ing,** *n.* —*v.t.* **1** deal a blow to; hit: *strike a person in anger.* **2** give forth or out; deal: *strike a blow in self-defense.* **3** attack: *The enemy struck the town at dawn.* **4** lower or take down (a flag, sail, tent, etc.). —*v.i.* **1** deal or aim a blow: *strike at a person with a whip.* **2** attack: *The enemy will strike at dawn.* —*n.* **1** a general stopping of work in order to force an employer or employers to agree to the workers' demands for higher wages, shorter hours, or other benefits. **2** baseball pitched through the strike zone and not swung at, any pitch that is swung at and missed, or any pitch that is hit foul under the rules of the game.

strode (strōd), *v.* pt. of **stride.**

struck (struk), *v.* pt. and a pp. of **strike.**

sty (stī), *n., pl.* **sties.** **1** pen for pigs. **2** any filthy or disgusting place. [Old English *stig* a building]

sua vi ty (swä′və tē, swav′ə tē), *n., pl.* **-ties.** smoothly agreeable quality or behavior; smooth politeness; blandness.

sub-, *prefix.* **1** under; below: *Subnormal = below normal.* **2** down; further; again: *Subdivide = divide again.* **3** near; nearly: *Subtropical = nearly tropical.* **4** lower; subordinate: *Subcommittee = a lower or subordinate committee.* **5** resulting from further division: *Subsection = section resulting from further division of something.* **6** slightly; somewhat: *Subacid = slightly acid.*

sub jec tive (səb jek′tiv), *adj.* **1** existing in the mind; belonging to the person thinking rather than to the object thought of: *subjective reasoning.* **2** influenced by personal feelings; not objective: *a subjective conclusion.*

sub merge (səb mėrj′), *v.,* **-merged, -merg ing.** —*v.t.* **1** put under water; cover with water: *land submerged by a flood.* **2** cover; bury: *His talent was submerged by his shyness.* —*v.i.* sink under water; go below the surface: *The submarine submerged.*

sub stan tial (səb stan′shəl), *adj.* **1** having substance; material; real; actual: *People and things are substantial; dreams and ghosts are not.* **2** strong; firm; solid: *The house is substantial enough to last a hundred years.* **3** large; important; ample: *make a substantial improvement in health.*

sub ter ra ne an (sub′tə rā′nē ən), *adj.* underground: *A subterranean passage led from the castle to a cave.*

sub tle (sut′l), *adj.,* **-tler, -tlest.** **1** delicate; thin; fine: *a subtle odor of perfume.* **2** so fine or delicate as to elude observation or analysis: *subtle distinctions.* —**sub tly** (sut′lē, sut′l ē), *adv.*

suf fo cate (suf′ə kāt), *v.,* **-cat ed, -cat ing.** —*v.t.* **1** kill by stopping the breath. **2** keep from breathing; hinder in breathing. **3** smother; suppress. —*v.i.* **1** gasp for breath; choke. **2** die for lack of oxygen; be suffocated.

sul len (sul′ən), *adj.* **1** silent because of bad humor or anger: *The sullen child refused to answer my question.* **2** showing bad humor or anger. **3** gloomy; dismal: *The sullen skies threatened rain.* [Middle English *soleine,* ultimately < Latin *solus* alone] —**sul′len ly,** *adv.* —**sul′len ness,** *n.*

sul try (sul′trē), *adj.,* **-tri er, -tri est.** hot, close, and moist.

sup¹ (sup), *v.i.,* **supped, sup ping.** eat the evening meal; take supper: *We supped on bread and milk.* [< Old French *souper* < *soupe* soup]

sup² (sup), *v.t., v.i.,* **supped, sup ping.** *n.* sip. [Old English *sūpan*]

super-, *prefix.* **1** over; above: *Superimpose = impose over or above.* **2** besides; further: *Superadd = add besides or further.* **3** in high proportion; to excess; exceedingly: *Superabundant = abundant to excess.* **4** surpassing: *Supernatural = surpassing the natural.*

su per nat ur al (sü′pər nach′ər əl), *adj.* above or beyond what is natural: *supernatural voices.*

sup pli cant (sup′lǝ kǝnt), *n.* person who asks humbly and earnestly: *She knelt as a supplicant at the altar.* [< Middle French, present participle of *supplier* supplicate]

sup press (sǝ pres′), *v.t.* **1** put an end to; stop by force; put down: *suppress a rebellion.* **2** keep in; hold back; keep from appearing: *She suppressed a yawn.*

sur ger y (sėr′jǝr ē), *n., pl.* **-ger ies.** BRITISH. a doctor's office.

sur ly (sėr′lē), *adj.,* **-li er, -li est.** bad-tempered and unfriendly; rude; gruff: *They got a surly answer from the grouchy old man.*

sur mise (sǝr mīz′, sėr′mīz), *n.* formation of an idea with little or no evidence; a guessing: *Their guilt was a matter of surmise; there was no proof.* [< Old French, accusation, ultimately *sur-* upon + *mettre* to put]

sus pend (sǝ spend′), *v.t.* **1** hang down by attaching to something above: *The lamp was suspended from the ceiling.* **2** hold in place as if by hanging: *We saw the smoke suspended in the still air.*

sus tain (sǝ stān′), *v.t.* **1** bear; endure: *The sea wall sustains the shock of the waves.* **2** suffer; experience: *sustain a great loss.* [< Old French < Latin *sustinere* < *sub-* up + *tenere* to hold]

su sur rus (sü sėr′ǝs), *n.* **1** whispering. **2** a rustling murmur. [< Late Latin *susurrationem* < Latin *susurrare* to whisper, hum]

swine herd (swīn′hėrd′), *n.* person who tends pigs or hogs.

swoon (swün), *v.i.* **1** faint: *swoon at the sight of blood.* **2** fade or die away gradually.

swoop (swüp), *v.i.* come down with a rush; descend in a sudden, swift attack: *Bats swooped down from the roof of the cave.*

---

tac tic (tak′tik), *n.* **1** detail of military tactics; maneuver. **2** any skillful move; gambit.

tan ge rine (tan′jǝ rēn′), *n.* a small, reddish-orange citrus fruit with a very loose peel and segments that separate easily. It is a kind of mandarin which is widely grown in the United States.

tan ta lize (tan′tl īz), *v.t.,* **-lized, -liz ing.** torment or tease by keeping something desired in sight but out of reach.

tarp (tärp), *n.* INFORMAL. sheet of canvas, plastic, or other strong waterproof material, used as a protective covering.

tat ter (tat′ǝr), *—v.t.* tear or wear to pieces; make ragged. *—v.i.* be or become tattered.

taunt (tônt, tänt), *v.t.* **1** jeer at; mock; reproach; deride. **2** get or drive by taunts; provoke: *taunt someone into taking a dare.*

taut (tôt), *adj.* **1** tightly drawn; tense: *a taut rope.* **2** in neat condition; tidy: *a taut ship.*

tech nol o gy (tek nol′ǝ jē), *n.* **1** the use of scientific knowledge to control physical objects and forces: *overcome problems by technology.* **2** science of the mechanical and industrial arts: *I studied engineering at a school of technology.* *—tech nol′o gist, n.*

tel e path ic (tel′ǝ path′ik), *adj.* having the ability to communicate with another mind without the aid of normal means of communication.

tem per ate (tem′pǝr it), *adj.* **1** not very hot and not very cold: *a temperate climate.* **2** using self-control; moderate: *She spoke in a temperate manner, not favoring either side especially.*

te nac i ty (ti nas′ǝ tē), *n.* **1** firmness in holding fast. **2** stubbornness; persistence.

ten don (ten′dǝn), *n.* a tough, strong band or cord of fibrous tissue that joins a muscle to a bone or some other part and transmits the force of the muscle to that part; sinew. [< Medieval Latin *tendonem* < Greek *tenōn;* influenced by Latin *tendere* to stretch]

ten e ment (ten′ǝ mǝnt), *n.* **1** tenement house. **2** any house or building to live in; dwelling house. **3** a dwelling, or part of a dwelling, occupied by a tenant. **4** abode; habitation.

---

a hat	i it	oi oil	ch child	⎧ a in about
ā age	ī ice	ou out	ng long	⎪ e in taken
ä far	o hot	u cup	sh she	ǝ ⎨ i in pencil
e let	ō open	u̇ put	th thin	⎪ o in lemon
ē equal	ô order	ü rule	ŦH then	⎩ u in circus
ėr term			zh measure	< = derived from

ten ta cle (ten′tǝ kǝl), *n.* one of the long, slender, flexible growths, usually occurring on the head or around the mouth of an animal, used to touch, hold, or move.

ten ta tive (ten′tǝ tiv), *adj.* **1** done as a trial or experiment; experimental: *We made tentative plans to work together for six months.* **2** hesitating: *—ten′ta tive ly, adv.*

ter mi nate (tėr′mǝ nāt), *v.,* **-nat ed, -nat ing.** *—v.t.* **1** bring to an end; put an end to; conclude: *terminate a partnership.* **2** occur at or form the end of; bound; limit. **3** dismiss from a job; fire. *—v.i.* **1** come to an end: *The contract terminates soon.* **2** stop short.

tes ty (tes′tē), *adj.,* **-ti er, -ti est.** easily irritated; impatient. *—tes′ti ly, adv.*

teth er (teŦH′ǝr), *—v.t.* fasten or confine with or as with a tether.

the o rist (thē′ǝr ist), *n.* person who forms theories or who speculates.

ther a py (ther′ǝ pē), *n., pl.* **-pies.** **1** treatment of diseases or disorders. **2** INFORMAL. psychotherapy.

throw back (thrō′bak′), *n.* **1** a throwing back. **2** setback or check. **3** reversion to an ancestral type or character. **4** an example of this: *The boy seemed to be a throwback to his great-grandfather.*

tick (tik), *v.t.* **1** mark with a tick or check. **2** BRITISH INFORMAL. **tick off,** reprimand; scold.

tier (tir), *n.* one of a series of rows arranged one above another: *tiers of seats in a stadium.* *—v.t., v.i.* arrange, or be arranged, in tiers. [< Middle French *tire,* originally, order <. *tirer* to draw]

tinge (tinj), *n.* **1** a slight coloring or tint: *a tinge of red in her cheeks.* **2** a very small amount; trace.

-tion, *suffix added to verbs to form nouns.* **1** act or process of ___ing: *Addition = act or process of adding.* **2** condition of being ___ed: *Exhaustion = condition of being exhausted.* **3** result of ___ing: *Reflection = result of reflecting.* [< Latin *-tionem*]

tip sy (tip′sē), *adj.,* **-si er, -si est.** tipping easily; unsteady.

tol e rate (tol′ǝ rāt′), *v.t.,* **-rat ed, -rat ing.** **1** allow or permit: *The teacher would not tolerate any disorder.* **2** bear; endure; put up with: *I cannot tolerate loud noises.*

tor ment (tôr ment′), *v.t.* **1** cause very great pain to. **2** worry or annoy very much. **3** torture.

tor por (tôr′pǝr), *n.* torpid condition or quality; apathy; lethargy.

trace (trās), *n.* either of the two straps, ropes, or chains by which an animal pulls a wagon, carriage, etc.

tram mel (tram′ǝl), *v.t.,* **-meled, -mel ing** or **-melled, -mel ling.** **1** hinder; restrain. **2** catch in or as if in a trammel; entangle. [< Old French *tramail* < Late Latin *trimaculum* < Latin *tri-* three + *macula* mesh]

tran quil (trang′kwǝl), *adj.,* **-quil er, -quil est** or **-quil ler, -quil lest.** free from agitation or disturbance; calm; peaceful.

trans-, *prefix.* **1** across; over; through, as in *transcontinental, transmit.* **2** on the other side of; beyond, as in *transatlantic.* **3** to a different place, condition, etc., as in *transmigration, transform.*

trans fix (tran sfiks′), *v.t.* **1** pierce through: *The hunter transfixed the lion with a spear.* **2** fasten or fix by piercing through with something pointed; impale. **3** make motionless or helpless (with amazement, terror, grief, etc.). *—trans fix′ion, n.*

trans for ma tion (tran′sfǝr mā′shǝn), *n.* **1** a change in form or appearance. **2** a being transformed. **3** (in mathematics) the

GLOSSARY

changing of the form of an expression or figure into another form.

trap line (trap′līn), *n.* a line or series of traps; the route along which such a line is set.

trel lis (trel′is), *n.* frame of light strips of wood or metal crossing one another with open spaces in between; lattice, especially one supporting growing vines.

tres pass (tres′pəs, tres′pas), *n.* **1** act or fact of trespassing. **2** a wrong; a sin. **3** an unlawful act done by force against the person, property, or rights of another.

trice (trīs), *n.* **1** a very short time; moment; instant. **2 in a trice,** in an instant; immediately.

trun dle (trun′dl), *v.t.,* **-dled, -dling. 1** roll along; push along: *The worker trundled a wheelbarrow full of cement.* **2** cause to rotate; twirl; spin; whirl.

tu mult (tü′mult, tyü′mult), *n.* **1** noise or uproar; commotion: *the tumult of the storm.* **2** a violent disturbance or disorder.

tun dra (tun′drə, tùn′drə), *n.* a vast, level, treeless plain in the arctic regions. The ground beneath the surface of the tundras is frozen even in summer. Much of Alaska and northern Canada is tundra. [< Russian]

tu nic (tü′nik, tyü′nik), *n.* **1** garment like a shirt or gown, usually reaching to the knees, worn by men and women in ancient Greece and Rome. **2** any garment like this.

tur ret (tėr′it), *n.* **1** a small tower, often on the corner of a building. **2** any of various low, rotating, armored structures within which guns are mounted, as in a warship or tank.

twang (twang), *v.t.* **1** make a sharp, ringing sound. **2** play, pluck, shoot, etc., with a twang. **3** speak (words, etc.) with a sharp, nasal tone. —*v.i.* **1** make a sharp, ringing sound: *The banjos twanged.* **2** speak with a sharp, nasal tone. [imitative]

tweak (twēk), *v.t., v.i.* seize and pull with a sharp jerk and twist: *tweak a person's ear.* —*n.* a sharp pull and twist.

twirl (twėrl), *v.t.* **1** revolve rapidly; spin; whirl: *twirl a baton.* **2** turn round and round idly. **3** twist; curl; flourish. —*v.i.* be twirled.

two-bit (tü′bit′), *adj.* SLANG. **1** worth a quarter of a dollar. **2** cheap; worthless.

-ty¹, *suffix added to numbers.* ___ tens; ___ times ten: *Seventy = seven tens, or seven times ten.* [Old English *-tig*]

-ty², *suffix added to adjectives to form nouns.* quality, condition, or fact of being ___: *Safety = condition or quality of being safe.*

un-¹, *prefix.* not ___; the opposite of ___: *Unequal = not equal; the opposite of equal. Unchanged = not changed.*

un-², *prefix.* do the opposite of ___; do what will reverse the act: *Unfasten = do the opposite of fasten. Uncover = do the opposite of cover.* [Old English *un-, on-*]

un can ny (un kan′ē), *adj.* **1** strange and mysterious; weird: *The trees took uncanny shapes in the darkness.* See **weird** for synonym study. **2** so far beyond what is normal or expected as to have some special power: *an uncanny knack for solving riddles.* —**un can′ni ly,** *adv.* —**un can′ni ness,** *n.*

un com pre hend ing (un′kom pre hend′ing), *adj.* not understanding the meaning of.

un con cerned (un′kən sėrnd′), *adj.* not concerned; not interested; free from care or anxiety; indifferent. —**un′con cern′ed ly,** *adv.* —**un′con cern′ed ness,** *n.*

un der mine (un′dər mīn′, un′dər mīn′), *v.t.,* **-mined, -min ing. 1** weaken by secret or unfair means: *undermine a person's reputation by scandal.* **2** weaken or destroy gradually: *Many severe colds had undermined her health.* —**un′der min′er,** *n.* —**un′der min′ing ly,** *adv.*

un err ing (un ėr′ing, un er′ing), *adj.* making no mistakes; exactly right: *unerring aim.* —**un err′ing ly,** *adv.* —**un err′ing ness,** *n.*

u nique (yü nēk′), *adj.* **1** having no like or equal; being the only one of its kind: *a unique specimen of rock.* **2** INFORMAL. very uncommon or unusual; rare; remarkable: —**u nique′ly,** *adv.*

un scal a ble (un skā′lə bəl), *adj.* not scalable; not climbable.

un wield y (un wēl′dē), *adj.,* **-wield i er, -wield i est.** not easily handled or managed, because of size, shape, or weight; bulky and clumsy: *an unwieldy package.* —**un wield′i ness,** *n.*

un yield ing (un yēl′ding), *adj.* not yielding; resisting.

vain ly (vān′lē), *adv.* **1** in vain. **2** with conceit.

val iant (val′yənt), *adj.* having or showing courage; brave; courageous: *a valiant soldier, a valiant deed.*

va por ous (vā′pər əs), *adj.* full of vapor; misty.

var mit (vär′mət), *n.* DIALECT. **1** vermin. **2** an objectionable animal or person. Also, **var′mint.**

ven er a ble (ven′ər ə bəl), *adj.* worthy of reverence; deserving respect because of age, character, or importance: *a venerable priest, venerable customs.*

ven om (ven′əm), *n.* the poison secreted by some snakes, spiders, scorpions, lizards, etc., and injected into their prey by biting, stinging, etc.

ve ran da or **ve ran dah** (və ran′də), *n.* a large porch or gallery along one or more sides of a house. [< Hindustani *varandā*]

ver ba tim (vər bā′tim), *adv., adj.* word for word; in exactly the same words: *a speech printed verbatim in the newspaper.*

ve to (vē′to), *n., pl.* **-toes. 1** the right or power of a president, governor, etc., to reject bills passed by a lawmaking body. **2** the right or power of any one member of an official body to prevent some action proposed by that body, as in the United Nations Security Council. **3** any power or right to prevent action through prohibition. **4** refusal of consent; prohibition.

vi bra tion (vī brā′shən), *n.* **1** a rapid movement to and fro; quivering motion; vibrating: *The buses shake the house so much that we feel the vibration.* **2** a rapid or slow movement to and fro.

vig il (vij′əl), *n.* a staying awake for some purpose; a watching; watch: *All night the mother kept vigil over the sick child.*

vig or ous (vig′ər əs), *adj.* full of vigor; strong and active; energetic; forceful: *wage a vigorous war against disease.* —**vig′or ous ly,** *adv.* —**vig′or ous ness,** *n.*

vin dic tive (vin dik′tiv). *adj.* feeling a strong tendency toward revenge; bearing a grudge.

vir tu al (vėr′chü əl), *adj.* being something in effect, though not so in name; for all practical purposes; actual; real. —**vir′tu al ly,** *adv.*

vir u lent (vir′yə lənt, vir′ə lənt), *adj.* **1** very poisonous or harmful; deadly: *a virulent poison.* **2** (of diseases) characterized by a rapid and severe malignant or infectious condition.

vi tal (vī′tl), *adj.* **1** of or having to do with life: *Growth and decay are vital processes.* **2** very necessary; very important; essential: *a vital question. Drainage of the nearby swamp was considered vital to the welfare of the community.* —*n.* **vitals,** *pl.* **a** parts or organs necessary to life. The brain, heart, lungs, and stomach are vitals. **b** essential parts or features of anything; essentials.

vix en (vik′sən), *n.* **1** a female fox. **2** a bad-tempered or quarrelsome woman. [Old English *fyxen* < *fox* fox]

viz., that is to say; namely [for Latin *videlicet*].

vor tex (vôr′teks), *n., pl.* **-tex es** or **-ti ces. 1** a whirling mass of water, etc., that sucks everything near it toward its center; whirlpool. **2** a violent whirl of air; cyclone; whirlwind. **3** whirl of activity or other situation from which it is hard to escape.

wa ger (wā′jər), *v.t., v.i.* make a bet; bet; gamble. —*n.* **1** something staked on an uncertain event. **2** act of betting; bet.

wane (wān), *v.i.*, **waned, wan ing. 1** lose size; become smaller gradually: *The moon wanes after it has become full.* **2** decline in power, influence, or importance: *Many great empires have waned.* **3** decline in strength or intensity. **4** draw to a close: *Summer wanes as autumn approaches.*

wan ton (won′tən), *adj.* **1** reckless, heartless, or malicious: *wanton cruelty.* **2** without reason or excuse: *a wanton attack, wanton mischief.* **3** frolicsome; playful: *a wanton breeze, a wanton child.* **4** not restrained: *a wanton mood.* **—wan′ton ness**, *n.*

war i ness (wer′ē nis, war′ē nis), *n.* caution; care.

warp (wôrp), *n.* the threads running lengthwise in a fabric. The warp is crossed by the woof.

war y (wer′ē, war′ē), *adj.,* **war i er, war i est. 1** on one's guard against danger, deception, etc.: *a wary fox.* **2** cautious or careful: *give wary answers to a stranger's questions.*

weal (wēl), *n.* well-being; prosperity: *Good citizens act for the public weal.* [Old English *wela* wealth, welfare]

wean (wēn), *v.t.* **1** accustom (a child or young animal) to food other than its mother's milk. **2** accustom (a person) to do without something; cause to turn away: *wean someone from a bad habit.*

weft (weft), *n.* **1** the threads running from side to side across a fabric; woof. **2** something woven or spun, as a web.

weird (wird), *adj.* **1** unearthly or mysterious: *They were awakened by a weird shriek.* See synonym study below. **2** odd; fantastic; queer: *The shadows made weird figures on the wall.*
Syn. 1 Weird, eerie, uncanny mean mysteriously or frighteningly strange. **Weird** describes something that seems not of this world or due to something above or beyond nature: *All night weird cries came from the jungle.* **Eerie** suggests the frightening effect of something weird or ghostly or vaguely and civilly mysterious: *The light from the single candle made eerie shadows in the cave.* **Uncanny** suggests a strangeness that is disturbing because it seems unnatural: *I had an uncanny feeling that eyes were peering from the darkness.*

wend (wend), *v.,* **wend ed** or **went, wend ing. —v.t.** direct (one's way): *We wended our way home.* **—v.i.** go.

whee dle (hwē′dl), *v.,* **-dled, -dling. —v.t. 1** persuade by flattery, smooth words, caresses, etc.; coax: *The children wheedled their parents into letting them go to the picnic.* **2** get by wheedling: *They finally wheedled the secret out of me.* **—v.i.** use soft, flattering words.

wheel house (hwēl′hous′), *n., pl.* **-hous es** (-hou′ziz). an enclosed place on the upper deck of a ship, sheltering the steering wheel and pilot; pilothouse.

whence (hwens), *adv.* **1** from what place; from where: *Whence do you come?* **2** from what place, source, or cause; from what: *Whence has he so much wisdom?* **—conj. 1** from what place, source, or cause: *She told whence she came.* **2** from which: *Let them return to the country whence they came.* [Middle English *whennes* < Old English *hwanone*]

whith er (hwiFH′ər), *adv., conj.* to what place; to which place; where. [Old English *hwider*]

wil y (wī′lē), *adj.,* **wi li er, wi li est.** using wiles or subtle tricks to deceive; crafty; cunning; sly: *a wily thief.* **—wil′i ly,** *adv.* **—wil′i ness,** *n.* [Middle English *wil* wile; a trick to deceive]

wipe out (wīp′out′), *n.* SLANG. **1** destruction; obliteration. **2** a fall from a surfboard or other sports equipment.

with draw (wiFH drô′, with drô′), *v.,* **-drew, -drawn, -draw ing. —v.t. 1** draw back; draw away: *He quickly withdrew his hand from the hot stove.* **2** take back; remove. **—v.i. 1** draw back; draw away: *I withdrew from the discussion before it became an argument.* **2** go away.

with drew (wiFH drü′, with drü′), *v.* pt. of **withdraw.**

with er (wiFH′ər), *v.i., v.t.* lose or cause to lose freshness, vigor, etc.; dry up; shrivel: *The grass withered in the hot sun.*

wol ve rine or **wol ve rene** (wúl′və rēn′, wúl′və rēn′), *n.* a heavily built carnivorous mammal of the forests of northern North America, Europe, and Asia, of the same family as the weasel and badger and having short legs and dark, shaggy fur; carcajou; glutton. [earlier *wolvering* < *wolf*]

won der ment (wun′dər mənt), *n.* **1** wonder; surprise. **2** object of wonder.

won drous (wun′drəs), *adj.* wonderful.

wraith (rāth), *n.* **1** ghost of a person seen before or soon after the person's death. **2** specter; ghost. [origin uncertain]

wrench (rench), *v.t.* **1** twist or pull violently: *The policeman wrenched the gun out of the man's hand.* **2** injure by twisting: *She wrenched her back in falling from the horse.*

wrest (rest), *v.t.* twist, pull, or tear away with force; wrench away: *She wrested the knife from her attacker.*

writhe (rīFH), *v.,* **writhed, writh ing. —v.i. 1** twist and turn; twist about: *writhe in pain. The snake writhed along the branch.* **2** suffer mentally; be very uncomfortable.

wroth (rôth, roth), *adj.* angry. [Old English *wrāth*]

wrought (rôt), *v.* ARCHAIC. a pt. and a pp. of **work.** **—adj. 1** made: *The gate was wrought with great skill.* **2** formed with care; not rough or crude. **3** manufactured or treated; not in a raw state.

-y¹, *suffix forming adjectives chiefly from nouns.* **1** full of ___: *Bumpy = full of bumps.* **2** containing ___: *Salty = containing salt.* **3** having ___: *Cloudy = having clouds.* **4** characterized by ___: *Funny = characterized by fun.* **5** somewhat ___: *Chilly = somewhat chill.* **6** inclined to ___: *Sleepy = inclined to sleep.*

-y², *suffix forming nouns from other nouns.* **1** small ___: *Dolly = a small doll.* **2** dear ___: *Daddy = dear dad.*

-y³, *suffix forming nouns from adjectives, nouns, and verbs.* **1** ___ condition or quality: *Jealousy = a jealous condition or quality.* **2** condition or quality of being ___: *Victory = condition or quality of being a victor.* **3** act or activity of ___ing: *Delivery = act of delivering.* [< Old French *-ie* < Latin *-ia* < Greek]

yaw (yô), *v.i.* **1** turn from a straight course; go unsteadily. **2** (of an aircraft) turn from a straight course by a motion about its vertical axis. **—n.** movement from a straight course. [origin uncertain]

yeo man (yō′mən), *n., pl.* **-men.** (in the United States Navy) a petty officer who performs clerical duties.

yield (yēld), *v.i.* **1** bear produce; be productive. **2** give up; surrender: *The enemy yielded to our soldiers.* [Old English *gieldan* to pay]

a hat	i it	oi oil	ch child	(a in about
ā age	ī ice	ou out	ng long	e in taken
ä far	o hot	u cup	sh she	ə = i in pencil
e let	ō open	ú put	th thin	o in lemon
ē equal	ô order	ü rule	FH then	(u in circus
ėr term			zh measure	< = derived from

GLOSSARY

INDEX OF READING AND LITERATURE TERMS

INDEX OF VOCABULARY EXERCISES

INDEX OF THINKING SKILLS

INDEX OF COMPOSITION ASSIGNMENTS

INDEX OF ENRICHMENT ACTIVITIES

INDEX OF FEATURES

INDEX OF AUTHORS AND TITLES

ACKNOWLEDGMENTS

All illustrations not credited are from Scott, Foresman and Company.

UNIT 1

1—Jay Johnson America's Folk Heritage Gallery, New York City; 5—© Vincent Di Fate; 15—© 1984 Will Barnet; 22—Francis Dodd, *Virginia Woolf*, 1908, Courtesy National Portrait Gallery, London; 25—© 1987 Detroit Institute of Arts, Gift of Dr. S. B. Milton, Dr. James A. Owen, Dr. B. F. Seabrooks and Dr. A. E. Thomas, Jr./Photo: Robert Koyton, Jr.; 28—Courtesy Random House/Photo: Carole Dufrechon; 35—Courtesy Louis L'Amour; 39—© 1987, Copyright by COSMO PRESS, Geneva; 45—© 1977 Keith Ferris; 53—The Bettmann Archive; 55—Courtesy Marlborough Gallery, NY; 59—© The Historic New Orleans Collection, Kemper and Leila Williams Foundation, 533 Royal Street, New Orleans; 63—illustration by Maurice Wilson from *The Jungle Book* by Rudyard Kipling, published by Schocken Books, 1984, Text © The National Trust, Illustrations © Macmillan Publishers Ltd. 1983. All rights reserved.; 72—W. Strang, *Rudyard Kipling, His Profile*, Courtesy National Portrait Gallery, London; 75—Courtesy E. John Robinson; 91—Scott Meredith Literary Agency, Inc.; 101—illustration by Wayne Anderson from *The Flight of Dragons* by Peter Dickinson. Illustration copyright © 1979 by Wayne Anderson. Reprinted by permission of Harper & Row Publishers, Inc.; 104—Photo: John Morris

UNIT 2

112,113—The Newark Museum, NJ. Purchase 1940, Felix Fuld Bequest Fund; 145—Courtesy Rod Serling; 149—Russ Kinne/© 1987 Comstock; 160—UPI/Bettmann Newsphotos; 165—Courtesy Martin Gale

UNIT 3

173,174—Dallas Museum of Art, Anonymous Gift; 175—Courtesy Brandywine River Museum; 181—AP/Wide World Photos; 185—Courtesy John Wilson; 187—AP/Wide World Photos; 191—Cincinnati Art Museum, Subscription Fund Purchase Acc. #1927.26; 207—illustration by Dougal MacDougal from *Snakes of the World* by John Stidworthy, copyright © 1971, 1974 by Grosset & Dunlap, Inc. All rights reserved. Copyright © 1969 by the Hamlyn Publishing Group Ltd.; 213—Photo © Sophie Baker; 218—Wide World Photos; 222—Photo courtesy Allan Stone Gallery; 224—Courtesy *Chicago Tribune*; 227—© Chris Mayger from *The Marine Painting of Chris Mayger*, A Peacock Press/© Bantam Books publication; 237—UPI/Bettmann Newsphotos

UNIT 4

240,241—Illustration from Lone Stars: A Legacy of Texas Quilts, 1836–1936, by Karoline Patterson Bresenhan and Nancy O'Bryant Puentes, Copyright © 1986 by the University of Texas Press. Reproduced by permission of the authors and the publisher.; 245—© 1952 Curtis Publishing Company, Printed by permission of the Estate of Norman Rockwell, Copyright © 1952 Estate of Norman Rockwell; 247—Photo courtesy Patricia Janis Broder *American Indian Painting and Sculpture*, Abbeville Press, NY Copyright © 1981 by Cross River Press, Ltd.; 252—(top) Metropolitan Museum of Art, Bequest of Benjamin Altman, 1913; 254—Courtesy John Ciardi; 255—Harry Ransom Humanities Research Center, The University of Texas at Austin; 261—From *Old Possum's Book of Practical Cats*, Copyright 1939

T. S. Eliot, copyright renewed © 1967 by Esme Valerie Eliot. Illustrations copyright © 1982 by Edward Gorey. Reprinted by permission of Harcourt, Brace, Jovanovich; 263—Museum of Art, Rhode Island School of Design-Jesse Metcalf Fund; 267—© Copyright illustration Tom Adams 1981; 268—AP/Wide World Photos; 268—Courtesy Harcourt Brace, Photo: Kay Bell; 275—Illustration by Marilena Pistoia from *The Language of Flowers* by Laura Peroni, copyright © 1984 Arnoldo Mondadori Editore S.P.A., Milan English translation copyright © 1985 Arnoldo Mondadori. Published United States 1985 Crown Publishers; 276—National Gallery of Art, Collection of Mr. and Mrs. Paul Mellon; 278 (top down)—E. Katterjohn, Waukegan, IL; Library of Congress; UPI/Bettmann Newsphotos; Photo by E. O. Hoppe, The Mansell Collection; 283—© James Lockhart; 287 (top down)—University of Pittsburgh Press; AP/Wide World Photos; Courtesy Doubleday & Company/Photo: Imogen Cunningham; 288—Metropolitan Museum of Art, Gift of William Church Osborn, 1949; 291 (top)—Courtesy Random House/Photo: Bob Fletcher; (bottom) Wilson Library, University of North Carolina, Chapel Hill 292—Fogg Art Museum, Harvard University, Grenville L. Winthrop Bequest; 294—Metropolitan Museum of Art, Bequest of Mrs. H. O. Havemeyer, 1929, The H. O. Havemeyer Collection; 297—(top) ©Fay Godwin; (bottom) Courtesy Mrs. Randall Jarrell; 301—University of Michigan, Bequest of Henry C. Lewis; 305—Detail of an original oil painting by Peter R. Berg; 307—© Glen Loates; 308—Photo courtesy Louis Meisel Gallery, NY; 309—(top, second from top) AP/Wide World Photos; 310—Frank Donato/Impact Photo, Inc., NY; 311—The Art Institute of Chicago, Henry Field Memorial Collection 1894.1063 © 1987 All rights reserved.

UNIT 5

327—(center) U.S. Department of Engraving and Printing, (others) Culver Pictures; 332, 337—AP/Wide World Photos; 339—Collection of Whitney Museum of American Art. Gift of Gertrude Vanderbilt Whitney 31.426; 345—Art Resource, NY, Photo: © Perry Brooks; 363—The Bettmann Archive; 379—NBC Photo/Bob Ganley; 385—E. O. Hoppe/Viking Press; 396—From *The Living Forest—A World of Animals*, by Rien Poortvliet. English translation © 1979 Harry N. Abrams, Inc.; 400—Courtesy Paul Annixter

UNIT 6

419—© Gordon Parks; 432—Photo: Andre Held, Lausanne; 441—Watercolor by Sylvie Selig from *Long, Broad and Sharpsight*, text copyright © 1971 by I. K. Junne, illustrations © 1971 by Sylvie Selig. Published by Doubleday & Co., Inc., Garden City, NY. All rights reserved.; 445—India Office Library, London

UNIT 7

450—Photo courtesy Matzke/Runnings Gallery, Seattle; 462—© Glen Loates; 474—© Daniel Schwartz 1987; 530—Courtesy E. P. Dutton, NY

UNIT 8

538 through 625—© Erich Lessing/Magnum

HANDBOOK

633—Illustration © 1984 Will Barnet; 647—Joseph Freamon, courtesy Joanna and Hy Dales

GLOSSARY

696—UPI/Bettman Newsphotos; 698, 704—Animals, Animals/Leonard Lee Rue III